why ? why ? why ?

What do my lungs do?

Sue Nicholson

This is a Parragon Book
First published in 2001

Parragon
Queen Street House
4 Queen Street
Bath BA1 1HE, UK

Produced by

David West ☖ Children's Books
7 Princeton Court
55 Felsham Road
Putney
London SW15 1AZ

British Library Cataloguing-in-Publication Data

A catalogue record for this book is available from
the British Library.

ISBN 0-75255-360-7

Printed in Italy

Designers
Aarti Parmar, Rob Shone, Fiona Thorne

Illustrators
Derek Bazell, Biz Hull, Julie Scott (Artist Partners)

Cartoonist
Peter Wilks (SGA)

Editor
James Pickering

CONTENTS

❓ Am I special?

Yes, because there's only one person like you in the whole wide world! We all have different coloured hair, skin and eyes, we may be tall or short and we all walk and talk differently.

What do you look like?

❓ What am I made of?

Your body is made up of millions of tiny cells. You have lots of different kinds of cells. Each kind has a special job to do. Your cells work together to keep you alive.

Fat cells

Muscle cells

Nerve cells

Blood cells

Skin cells

? *What can my body do?*

All sorts of amazing things! The different parts of your body – both the outside parts and the inside parts like your heart, bones and muscles that you can't see – all work together so you can laugh, cry, walk, talk, jump, hop, run, think, read and sleep!

? What's my skin for?

Your skin keeps the insides of your body safe. It helps to keep out water and harmful germs. It also makes sure you don't get too cold or too warm. Your skin grows with you as you grow.

?Why do my fingers go wrinkly in the bath?

Your skin contains oil that helps to make it waterproof, like a raincoat. Fingers and toes don't have this oil, so the ends get wrinkly if you stay in water for a long time.

?Why do some people have freckles?

Skin contains a special colouring called melanin, which protects it from strong sunlight. Freckles are patches of extra melanin, which can appear on fair skin when it has been in the sun. Dark skin has more melanin than pale skin.

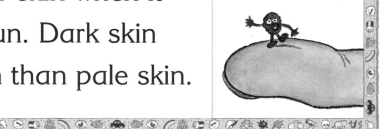

Why do I need haircuts?

Your hair is always growing, that's why! Hair grows quite slowly though, at about 2 mm every week. It grows a bit faster in the summer than in the winter. Hair is made out of keratin. So are your fingernails and toenails.

? Why do I get goosebumps?

Your whole body is covered with tiny hairs except on the palms of your hands and the soles of your feet. When you get chilly, little muscles in your skin push the hairs up to trap warm air, and you get goosebumps.

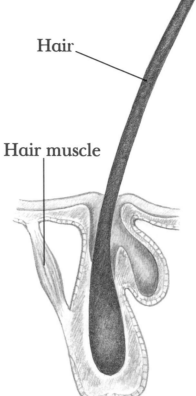

Hair

Hair muscle

? Why is some hair straight and some curly?

Hair grows out of tiny holes in our skin. If the hole is round, then our hair grows straight. If the hole is flat, our hair grows curly.

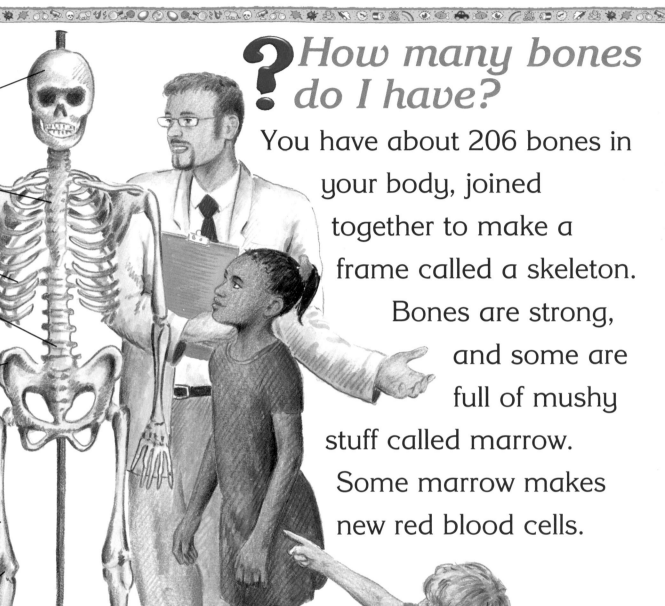

Skull

Breast bone

Ribs

Backbone

Arm bone

Hip bone

Hand bones

Thigh bone

Knee bone

Shin bone

? *How many bones do I have?*

You have about 206 bones in your body, joined together to make a frame called a skeleton. Bones are strong, and some are full of mushy stuff called marrow. Some marrow makes new red blood cells.

? What are bones for?

Bones hold you up. Without them you'd be a floppy jellyfish! Your bones also help to protect the soft parts inside your body – your skull protects your brain, and your ribs protect your heart and lungs. Your bones help you make lots of different movements.

? Where is my funny bone?

Your funny bone is on your elbow. It has a big nerve running over it. If you bang it you may feel a strange tingle that can hurt.

You shrink a bit every day.

TRUE. You shrink about 1 cm every day because your back bones get squashed together. They stretch out again when you're asleep.

Bones can be broken.

TRUE. Broken bones are wrapped in plaster or plastic while they mend.

What do muscles do?

Muscles help you move. Muscles in your arms lift and pull. Muscles in your thumbs help you to hold things. Muscles in your chest help you to breathe. You have more than 600 muscles to help you move different parts of your body.

? How do muscles work?

Muscles are fixed to your bones and usually work in pairs. They tighten to pull a bone one way, and loosen to let the bone move back again.

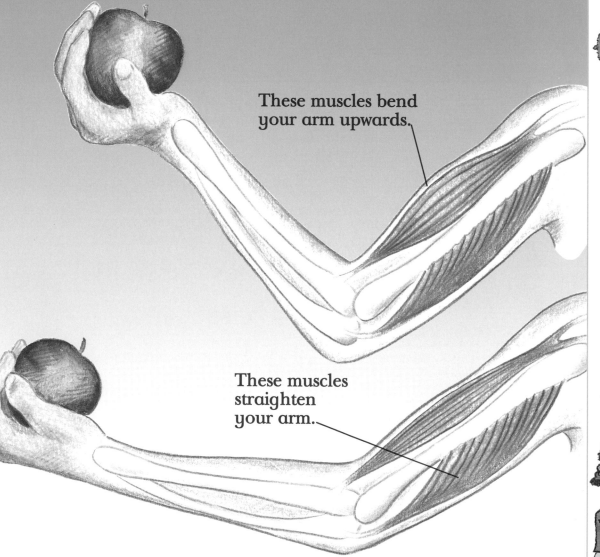

These muscles bend your arm upwards.

These muscles straighten your arm.

❓ Where does my food go?

When you eat, food goes down a long tube into your stomach. Juices in your stomach mush the food into a soup then the mush is squeezed through a long, coiled tube called your intestines. There, goodness from the food passes into your blood to be carried all round your body.

Throat

Liver (helps to break down your food)

Stomach

Kidneys (help to get rid of waste water)

Intestines

Appendix

Rectum

? What are teeth for?

Teeth chomp your food into tiny bits so that it's easier to swallow. Sharp incisors cut it up, pointed canines tear it and big molars at the back crush it.

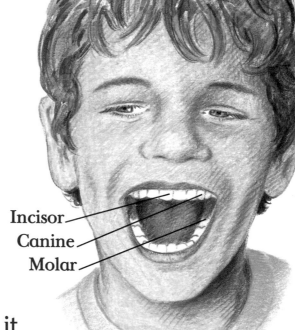

Incisor
Canine
Molar

? Why do I go to the toilet?

Your body can't use all the food you eat. The bits you don't need pass out of your body as poo. You also go to the toilet to wee. Wee (or urine) is waste water.

? What's blood for?

Blood carries oxygen and goodness from the food you eat to all the tiny cells in your body to keep them working properly. It travels around your body in narrow tubes called blood vessels.

? What does my heart do?

Your heart is a special muscle that keeps working all the time – even when you're fast asleep. Its job is to pump blood all around your body.

From body

To body

To lungs

To lungs

From lungs

Arteries carry blood with oxygen and food to all the parts of your body.

Heart

Veins carry blood without oxygen and food back to your heart.

? Where's my heart?

Your heart is right in the middle of your chest, just a little bit to the left, between your lungs. It's about as big as your fist.

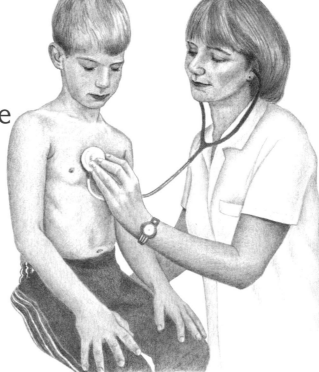

? Can I feel my heart beating?

You can sometimes feel your heart beating in your chest if you've been running fast. Or, if you put your fingers on the inside of your wrist, you can feel the throb of your blood moving in time to your heartbeat.

What do my lungs do?

Your lungs take in a gas called oxygen from the air and pass it into your blood. Your blood carries the oxygen from your lungs to the rest of your body. We need oxygen to stay alive. Your lungs are very large. A grown-up's lungs can hold about three litres of air.

What makes me yawn?

You yawn when you haven't been breathing deeply because you're tired or have been sitting still for a long time and you're not getting enough oxygen to your lungs. To take in more oxygen, you suddenly take a big gulp of air through your mouth.

? *What happens when I breathe?*

When you breathe in, your chest expands, your lungs get bigger and air goes up your nose, down your windpipe and into your lungs. When you breathe out, your chest and lungs become smaller and your diaphragm arches upwards to squeeze out stale air. All this happens in just a few seconds.

Windpipe

Lung

Diaphragm

19

Brain

? *What are nerves?*

Nerves carry messages to and from your brain, telling it if you're hungry, hot, cold or in pain. Nerves run from your spinal cord – a thick rope of nerves inside your backbone – to every part of your body.

Spinal cord

Nerves

❓ Why do I get pins and needles?

If you lie on your arm or leg for a long time, the tiny nerves in them get squashed. When you move again, the nerves may tingle and throb as they start to work again.

❓ What does my brain do?

Your brain sends signals along your nerves telling your body how to work. It stores all your thoughts and memories and controls everything you do.

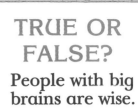

? How do my eyes help me see?

Each of your eyes is a ball. At the front, there's a black hole called the pupil, which lets in light. Behind the pupil is a lens that helps you to see things close to or far away. The optic nerve carries messages about what you see to your brain.

An upside down picture of what you see is sorted out by your brain, so that you see things the right way up.

Pupil

Iris

Lens

Optic nerve

Muscles (move eyeball up and down and from side to side)

?How do my ears help me hear?

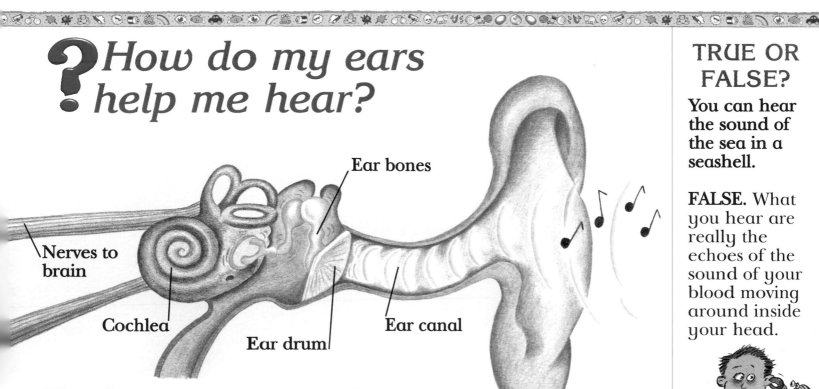

Ear bones

Nerves to brain

Cochlea

Ear drum

Ear canal

The flappy outer parts of your ears collect sounds from the air. The sounds enter your ears as tiny, invisible waves. The waves make your eardrum move up and down, and tiny bones deep inside your ears move, too. Nerves carry sound messages from your ears to your brain.

23

TRUE OR FALSE?

You can hear the sound of the sea in a seashell.

FALSE. What you hear are really the echoes of the sound of your blood moving around inside your head.

Carrots help you see better.

TRUE. Carrots contain special vitamins that might help you to see a little better in the dark.

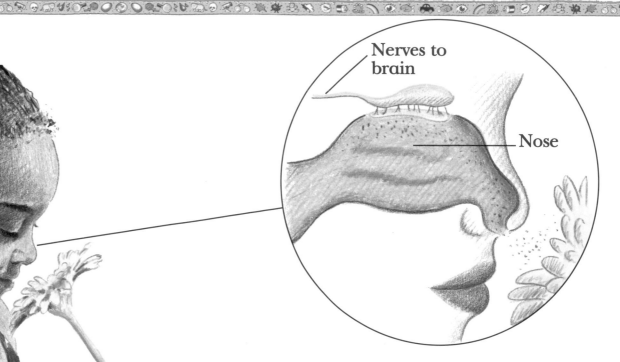

Nerves to brain

Nose

? *What's my nose for?*

Your nose is for smelling things, such as a flower, a tasty snack or stinky rubbish. Tiny bits of food or dirt go up your nose when you breathe in. These bits are too small to see but nerves inside your nose send messages about them to your brain.

? Why can't I taste food if I have a cold?

Your sense of smell and taste work together, so if you're eating a crunchy apple, your nose smells how sweet it is and tiny bumps on your tongue (called taste buds) pick up its flavour. When you have a cold, your nose often gets bunged up so it's hard to smell and taste things.

Bitter

Sour

Sweet

Salty

Taste areas of the tongue

? *What is chickenpox?*

Chickenpox is a disease, like mumps and measles. It's quite easy to catch but once you've had it you don't usually get it again. Sometimes, we have injections to stop us catching serious diseases that can make us very ill.

Why do I sometimes get sick?

You get sick when tiny harmful germs get into your body. Your white blood cells destroy germs by eating them, so that you get better again.

White blood cells eating the invading germs.

How do I stay healthy?

To stay healthy, you need to eat food that's good for you, drink lots of water, take plenty of exercise and get lots of sleep.

TRUE OR FALSE?

Watching TV is bad for you.

TRUE. If you watch it for several hours a day! TV is fun but everyone needs plenty of exercise like running, swimming or football as well.

Washing gets rid of germs.

TRUE. Germs can get into your body if you rub your eyes or eat with dirty hands, so it's important to keep your hands clean and always wash them before a meal.

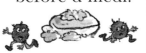

Where did I come from?

You began when a sperm from your father joined with an egg from your mother. A cell formed and began to make more and more cells and a baby – YOU – began to grow. A baby grows inside its mother's womb for nine months.

Sperm

Egg

TWO MONTHS

The baby's heart is beating.

SIX MONTHS

The baby weighs as much as a bag of sugar. It may suck its thumb.

SEVEN MONTHS

The baby can swallow and hear and recognise its mother's voice.

? *What's my tummy button?*

Your tummy button, or your navel, is the place where you were once joined to your mother by a cord called the umbilical cord when you were inside her womb. You got all the food and oxygen you needed to grow through this cord.

NINE MONTHS

At nine months, the baby is plump and strong and nearly ready to be born. It is around 50 cm long and weighs around 3.4 kg.

You are still growing.

TRUE. You get taller and stronger and you carry on changing shape, until you're about 18 years old.

Some mothers have more than one baby at a time.

TRUE. Two babies are called twins, four are called quadruplets and six babies are called sextuplets.

?Why do I sleep?

You need to sleep to stay healthy. While you're asleep, your body is resting, growing and repairing itself, getting ready for another busy day, and your brain is sorting out your thoughts.

? *Why do I dream?*

Dreams are times during the night when you sleep lightly. Everyone has about five dreams a night but we don't always remember them. Scary dreams are called nightmares. Some are so frightening, they may wake you up.

? *What's sleepwalking?*

Sleepwalking is when someone gets out of bed and walks around when they're still fast asleep. Sleepwalking is quite rare, and no one knows why some people do it.

Index

Human Factors in Simulation and Training

Human Factors in Simulation and Training

Edited by

Dennis A. Vincenzi
John A. Wise
Mustapha Mouloua
Peter A. Hancock

CRC Press
Taylor & Francis Group
Boca Raton   London   New York

CRC Press is an imprint of the
Taylor & Francis Group, an **informa** business

CRC Press
Taylor & Francis Group
6000 Broken Sound Parkway NW, Suite 300
Boca Raton, FL 33487-2742

© 2009 by Taylor & Francis Group, LLC
CRC Press is an imprint of Taylor & Francis Group, an Informa business

No claim to original U.S. Government works
Printed in the United States of America on acid-free paper
10 9 8 7 6 5 4 3 2 1

International Standard Book Number-13: 978-1-4200-7283-9 (Hardcover)

Library of Congress Cataloging-in-Publication Data

Human factors in simulation and training / editors, Dennis A. Vincenzi ... [et al.]
     p. cm.
   "A CRC title."
   Includes bibliographical references and index.
   ISBN 978-1-4200-7283-9 (alk. paper)
   1. Simulation methods. 2. Occupational training. 3. Human engineering. I. Vincenzi, Dennis A. II. Title.

T57.62.H845 2008
620.8'2--dc22   2008009818

Visit the Taylor & Francis Web site at
http://www.taylorandfrancis.com

and the CRC Press Web site at
http://www.crcpress.com

Contents

SECTION I Theory

SECTION II   Application

Preface

As we look toward the future we find that it is neither totally random nor is it totally predictable. If it were completely predictable, there would be no point looking forward because we would already know what was to come. If it were completely random, we would not bother because we could not know anything systematic about forthcoming events. That life lies between these two polar extremes gives us both the motivation to try to understand the future and the belief that we can do so, at least to a useful degree. Indeed, the triumphs of science encourage us to believe that we are making "progress" insofar as our predictions of the future. At least in relation to many physical processes, these are growing more accurate as the years progress. And, of course, the more we can know about the future, the more we can generate rational courses of action based upon this understanding. This respective confluence of ideas encourages us to develop theories, models, methodologies, and other such instruments to continue to improve our predictive capabilities.

However, although certain forms of prediction work well for some of the more simple physical processes, there are many forms of complex interactions in which our predictive capacities are at present rudimentary at best. Unfortunately, many of these complex processes—global warming, for example—may prove so dangerous to our species that we cannot afford to assert predictions that are radically incorrect. Flawed prediction here can spell our end. As a consequence, we are in ever greater need of technologies that allow us to generate and refine predictions as well as explore alternative potentialities found to be countertheses and antitheses to these various propositions. One such technology is simulation.

As a tool, simulation is an aid to the imagination. It allows us to create, populate, and activate possible futures and explore the ramifications of these developed scenarios. However, in common with all tools, it performs its task only to the degree that it is open to facile interaction with the user. One can imagine that on many occasions, a poor simulation with its impoverished or wildly inaccurate outcomes might be of even more harm than good. Thus, as with all tools and technologies, we certainly need the application of the branch of science that turns user–machine antagonism into user–machine synergy. That branch of science is human factors. Hence, the focus of this present work is on human factors issues as they pertain to simulation. In general these issues revolve around two central themes. The first theme concerns the application of human factors principles in order to generate, facilitate, and improve all of simulation. Indeed, there are many techniques and insights from the behavioral sciences that can help us to construct better ways in which to create and visualize possible futures. The second theme is more pragmatic and utilitarian in nature because it now reflexively asks how simulation itself can help address human factors issues such as training, design, evaluation, testing, and visualization. In this way, human factors seeks to both refine and improve the technology of simulation and then, in turn, benefit itself from those very improvements. The chapters presented in the following text reflect these general concerns.

One evident focus of this notion of usage derives from the ongoing concerns over training. More than ever, as we put individuals in circumstances that require flawless response or require them to act under extremes of stress or cognitive workload, we can no longer rely on the hope and expectation that they will perform such functions effectively the first time they are exposed to them. Training has always been a traditional answer to this inherent uncertainty and as more individuals are asked to work with ever more complex technologies, training has assumed growing importance. Also, the strictures of conflict are as ever unforgiving. The military finds itself under an ever-harsher mandate for flawless performance, and training continues to be touted as the answer. But, of course, training for unique circumstances is, almost by definition, untenable. The contemporary solution to this conundrum is through simulation. Inevitably, the simulation solution brings forth the issue of performance transfer, and it is one addressed at length in the present text. However, the optimistic view of this concern is that our simulations are improving along many dimensions and, indeed, our techniques for deriving validation metrics and measures of transfer have likewise increased across the recent decades. These gains encourage further investment in the simulation strategy, and the path to even greater improvements appears to be going directly through human factors. It is the synthesis of these various developments that give rise to the present text.

In this work, we have solicited chapters that deal with a wide variety of topics, beginning with theory and application, in areas ranging from traditional training to augmented reality to virtual reality. Areas of coverage include fields related to surface ships, submarines, naval aviation, commercial aviation, and space. The theory-based section of the book focuses on human factors aspects of simulation and training ranging from the history of simulators and training devices to future trends in simulation from both civilian and military perspectives. Chapters expand on concepts of interest to the simulation and training communities regarding simulator usage, particularly with respect to the validity and functionality of simulators as training devices. Chapters are comprised of in-depth discussions of specific issues including fidelity, interfaces and control devices, transfer of training, simulator sickness, effects of motion in simulated systems, and virtual reality. Enveloping both theory and application, this book addresses in detail numerous issues and concepts pertaining to human factors in simulation, gathering this important information into one comprehensive volume.

Dennis A. Vincenzi
John A. Wise
Mustapha Mouloua
Peter A. Hancock

Editors

Dennis A. Vincenzi, Ph.D. Dr. Vincenzi is a research psychologist for the Naval Air Warfare Center Training Systems Division (NAWCTSD) in Orlando, Florida. He earned his Ph.D. in human factors psychology from the University of Central Florida in 1998. He has performed extensive work in the areas of simulation, training, human performance, and systems testing and evaluation. Dr. Vincenzi is currently the lead researcher on an Office of Naval Research (ONR)–funded research project involving Next Generation Helmet Mounted Display Systems (NGHMOS) and is the technical point of contact for a number of cutting-edge small business innovative research (SBIR) initiatives.

Dr. Vincenzi's primary duties and responsibilities at NAWCTSD Orlando involve providing technical leadership, vision, and guidance resulting in efficient management of resources for a variety of efforts. Past training technology programs include Synthetic Teammates for Real-time Anywhere Training and Assessment (STRATA), and Virtual Submarine Officer of the Deck Training (VESUB), DDG 1000, Virtual Technologies and Environments (VIRTE), Debriefing Distributed Simulation-Based Exercises (DDSBE), and Deployable REdiness Devices (DRED).

John A. Wise, Ph.D., CPE Dr. Wise has over 25 years of experience in the practice, research, and project management of information science, human factors engineering, and display system design applied to aviation and aerospace systems. Dr. Wise has a long history of widely recognized research in aviation human factors, primarily addressing issues of information systems, automation, and future systems. He has led international interdisciplinary teams on projects sponsored by government agencies (e.g., NOAA, FAA, NASA, NATO, Eurocontrol, DGAC, Centre d'Etudes de la Navigation Aerienne), as well as various corporate sponsors (including Boeing). His research has impacted the design of a wide variety of systems including the F/A-18, F-15E, AV-8B, high-definition television standards, nuclear power plants, computer interfaces, and training systems. Despite this focus on applied research, the research has been published nationally and internationally, and he has been invited to both publish and speak in a wide variety of national/international venues. He has served on the faculty at the University of Pittsburgh, Embry-Riddle University, and is currently on the visiting faculty at the Ecole Nationale de l'Aviation Civile. In addition, he was a U.S. Air Force pilot for five years. He has published over 100 technical papers and 8 books.

Mustapha Mouloua, Ph.D. Dr. Mouloua received his Ph.D. (1992) and M.A. (1986) degrees in applied/experimental psychology from the Catholic University of America, Washington D.C. He is currently a professor of applied/experimental and human factors psychology, associate director of the applied/experimental and human factors doctoral program, and director of the Center of Applied Human Factors in Aviation (CAHFA) at the University of Central Florida, Orlando. Before joining the faculty at UCF in 1994, he was a postdoctoral fellow at the Cognitive Sciences Laboratory of Catholic University of America from 1991 to 1994 where he studied and researched several aspects of human–automation interaction topics sponsored by NASA and the Office of Naval Research (ONR). He was director of human factors research at the Center for Advanced Transportation Systems Simulation (CATSS) from 1999 to 2001, and a consulting faculty for the Florida Space Institute (FSI) at the University of Central Florida. He has over 25 years of experience in the teaching, practice, research, and development of complex human–machine systems. During his tenure at UCF, Dr. Mouloua directed three NASA/ONR research conferences on automation technology and human performance. He has taught a variety of undergraduate courses on subjects including research methods in psychology, experimental psychology, advanced research methods in psychology, human performance in systems, advanced human–computer interaction, and human factors in system design and evaluation. His research interests include human performance evaluation, human–automation interaction, pilot-alerting systems interaction, automation and workload, pilot training and detection of automation failures, adaptive function allocation and human monitoring of systems, cognition and performance of older pilots and drivers, simulation technologies, and training in transportation systems.

Dr. Mouloua was the editor of *Aging and Human Performance*, a special section of the *Human Factors Journal* (2005), *Human Performance in Automated Systems: Current Research and Trends* (1994, Lawrence Erlbaum Assoc.), *Human–Automation Interaction: Research and Practice* (1997, Lawrence Erlbaum Assoc.), *Automation and Human Performance: Theory and Applications* (1996, Lawrence Erlbaum Assoc.), and *Automation Technology and Human Performance: Current Research and Trends* (1999, Lawrence Erlbaum Assoc.). Dr. Mouloua has over 150 publications and scientific reports published in journals such as *Experimental Aging Research, Human Factors, Journal of Experimental Psychology: Human Perception and Performance, and Ergonomics in Design*. He has made more than 100 presentations at national and international meetings, 50 invited colloquia and lectures at local and regional meetings, and 42 interviews in local, national, and international newspapers, radio, and television. Dr. Mouloua was the recipient of the prestigious Jerome Hirsch Ely (1997) and Tidewater Awards (1999) from the Human Factors and Ergonomics Society; the NASA 2003 Award; and the Automation, Situation Awareness, and Human Performance Conference Chair's awards in 2005. His research programs have been supported by several state, federal, and private agencies including the Office of Naval Research, DARPA, NASA, ARO, Department of Transportation, AAA Foundation, and Lockheed Martin Systems. Dr. Mouloua has served as a consultant on several government-sponsored projects related to reducing the symptomatology of motion sickness in space (NASA), development of computerized batteries for the assessment of cognitive readiness and fitness for duty for the U.S. Army, and tests of visual perception, depth perception, and so forth.

Peter A. Hancock, Ph.D.   Dr. Hancock is Provost Distinguished Research Professor in the Department of Psychology, the Institute for Simulation and Training, and in the Department of Civil and Environmental Engineering, all at the University of Central Florida. In his previous appointment, he founded and was director of the Human Factors Research Laboratory at the University of Minnesota. At Minnesota he held appointments as full professor in the departments of computer science and electrical engineering, mechanical engineering, psychology, and kinesiology, as well as at the Cognitive Science Center and the Center on Aging Research. He currently holds a courtesy post as an adjunct senior research scientist at the Transportation Institute of the University of Michigan. Dr. Hancock is the author of over 500 refereed scientific articles and publications as well as the editor of numerous books including *Human Performance and Ergonomics* in the *Handbook of Perception and Cognition* series, published by Academic Press in 1999; and *Stress, Workload, and Fatigue,* published in 2001 by Lawrence Erlbaum Assoc. He is the author of the 1997 book, *Essays on the Future of Human–Machine Systems.*

He has been continuously funded by extramural sources for every year of his professional career, including support from NASA, NIH, NIA, FAA, FHWA, the U.S. Navy and the U.S Army, as well as numerous state and industrial agencies. He was the principal investigator on a multidisciplinary university research initiative, in which he oversaw $5 million of funded research on stress, workload, and performance. In 1999 he was the Arnold Small Lecturer of the Human Factors and Ergonomics Society and in 2000 he was awarded the Sir Frederic Bartlett Medal of the Ergonomics Society of Great Britain for lifetime achievement. Dr. Hancock was the keynote speaker for the International Ergonomics Association and the Human Factors and Ergonomics Society at the 2000 combined meeting in San Diego. In 2001 he won the Franklin V. Taylor Award of the American Psychological Association as well as the Liberty Mutual Prize for Occupational Safety and Ergonomics from the International Ergonomics Association. In association with his colleagues Raja Parasuraman and Anthony Masalonis, he was the winner of the Jerome Hirsch Ely Award of the

Human Factors and Ergonomics Society for 2001, the same year in which he was elected a fellow of the International Ergonomics Association. He was awarded a doctor of science degree from Loughborough University in December 2001. In 2002, he was awarded the Jastrzebowski Medal of the Polish Ergonomics Society for contributions to world ergonomics and in the same year was named a fellow of the Ergonomics Society of Great Britain. He has been elected to a three-year term as a member of the National Research Council's Committee on Human Factors, which will run concurrently with his membership on the executive council of the Human Factors and Ergonomic Society. In 2003 he won the Liberty Mutual Medal of the International Ergonomics Association, a worldwide competition for innovative advances in occupational safety and ergonomics. In 2006 he won the Norbert Wiener Award of the Systems, Man and Cybernetics Society of the IEEE. It is of interest to note that the company Geek Squad, which was featured on *60 Minutes* in January of 2007, was founded by Robert Stephens while working in Dr. Hancock's laboratory at Minnesota.

Dr. Hancock's current experimental work concerns the evaluation of behavioral response to high-stress conditions. His theoretical work concerns human relations with technology and the possible futures of this symbiosis. He is a fellow of and past president of the Human Factors and Ergonomics Society. He collects and studies antique maps and is a committed Ricardian.

Contributors

Robert C. Allen, Ph.D., CPE
Project Engineer–Human Factors
Worldwide Safety and Accessibility
Walt Disney World
Lake Buena Vista, Florida

Benjamin Bell, Ph.D.
Director, Business Development
CHI Systems, Inc.
Fort Washington, Pennsylvania

Elizabeth L. Blickensderfer, Ph.D.
Assistant Professor
Human Factors and Systems Department
Embry-Riddle Aeronautical University
Daytona Beach, Florida

Robert S. Bolia
Chief, Asia-Pacific Branch
AFRL International Technology Office
  (AFRL/XPPI)
Wright-Patterson Air Force Base
Dayton, Ohio

Cheryl A. Bolstad, Ph.D.
Senior Research Associate
SA Technologies
Forest Hill, Maryland

Michael T. Brannick, Ph.D.
Professor
Psychology Department
University of South Florida
Tampa, Florida

Gloria L. Calhoun
Senior Engineering Research Psychologist
Air Force Research Laboratory AFRL/RHCI
Wright-Patterson Air Force Base
Dayton, Ohio

Meredith B. Carroll
Senior Research Associate
Design Interactive, Inc.
Oviedo, Florida

Joseph Cohn, Ph.D., MSC, USN
Manpower, Personnel, Training, and
  Education Strategic Analyst
Strategic Affairs Office, Strategic
  Concepts Branch
Navy Annex
Washington D.C.

John E. Deaton, Ph.D.
Professor and Director of Research
Chair, Human Factors Program
College of Aeronautics
Florida Institute of Technology
Melbourne, Florida

Jared Freeman, Ph.D.
Senior Vice President, Research
Aptima, Inc.
Washington D.C.

Steven Hall, Ph.D.
Senior Manager, HR Research and
  Analytics
Marriott Vacation Club International
Orlando, Florida

Peter A. Hancock
Provost Distinguished Research
  Professor
University of Central Florida
Institute for Simulation and Training
Orlando, Florida

Cullen Jackson, Ph.D.
Senior Cognitive Scientist
Aptima, Inc.
Woburn, Massachusetts

Joan H. Johnston, Ph.D.
Senior Research Psychologist
Naval Air Warfare Center Training
  Systems Division AIR 4651
Orlando, Florida

Robert S. Kennedy, Ph.D.
President
RSK Assessments
Orlando, Florida

Stephanie J. Lackey
Deputy Director
Concept Development and Integration Lab
Naval Air Warfare Center Training Systems
  Division Partnership One
Orlando, Florida

Kristen K. Liggett, Ph.D.
Technical Adviser
System Control Interface Branch
Warfighter Interface Division
Human Effectiveness Directorate
Air Force Research Laboratory
  AFRL/RHCI
Wright-Patterson Air Force Base
Dayton, Ohio

Michael G. Lilienthal, Ph.D., CPE
Capt. MSC USN
Deputy Director, Biometrics Task Force
Arlington, Virginia

Dahai Liu, Ph.D.
Assistant Professor
Department of Human Factors and
  Systems
Embry-Riddle Aeronautical University
Daytona Beach, Florida

Ronald J. Lofaro, Ph.D.
Aviation Psychologist
Adjunct Associate Professor
Embry-Riddle Aeronautical University
Orange Beach, Alabama

Nickolas D. ("Dan") Macchiarella, Ph.D.
Assistant Professor
Department of Aeronautical Science
Embry-Riddle Aeronautical University
Daytona Beach, Florida

Phillip M. Mangos, Ph.D.
Research Psychologist
Naval Air Warfare Center Training Systems
  Division AIR 4651
Orlando, Florida

William F. Moroney, Ph.D., CPE
Director, Experimental Psychology and Human
  Factors Program
Department of Psychology
University of Dayton
Dayton, Ohio

Mustapha Mouloua, Ph.D.
Professor of Psychology
Psychology Department
University of Central Florida
Orlando, Florida

W. Todd Nelson, Ph.D.
Senior Research Psychologist
Air Force Research Laboratory
Wright-Patterson Air Force Base
Dayton, Ohio

Denise Nicholson, Ph.D., CMSP
Director
Applied Cognition and Training in Immersive
  Virtual Environments Lab (ACTIVE)
  Institute for Simulation and Training
University of Central Florida
Orlando, Florida

Tiffany Nickens
Systems Engineer
Rockwell Collins
Cedar Rapids, Iowa

Kristie Norman, CPT
Operations Research Analyst
Office of the Chief of Naval Operations
Total Force Integration Branch
Orlando, Florida

Stacie N. Pratt, USAF
T-6A Instructor Pilot
Laughlin Air Force Base
Laughlin, Texas

Joan M. Ryder, Ph.D.
Consultant
CHI Systems, Inc.
Maple Glen, Pennsylvania

William J. Salter, Ph.D.
Senior Cognitive Scientist
Aptima, Inc.
Woburn, Massachusetts

Mark W. Scerbo, Ph.D.
Professor
Department of Psychology
Old Dominion University
Norfolk, Virginia

Elizabeth A. Schmidt-Panos, M.S.
Old Dominion University
and
Eastern Virginia Medical School
Virginia Beach, Virginia

Dylan Schmorrow, Ph.D., MSC, USN
Program Manager
Office of Naval Research
Arlington, Virginia

Alton G. Seamon
Submarine Training Systems Program Manager
Naval Air Warfare Center Training Systems
  Division (NAWCTSD)
Orlando, Florida

Kevin M. Smith
United Airlines Captain (Ret.);
  USN Reserve Captain (Ret.)
Mesquite, Nevada

Janan A. Smither, Ph.D.
Associate Professor
Psychology Department
University of Central Florida
Orlando, Florida

Kay M. Stanney, Ph.D.
President
Design Interactive, Inc.
Oviedo, Florida

Emily M. Stelzer, Ph.D.
Cognitive Scientist
Aptima, Inc.
Washington D.C.

Laura D. Strater
Senior Research Associate
SA Technologies, Inc.
Carrollton, Texas

Trena N. Thompson
Embry-Riddle Aeronautical University
Daytona Beach, Florida

Linda Trocine, Ph.D.
President
Venutek, LLC
Oviedo, Florida

Michael A. Vidulich, Ph.D.
Principal Research Psychologist
Air Force Research Laboratory
  (AFRL/HEC)
Wright-Patterson Air Force Base
Dayton, Ohio

Dennis A. Vincenzi, Ph.D.
Research Psychologist
Naval Air Warfare Center Training Systems
  Division AIR 4651
Orlando, Florida

Emily E. Wiese
Senior Human Factors Engineer
Aptima, Inc.
Woburn, Massachusetts

Section I

Theory

1 Human Factors in Simulation and Training
An Overview

William F. Moroney and Michael G. Lilienthal

CONTENTS

INTRODUCTION

This chapter provides a broad overview of human factors and simulation with an emphasis on areas that will not be addressed in subsequent chapters; it addresses more global issues. It begins with a discussion of the pervasiveness of simulation, and delineates differences between simulation and modeling. This is followed by a section titled "Why Simulate?" that describes the advantages and disadvantages of simulation from a human factors perspective. Following this is a brief history of simulation that focuses on war gaming and aviation and includes a section on 21st-century simulators. Then the simulation development process is addressed, with particular emphasis on the often neglected area of Verification, Validation, and Accreditation (VV&A). This is followed by a section on simulating human behaviors in systems—a topic that will not be addressed in other chapters. This chapter closes with the authors' perceptions of future challenges in the areas of human factors and simulation.

Simulation is pervasive. Indeed, we probably received simulators during the first days if not hours of our lives. Interestingly, the devices were called pacifiers. While the name may have been provided by parents seeking a respite, a pacifier serves as both a simulator and a stimulator (see Appendix B for definitions). It simulates the nipple of a mother's breast or a feeding bottle and stimulates sucking and rooting reflexes, thus improving infant muscle tone.

Young children simulate as they play with their toys, athletes envision success, would-be fighter pilots do battle in the safety of their homes, while actual and aspiring politicians rule simulated cities. For engineers, educators, and trainers, simulation is a standard tool of their trades. Business relies heavily on simulation as part of its planning process. Simulation is not a relatively modern development attributable to technological and mathematical advances. Simulation has a much longer history. We use or have used simulation in many ways in our daily life. Consider the following examples of simulation (modified from Raser, 1969):

- Make-believe: a child engages in play-based learning as he or she manipulates blocks and model toys of various scales. It is interesting to note that as children mature, the level of expected fidelity increases. Thus, for most young children, scale is irrelevant and they see no inconsistency in playing with toy vehicles of various sizes. However, scale is critical for adults, for example, when creating a diorama.
- Artificial: an artificial Christmas tree is an example.
- Substitution: margarine used as a replacement for butter; clothing made of natural or synthetic material in lieu of animal fur.
- Imitation: faux leather purses; wallets made of Naugahyde or similar material.
- Deception: simulated storefronts used in movies and on theatrical stages; inflated military vehicles positioned where they can be observed by aerial reconnaissance or satellites.
- Mimicry: calls used by hunters to lure animals; vibration devices built into bouncing infant seats to provide a surrogate for parental rocking motion.
- Metaphor: Shakespeare's *Henry V* is a morality play applicable to modern warfare.
- Analogy: simulated sunlight used to reduce the effects of seasonal-adaptive disorders.
- Representation:
  - Mathematical: a graph representing the dynamics of a stock market.
  - Logical: a "you-are-here" map.
  - Physical: toys (scaled representations); Tinker toy-like representations of chemical bonds or DNA and 3-D and even 4-D holographic images.
  - Mental: our perception or belief of how hardware, software, or a system works.

Where would society be if humans did not have the ability to simulate? Where would the world be if individuals like Lincoln, Roosevelt, Churchill, Gandhi, Martin Luther King, Walt Disney, Bill Gates, and Steven Spielberg had no dreams or visions (simulations) of a different world? Indeed, one could speculate that at some level, the ability or drive to simulate is an essential part of proactive evolution. This ability is essential to human creativity, as Hofstadter (1979, p. 643) opined: "How immeasurably poorer our mental lives would be if we did not have this creative capacity for slipping out of the midst of reality into soft "what ifs"!"

On a higher intellectual plane, Rescher (1969) devotes a chapter of his book titled *Essays in Philosophical Analysis* to the concept of nonexistent possibilities, also known as nonentities, unactualized possibilities, negative things, unreal particulars, or nonexistent individuals. Aristotle believed that actual existence was not necessary for something to be considered in thought and discourse. Aristotle held that unactualized possibilities were meaningful, but statements about unactualized probabilities could not be considered true. St. Thomas Aquinas addressed the question of God's knowledge of nonexistents and concluded that God had full knowledge of nonexistents because otherwise he would not be omniscient. Descartes and Kant considered nonexistents as purely conceptual. While the issue of nonexistent probabilities has a long philosophical history, discussing them requires that we simulate their existence and the existence of their attributes.

On a more practical plane, Schrage (2000) stated, "We shape our models, and then our models shape us" (p. 13). To a large extent, our internal models determine our perceptions that in turn may influence and perhaps determine our behaviors in the real world. Individuals routinely utilize simulation when we engage in what is colloquially described as "wishful thinking" and cited in the psychological literature as "counterfactual thinking" (Roese and Olson, 1995). Counterfactual thinking is often characterized by a conditional statement including an antecedent ("if only...") followed by a consequence statement ("then..."). Sternberg and Gastel (1989a, 1989b) describe counterfactual thinking as an important component of intelligence. Tetlock and Belkin (1996) provide interesting reading regarding the role that counterfactual thinking has played in world politics including the rise of Hitler, Western perceptions of Soviet politics, and the Cuban missile crisis.

During World War II, simulation supported flight training through use of a "blue box" that held instruments within an enclosed cockpit and exhibited minimal physical displacement. During the 1970s, the word *simulation* invoked images of moving-based simulators tossing about cockpits atop platforms supported by giraffe-like hydraulic legs. The simulators were housed in special air-conditioned buildings and supported by highly skilled technical staff. In many ways, we should acknowledge the support of an unlikely hero who supported simulation for training and also the research and development (R&D) that made simulation what it is today. Senator Barry Goldwater, himself a pilot, began a series of hearings on simulation and training in the mid to late 1970s. The hearings brought focus and R&D funds to bear on the technology and effectiveness of simulation for training.

Simulations of cognitive processes emerged in the 1980s. Kahneman and Tversky (1982) developed a simulation heuristic describing how decision makers develop mental simulations. The five functions of their simulation heuristic are:

1. Generating predictions
2. Assessing event probabilities
3. Generating conditional probabilities
4. Assessing causality
5. Generating counterfactual assessments

Klein and Crandall (1995) defined mental simulation as "the process of consciously enacting a sequence of events" (p. 324). They describe how urban fire ground commanders (FGCs) use mental simulation to allocate resources and direct their firefighters. According to Klein and Crandall, 72% of the accounts of mental simulation in their database referred explicitly to visual imagery. Visual imagery is also used in athletic events; indeed, it is taught at the high school, college, and Olympic levels (Munroe, Giacobbi, Hall, and Weinberg, 2000; Weinberg, Butt,

Knight, Burke, and Jackson, 2003). Athletes are taught to visually simulate their performances in their particular events. This technique has been applied to events ranging from badminton (Callow, Hardy, and Hall, 1998) to swimming (Casby and Moran, 1998) to rowing (Barr and Hall, 1992).

For many years, higher-level simulation was the domain of technologists. However, with improved interfaces and increased accessibility to more capable and affordable personal computers, simulation is used almost daily by less technically oriented people. In the workplace, simulations such as weather and climate forecasts, expected aircraft delays, stock market projections, mortgage cost estimates, and retirement projections are common tools. Simulation tools used during play range from "first person" games such as those found on phones to massive multiplayer online games such as World of Warcraft, EverQuest, Ultima Online, Ragnarok Online, and Sims Online. For young children play is work. It starts with building blocks, then moves on to dollhouses. Play is computerized for 3-year-olds and older children, for example, the earth moving equipment available in the Tonka Dig 'N' Rigs Playset developed by Atari. Indeed, the distinction between simulators for work and play blurs when one considers simulations such as those for designing a house or landscape and Microsoft's flight simulator that allows both pilots and nonpilots to experience "flying" a variety of historic and current aircraft (Breeden, 2003).

Within the civilian aviation community, individuals have not only developed their own aircraft simulations (Wise, 2003), but are building personal moving-base simulators (Stibbe, 2003). The pervasiveness of simulations becomes more apparent when one considers the millions of Nintendo Wii, Microsoft Xbox 360, and Sony PlayStation users. These games produced interesting side effects ranging from a medical condition referred to as Nintendo thumb to the ability to improve visual attention (Green and Bavelier, 2003). The increase in simulator use may be attributed to the fusion of inexpensive computation power, affordable broadband, and wireless networks into the creation of a persistent environment available 24/7.

SIMULATION VERSUS MODELING

What is simulation? What is a model? While the terms are used interchangeably, is there a meaningful difference between simulation and modeling? Schrage (1999) commented, "Once upon a time there was a fighting chance to answer this question simply and clearly. Today, technologies have conspired to turn any answer into a confusing jumble of semantics that obscures understanding." (p. 7). Indeed, the terms are linked so closely that the Department of Defense (DoD) Directive 5000.59 (1994) provides a joint definition for modeling and simulation (M&S) as "the use of models, including emulators, prototypes, simulators and stimulators, either strategically or over time, to develop data as a basis for making managerial or technical decisions." Raser (1969) describes a simulation as "a special kind of model, and a model is a special way of expressing theory.... A 'theory' is a set of statements about some aspect of reality, such as the past reality, present reality or future reality. A theory attempts to describe the components of that reality and to specify the nature of the relationships among those components" (p. 6). Thus, for Raser, a model is a specific form of a theory, while a simulation is "an operating model that displays processes over time and that thus may develop dynamically" (p. 10).

It may be helpful to compare the usage of the terms simulation and modeling as nouns and verbs. According to DoD Instruction 5000.61, *simulation* (the noun) is defined as an executable implementation of a model, or execution of an implemented model, or a body of techniques for training, analysis and experimentation using models. *Model* (the noun) is defined as a "physical, mathematical, logical, or other representation of a system, entity, phenomenon or process." The Institute for Electrical and Electronics Engineers (IEEE) provides an even more encompassing definition of a model as an approximation, representation, or idealization of selected aspects of the structure, behavior, operation, or other characteristics of a real-world process, concept, or system (IEEE 610.12-1990).

This distinction is also reflected in differentiating between the verbs *simulating* and *modeling*. According to DoD Directive 5000.59 (1994), simulating is defined as "a method for implementing a model over time." Modeling is the "application of the standard, rigorous, structured methodology to create and validate a physical, mathematical or otherwise logical representation of a system, entity, phenomenon or process." According to the above definitions, the distinguishing feature is that a model is used to produce a simulation, while a simulation implements a model. Within the training community that focuses on the outcomes of modeling, the terms are often used interchangeably. Individuals who perceive modeling as a descriptive process see the model as the end product rather than the simulation of that model as the end product. Since the terms are more commonly used interchangeably, the authors have also used them interchangeably throughout the remainder of this chapter.

DoD, a leading developer and procurer of models and simulations, has developed fairly concise and pragmatic definitions of simulation and modeling terms. Other professional organizations such as IEEE and the Military Operations Research Society (MORS) have also made efforts to standardize the terminology. Appendices A (Modeling) and B (Simulation) are provided to help clarify the ambiguities associated with these terms and facilitate the reading and understanding of the material contained in subsequent chapters and related readings. Updated online modeling and simulation glossaries are maintained at https://www.dmso.mil/public/resources/glossary/ and http://vva.dmso.mil/ (select glossary).

DOMAINS AND DIMENSIONS OF MODELING AND SIMULATION

According to the Modeling and Simulation Information Analysis Center (MSIAC, 2006), the three primary domains of modeling and simulation are:

1. Training domain comprised of exercises, education, and military operations
2. Analysis domain comprised of operations and evaluation
3. Acquisition domain comprised of research and development (R&D), testing and evaluation (T&E), and production and logistics (P&L)

Current discussions at DoD show a shift toward identifying communities of interest that look to bring people with common interests together to define their communities and visions for the use of M&S and to speak as one voice. The intent is to break down barriers and silos within different organizations and better coordinate the management of the billions of dollars DoD invests annually for modeling and simulation. Currently the discussions include communities for acquisition, analysis, planning, training, testing, and experimentation.

Andrews, Brown, Byrnes, Chang, and Hartman (1998) provide two dimensions of simulation. In their first dimension, a simulation can be described as live, virtual, constructive, and hybrid. Live simulations involve live people using real systems (e.g., field exercises). Virtual simulations involve real people using simulated systems (e.g., moving-based flight simulators). Constructive simulations involve real people controlling simulation systems and simulated people (e.g., war games). Finally, a hybrid simulation "combines constructive, live, and/or virtual simulations, typically in a distributed environment" (DoD 5000.59-M, p. 119). Hybrid simulations used in R&D T&E may involve live people with current or proposed operational equipment in a simulated operational environment.

In their second dimension, simulations are classified as local or distributed. Local simulations are constrained to actual physical locations, while distributed simulations are interoperable and use communication networks to share information from a variety of locations. MSIAC (2006) indicates that models and the resultant simulations can differ on certain dimensions: level of resolution, degree of human participation, degree of physical realism, time management method, time stamp resolution, degree, distribution, and complexity.

WHEN IS A SIMULATOR NOT A SIMULATOR?

Generally devices that use simulation are considered simulators. However, the Federal Aviation Administration (FAA) does not classify all such devices as simulators. Its advisory circular titled *Airplane Simulator Qualification* (AC120-40C, 1995) defines an airplane simulator as "a full-size replica of a specific type or make, model and series airplane cockpit, including the assemblage of equipment and computer programs necessary to represent the airplane in ground and flight operations, a visual system providing an out-of-the-cockpit view, and a force-cueing system" (pp. 3, 4).

This advisory circular specifies four levels of simulators ordered in increasing complexity from Levels A through D. Every simulator must have a motion system with at least three degrees of freedom. With respect to optical systems, a Level A or B simulator must include a night visual system with a minimum field of view (FOV) of 45 degrees horizontal and 30 degrees vertical for each pilot station. Level C must have a night and dusk visual system with minimum FOVs of 75 degrees horizontal and 30 degrees vertical. Level D must provide daytime, dusk, and night visual systems and FOV of 75 degrees horizontal and 30 degrees vertical. Simulators meeting these requirements are used primarily for training and evaluating the performance of air carrier crew members. However, many devices that most people would classify as simulators do not meet the FAA's definition of a simulator and are classified as flight training devices (FTDs) or personal computer-based aviation training devices (PCATDs). FAA's *Airplane Flight Training Device Circular* (AC 120-45A, 1992) defines an FTD as "a full-scale replica of an airplane's instruments, equipment, panels, and controls in an open flight deck area or an enclosed aircraft cockpit, including the assemblage of equipment and computer software programs necessary to represent the airplane in ground and flight conditions to the extent of the systems installed in the device; does not require force (motion) cueing or visual system" (p. 4).

There are seven levels of FTDs and the level of realism required increases from Level 1 to Level 7. Legacy trainers that have FAA conferred status may meet Level 1 criteria. A Level 7 FTD must have the same lighting as the aircraft; use aircraft seats that can be positioned at the design–eye position; simulate all applicable flight, navigation, and system operations; and provide significant aircraft noises (precipitation, windshield wipers, etc.). Change 21 (March 2001) to FAA Order 8700.1, *General Aviation Operations Inspector's Handbook*, Volume 2, Chapter 34, maintained the distinction between FTDs and flight simulators and closely linked the required characteristics and components of these devices to the purposes of the FTD and simulators.

The newest category, PCATDs, was created when the increased capability of personal computers allowed manufacturers to provide more realistic flight simulations. The FAA responded by providing guidance for the qualification and approval of PCATDs in *Advisory Circular 61-126* (1997). This circular also specifies criteria for obtaining the required flight-hour training time for an instrument rating on a PCATD. Martin (2007) described the U.S. Air Force approach for the development of flight simulator specifications. Well-crafted generic specification paragraphs provide both samples of all requirements and recommendations and rationales for the specifications language and verification. The cut-and-paste software derived from this document should facilitate the development of simulator specifications.

Boothe (1994) commented that in simulators and FTDs, the emphasis is not simply on accomplishing the required task. To achieve maximum "transfer of behavior," the task must be performed exactly as it would be in the aircraft. Thus the same control strategies and control inputs must be provided in both the aircraft and the simulator. Boothe believed that the emphasis should be on appropriate cues, as identified by pilots, who are the subject matter experts. To achieve this end, Boothe argued for replication of form and function, flight and operational performance, and perceived flying (handling) qualities. He noted that these advisory circulars are developed by government and industry working groups that utilize realism as their reference and safety as their justification.

Roscoe (1991) offered a counterposition. He argued that "qualification of ground-based training devices for training needs to be based on their effectiveness for that purpose and not solely on their verisimilitude to an airplane" (p. 339). Roscoe concluded that pilot certification should be based on demonstrated competence, not hours of flight experience. Lintern, (1991) argued "The transfer observed following training on a task that differs in some specific respects from the criterion task is often better than transfer observed following equivalent training on the criterion task itself" (p. 261). Caro (1988) emphasized, "The cue information available in a particular simulator, rather than stimulus realism per se, should be the criterion for deciding what skills are to be taught in that simulator" (p. 239). Thus, important differences of opinion surround both the definitions of and the requirements for the qualification of simulators. We will return to this discussion later in this chapter in the section covering the modeling and simulation development processes.

WHY SIMULATE?

Before examining simulation in more detail, it is appropriate to ask why simulation evolved. It may have evolved for a variety of reasons, but its origins may be best attributed to an organism's parsimonious strategy of accomplishing tasks with the least amount of effort, thus conserving energy, avoiding overload, and maintaining homeostasis. This strategy is perhaps most apparent in our development of schema that constrain our perceptions as we transform data into information. Apparently, we simulate for the same reason we stereotype: simulation is both effective and efficient.

The reasons we simulate may be reflected in an examination of our uses of simulations and simulators. Currently, simulators are most frequently used for training of operators (air crews, physicians, bus and truck drivers, ship navigators, nuclear power plant operators, etc.) and maintainers (technicians who perform trouble shooting). Simulators are also used to maintain and/or evaluate proficiency levels and allow individuals to qualify for particular positions or ratings, for example, a pilot of a single-seat aircraft, a surgeon, or a nuclear power plant operator. Manufacturers routinely use digital prototypes for product R&D (e.g., automobile and aircraft cockpit prototypes). Systems engineers routinely use M&S as a prime means for managing the cost of developing, building, and testing increasingly complex systems. T&E experts rely on M&S to help design test scenarios and experiments. Since M&S is so essential to many human endeavors, its advantages, disadvantages, and limitations merit consideration.

ADVANTAGES OF M&S

Cost Effectiveness

Simulation and simulators are used primarily because they are cost effective, saving both time and money while effectively achieving the desired end. One objective of an effective training system is to provide the required level of training at the lowest possible cost. As Baudhuin (1987) stated, "The degree of transfer from the simulator to the system often equates to dollars saved in the operation of the real system and in material and lives saved" (p. 217). Within the aviation community, the effectiveness of simulators is accepted as an article of faith. Indeed, the aviation industry could not function without simulators and FTDs, both of which are mandated by FAA regulations (1992). As early as 1949, Williams and Flexman documented the effectiveness of aviation training devices (early simulators) as measured by the reduction in the number of trials and flight hours required to qualify pilots.

Flexman, Roscoe, Williams, and Willeges (1972) provided additional documentation regarding cost effectiveness and training effectiveness. In a very detailed analysis of cost effectiveness, Orlansky and String (1977) reported that flight simulators for military training operate at 5% to 20% of the cost of operating the aircraft simulated; median savings equaled approximately 12%. They also reported that commercial airlines can amortize the cost of a simulator in fewer than 9 months and the cost of an entire training facility in fewer than 2 years. Commercial airlines that use simulators accrue additional savings because they do not incur the loss of revenue associated with using aircraft for in-flight training.

Roscoe's seminal work (1980) documented the economic-versus-skill tradeoff between simulated hours and in-flight hours and became the "gold-standard" for determining the effectiveness of fixed-base simulators. Spears, Sheppard, Roush, and Richetti (1981) provided detailed summaries and evaluations of 196 research and development reports related to simulator requirements and effectiveness. Pfeiffer, Horey, and Butrimas (1991a, 1991b) supplied additional support in their report of positive transfer of instrument training to instrument and contact flight in an operational flight training aircraft (U.S. Navy T-2C).

The U.S. Air Force documented an even better example of training. In 1986, its MH-53H Pave Low Combat Crew Qualification Course was almost entirely aircraft-based. The Air Force replaced the MH-53H with the MH-53J in 1990. Due to the high hourly operating cost for this very complex multimission aircraft, training was shifted to simulators and part-task trainers. One of the most mentally demanding training tasks of the Pave Low was integrated sensor operations. In 1990, training consisted of 18 aircraft sorties of 2 hours each, changed in 1992 to 12 simulators and 3 aircraft sorties. The 1993 hourly cost for the MH-53J was $3100, while the weapons system trainer cost $800 to $1000 per hour (Selix, 1993).

Rakip, Kelly, Appler, and Riley (1993) surveyed experienced Pave Low crew members and their commanders in operational units to rate their perceptions of new crew members, all of whom completed the same curriculum but only some of whom trained on a Pave Low weapons systems trainer. Respondents rated those trained in the simulator as superior to their aircraft-only training counterparts on all criteria except night vision goggles on which they rated virtually the same. Training time was reduced significantly as simulator-trained individuals met operational standards in 2 to 3 months compared to 12 months for members of the nonsimulator group.

Often, because of the high cost of true transfer of training experiments, quasi-experiments are performed to determine the transfer between an FTD or part-task trainer and a representative high-fidelity simulator that serves as a surrogate for real aircraft. However, Jacobs, Prince, Hays, and Salas (1990), in a meta-analysis of data culled from 247 sources, identified 19 experiments in which training transfer between the simulator and actual jet aircraft was evaluated. They concluded that simulators reliably produced superior training relative to aircraft-only training. They also reported that jet aircraft takeoffs, landings, and approaches benefitted from the use of a simulator, with the landing approach showing the greatest benefit. However, similar conclusions regarding the effectiveness of helicopter simulators could not be drawn because only seven experiments involving helicopters met the criteria for inclusion in the meta-analysis.

Today's effectiveness questions still focus on how the required skills can be taught rapidly and inexpensively. Thus, we see an emphasis on the systems approach to training (Department of the Army, 1990) that, like the instructional systems development (ISD) approach, emphasizes requirement definition and front-end analysis (FEA) early in systems development and evaluation at the end. The *Handbook of Simulator-Based Training* by Farmer et al. (1999) provides details on FEA, program design, media selection, and training evaluation. Roscoe and Williges (1980), Roscoe (1980), and Baudhuin (1987) provided excellent descriptions of strategies for evaluating transfer of training, including the development of transfer effectiveness ratios (TERs), incremental transfer effectiveness functions (ITEFs), and cumulative transfer effectiveness functions (CTEFs).

All of these approaches attempt to measure the degree to which performing a desired task in an actual aircraft is facilitated by learning an intervening task on a training device or simulator. The resulting measure is usually expressed in terms of time saved. The critical concern as emphasized by Roscoe (1980) was not simply measuring effectiveness, but also determining cost effectiveness. Specifically, Roscoe was concerned with identifying the region in which increasing the investment in a training device (by improving fidelity, adding additional instructional features, etc.) did not result in a significant increase in transfer. However, as noted by Beringer (1994), because the cost of simulation has decreased as the capabilities of simulators have increased, today's question is more often: "If we can get more simulation for the same investment, what is the 'more' that we should ask for?" Thus, according to Beringer, cost is seen as a facilitating rather than a prohibitive factor.

Within the DoD, the use of simulation has significantly reduced the costs associated with live fire training. Bailey and Hodak (1994) reviewed several studies that examined the use of simulation in lieu of live fire for small arms training for U.S. Marines. At that time, the live fire cost to qualify a Marine with an M16 was $1762. Many empirical studies demonstrated that performance in the simulation was at least equal to live fire training and at lower cost. For example, Marines using the Multipurpose Arcade Combat Simulator expended fewer rounds during live fire qualifications and fewer candidates failed to qualify compared to those who underwent traditional training. The Precision Gunnery Training System was highlighted as an inexpensive trainer for Dragon and Tow missiles whose rounds cost $11,500 and $19,145 (in 1994 dollars, making live training prohibitively expensive). Several studies supported the simulated marksmanship training as a good investment that would increase the overall quality and effectiveness of training while significantly reducing annual cost (Berg, Adedeji, and Steadman, 1993; Berg, Adedeji, and Trenholm, 1993).

While cost effectiveness has traditionally been associated with training systems, it is now associated with simulations used at testing facilities. Consider, the F/A-18 Weapons Software Support Facility at China Lake, California, that includes avionics hardware, operator stations, and weapons and flight dynamic simulations. The facility provides test information that reduces the number of actual flights required. In 1996, the simulator facility operating cost was $930 per hour compared to $2800 per hour for an F/A-18 flight (Worley et al., 1996). The manned flight simulator (MFS) at Naval Air Station Patuxent River, Maryland, was heavily involved in R&D and T&E of emerging aircraft and systems. The facility has a motion-based system to provide acceleration cues for conventional takeoffs and landings, hovers, and transitions; a 40-foot, 360-degree dome; two laboratory stations; and a helmet-mounted display visual system. The modular approach employed at the MFS can support several aircraft simulators networked at the site or other live, virtual, or constructive simulations across a distributed high-speed encrypted network across the United States. A variety of high-fidelity cockpits are available including F-14D, a single-seat F/A-18A/C, a dual-seat F/A-18E/F, a V-22, a side-by-side generic helicopter, and a single-seat multi-reconfigurable cockpit. As system complexity increases and testing must become more environmentally friendly, the demands for simulation at test facilities will increase.

Likewise, the value of M&S has been documented for designing and producing new systems. A DoD study (Patenaude, 1996) compared the traditional engineering approach to design with a new process that leveraged M&S. Table 1.1 summarizes this comparison for six commercial manufacturers and three government organizations. Savings are reported as reductions in the number of personnel and man hours required to accomplish a task (translating to cost savings). For example, TRW Corporation reduced the time required for designing a radar warning system by 50 man-months. These savings were derived by the use of computer-aided design/computer-aided manufacturing (CAD/CAM) capabilities. The level of savings shown in Table 1.1 varies from 50% to 3000%. The level of saving depends on the situation, but as simulations have become more complex and interfaced with other models and simulations, their effectiveness and value have increased.

Some companies and government offices currently show no cost savings from the use of M&S because they had planned to use M&S when projects were initiated. Thus, M&S was engrained into their systematic approaches to product development. However, when possible, documentation of cost savings resulting from M&S should be obtained. These data can be used to justify

TABLE 1.1

U.S. Department of Defense Study of Effectiveness of M&S for System Acquisition

	Demonstrated Value of M&S for Design and Productivity		
Who	**What**	**Traditional**	**New Process w/ M&S**
TRW Corp.	Radar warning system research	96 man-months	46 man-months
TARDEC	Bradley Fighting Vehicle engineer analysis	4–6 man-months	0.5 man-months
	Low silhouette tank design	55 engineers—3 yr	14 engineers—16 months
GE	Engine fan blade	4 weeks	A few hours
Lockheed-Martin	Engineering mock-ups	2100 h	900 h
	Changes per final drawing	Four changes	2.2 ($108 million/yr)
	Solid modeling		Eliminated physical mock-ups @ $30 million each
	Design verification		30–50% reduction
IBM	M&S and integrated process team	S.38 computer with 10 K parts in 4 yr	AS 400 computer with < 4K parts in < 2 yr
Motorola	Application specific integrated circuits		50% reduction in design cycle time
	Cellular communication products		Product cycle reduced 50%
Sikorsky Aircraft	External working drawings	CH-53E—38 draftsman—6 months	RAH-66—one engineer in 1 month
NAVSEA	Seakeeping analysis	1985—27 d	1994—3.5 d
	Radar cross section analysis	1990—57 d	1997—17 d
Comanche Program Management Office	Mission and engineering simulators	$500 million UH—60 fly-off prototype	$20 million RAH-66 Simulator and Surrogate A/C Fly-off

Source: Based on Patenaude, A., 1996, Study on Effectiveness of Modeling and Simulation in Weapons Systems Acquisition Process (study conducted for the Deputy Director, Test Systems Engineering and Evaluation, Office of the Secretary of Defense), McLean, VA: Science Applications International Corporation.

and encourage further M&S development. Readers interested in additional details about DoD's interests in M&S in manufacturing and acquisition can consult the National Research Council's 2002 report.

Availability

Many simulations are available 24/7, and do not require the physical presence of the object simulated. However, some aircraft and ships have built-in simulations that allow training in the actual vehicle while using onboard operational systems. A simulator can allow immediate access to a simulated location (described by latitude and longitude) under specified environmental conditions (day, night, fog, sea state, etc.). Thus, the simulation of a physical presence at a location under specific environmental or operational conditions can be achieved. For example, a simulator allows a student to complete an instrument landing system (ILS) approach and return immediately to the final approach fix (FAF) to commence the next ILS approach without consuming the time and fuel required to re-enter the landing pattern. Indeed, since simulators allow an instructor to control reality, conflicting traffic in a landing approach can be eliminated to further increase the number of approaches flown per training session. In short, simulators provide more training opportunities than could be provided by an actual aircraft in the same amount of time. As noted by Jones (1967), simulators can provide training time in nonexistent aircraft or in aircraft in which first performance in a new system is critical (e.g., the early space shuttle landings and flights in single-seat aircraft).

Safety

Simulation provides a means for experiencing normal conditions in a safe and nonthreatening environment. It also allows exposure to controlled critical conditions that trainees hope they will never encounter such as loss of control of a vehicle or need for egress during a fire. Simulation also provides opportunities for initial qualification or requalification in a variety of work places such as control rooms of nuclear power plants and vehicles such as the space shuttle. For some tasks, the ability to control a simulated environment, for example, in a hyperbaric chamber, is critical. Within the aviation domain, due to safety concerns, a simulator may be the only way to teach certain flight maneuvers or expose air crews to conditions they are unlikely to experience under actual flight conditions (e.g., engine separation at take-off, wind sheer, loss of hydraulic systems, and engine fire).

Simulation is routinely used for crew resource management (CRM) research and training. CRM evolved from cockpit resource management (Weiner, Kanki, and Helmreich, 1993). The original objective of CRM was to reduce the number of aviation accidents and incidents by increasing the effectiveness of cockpit crew coordination and flight deck management. Since its introduction in 1978, CRM training has been expanded to include both cockpit flight and cabin crew members, dispatchers, maintenance personnel, and security staff. Its effectiveness is well documented (Helmreich et al., 1990; Salas, Rhodenizer, and Bowers, 2000; Weigmann and Shappell, 1999). CRM has begun to be incorporated into the training of medical teams, particularly in operating rooms (Bond et al., 2007; Helmreich and Schafer, 1998).

Additionally, automation has increased the need for simulators, as Wiener and Nagel (1988, p. 453) commented, "It appears that automation tunes out small errors and creates the opportunities for larger ones." In automated glass (cathode ray tube, liquid crystal flat panel) cockpits, improvements in system reliability have reduced the probability and frequency of system problems and situational awareness while inducing a sense of complacency on the part of air crew members. However, when an unanticipated event occurs, a crew must be trained to respond rapidly and correctly. Simulators provide opportunities for that type of training.

Surrogate Value

When simulator hours are accepted in lieu of hours using an operational system, the usage of the actual system is reduced. Thus, simulator usage for ground transportation and aviation systems reduces the exposure and number of hours on vehicles, which in turn reduces mechanical wear and tear, maintenance costs, and infrastructure loads on highways and the national airspace system. Additionally, in the case of commercial airlines, aircraft not required for training purposes can be utilized on revenue-producing flights.

Environmental Problem Reduction

Simulated vehicles do not pollute, consume fuel, create noise, or leak hazardous substances such as radiation, nor do they damage people or property. Indeed, simulated patients and bomb-damaged areas can be "repaired" at the flick of a reset switch. The U.S. Navy has a requirement to determine the survivability of its new ship classes from near-miss explosions of torpedoes and underwater mines. Traditionally, the Navy performed full ship shock tests in which a ship was subjected to a significant underwater explosion. Environmental impact studies are required for this type of exercise. In the future, it may become difficult for the Navy to gain permission to conduct such open ocean tests. Advances in finite element analyses of structures and high performance computing systems may enable the Navy to conduct less severe tests or entirely eliminate the need for such large shock tests.

Improved Training Environment

Simulators incorporate instructional features that enhance student learning and facilitate instructor intervention. Moroney and Moroney (in press) provide a detailed listing of instructional features incorporated into modern simulators including:

- Simulator instructor options such as preset and reset capability, crash and kill overrides, playback, replay, motion, and sound
- Ability to set task conditions such as time of day, season, weather, wind direction, velocity, degree of realism, aircraft stability, and instrument malfunction
- Performance analysis and monitoring features such as automated performance measurement, debriefing aids, warnings, and advisories that a preset parameter is about to be or has been exceeded

Standardized Training Environments

Simulators can provide identical flight dynamics and environmental conditions from training session to training session. Thus, the same task can be repeated until the required criteria are attained and indeed until the task is overlearned (automated). Unlike an airborne instructor, a simulator instructor (SI) can focus on teaching a task without flight responsibilities or concerns about safety and violations of regulations. Thus, he or she may deliberately allow a student to make mistakes such as illegally entering a terminal control area or flying below an assigned altitude.

Provision of Data

Simulation provides opportunities for data collection that are not available in the real world. While the critical issue of collecting accurate data is beyond the scope of this chapter, data collection permits:

- Performance comparison: as part of the diagnosis process, student performance can be compared with performance criteria and with the performances of other students at the same stage of training.
- Performance and learning diagnosis: having evaluated a student's performance, an instructor can gain some insight into the student's learning processes and suggest new approaches in problem areas.
- Performance evaluation: performance measurement can be used to evaluate the efficacies of different approaches to training a particular task.

Lack of Realism

Despite the emphasis on high fidelity and realism, simulators are not realistic; rather they allow us to manipulate reality. Paradoxically, this lack of realism contributes to their effectiveness. Lintern (1991) stated that transfer could be enhanced by "carefully planned distortions of the criterion task" (p. 251). Additionally, most instructional features found in simulators do not exist in the cockpit or the device simulated. Indeed, if real cockpits had the same features as simulators, the reset button would be used routinely because it can undo and defy the laws of physics. The entertainment industry relies on this ability to suspend reality to move audiences to nonexistent worlds. Viewers readily suspended reality when the USS Enterprise on *Star Trek* accelerated to warp speed and when repulsion technology was used to power the Land Speeders in *Star Wars*.

Disadvantages of Simulation

Failure to Reflect Real-World Performance

While performance in a simulation with reasonable fidelity is probably indicative of expected performance in the real world, we must recognize that performance in a simulator does not necessarily reflect how an individual will react in the real world. There are at least three reasons for this:

- Because there is no potential for an actual accident in a simulator, it would seem reasonable to expect that a trainee's stress level would be lower in a simulator. However, the stress level may increase when an individual's performance is evaluated or when he or she is competing for a position or a promotion.
- To the extent that teams or individuals, being evaluated or seeking a qualification, expect an emergency or unscheduled event during their time in the simulator, their performance in a simulator may not reflect in-flight performance. A trainee would, in all probability, have reviewed operating procedures prior to the start of his or her period in the simulator. Nonetheless, it should be recognized that a review of procedures even in preparation for an evaluation is of value.
- Trainee and crew member performance (particularly vigilance and situational awareness) during evaluation in a simulator rarely reflects the fatigue and/or boredom common to many cockpits. Because the person being evaluated expects the evaluator to create multiple malfunctions in an effort to determine his or her proficiency level, he or she is hypervigilant. Thus performance in a simulator may exceed actual in-flight performance.

Equipment and Facility Costs

The cost of computer-based simulation has decreased dramatically in the past 30 years as processing speed and input–output capability have increased. In addition, the requirements for supporting infrastructure (particularly cooling and space requirements) have decreased. However, more sophisticated simulations, particularly dome and motion-based simulators, usually require unique air-conditioned facilities and maintenance personnel, thus reducing assets available to operational personnel.

Surrogate Value

The advantages of using a simulator as a replacement for an operational system were described earlier, but their surrogate value has a downside. Reduced utilization of the operational system will require fewer maintenance personnel and achieve reduced supply chain requirements. These apparent savings may create personnel shortages and logistic problems when the operational tempo rises beyond the training level.

User Acceptance

The acceptance and use of simulators are subject to the attitudes of simulator operators, instructors, trainees, management, and evaluating agencies. The increased use of computers from preschool to college has increased their acceptance in the education and training processes. However, trainees often voice the expectation of "using a real system, not a simulation." User acceptance can be significantly influenced by a management policy that monitors the appropriate use of simulation. A critical element in this process is determining the appropriate performance metrics.

Measuring effectiveness is a fairly complicated process that has performance measurement at its core. Lane's (1986) report is a "must read" for individuals interested in measuring performance in both simulators and the real world. Mixon and Moroney (1982) provided an annotated bibliography of objective pilot performance measures in aircraft and simulators. Gawron (2000) provided a compilation and review of performance measurement techniques that could be used with operational systems and simulations. Readers interested in measuring transfer effectiveness are referred to Boldovici's chapter (1987) on sources of error and inappropriate analysis for estimating transfer effectiveness. Overall, the advantages of M&S significantly outweigh any real or perceived disadvantages as evidenced by the general acceptance of simulators by both users and regulatory agencies.

BRIEF HISTORY OF SIMULATION

After considering the many facets of simulation covered earlier, the authors realize that any detailed discussion of all the areas in which human factors and ergonomics professionals use simulation is beyond the scope of this chapter. Therefore, we examined two different human-related domains that have played a major role in the history of simulation—namely, war gaming and aviation. War gaming, originally focused on decision making and strategy development, has evolved into distributed mission training at multiple locations on a distributed simulation network. Aviation has pushed the development of simulation technology from manually manipulated simulators to multiple aircraft at different locations engaged in simulated air combat mission (ACM) training simulations.

War Gaming

The ubiquitous Internet began as a Defense Advanced Research Project Agency (DARPA) effort to ascertain whether critical information could successfully pass over multiple communication paths despite the destruction of some nodes. Many other innovations, including emergency medical services, blood plasma, and lasers claim their origins in warfare. Modern simulation is no exception; it evolved from war fighting strategies.

Simulating battles through games can be traced back to the Hindu game known as "Chaturanga" and the Eastern game called "Go" (Allen, 1987). McLean (1978) notes that roles, rules, unforeseen chance factors, and time compression are characteristics of war games. He also notes that resources are allocated in proportion to the capabilities of the conflicting nations. Within Western culture, chess is sometimes considered an early example of simulation. Consider the elements involved in chess. All the actors (knights, kings, queens, bishops, rooks, etc.) have roles, predetermined start points, and specific rules of engagement with which they must comply. Chess involves both deterministic (rule compliance) and probabilistic (anticipation of opponent's moves) elements.

According to Allen, the Prussians used military chess and toy soldiers for warfare training and planning during the 17th century. They employed formal tactics subject to rules and mathematics. During the 18th century, a game known as Kriegsspiel (war play) employed a 60 square by 60 square playing board representing the terrain of the Franco–Belgian border and required a 60-page rule book to set up the scenario and adjudicate the moves. As more data were incorporated into the game, it became more rigid. Over time, a less rigid, more practical (free) Kriegsspiel based on the judgments of umpires evolved. During the mid-1800s, major European countries expanded the concepts of war games from tactical situations to strategic situations. Late in the 1800s, the Japanese employed war gaming effectively in preparing for the Russo–Japanese War of 1904.

During the 1880s, Major William R. Livermore's book titled *American Kriegsspiel* introduced war gaming to the United States military. Look-up tables were used to determine some outcomes. Casualty rates were determined as functions of range, firepower, duration of exposure, and so forth. A roll of the dice added the element of chance to the probability of the outcomes. In 1889, the U.S. Navy introduced war gaming at the Navy War College (established in 1885).

The practice was soon institutionalized. Allen (1987) provided a foreboding description of a scenario assigned in 1897 to the Navy War College as a "special problem" by Assistant Secretary of the Navy Theodore Roosevelt. Roosevelt's scenario was, "Japan makes demands on Hawaiian Islands. This country intervenes. What force will be required to uphold intervention? Keep in mind possible complications with another power in the Atlantic" (Allen, 1987, p. 120). One task in 1900 was preventing a Japanese invasion of California; while in 1911, one plan called for a naval blockade of Japan.

During the late 1800s and early 1900s, General Alfred Graf von Schlieffen used war games to develop a war plan that involved a swing by German forces through the Low Countries and on to Paris. However, the Germans had not anticipated that the British would share the outcomes of their war games with the French and Belgians. Thus, the allied forces blocked the German invaders early in World War I. During the period between the wars, the German military, whose size was restricted by the Treaty of Versailles, trained its officers by developing war games that led to the development of the blitzkrieg tactics in World War II.

Outcomes of the war games impacted the development of both technologies and tactics. During war games in the early 1900s that pitted the U.S. Navy and the British Navy against each other, it was observed that the longer ranges of the British guns allowed them to attack U.S. vessels at ranges that precluded attacks by U.S. Navy vessels. This finding, among others, led to the U.S. Navy's development of longer range guns with higher elevations, improved gunnery training, and thicker deck plates to protect against British shells.

As the use of war game simulations increased, the need for more appropriate models also increased. During the 1930s, Fletcher Pratt developed a mathematical formula now considered a model. The parameters of his formula for calculating the probabilities of suffering damage and inflicting damage included armor thickness, ship speed, gun calibers, and numbers of guns. In describing the model, Pratt wrote, "It is extremely arbitrary; but the only answer is that it works out in practice better than some more common methods of computation" (Allen, 1987, p. 124). As evidence of the validity of his model, Pratt applied it to examine the damage inflicted on the Nazi battleship *Graf Spee* in 1939. Based on firepower and armor alone, the battleship should have destroyed the three more lightly armed cruisers that attacked it; but as Pratt's model would have predicted, they damaged the *Graf Spee* so effectively that it had to be scuttled.

In September 1941, the Japanese Naval War College played a war game for 11 days that ended with a surprise attack on Pearl Harbor. Allen (1987) reported that Vice Admiral Nagumo, who subsequently led the attack on Pearl Harbor, played himself during the game. Allen also noted that games played by Japanese war planners were used to convince Japanese politicians that Japan would win a war with the United States.

Senior U.S. Navy leaders had been exposed to war gaming at the Navy War College prior to the outbreak of WWII. Allen (1987) quotes Admiral Nimitz as saying, "The war with Japan had been reenacted in the game rooms at the Navy War College by so many people and so many different ways, that nothing that happened during the war was a surprise, absolutely nothing except the kamikaze tactics toward the end ...; we had not visualized these" (p. 127). As an aside, it should be noted that simulations were used to develop tactics to counter kamikaze attacks.

Perla (1990) provided an intriguing discussion about Japanese war games and the Battle of Midway. In May 1942, aboard the flagship *Yamato*, the invasion of Midway was simulated during a war game. In the course of the simulation, U.S. planes from Midway attacked the Japanese carriers and on the basis of a die toss, nine hits resulted in the sinking of two Japanese carriers. This loss was overruled by the presiding officer, Rear Admiral Ugaki, who determined that only one aircraft carrier was sunk and the other was only slightly damaged. After the conclusion of the game, Ugaki inquired about a contingency plan in case a U.S. Navy carrier task force opposed the Japanese invasion. He received an ambiguous reply that led him to caution that such a possibility should be considered (Perla, 1990). A month later, the real battle of Midway was fought. Land-based planes did little damage to the Japanese fleet, while the unexpected U.S. carrier task force effectively destroyed Japanese carrier-based air power. With respect to Ugaki's decision, Perla noted that the land-based aircraft did not score a single hit on Japanese carriers, thus validating Ugaki's inquiry. Regarding the Battle of Midway, Perla emphasized that the outcome of the Japanese war game might have been different if the individual representing the commander of the American forces behaved in a manner more characteristic of an American commander. Lesson developers and simulation users should learn from this error that the fidelity of the players is an essential element of a valid war game. Readers interested in more details on war games can consult the 32-page war game bibliography prepared by Aegis Research Corporation (2002).

While war gaming is performed on a macro level, mission planning is performed on a micro level and is another area of considerable interest to DoD. Human factors, particularly within the domains of decision making and teamwork, have been and will continue to act as factor in the development and utilization of both types of simulations. Human factors professionals can aid modelers in areas such as requirements definition, variable selection, data selection and analysis, information processing, information presentation, model validation, after-action reviews, and interface design.

AVIATION

The U.S. Army Signal Corps' Specification 486 (1907) for its first "air flying machine" imposes one very straightforward user-centric requirement: the device should be sufficiently simple in its construction and operation to permit an intelligent man to become proficient in its use within a reasonable period. Apparently, the "intelligent man" needed help or the flying machine was too complex. Within 3 years, Haward (1910, as quoted in Rolfe and Staples, 1986) described an early flight simulator as "a device which will enable the novice to obtain a clear conception of the workings of the control of an aeroplane, and of the conditions existent in the air, without any risk personally or otherwise" (p. 15).

As early as 1910, the Wright Brothers used a "kiwi bird" flight simulator in their training school at Huffman Prairie (Bernstein, 2000). Students learned rudimentary flight control while seated in a defunct Wright Type B Flyer mounted atop a trestle. Motion was induced by a motor-driven cam. With respect to cost, Bernstein reports a Bernard Whelan as saying the simulator "was the only thing that I know that cost more then than it does today. It cost sixty dollars an hour to take flight training at the Wright School. That's a dollar a minute. And they didn't sign you up for anything less than four hours" (p. 123).

A similar device was described by Adorian, Staynes, and Bolton (1979). The Antoinette Trainer (circa 1910) required that a student maintain balanced flight while seated in a barrel (split the long way) equipped with short "wings." The barrel, with a universal joint at its base, was mounted on a platform slightly above shoulder height so that instructors could push or pull on these "wings" to simulate disturbance forces. The student's task was to counter the instructors' inputs and align a reference bar with the horizon by applying appropriate control inputs through a series of pulleys. Figure 1.1 shows an Antoinette, one of the earliest rudimentary trainers (circa 1910).

The French Foreign Legion utilized a more dynamic simulator. The legion realized that an airframe with minimal fabric on its wings would provide trainees with insight into the flight characteristics of the aircraft while limiting damage to the real aircraft and the student (Caro, 1988). In 1917, Winslow, as reported in Rolfe and Staples (1986), described this device as a "penguin" capable of hopping at about 40 miles per hour. Although of limited use, it exhibited considerable improvement over the earlier flight training method of self-instruction by which trainees practiced solo until they learned basic flight maneuvers. Instructors participated in in-flight training only after the trainees learned the relationship between input and system response through trial and error (Caro, 1988). Apparently, the legionnaires understood the value of a skilled flight instructor.

FIGURE 1.1 One of the earliest rudimentary trainers, an Antoinette Trainer (ca. 1910).

The origins of modern flight simulators can be traced to 1929, when Edward A. Link received a patent for a generic, three-degree-of-freedom (yaw, pitch, and roll), ground-based flight simulator (Figure 1.2). His initial trainer with stubby wings and rudders was designed to demonstrate simple control surface movements and make them apparent to an instructor. Later a hood was installed over the cockpit that, with appropriate instruments in the cockpit, allowed the device to be used for

FIGURE 1.2 "Blue Box" Link Trainer and associated instrument table.

instrument flight training. Link based his design on the belief that the trainer should be as analogous to the operational setting as possible. The use of compressed air that actuated bellows allowed a trainer to simulate pitch, yaw, and roll, enabling student pilots to gain insight into the relationship of stick inputs and movements in three flight dimensions.

A patent for an aviation training machine that used an air-operated motor was granted to Levitt L. Custer of Dayton, Ohio, in 1930. Link's invention was originally marketed as a coin-operated amusement device (Fischetti and Truxal, 1985), but the value of Link's simulator was recognized when the Navy and Army Air Corps began purchasing trainers in 1934. Flight instructors, watching from outside the "blue box" monitored the movements of the ailerons, elevator, and rudder to assess a student's ability to activate the control inputs necessary for various flight maneuvers. A plotting table (Figure 1.2) allowed instructors to observe the ground track and speed of an aircraft.

History has repeated itself with Microsoft's Flight Simulator software. Originally sold as a game, the simulator has evolved into a PC-based training device. Grupping (2005) documented the development of the PC-based program. It was originally developed by Bruce Artwick as part of his master's program at the University of Illinois in 1975. It was released by subLOGIC as FS1 for Apple II computers in January 1980. In November 1982, Microsoft began distributing it as Flight Simulator 1.01, and multiple upgrades have been released since then. In 2006, Microsoft released the newest version as Flight Simulator X covering 21 new and current aircraft such as the Airbus 321 and Boeing 737-800 and legacy aircraft such as the Piper Cub and Cessna 172. The simulated aircraft can be flown to and from thousands of airports (with dynamic airborne and ground traffic and ground support equipment).

When the United States entered World War II, more than 1600 trainers were in use throughout the world. The number increased as the Allied forces rushed to meet the demand for pilots. During the war years, the U.S. military utilized approximately 10,000 Link trainers (Caro, 1988; Stark, 1994). In 1943, an operational flight trainer for the U.S. Navy's PBM-3 aircraft was produced by Bell Telephone Laboratories (Pohman and Fletcher, 1999). This trainer used analog circuitry to solve flight equations in real time and presented the results using the controls and instruments available in the aircraft. During World War II, considerable assets were devoted to the development of electronic digital computers. In 1944, with U.S. Navy funding, the Massachusetts Institute of Technology (MIT) undertook the development of an electronic flight simulator (Waldrop, 2001). Prior development efforts focused on batch-processing computers. This type of computer solved an equation and then waited for the next one. The MIT developers recognized the need for a computer that responded in real-time to constantly changing pilot inputs and dynamic responses of simulated aircraft. They built Whirlwind, the first real-time digital computer that was the basis of the modern personal computer. Its performance in 1951 was equivalent to the 1980 TRS-80 personal computer (1.774 MHz, 12K ROM, 4–48K RAM), but its vacuum tube electronics required an area approximately the size of small house along with unique electrical and cooling requirements.

After the war, simulations developed for military use were adapted by commercial aviation. Loesch and Waddell (1979) reported that by 1949, the use of simulation reduced airline transition flight training time by half. Readers interested in details of the intriguing history of simulation would do well to consult the Royal Aeronautical Society's excellent three-volume history titled *Fifty Years of Flight Simulation* (1979). Also, Jones, Hennessy, and Deutsch (1985), in *Human Factors Aspects of Simulation*, provide an excellent overview of the state of the art of simulation and training through the early 1980s. Finally, a chapter about flight simulation by Moroney and Moroney (in press) provides additional detail.

Following World War II and throughout the 1950s, aircraft diversity and complexity created the need for aircraft-specific simulators, that is, simulators that represented specific models of aircraft in instrument layout, performance characteristics, and flight handling qualities. Successful representation of instrument layout and performance characteristics was readily accomplished, but the accurate reproduction of flight handling qualities was a more challenging task (Loesch and Waddell, 1979).

Exact replication of flight is based on the unsupported belief that higher fidelity simulation would result in greater transfer of training from the simulator to the actual aircraft. This belief has prevailed for years and continues today. However, even 50 years ago, researchers questioned the need to have a simulator duplicate every aspect of flight (Miller, 1954; Stark, 1994).

Spannaus (1978) lists three characteristics of simulations used in an educational context: (1) they are based on a model of reality, (2) the objectives must be at the level of application, and (3) the participants must deal with the consequences of their decisions. He believed that students could not simply act as observers. They had to be involved for an activity to be called a simulation. Today's educators and trainers call this process active learning. Ricci, Salas, and Cannon-Bowers (1996) provide experimental support for the advantages of active learning, specifically computer-based gaming, in knowledge acquisition and retention.

Caro (1979) emphasized that a flight training simulator's purpose was "to permit required instructional activities to take place" (p. 84). However, from his 1979 examination of existing simulators, design procedures, and the relevant literature, Caro concluded that "designers typically are given little information about the instructional activities intended to be used with the device they are to design and the functional purpose of those activities" (p. 84). Fortunately, some progress has been made in this area. Today, as part of the system development process, designers (knowledgeable about hardware and software), users and instructors (knowledgeable about the tasks to be learned), and trainers and psychologists (knowledgeable about skill acquisition and evaluation) interact as a team when developing training systems (Stark, 1994). The objective of this development process is to maximize training effectiveness while minimizing the cost and time required to reach the training objective (Stark, 1994).

To fully exploit the tremendous progress in simulation technology, Salas, Bowers, and Rhodenizer (1998) propose that we reduce the emphasis on fidelity and realism and focus on enhancing the learning of complex skills by bridging the gap between training research findings and the use of training technology. They challenge the assumptions that (1) simulation is all you need; (2) more fidelity is better; and (3) a device is good if aviators like it. They propose that the emphasis shift from technology to learning, specifically, to a trainee-centered approach with a more holistic consideration of the training process.

The capabilities of aircraft and flight simulators continue to evolve. Modern flight simulators are used for initial and advanced training and for proficiency maintenance and evaluation. They have become integral aspects of the research, development, test, and evaluation (RDT&E) cycle. The development of the glass/digital cockpit with onboard computers and associated recording media (including the Black Box) allows simulators to be used to reconstruct aircraft accidents and in some cases identify appropriate recovery procedures.

In 1994, flight simulation was a worldwide industry involving many competitors (Sparaco, 1994). The industry achieved annual sales of $3 billion to commercial airlines and $2.15 billion to DoD. Simulators ranged in price from $3000 for a basic PC-based flight simulator with joystick controls up to $13 million for a motion-based simulator (down from $17 million in the early 1990s). In December 2006, Frost & Sullivan, an organization that studies markets, reported that within North America, revenues for commercial and military ground-based flight simulation (GBFS) totaled $2.01 billion in 2005 and were expected to reach $2.78 billion in 2012. Its August 2006 report notes that in 2005 the commercial GBFS segment in North America accounted for 36.3% of total revenues; the military segment accounted for 63.7%. Frost & Sullivan predicts GBFS market growth based on the introduction of new aircraft (such as the Boeing 787 and the Airbus 380) along with high fuel and maintenance costs. The military sector faces the additional pressure of aircraft and instructor unavailability due to operational commitments. Frost & Sullivan also predict simulator growth in the very light jet (VLJ) air taxi and business markets. The final factor is the need to train individuals with minimal or no flight experience to operate unmanned air vehicles (UAVs) that will share airspace with manned vehicles carrying passengers.

Consolidation within the aviation industry has reduced the number of competitors in the GBFS market since the 1990s. This consolidation has contributed to advances in technology and the emphasis on leaner, more efficient, core business-focused organizations (Wilson, 2000). According to L-3 CEO Frank Lanza, "Simulators that used to cost $40 million per copy now cost $7 to $10 million each. And we are driven by commercial technology because the explosion of precision graphics and visuals for the multimedia industry is directly transferable to the military" (Wilson, 2000, p. 19). In 2003, Lanza expanded on this theme during an interview with Diane Bradley: "In 1986, we sold simulators for F-16s for $35 million apiece. Now we can build them for about $2 million to $3 million apiece. Moreover, we can do much more with each one. We used to have to build dedicated simulators for each type of aircraft. Now we have simulators that can train six types of air crews simultaneously." This reduction in hardware cost for display technologies changed the traditional focus from hardware driven to software driven. Major industry suppliers now focus on ways to incorporate the Internet and virtual reality into training systems.

21ST-CENTURY SIMULATORS

Modern simulation is demarcated by the conceptualization, development, and demonstration of the power of networked simulations. In 1987, Captain Jack Thorpe of the U.S. Air Force delivered a seminal but unpublished paper titled "Future Views: Aircrew Training, 1980–2000" that predicted the development of today's distributed simulations (Hapgood, 1997; Van Atta, 1991). Before the 1980s, simulators were very expensive stand-alone systems that mimicked actual systems found in aircraft and submarine control stations. At DARPA in 1982, Thorpe began the development of SIMNET, a simulator network that dedicated high-speed phone lines and massive computers. The simulators were practically hand-made, which facilitated quality control but made mass production costly and slow. SIMNET communications began with local area networks (LANs at Fort Knox and in Germany) and expanded to long-haul phone networks with rudimentary Internet capabilities. Displays and controls to enable simulated local and distant combat systems were connected to the communication system and allowed the dispersed sites to interact.

Bandwidth was then so expensive and narrow that the objective of the design team was to provide selective functional fidelity rather than completely replicate the exact physical hardware of a tank or airplane. Fidelity was driven by those functions needed to meet group training objectives. In 1986, Schwab and Gound evaluated collective training for tank teams through network simulations. Members of the network simulation group improved their average group score by 13%, while the control (no network) group improved by only 6%. Similar research continued until SIMNET became operational in 1990 (Thorpe, 1987). At the SIMNET graduation demonstration in March 1990, long-haul networking supported hundreds of manned players for the first time. Alluisi (1991) and Orlansky (1992) provide background of the early development of networked simulation for training. SIMNET can be seen as the first massive multiplier online game, even though by today's Internet standards, it lacked a massive environment and did not support many online players simultaneously.

Recognizing the power of networking simulators to train people as fighting teams, the U.S. Army led the way in developing networked training systems. Perhaps the best example is the close combat tactical trainer (CCTT), a distributed system of manned simulators and workstations that trains teams for collective tasks. These selective fidelity simulators all operate in a common synthetic environment encompassing, terrain, weather, and semi-automated forces (SAFs) of friendly and enemy forces. Command and control workstations have also been integrated into the CCTT system. The manned simulators can experience mechanical failures, combat damage from direct fire or land mines, and even problems from running out of fuel. The CCTT has added dismounted infantry portals that allow leaders to enter the same synthetic battlefields as personnel who man simulated vehicles. The infantry leaders can practice tactical decision making including navigation, direct computer-generated infantry, and order movements and fire control. More detailed information about CCTT can be found at www.amso.army.mil/smart/conf/2000/day-1/cctt-barlow. The CCTT has expanded to include interoperable simulation capabilities for helicopter crews (aviation combined arms tactical trainer–aviation [AVCATT-A]); field artillery (fire support combined arms tactical trainer [FSCATT]); combat engineers (engineer combined arms tactical trainer [ENCATT]); and air defense systems (air defense combined arms tactical trainer [ADCATT]).

The Air Force also joined the movement to team training with the distributed mission training (DMT) system that included 14 simulator sites worldwide. Each site had four fighter aircraft that could be networked locally or linked with other remote sites. The synthetic environment includes threat systems, combat environments, and briefing–debriefing capabilities. This capability initiated in 1998 expanded beyond F-15 systems to include other aircraft in the Air Force's inventory such as F-16s and AWACS controller aircraft. The Air Force plans to add more aircraft simulators to this system over the next decade as it creates a ubiquitous synthetic environment in which pilots and air crew can train, practice, and conduct mission rehearsals at any time. The Navy developed a similar DMT system for its F/A-18 aircraft pilots. Additional details on DMT systems are available at https://www.spider.hpc.navy.mil/index.cfm?RID=WEB_OT_1000438.

The Navy also developed the battle force tactical trainer (BFTT) that uses equipment onboard a ship and simulates a tactical environment. By introducing signals after the sensor level, it stimulates system responses on the onboard equipment. System operators who may be aboard other vessels can see and respond to the same stimulants on the shipboard equipment they would actually use under combat conditions. BFTT can connect ships in port via data links to ships at sea. A hybrid BFTT simulation of battle space environment supports joint and allied exercise interoperability and provides commanding officers and battle group and battle force commanders with the ability to conduct coordinated, real-time, realistic, high-stress combat system training. The BFTT has the ability to passively monitor data from its own ship's tactical systems, recording data for post-event processing, and providing passive and dynamic replays to assist in self-assessment.

The CCTT, DMT, and BFTT systems have components that execute similar functions, that is, they contain simulations of operator platforms, weather, semi-automated and automated opponents, weapons, debriefing stations, and local and distributed network infrastructures. The military is evolving technologies through standards like high level architecture (HLA) that will eventually meld into a truly synthetic environment in which the services can train, practice, and rehearse in a joint manner the full spectrum of warfare.

DEPLOYABLE TRAINERS

The U.S. Navy is considering using flight simulators aboard ships (Muth and Lawson, 2003). During a demonstration in 1998, an F/A-18 weapons system trainer was deployed aboard the carrier USS *Independence*. While the exercise was a demonstration and not a controlled experiment, the participants reported no simulator sickness. However, it should be noted that no major storms occurred at sea during the demonstration. In an experiment by Mark and Lowson (2003) test participants showed minimal symptoms of nausea and similar sickness after completing a 1-hour simulated flight aboard a 108-foot coastal patrol boat. The authors note that their study examined a best-case scenario "in which a minimal provocative ship motion stimulus was combined with a minimally provocative flight simulator" (p. 504). The authors proposed that flight simulators be located near a ship's center of rotation where motion is not as provocative in order to minimize the interaction of ship motion and the apparent motions of the aircraft and earth.

In a follow-on study by Muth, Walker, and Fiorello (2006), ten subjects completed a simulated driving task while riding in the backseat of an automobile. Their task completion time was significantly longer when the vehicle was in motion and results were less accurate. In addition, their scores on the motion sickness and simulator sickness questionnaires were significantly higher under the vehicle-in-motion condition. The findings show the impact of a more provocative environment and present implications for tasks such as controlling remote vehicles from a moving vehicle.

Since virtual reality systems require considerably less space than weapon systems trainers, it is reasonable to assume that efforts will be made to introduce virtual reality (VR) and virtual environment (VE) technologies to ships and other moving environments. This expectancy increases the need for research into the use of virtual reality in dynamic environments. The research could build on basic etiological research on the undesirable side effects of virtual environments in static environments and the development of appropriate countermeasures.

The convergence of computational power, increased bandwidth, inexpensive display and computer-user interface technology, artificial intelligence, and improved M&S techniques led to improvements of virtual reality systems, which are discussed in the next section.

VIRTUAL REALITY AND VIRTUAL ENVIRONMENTS

Virtual reality (VR) and virtual environments (VEs) developed considerably during the 1990s and continue to undergo explosive growth. VR/VE technology, sometimes called artificial reality and the virtual world, has been described as:

- An artificial environment, created with computer hardware and software, presented to users in such a way that it appears and feels like a real environment (Webopedia, 2004).
- The simulation of a real or imagined environment that can be experienced visually in the three dimensions of width, height, and depth and that may additionally provide an interactive experience visually in full real-time motion with sound and possibly with tactile and other forms of feedback. The simplest form of virtual reality is a 3-D image that can be explored interactively at a personal computer, usually by manipulating keys or a mouse so that the content of the image moves in some direction or zooms in or out. More sophisticated efforts involve such approaches as wrap-around display screens, rooms augmented with wearable computers, and haptic joystick devices that let you feel display images (searchsmallbizit.techtarget.com, 2004).

VR/VE exists in one of three possible contexts: (1) as a simulation of an *existing* environment such as the interior of a building; (2) as a *proposed* environment such as a Mars-bound space station; or (3) as an *imaginary* environment such as that found in a PC-based adventure game. These environments are designed to achieve an educational or entertainment goal.

The two VR/VE levels are nonimmersion and immersion (Kuntz-Rangal, Guimaraes, and De Assis-Correa, 2002). At the nonimmersion level, images are presented on a computer display and the user is aware of his or her real-world surroundings. The immersion level involves efforts to convince an individual that he or she is actually present in the environment through the use of devices such as helmet-mounted displays (HMDs). These devices project computer-generated images onto the inside of a visor while preventing any view of the real world. Controlling the auditory input through earpieces or surround sound technology can increase the depth of immersion. Haptic (tactile) information can be provided by the use of body gloves. When locomotion is simulated, the VE may include a small treadmill-like platform on which a trainee can walk with minimal real displacement. At a higher level of immersion, a trainee wearing an appropriate VR projection system is enclosed in an 8.5-foot diameter sphere that rotates in every direction as the trainee walks, runs, crawls, and so forth. (VirtuSphere, 2006).

Stone (2001) describes utilization of VR for training in diverse environments including metal forges in the automotive industry, minimal invasive surgery trainers (MISTs) for laparoscopic surgeries, repair work on the Hubble telescope, fire fighting training, and avionics repairs. In most cases, more learning was achieved at less cost in VEs.

The medical community is gradually accepting the use of VR for both training and surgical rehearsals. It is a small step from looking at three-dimensional magnetic resonance images (MRIs) in planning a surgery (Hoell et al., 1999) to real-time simulated surgical interactions with those images (Larsen et al., 2001). At the 48th annual meeting of the Human Factors and Ergonomics Society (2004), Mark Bowyer, director of surgical simulation at the National Capital Area Medical Simulation Center in Bethesda, Maryland, noted that simulators unlike operating rooms "give permission to fail." He also mentioned two practical interacting reasons to increase the use of simulation in the medical teaching community: (1) in an effort to reduce medical costs, fewer patients are available for shorter periods; and (2) new laws limit the number of hours residents can work each week. This combination reduces the opportunities for residents to observe and participate in surgical procedures. Without simulation, they will face fewer opportunities for learning. Simulation is under consideration by the medical community as a tool for continuing education and certification. Additional details including descriptions of 17 surgery-related simulators are available in an issue of *Laparoscopy Today* dedicated to simulation (Volume 3, No. 2, 2004). The journal also includes an article describing how a simulation of "Top Gun" air combat served as a model for training surgeons (Rosser and Young, 2004).

Despite its high technology attractiveness, VE does not lack side effects that have social, legal, and economical repercussions (Stanney et al., 2003). In 1992, McCauley and Sharkey used the term *cybersickness* to describe VR-induced motion sickness. Kennedy, Hettinger, and Lilienthal (1990) cautioned that the increased fidelity promised by VR might lead to a higher incidence of simulator sickness. Indeed, adverse effects similar to those described for simulator sickness have been reported. Specifically, problems noted during and after exposure include prolonged after-effects involving disturbed proprioception and postural instability. Stanney et al. (2003) reported that a variety of factors common to simulation may induce these effects. The factors include navigational control, scene complexity, and exposure duration. Navigational control is the ability of a subject to self-initiate control of his or her visual field (i.e., an automobile driver can change a vehicle's direction and velocity; a passenger cannot). Scene complexity involves both visual flow rate and the size of the visual field. Scenes with greater texture, greater flow rates, and wider visual fields induced higher levels of vection and increased levels of cybersickness. Longer exposure durations in VEs generally produced increased levels of cybersickness. Furthermore, individual factors such as gender and motion sickness histories influenced the level of sickness.

Stanney et al. (2003) performed a multifactorial experiment involving 1102 participants ranging in age from 15 to 53 years. Participants in a VE performed a battery of tasks involving locomotion, object manipulation, and choice reaction time. Eighty-one percent of the participants reported higher sickness symptomatology on their simulator sickness questionnaires (SSQs) immediately after exposure. Their findings included:

- Duration: as exposure time increased, symptom severity, drowsiness, and dropout rate increased.
- Navigational control: the severity of the symptoms increased as the degrees of freedom (for navigational control) available to the subjects increased.
- Scene complexity: sickness level was not significantly related to scene complexity. However, the authors note that the levels of scene complexity used in their study may not have induced sufficient differences in vection so additional studies are needed in this area.
- Gender: males reported significantly fewer symptoms than females.
- Prior adverse experience: participants with histories of prior sickness symptomatology reported more symptoms under VE conditions.
- After-effects: more than 4 hours after exposure, 35% of the participants reported symptoms higher than preexposure levels.

If VEs are to successfully provide training, designers must develop strategies to reduce high dropout rates (~50% after 1 hour of exposure) and symptom severity. Possible solutions include simplification of imagery and restricting the degrees of navigational freedom. Stanney et al. (2003) provide two excellent tables describing the adverse effects and proposing sickness mitigating guidelines for use of head-coupled, PC-based, immersive VE systems. Readers desiring additional information on virtual environments should consult the *Handbook of Virtual Environments: Design, Implementation, and Applications*, edited by Stanney (2002). For a good description of the technology used in flight simulators to create VEs, readers can consult Lee (2005).

ONLINE GAMING

The entertainment and gaming industries are also developing simulations and simulators. The increased power of personal computers, increased bandwidth for the Internet, and affordable Internet-capable game consoles such as Nintendo's Wii, Microsoft's Xbox, and Sony's PlayStation are fueling the commercialization of affordable distributed networking developed earlier for SIMNET at a cost of millions of dollars. Many games have both stand-alone capability and the ability to connect with other players through broadband commercial networks.

Private industry and the military are examining this commercial capability for its utility for increasing market share or fighting wars. In 1997, the National Research Council recommended joint research for defense and entertainment modeling and simulation (Zyda and Sheehan, 1997). One of the more successful government investments into Internet games was America's Army: Operations. The U.S. Army funded the Navy Postgraduate School's development of this free online game as a means to recruit computer-savvy teens by exposing them to opportunities for high-technology positions in the Army (Zyda, 2003).

MODELING AND SIMULATION DEVELOPMENT PROCESSES

A model or simulation is developed to represent a system, concept, or process for exploring a problem space, reducing risk, answering a question, or creating a new capability. A model can be developed to exist and perform only in a virtual world (e.g., an antigravity vehicle created for a video game) or may mimic a portion of the real world (e.g., a commercial motorcycle design that follows the rules of physics). The model development process requires discipline much like that required for software development. The process is straightforward: define the end state and objectives (criteria for acceptance) and follow a consistent systems engineering process.

System engineering approaches may vary (ANSI/EIA 632, 1999; ISO/IEC 15288, 2008), but they all provide disciplined processes (models and simulations) for the development of system solutions. System engineering is an iterative, interactive exchange between the customer and the model developer. Basically, any model development must start with a requirements analysis that articulates the customer's needs and describes them via manageable details and programmable functional requirements. Systems engineering provides a common, structured approach that facilitates communication between developer and customer. The detailed requirements define performance and design constraints for the modeler to follow. This is one of the most critical steps in model development because it defines the assumptions—what the model must do and the simulated environment in which it must interact. Based on these functional requirements, a plan is developed, a conceptual model is built, and software is written, tested, and implemented. Figure 1.3 illustrates the process, starting in the upper left section with the problem to be solved, continuing through the formalization of objectives, and leading to application of the results. After a modeling and simulation method is selected as a part of the solution, the development process follows the general path outlined in the middle section.

A model is an abstraction of the real world, but not all aspects of the environment or real world are represented. A model will ignore or even misrepresent some aspects of the real world; its accuracy and utility to the customer are limited. As with any project, finite amounts of time and money are dedicated to developing a capability. Trade-offs among the available resources determine what can be developed. Developers and users of M&S must make assumptions about the relevance of specific factors related to model performance. Without assumptions, they will run out of time and

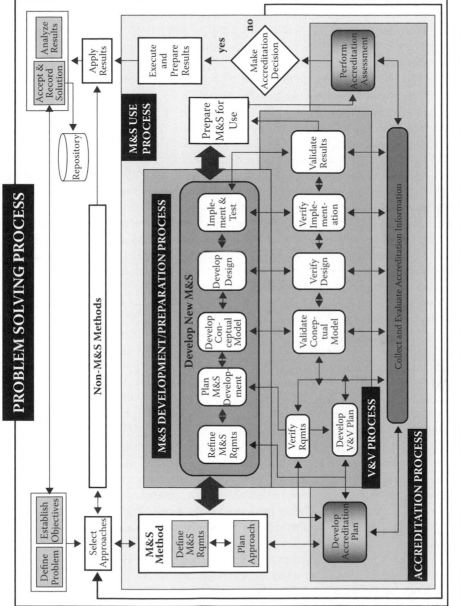

FIGURE 1.3 VV&A and new M&S development (DoD Recommended Practices Guide; used with permission of the Defense Modeling and Simulation Office.)

money while trying to model and simulate every factor. For example, a representation of the human sensory capability of smell may be excluded from a truck driving model because it is irrelevant to a human who relies on visual, auditory, and tactile cues in learning the task. However, smell may be very relevant to a physician who uses his sense of smell to determine whether a simulated wound is infected. Because a model is a "compromised reality," a developer must convince the user that the model meets his needs and requirements.

The most important characteristic of a model or a simulation is its credibility to a customer. Development of a credible model requires scrutiny through verification, validation, and accreditation (VV&A) steps. The VV&A process is more essential to M&S than it is to other software development activities. Verification is the process for determining whether a model achieves what the customer intended and operates relatively free of errors. Verification answers the question, "Does the model actually represent the design intent and accurately reproduce the model specifications?" The intent and the specifications should have been made explicit during the earlier interactions of the customer and model developer.

Validation is a process for determining how well a model matches the real world and the customer's needs. It answers the question, "Does the model adequately depict the 'real' world that it was designed to represent?" Subject matter experts routinely "run a model through its paces" to determine whether it acts and interacts as expected in a simulated world. A car test driver may be the ideal expert to determine whether the simulated handling characteristics of a new model that only exists in a computer is an acceptable representation.

Accreditation is an official certification that sufficient evidence indicates that a model is credible and suitable for a particular purpose. It answers the question, "Does the model provide acceptable answers to my particular questions and can it be used for my specific purpose?" Accreditation confirms that a simulation can meet the specific requirements developed in response to the objectives established at the beginning of the M&S development process.

The bottom section of Figure 1.3 provides a general description of the VV&A process that must be conducted *in parallel* to model development. If VV&A is not an integral part of model development at the start, it will be difficult if not futile to attempt to integrate VV&A after model development is complete. Without VV&A, a customer/user will not know the capabilities or the limitations of a model. A customer or user who lacks confidence in a model or simulation will not use it, or even worse, may use it incorrectly. VV&A consists of three intertwined processes that increase the credibility of a model, reduce risk, and increase user confidence. In essence, VV&A provides risk reduction by ascertaining whether a simulation supports the user's objectives. It calibrates the credibility of a model or simulation for its intended use.

For human behavioral representation (HBR) modeling, as with any software program, the articulated requirements serve as the foundation for validation. Before the model or simulation is developed, the ultimate user defines the tasks that the simulated humans will perform and the level of cooperation with a human in the loop or another human simulation (e.g., a simulated associate with defined cognitive capabilities). The user also defines the levels of behavior moderators (fatigue, emotion, physiological limits, personality differences, motivation, etc.).

No single "cookie cutter" VV&A process can be applied to the development of every model and simulation. VV&A must be tailored to the nature of the problem. How much VV&A and what aspects are employed (i.e., resources expended) depend greatly on the importance of decisions that will be made based on the simulation. The VV&A process can make a model transparent enough for people to understand its assumptions and limitations. Currently, the most common technique used to validate human models is the use of subject matter experts (SMEs) who "drive" the human performance model through typical scenarios and observe the resulting performance of the simulation. SMEs determine, often qualitatively, whether a model meets the user's realism requirements. This type of testing should be only one of a number of validations.

Unfortunately, technology and techniques for validation have not kept pace with the explosion in computational capability. As the demand for M&S continues to grow, the VV&A process continues to evolve. VV&A is still in adolescence. Both DoD and NASA have instituted process action teams to develop best business practices. Universities are integrating VV&A into their curricula and related scientific symposia are held periodically. The lessons learned from modelers who deliver products to gaming, commercial, and military customers are now applied to advance the state of the art of M&S and with it the state of the art of VV&A. HBRs, for example, use data from humans performing a variety of tasks as criteria against which to validate simulated performance. Psychological, sociological, and physiological theories are serving as baselines for the behaviors of simulated humans under various conditions and circumstances. Guidance for future HBR validation activities continues to develop as modelers are required to increase the realism of the simulated worlds they populate with simulated humans of increasingly higher fidelity. As these techniques evolve so does the VV&A lexicon, portions of which are included in Appendix C.

OTHER SIMULATION AREAS

This book describes simulations used in a variety of the environments (space exploration, aviation, ships, nuclear power plants), but does not directly address simulating human behavior, the use of simulation in learning, and workplace simulations. Therefore, we have included brief discussions of these areas in this chapter.

SIMULATING HUMAN BEHAVIOR

Simulations of human behavior or human-like behavior have become more available to the general public as the capabilities of and access to the Internet and computational capability have increased. Gamers use simulations of human behavior when they play Doom or the variety of Dungeons and Dragons role-playing games. Since 1989, SimCity players who serve as "mayors" use models of human behavior as they attempt to manage an urban society while attending to the crimes and crises associated with city life. Players must also negotiate trade-offs among competing interests (Grossman and Song, 2002).

In 2000, SimCity was the best selling (>34 million copies) computer game. In The Sims game, a player is a member of a simulated suburban family and must cope with the vicissitudes of daily life (e.g., earning a living by establishing a business). In late 2002, Sims Online was released. It allows real players to interact via the Internet in a three-dimensional virtual world in which each player controls the behavior of his or her character (Croal et al., 2002). In 2004, The Sims 2 was released. This version allows players to advance from infancy to old age over an average of 25 hours of playing time (Taylor, 2004). The perceived value of SimCity as an educational tool is indicated by the use of SimCity 3000 software at the National Engineers Week Future City Competition in which seventh and eighth grade students compete at local, regional, and national levels (Future City, 2006).

On a commercial level, perhaps the best known example of effective use of a human operator model is provided by Gray, John, and Atwood (1993). Using the GOMS (goals, operators, methods, selection rules) model, they determined that the new equipment NYNEX (the parent company of New England Telephone) was considering for purchase would have increased customer transaction time for a telephone operator by an average of 0.63 seconds. While the time increase may seem minimal, it would have cost NYNEX $3 million annually.

DoD has invested heavily in the development and use of simulations of human behavior. DoD's term for describing simulations of human behavior is *human behavior representation* (HBR). For Pew and Mavor (1998), HBR denotes "a computer-based model that mimics the behavior of a single human or the collective action of a team of humans" (p. 11). Space limitations preclude a detailed consideration of this topic. However, their text titled *Modeling Human and Organizational Behavior* describes models of individuals, attention and multitasking, memory and learning, human decision making, situation awareness, and planning. Behavior moderators and modeling at unit level are also discussed. Readers who consult this excellent text will find superb descriptions of a number of models simulating human behavior of individuals and as system components. The models include:

- ACT-R (Adaptive Control of Thought)—higher level cognition models
- COGNET (COGnition as a NEtwork of Tasks)—creates and exercises models of human operators engaged in cognitive tasks
- HOS (Human Operator Simulator)—simulates the perceptual, cognitive, and psychomotor responses of a human operator and generates timelines and accuracy data
- MicroSAINT (Micro Systems Analysis of Integrated Networks of Tasks)—a discrete-event network simulation used to analyze and describe the performances of complex systems in which human operators are components
- MIDAS (Man–Machine Integrated Design and Analysis System)—evaluates human machine system designs

Comparisons of these and other models are provided. The authors provide an interesting discussion on incorporating behavior moderators into simulations. They differentiate external moderators (noise, vibration, fatigue, and cognitive overload) from internal moderators (intelligence, expertise, personality, emotions, attitudes, and cultural values). They also address modeling of behavior at the unit level and information warfare. Pew and Mavor conclude with a chapter on methodological issues and approaches for developing, verifying, validating, and accrediting human behavior models. They emphasize that acceptance of these simulations requires human behavior representations that conform to behaviors expected by subject matter experts.

Gluck and Pew (2005) continue to work in this area as part of the Agent-Based Modeling and Behavior Representation Project. They reported on a comparison of models applied to multitasking and category learning. Four teams applied models (COGNET/iGEN, DCOG, ACT-R, and EASE) to an abstracted version of an air traffic control. The same tasks were completed by 16 human participants, all of whom were video game players. The performance measures utilized included accuracy, response time, workload rating, and learning rate. While each model exhibits unique advantages and disadvantages, COGNET/iGEN showed the best fit to human data, followed by ACT-R, DCOG, and EASE. Their detailed analyses of the efficacies of these models provide insights for all model users and developers. Readers interested in learning more are referred to Gluck and Pew (2005).

A book by Ness, Tepe, and Rirzer (2004) titled *The Science and Simulation of Human Performance* describes models and simulations of individual and small unit or team performance, primarily with a military focus. It is divided into four sections. The first reviews the state of the art in human performance, research, training, and assessment. The second and largest section describes theories and measurements of human performance and provides insights related to developing standardized operational definitions, methods, and metrics for data collection appropriate for M&S use. The chapters focus on cognition, physiology, team performance, and a neurochemical perspective on performance measurement. The third section critically analyzes existing human performance models and provides recommendations for the future. The last section identifies resources and provides an overview of human performance research and modeling at DoD laboratories.

Representations of human behavior are not limited to efforts by DoD. In December 2002, moviegoers who attended the second film in the *Lord of the Rings* trilogy observed a battle scene involving approximately 50,000 computer-generated fighters (Koeppel, 2002). These computer-generated actors exhibited medieval fighting behavior based on unique and unpredictable choices made by individual avatars engaged in battle. Each individual was capable of about 350 potential human-like actions (step forward, step back, move to next rung on a ladder, raise sword, lower sword) and had specific body attributes (height, weight, muscular or thin physique) and behavior characteristics (aggressivity or passivity). Unlike characters in previous animations, the behaviors of these agents were not predictable because the software animating them relied on fuzzy logic. Thus, each agent appeared to be unique, goal-oriented, and sentient—responsive to the laws of physics and changes in the environment. In 2002, Karl Sims, the creator of these actors, said, "Right now you can usually tell when something is synthetic, but we'll soon be crossing over into a time where that's not possible. It's going to be a very interesting moment" (Koeppel, 2002, p. 44). We are progressing down that path quickly. In 2007, Roush described a three-dimensional VR Internet that integrates the social virtual world (Second Life) with mapping technology (Google Earth).

SIMULATION AND LEARNING

During the past two decades, major corporations established virtual universities to meet the educational needs of their employees. Many academic and corporate universities utilize e-learning as part of their educational processes. The first academic institution to significantly capitalize on e-learning opportunities was the University of Phoenix. E-learning started slowly in the mid-1980s when IBM introduced Authoring System and Apple introduced Hypercard as tools for classroom use. As PC and Internet usage increased, tools like Authorware, Toolbox, QuickPlace, and WebCT were developed for use in academia and by trainers. The use of simulation and games in education also increased in the 1980s.

Aldrich (2004), whose focus is on training, describes simulations and their use for improving the learning process. While his book specifically describes the development of a leadership learning simulation, he provides insights on the interactions of simulation and learning. He describes how simulation provides opportunities to deviate from a traditional linear learning model to a more realistic nonlinear model that allows for increased experimentation and has greater applicability to the real world. His guidance regarding the use of simulation is particularly interesting when he reflects on what performance should be measured and how it should be scored.

Should absolute scores be reported? Are we more interested in improvement (change scores)? Should data with diagnostic value be obtained? These critical questions must be asked before any simulation is developed. Debriefing, an often ignored component of the simulation process, emphasizes scoring and evaluation. Aldrich (2004) credits Jane Boston, general manager of Lucas Learning Ltd., with the following statement: "The most critical elements of a simulation come after the game itself. Debriefing what has happened—what a player experienced, felt during the simulation and is still feeling afterwards, what strategies were tried and what happened, what other strategies might have been applied, what else the player needed to know or be able to do, analogies to real life situations, how the player's own values and experience influenced their actions—are all important items for discussion" (p. 204). Aldrich believes that the increased use of simulations and their ability to engage students and trainees will significantly improve the education and training processes.

WORKPLACE SIMULATIONS

This section describes simulations used by ergonomists, industrial designers, and mechanical engineers to design, develop, and evaluate workplaces. These models have been used to design assembly lines producing automobiles, aircraft, tanks, earth moving machinery, construction and farm equipment; office workplaces; nuclear power plants; and space stations. The models are designed to ascertain whether users and maintainers can be physically accommodated and accomplish the tasks required with the least risk of injury. They are integral to commercially available computer-aided design (CAD) software or may be imported into CAD software. Many current models were developed by and rely on data collected by DoD.

Paquette (1990) reviewed the 1990 state of the art by comparing six workplace simulations (CYBERMAN, COMBIMAN, CREW CHIEF, JACK, SAMMIE, and MANNEQUIN) that performed one or more of the following functions: (1) anthropometric accommodation analysis, (2) biomechanical and strength modeling, and (3) human–machine interface analysis. His report describes the developmental backgrounds of all six models and their capabilities. Badler, Phillips, and Webber (1993) described efforts to create a three-dimensional computer graphics surrogate human to support human-centered design processes. This surrogate developed at the Center for Human Modeling and Simulation at the University of Pennsylvania is known as JACK. In 1995, Das and Sengupta updated Paquette's report and compared updated versions of the same simulations.

As computer graphics improved and became more accessible, these software packages migrated from dedicated machines to PCs. Space limitations preclude detailed analyses of the various packages, so the authors will limit their description to JACK, a system that provides a three-dimensional interactive environment for controlling articulated figures. It includes a dynamic human model along with realistic behavioral controls, anthropometric scaling, animation and evaluation systems, view analysis, reach-and-grasp capability, collision detection and avoidance, and other useful tools for a wide range of applications. JACK or JACK-like variants are used in software developed by Unigraphics (www.ugs.com) and Delmia (www.delmia.com).

CHALLENGES AND OPPORTUNITIES IN HUMAN FACTORS AND SIMULATION

Since subsequent chapters will address needs specific to their particular domains, this is an appropriate place to address global needs pertinent to human factors and simulation. Simulation users expect more than simple representations of the physics of a phenomenon, machine, or human–machine interactions. Models describing human, team, and organizational behaviors in depth are needed. The ever-increasing use of the World Wide Web to connect people, organizations, and processes requires the scientific community to understand individual and group dynamics, and model distributed emergent organizations and online societies. Fortunately, the Web is a readily available real-world laboratory that can improve our understanding and allow us to model that behavior as we design and test systems for the ubiquitously connected and computationally friendly society of the near future.

Models "must be able to make predictions that designers care about" and the time and expertise required to use these models must be within practical limits (Freed, 1999). We need credible human models that researchers, analysts, designers, decision makers, trainers, and trainees can understand and use. We are just now recognizing that the psychologies of human interactions, group behaviors, and cultural and national differences must be better understood. The "softer" sciences of psychology, sociology, and anthropology follow basic principles and require data that can be modeled and simulated. This is a greater challenge than modeling most physical phenomena but represents the direction in which human factors and simulation must progress.

A major challenge to the development of human models is proper representation of the wide range of human behavior, decision making, and performance factors. Consider the complexity of a typical conversation described by Jay Forrester (MIT's "guru" of system dynamics): "The mental model is fuzzy. It is incomplete. It is imprecisely stated. Furthermore, within one individual, a mental model changes with time and even during the flow of single conversation. The human mind assembles a few relationships to fit the context of a discussion. As the subject shifts, so does the model. Each participant in a conversation employs a different mental model to interpret the subject. Fundamental assumptions are different but are never brought into the open" (Schrage, 1999, p. 13). Forrester captured the complexity of the task facing developers of communication models. Human flexibility makes modeling difficult, but allows for the innovations so essential to humankind. The journey will not be easy but modeling and simulation techniques have reached a new level, as readers of the following chapters will discover. As we close this chapter, we would like to provide our perceptions of specific human factor modeling and simulation challenges to be addressed:

- Developing better techniques for clearly articulating the requirements for modeling and simulation.
- Developing new techniques for synthesizing and visualizing large amounts of heterogeneous data into easily understood information.

- Developing techniques to facilitate the incorporation of VV&A into modeling and simulation development processes for the "softer" sciences.
- Developing more intuitive interfaces to encourage the use of complex models by individuals who are not model developers.
- Developing and/or improving strategies for determining (1) which human behavior and physiological responses to model; (2) how to select and obtain appropriate measures for validating a model; and (3) when and where in the system development process to apply these models.
- Designing simulations and simulators that instructors can use to seamlessly merge classroom educational techniques with training and experiential learning.
- Designing interoperable M&S tools and environments through the use of readily available and easily used standard toolkits.

Readers seeking broad perspectives on future challenges to M&S are referred to the *Proceedings of the International Conference on Grand Challenges for Modeling and Simulation* (Lunceford and Page, 2002). The challenges described range from simulating consciousness to simulating the national airspace system. Individuals desiring more active roles in human performance modeling are encouraged to join the Human Performance Modeling Technical Group of the Human Factors and Ergonomics Society, an organization concerned with "the development and application of predictive and reliable, quantitative models of human performance. In distinction to other approaches to behavioral and cognitive modeling, human performance modeling considers the human, engaged in some goal-directed behavior, in the context of a designed task environment" (Human Factors and Ergonomics Society, 2006).

Finally, we face the issue of emerging technologies. Virtual reality is in its adolescence and will continue to improve, become more readily available, and continuously incorporate new technologies. How will capabilities such as three-dimensional holographic displays be best utilized to train, educate, and evaluate? This is only one question that must be raised and answered. The authors expect that readers will conclude from reading this and subsequent chapters that much progress has been made but much work remains to be done. We live in exciting times.

ACKNOWLEDGMENTS

The authors acknowledge the assistance of their colleagues, including students at the University of Dayton. Critical readings by Dennis McBride and Paul Chatelier deserve particular recognition. The assistance of friends in the modeling and simulation community who shared materials from their archives and reviewed portions of this chapter is also recognized. Finally, the authors thank their wives, Kathy and Darleen, for their patience and support.

REFERENCES

Adorian, P., Staynes, W.N., and Bolton, M. (1979). The evolution of the flight simulator. *Proceedings of Conference: Fifty Years of Flight Simulation*, Vol. 1. London: Royal Aeronautical Society, p. 1.

Aegis Research Corporation. (2002). War games bibliography. In Lunceford, W.H. and Page, E.H., Eds., *International Conference on Grand Challenges for Modeling and Simulation*. Society for Modeling and Simulation (www.scs.org).

Aldrich, C. (2004). *Simulations and the Future of Learning*. San Francisco: Pfeiffer.

Allen, T.B. (1987). *War Games*. New York: McGraw-Hill.

Alluisi, E.A. (1991). The development of technology for collective training: SIMNET, a case history. *Human Factors*, 33, 343.

American National Standards Institute. (1991). *American National Dictionary for Information Systems*. (FIPS Publication 11-3).

American National Standards Institute/Electronic Industry Alliance. (1999). *Processes for Engineering a System*, 632.

Andrews, D.H. et al. (1998). Enabling technology: analysis of categories with potential to support the use of modeling and simulation in the United States Air Force. Mesa, AZ: Air Force Research Laboratory (DTIC Report ADA3518899).

Badler, N.I., Phillips, C.B., and Webber, B.L. (1993). *Simulating Humans: Computer Graphics, Animation, and Control*. Oxford: Oxford University Press.

Bailey, S.S. and Hodak, G.W. (1994). *Live Fire versus Simulation: A Review of the Literature*. NAWCTSD-SR-94-002. Orlando, FL: Naval Air Warfare Center, Training Systems Division.

Barr, K. and Hall, C. (1992). The use of imagery by rowers. *Int. J. Sport Psychol.*, 23, 243.

Baudhuin, E.S. (1987). The design of industrial and flight simulators. In Cormier, S.M. and Hagman, J.D., Eds., *Transfer of Learning*. San Diego, CA: Academic Press, p. 217.

Berg, R.M., Adedeji, A.M., and Steadman, G.W. (1993). *Simulation Offset to Live Fire Training Phase 2 Results: Application of at Least Equal Effectiveness Methodology to Simulator Use in Marine Corps Infantry Training Programs*. Alexandria, VA: CRM-93-112, Center for Naval Analyses.

Berg, R.M., Adedeji, A.M., and Trenholm, C. (1993). *Simulation Offset to Live Fire Training Study: Assessment of Marine Corps Live Fire Training Support*. Alexandria, VA: CIM-238, Center for Naval Analyses.

Beringer, D.B. (1994). Issues in using off-the-shelf PC-based flight simulation for research and training: historical perspective, current solutions and emerging technologies. *Proceedings of the Human Factors and Ergonomics Society 38th Annual Meeting*. Santa Monica, CA: Human Factors and Ergonomics Society, p. 90.

Bernstein, M. (2000). *Grand Eccentrics: Turning the Century: Dayton and the Inventing of America*. Wilmington, OH: Orange Frazer Press.

Boldovici, J.A. (1987). Measuring transfer in military settings. In Cormier, S.M. and Hagman, J.D., Eds., *Transfer of Learning*. San Diego, CA: Academic Press, p. 239.

Bond, W.F. et al. (2007). The use of simulation in emergency medicine: a research agenda. *Acad. Emerg. Med.*, 14, 353.

Boothe, E.M. (1994). *A Regulatory View of Flight Simulator Qualification: Flight Simulation Update,* 10th ed. Binghamton, NY: State University of New York, Watson School of Engineering.

Bowyer, M.W. (2004). Personal communication during panel discussion at 48th annual meeting of the Human Factors and Ergonomic Society, New Orleans, LA.

Bradley, D. (March 28, 2003). Silicon Valley goes to war. *Business Week On Line*. http://www.businessweek.com/bwdaily/dnflash/mar2003/nf20030328_4292_db069.htm?chan=search

Breeden, J., II. (August 10, 2003). Microsoft Flight Simulator 2004: A century of Flight. *Washington Post*, p. F8.

Callow, N., Hardy, L., and Hall, C. (1998). Effect of a motivational mastery imagery intervention on the sport confidence of three elite badminton players. *J. Appl. Sport Psychol.*, 10, S135.

Caro, P.W. (1979). Development of simulator instructional feature design guides. *Proceedings of Conference: Fifty Years of Flight Simulation*. London: Royal Aeronautical Society, p. 75.

Caro, P.W. (1988). Flight training and simulation. In Weiner, E.L. and Nagel, D.C., Eds., *Human Factors in Aviation*. New York: Academic Press, p. 229.

Casby, A. and Moran, A. (1998). Exploring mental imagery in swimmers: a single case study design. *Irish J. Psychol.*, 19, 525.

Croal, N. et al. (November 25, 2002). Sims Family Values. *Newsweek*. Vol. 140, p. 46.

Custer, L.L. (1930). Aviation training machine. U.S. Patent 481,831. Washington D.C.

Das, B. and Sengupta, A.K. (1995). Computer-aided human modeling programs for workstation design. *Ergonomics*, 38, 1958.

Defense Modeling and Simulation Office. (August 2004). *VVA: Recommended Practices Guide*. Available at http://vva.dmso.mil/

Department of Defense. (January 1994). Directive 5000.59. Modeling and Simulation (M&S) Management.

Department of Defense. (January 1998). Directive 5000.59-M. Modeling and Simulation (M&S) Glossary.

Department of Defense. (May 13, 2003). Instruction 5000.61, DoD Modeling and Simulation (M&S).

Department of the Army. (1990). *Systems Approach to Training Analysis*, Pamphlet 351-4. Fort Monroe, VA: U.S. Army Training and Doctrine Command.

Farmer, E. et al. (1999). *Handbook of Simulator Based Training*. Aldershot, UK: Ashgate Publishing.

Federal Aviation Administration. (1992). *Advisory Circular: Airplane Flight Training Device*, AC 120-45A.

Federal Aviation Administration. (1995). *Advisory Circular: Airplane Simulator Qualification*, AC 120-40C.

Federal Aviation Administration. (1997). *Advisory Circular: Qualification and Approval of Personal Computer-Based Aviation Training Devices*, AC 61-126.

Federal Aviation Administration. (December 12, 2003). *FAA Order 8700.1: General Aviation Operations Inspector's Handbook*, vol. 2, chap. 34.

Fischetti, M.A. and Truxal, C. (March 1985). Simulating "the right stuff." *IEEE Spectrum*, 38.

Flexman, R.E. et al. (1972). Studies in pilot training: the anatomy of transfer. Aviation Research Monographs. Champaign, IL: University of Illinois Aviation Research Laboratory.

Freed, M. (1999). Human–machine system design: when does simulation pay? http://human-factors.arc.nasa. gov/cognition/papers/freed/interact99.html

Frost & Sullivan. (August 2006). New aircraft spur North American ground-based flight simulation solutions market. http://aero-defense.ihs.com/news/2006/frost-flight-simulation.htm (retrieved June 18, 2007).

Frost & Sullivan Research Services. (December 2006). North American commercial and military ground-based flight simulation market. http://www.frost.com/prod/servlet/report-brochure.pag?id=F898-01-00-00-00 (retrieved June 18, 2007).

Future City. (August 2006). http://www.futurecity.org/

Gawron, V.J. (2000). *Human Performance Measures Handbook*. Hillside, NJ: Lawrence Erlbaum.

Gluck, K.A. and Pew, R., Eds. (2005). *Modeling Human Behavior with Integrated Cognitive Architectures: Comparison, Evaluation and Validation*. Mahwah, NJ: Lawrence Erlbaum.

Gray, W.D., John, B.E., and Atwood, M.E. (1993). Project Ernestine: validating a GOMS analysis for predicting and explaining real-world task performance. *Hum. Comp. Interaction*, 8, 237.

Green, G.S. and Bavelier, D. (2003). Action video game modifies visual selective attention. *Nature*, 423, 534.

Grossman, L. and Song, S. (November 25, 2002). Sim Nation. *Time*, vol. 160, p. 78.

Grupping, J. (2005). The story of flight simulator. http://fshistory.simflight.com/fsh/versions.htm (retrieved June 26, 2007).

Hapgood, F. (April 1997). Simnet. *Wired*, vol. 5.

Helmreich, R.L. and Schaefer, H.G. (1998). Team performance in the operating room. In Bogner, M.S., Ed., *Human Error in Medicine*. Hillside, NJ: Lawrence Erlbaum.

Helmreich, R.L. et al. (1990). Preliminary results from the evaluation of cockpit resource management training: performance ratings of flightcrews. *Av. Space Env. Med.*, 61, 576.

Hoell, T. et al. (1999). The value of 3D magnetic resonance imaging in the planning of neurosurgery. *Controv. Neurooncol.*, 33, 88.

Hofstadter. D R. (1979). *Godel, Escher, Bach: An Eternal Golden Braid*. New York: Vintage Books.

Human Factors and Ergonomics Society. (August 2006). Human Performance Modeling Technical Group. http://www.hfes.org/web/TechnicalGroups/technicalgroups

Institute of Electrical and Electronics Engineers. (1990). *IEEE Standard Glossary of Modeling and Simulation Terminology*. Standard 610.3.

Institute of Electrical and Electronics Engineers. (1990). *IEEE Standard Glossary of Software Engineering Terminology*. Standard 610.12.

International Organization for Standardization/International Electrotechnical Commission. (2008). System Life Cycle Processes, 15288.

Jacobs, J.W. et al. (1990). A meta-analysis of the flight simulator research. Technical Report 89-006. Orlando, FL: Naval Training Systems Center.

Jones, E.R. (1967). *Simulation Applied to Education*. St. Louis: McDonnell-Douglas Corporation.

Jones, E., Hennessy, R., and Deutsch, S., Eds. (1985). *Human Factors Aspects of Simulation*. Washington D.C.: National Academy Press.

Kahneman, D., Slovic, P., and Tversky, A. (1982). *Judgment under Uncertainty: Heuristics and Biases*. Cambridge: Cambridge University Press.

Kennedy, R.S., Hettinger, L.J., and Lilienthal, M.G. (1990). Simulator sickness. In Crampton, G.H., Ed., *Motion and Space Sickness*. Boca Raton, FL: CRC Press, p. 317.

Klein, G.A. and Crandall, B.W. (1995). The role of mental simulation in naturalistic decision making. In Hancock, J. et al., Eds., *Local Applications of the Ecological Approach to Human–Machine Systems*, Mahwah, NJ: Lawrence Erlbaum, vol. 2, p. 324.

Koeppel, D. (December 2002). Massive attack. *Pop. Sci.*, 38.

Kuntz-Rangal, R. et al. (2002). Development of a virtual flight simulator. *Cyber Psychol. Behav.*, 5, 461.

Lane, N.E. (1986). *Issues in Performance Measurement for Military Aviation with Applications to Air Combat Maneuvering*. Orlando, FL: Naval Training Systems Center.

Larsen, O.V. et al. (2001). The virtual brain project: development of a neurological simulation. *Studies Health Technol. Info.*, 81, 256.

Lee, A.T. (2005). *Flight Simulation: Virtual Environments in Aviation.* Burlington, VT: Ashgate Publishing.

Lintern, G. (1991). An informational perspective on skill transfer in human–machine systems. *Hum. Fact.*, 33, 251.

Lintern, G., Roscoe, S.N., and Sivier, J.E. (1990). Display principles, control dynamics, and environmental factors in augmentation of simulated visual scenes for teaching air-to-ground attack. *Hum. Fact.*, 32, 299.

Loesch, R.L. and Waddell, J. (1979). The importance of stability and control fidelity in simulation. *Proceedings of Conference: Fifty Years of Flight Simulation.* London: Royal Aeronautical Society, p. 90.

Lunceford, W.H. and Page, E.H., Eds. (2002). International Conference on Grand Challenges for Modeling and Simulation. Society for Modeling and Simulation (www.scs.org).

Martin, E.A. (2007). Guidance for Development of a Flight Simulator Specification. AFRL-HE-WP-SR-2007-0002. Wright Patterson Air Force Base, OH, ADA473149.

McCauley, M.E. and Sharkey, T.J. (1992). Cyberspace: perception of self-motion in virtual environments. *Presence*, 1, 311.

McLean, H.V. (May 1978). Are simulations and games really legitimate? *Audiovis. Instr.*, 12.

Military Operations Research Society. (October 27, 1989). Report: A Taxonomy for Warfare Simulation (SIMTAX).

Miller, R.B. (1954). Psychological considerations in the design of training equipment. Technical Report 54-563. Wright Patterson Air Force Base, Ohio.

Mixon, T.R. and Moroney, W.F. (1982). Annotated bibliography of objective pilot performance measures. Report NAVTRAEQUIPCEN IH 330. Orlando, FL: Naval Training Equipment Center.

Modeling and Simulation Analysis Center. (2006). http://www.msiac.dmso.mil/

Moroney, W.F. and Moroney, B.W. (in press). Flight simulation. In Garland, D. et al., Eds., *Handbook of Aviation Human Factors.* Boca Raton, FL: Taylor & Francis.

Munroe, K.J. et al. (2000). The four Ws of imagery use: where, when, why, and what. *Sport Psychol.*, 14, 119.

Muth, E.R. and Lawson, B. (2003). Using flight simulators aboard ships: human side effects, optimal scenario with smooth seas. *Av. Space Env. Med.*, 77, 497.

Muth, E.R, Walker, A.D., and Fiorello, M. (2006). Effects of uncoupled motion on performance. *Hum. Fact.*, 48, 600.

National Research Council. (2002). *Modeling and Simulation in Manufacturing and Defense Acquisition: Pathways to Success.* Washington D.C.: National Academy Press.

Ness, J.W., Tepe, V., and Rirzer, D.R. (2004). *The Science and Simulation of Human Performance.* Amsterdam: Elsevier.

Orlansky, J. and String, J. (1977). Cost effectiveness of flight simulator for military training. Reports IDA HQ 77-19470 and AGARD-CP-268. Arlington, VA: Institute for Defense Analysis.

Orlansky, J., Ed. (1992). *Training Strategies for Networked Simulation and Gaming.* Brussels: NATO Defense Research Group.

Paquette, S.P. (1990). Human and Analogue Models for Computer-Aided Design and Engineering Applications. Technical Report, NATICK/TR-90/054, Natick, MA: Natick Research, Development and Engineering Center.

Patenaude, A. (1996). Study on Effectiveness of Modeling and Simulation in Weapons Systems Acquisition Process (Conducted for Office of the Secretary of Defense). McLean, VA: Science Applications International.

Perla, P.P. (1990). *The Art of War Gaming.* Annapolis, MD: Naval Institute Press.

Pew, R.W. and Mavor, A.S., Eds. (1998). *Modeling Human and Organizational Behavior: Application to Military Simulations.* Washington D.C.: National Academy Press.

Pfeiffer, M.G., Horey, J.D., and Butrimas, S.K. (1991). Transfer of simulated instrument training to instrument and contact flight. *Int. J. Av. Psychol.*, 1, 219.

Pohman, D.L. and Fletcher, J.D. (1999). Aviation personnel selection and training. In Garland, D. et al., Eds., *Handbook of Aviation Human Factors.* Boca Raton, FL: Taylor & Francis.

Rakip, R. et al. (1993). The role of the MH-53J III E Pave Low weapon system trainer/mission rehearsal system (WST/MRE) in preparing students for Operation Desert Storm, and future operations. *Proceedings of 5th Interservice/Industry Training Systems and Education Conference.* Washington D.C.: American Defense Preparedness Association, p. 432.

Raser, J.R. (1969). *Simulation and Society: An Exploration of Scientific Gaming.* Boston: Allyn & Bacon.

Rescher, N. (1969). *Essays in Philosophical Analysis.* Pittsburgh, PA: University of Pittsburgh Press.

Ricci, K.E., Salas, E., and Cannon-Bowers, J.A. (1996). Do computer-based games facilitate knowledge acquisition and retention? *Mil. Psychol.,* 8, 295.

Roese, N.J. and Olson J.M. (1995). *What Might Have Been: The Social Psychology of Counterfactual Thinking.* Mahwah, NJ: Lawrence Erlbaum.

Rolfe, J.M. and Staples, K.J., Eds. (1986). *Flight Simulation.* Avon: Cambridge University Press.

Roscoe, S.N. (1980). Transfer and cost effectiveness of ground-based flight trainers. In Roscoe, S.N., Ed., *Aviation Psychology.* Ames: Iowa State University Press, p. 194.

Roscoe, S.N. (1991). Simulator qualification: just as phony as it can be. *Int. J. Av. Psychol.,* 1, 335.

Roscoe, S.N. and Williges, B.H. (1980). Measurement of transfer of training. In Roscoe, S.N., Ed., *Aviation Psychology.* Ames: Iowa State University Press, p. 182.

Rosser, J.C. and Young, S.M. (2004). The Top Gun Laparoscopic Skills and Suturing Program. *Laparosc. Today,* 3, 14.

Roush, W. (2007). Second Earth. *Technol. Rev.,* 110, 38.

Royal Aeronautical Society. (1979). *Proceedings of Conference: Fifty Years of Flight Simulation.* London: Royal Aeronautical Society.

Salas, E., Bowers, C.A., and Rhodenizer, L. (1998). It is not how much you have but how you use it: toward a rational use of simulation to support aviation training. *Int. J. Av. Psychol.,* 8, 197.

Salas, E., Rhodenizer, L., and Bowers, C.A. (2000). The design and delivery of crew resource management trainees: exploiting available resources. *Hum. Fact.,* 42, 490.

Schrage, M. (1999). *Serious Play: How the World's Best Companies Simulate to Innovate.* Boston: Harvard Business School Press.

Schwab, J.R. and Gound, D. (1986). Concept Evaluation of Simulation Networking (SIMNET). TR 86-CEP345. Fort Knox, KY: U.S. Army Armor and Engineer Board.

Searchsmallbizit. (July 24, 2004). http://searchsmallbizit.techtarget.com/sDefinition/0,sid44_gci213303,00.html

Selix, G.A. (1993). Evolution of a training program: Effects of simulation on the MH-53J Pave Low combat crew qualification course. *Proceedings of 15th Interservice/Industry Training Systems and Education Conference.* Washington D.C.: American Defense Preparedness Association, p. 422.

Spannaus, T.W. (May 1978). What is a simulation? *Audiovis. Instr.,* 16.

Sparaco, P. (June 1994). Simulation acquisition nears completion. *Av. Week Space Technol.,* 71.

Spears, W.D. et al. (1981a). Simulator training requirements and effectiveness study (STRES). Technical Report AFHRL-TR-80-38, Part I. Dayton, OH: Logistics and Technical Training Division.

Spears, W.D. et al. (1981b). Simulator training requirements and effectiveness study (STRES) Technical Report AFHRL-TR-80-38, Part II. Dayton, OH: Logistics and Technical Training Division.

Stanney, K.M. (2002). *Handbook of Virtual Environments: Design, Implementation, and Applications.* Mahwah, NJ: Lawrence Erlbaum.

Stanney, K.M. et al. (2003). What to expect from immersive virtual environment exposure: influences of gender, body mass index, and past experience. *Hum. Fact.,* 45, 504.

Stark, E.A. (1994). Training and human factors in flight simulation: flight simulation update. Binghamton: State University of New York Watson School of Engineering.

Sternberg, R.J. and Gastel, J. (1989a). Coping with novelty in human intelligence: an empirical investigation. *Intelligence,* 13, 187.

Sternberg, R.J. and Gastel, J. (1989b). If dancers ate their shoes: inductive reasoning with factual and counterfactual premises. *Mem. Cognit.,* 17, 1.

Stibbe, M. (2003). *Homegrown Simulators: Air and Space.* Washington D.C.: Smithsonian Institution, p. 36.

Stone, R. (2001). Virtual reality for interactive training: an industrial practitioner's viewpoint. *Int. J. Hum. Comp. Studies,* 55, 699.

Taylor, C. (May 24, 2004). Virtually mortal. *Time,* 163, 89.

Tetlock, P.E. and Belkin, A. (1996). *Counterfactual Thought Experiments in World Politics: Logical, Methodological and Psychological Perspectives.* Princeton, NJ: Princeton University Press.

Thorpe, J.A. (1987). The new technology of large scale simulator networking: implications for mastering the art of war fighting. *Proceedings of 9th Interservice Industry Training Systems Conference,* American Defense Preparedness Association.

U.S. Air Force. (1997). *Guide Specification: Simulators, Flight.* AFGS-87241A, Washington D.C.

U.S. Army Signal Corps. (1907). Specification 486: advertisement and specification for a heavier-than-air flying machine. Washington D.C.: Department of the Army (on display at U.S. Air Force Museum, Wright Patterson Air Force Base, OH).

Van Atta, R.H., Reed, S., and Deitchman, S.J. (1991). DARPA Technical Accomplishments: An Historical Overview of Selected DARPA Projects. Institute for Defense Analysis, Paper P-2429.

VirtuSphere Home Page. (2006). http://www.virtusphere.com/ (retrieved June 29, 2007).

Waldrop, M.M. (2001). The origins of personal computing. *Sci. Amer.*, 285, 84.

Webopedia. (July 24, 2004). http://webopedia.internet.com/TERM/V/virtualreality.html

Weigmann, D.A. and Shappell, S.A. (1999). Human error and crew resource management failures in naval aviation mishaps: a review of U.S. Naval Safety Center data, 1990–96. *Av. Space Env. Med.*, 70, 1147.

Weinberg, R. et al. (2003). The relationship between the use and effectiveness of imagery: an exploratory investigation. *J. Appl. Sport Psychol.*, 15, 26.

Wiener E.L. and Nagel, D.C. (1988). *Human Factors in Aviation*. New York: Academic Press.

Wiener, E.L., Kanki, B.G., and Helmreich, R.L. (1993). *Cockpit Resource Management*. San Diego: Academic Press.

Williams, A.C. and Flexman, R.E. (1949). Evaluation of the Link SNJ operational trainer as an aid in contact flight training (SDC-71-16-3). Port Washington, NY: Navy Special Devices Center.

Wilson, J.R. (June 2000). Technology brings change to simulation industry. *Interavia Bus. Technol.*, 55, 19.

Wise, J. (August 2003). Austin and Goliath. *Pop. Sci.*, 36.

Worley, D.R. et al. (1996). *Utility of Modeling and Simulation in the Department of Defense: Initial Data Collection*. Alexandria, VA: Institute for Defense Analysis.

Zyda, M. (June 2003). This year in the MOVES Institute. *Proceedings of 7th International Conference on Telecommunications*. Zagreb, Croatia, p. 37.

Zyda, M. and Sheehan, J., Eds. (1997). *Modeling and Simulation: Linking Entertainment and Defense*. Washington D.C.: National Academy Press.

2 Justification for Use of Simulation

Trena N. Thompson, Meredith B. Carroll and John E. Deaton

CONTENTS

INTRODUCTION

Simulation involves the interaction of human and system with elements of cost efficiency and safety to the user and system, while providing an effective means of training, evaluation, and analysis. To sufficiently justify and validate simulator usage and applicability as a training device and systems engineering tool, advantages as well as disadvantages must be expanded upon. Although disadvantages do exist, they are surpassed by the magnitude of overall benefits. Simulators are a viable, safe, and cost-effective method for both training and system evaluation, justifiably extending application to a multitude of environments and situations.

Simulation is an interactive system that represents the operational system through artificial duplication or replication of the system and its equipment, environment, and capabilities (Jones, Hennessy, and Deutsch, 1985). Advancements in computer hardware and software technology allow for the creation, manipulation, and control of complex, realistic situations and environments (Jones, Hennessy, and Deutsch, 1985). Advancement in virtual reality (VR) and artificial intelligence add to the range of applicability of simulation usage. Such advancements can even be experienced on the Internet. For example, today an individual interested in buying a home may take a simulated, virtual tour through a prospective home on a real estate Web site.

Typically, most simulators are classified as training devices, while research simulators are classified as laboratory or experimental equipment. Engineering simulators are used for design, development, and evaluation processes (Jones, Hennessy, and Deutsch, 1985). Simulation is widely accepted in a vast array of domains in part due to the immense training opportunities provided to the user, which may not be safe or feasible in a real-world or operational environment. The value of this safety feature is priceless, with respect to cost efficiency and human safety, both illustrated in terms of reduced accident rates, equipment or system damage, aborted missions, and equipment or system failures (Jones, Hennessy, and Deutsch, 1985).

Simulation used for systems engineering purposes involves research in many domains. These include human performance and human–computer interaction, system design, development, test, and evaluation, and the analysis and evaluation of standards and procedures, specifically for licensing and certification (Jones, Hennessy, and Deutsch, 1985). Acceptance of the simulation as a training device is demonstrated through the reliance and confidence of the transfer of training to the real-world environment. This acceptance is such that licenses, certifications, and qualifications may be received from simulator training alone. The use of simulation for engineering purposes as well as training applications will be discussed in the following text.

SYSTEM ENGINEERING EVALUATION

Although training is the principal application of simulators, simulation is also extremely valuable as a systems engineering tool. Simulations are utilized for system design and development processes involving a multitude of applications. These include system demonstrations, parametric studies, alternate configurations, subsystem and system evaluation, prototype assessments, procedures development, tactics development, mission capability assessment, and modification studies (Jones, Hennessy, and Deutsch, 1985). Simulations are also used for test and evaluation purposes of system and subsystem performance, and operational capabilities and limitations (Jones, Hennessy, and Deutsch, 1985).

Simulations used in research applications typically involve investigations of human–computer interactions, visual/motion systems, and human performance assessments, such as measurements of workload, decision-making skills, psychomotor abilities, multitasking abilities, situation awareness, stressor effects, and spatial abilities (Jones, Hennessy, and Deutsch, 1985; Farmer, Rooij, Riemersma, Jorna, and Moraal, 1999). Simulators have also been used in studies exploring team process and team performance measures. Examples of these research applications are discussed below.

The air force is in the process of developing adaptive automation aviation displays in which the display changes with the changing needs of the pilot (Haas, Nelson, Repperger, Bolia, and Zacharias, 2001). Evaluations of these interfaces, and the human–computer interactions involved, have been conducted on a high-tech simulator in the U.S. Air Force Laboratory's Synthesized Immersion Research Environment (Haas et al., 2001).

Simulation has also been used as a means of evaluating situation awareness associated with certain system displays. A study conducted by Williams (2002) tested the situational awareness of 36 pilots associated with the highway-in-the-sky (HITS) display. These pilots were tested on the Advanced General Aviation Research Simulator (AGARS) at the Federal Aviation Administration (FAA) Civil Aeromedical Institute (CAMI). In the past decade there has been increased interest in team performance and many researchers have expressed their support for using simulator technology in team process research (Salas, Prince, Baker, and Shrestha, 1995; Weaver, Bowers, Salas, and Cannon-Bowers, 1995; Kaber and Endsley, 1998). A study conducted by Brannick, Prince, Prince, and Salas (1995) explored the construct validity of measures of team processes using simulated missions. The researchers concluded that important team process behaviors could be identified and rated in this type of test simulation given ample observation (Brannick et al., 1995). This simulator-based team research has become widely accepted and has been essential in furthering the understanding of team process variables.

Engineering simulators are also used for the evaluation of standards and procedures as well as criterion development (Jones, Hennessy, and Deutsch, 1985). The FAA has used simulators in determining such standards and procedures necessary for the effective training and nurturing of pilot knowledge and skill. The types of simulators discussed in this section are typically found in government laboratories, universities, and civilian industry (Jones, Hennessy, and Deutsch, 1985).

TRAINING EFFECTIVENESS AND VALUE

"Measuring effectiveness is a fairly complicated process that has performance measurement at its core" (Moroney and Moroney, 1999, p. 361). To ensure training effectiveness, a detailed analysis must be performed of the training task, purpose, specific objectives, and necessary outcomes of the simulator between customer, manufacturer, regulatory agencies, maintenance personnel, instructor, and user (Jones, Hennessy, and Deutsch, 1985). This process must also include subsequent evaluations to verify effective training requirements and specifications (Rolfe and Staples, 1986). The desired goal of any training simulation is to teach the required skills quickly and inexpensively (Moroney and Moroney, 1999).

Training is the "systematic modification of behavior through instruction, practice, measurement, and feedback. Its purpose is to teach the trainee to perform tasks not previously possible or to a level of skill or proficiency previously unattainable" (Caro, 1988, p. 229). As a training device, simulators make their contribution in skill development, maintenance, and assessment (Rolfe and Staples, 1986).

The operator uses simulators for many different training purposes. These include initial training, instrument training, normal and emergency procedures training, upgrade, and transition and recurrent/refresher training. Also included are tactics and mission training, individual and team assessment, accident investigation, and selection (i.e., initial selection, screening for training courses, allocation to specialization, and to individualize and assess the training program) (Jones, Hennessy, and Deutsch, 1985; Marohn, 1989; Farmer, Rooij, Riemersma, Jorna, and Moraal, 1999). System maintenance personnel also use simulators for procedures and troubleshooting training (Jones, Hennessy, and Deutsch, 1985).

One area of training in which simulation has gained increasing support is crew resource management (CRM) training. This approach to teaching aircrews how to utilize every resource available to them has gained momentum over the past few decades with pressure from the National Transportation Safety Board (NTSB) to improve upon aircrew coordination. Though CRM incorporates many elements, including conventional lecture-based training and role play, one critical segment, line-oriented flight training (LOFT), takes place in the simulator. LOFT consists of realistic scenarios in which an aircrew flies a full mission on a high-fidelity simulator. This method incorporates hands-on learning and practice, and feedback, available to the crew afterward in the form of a video recording of the flight. This use of simulation in CRM training is well accepted by the aviation industry and is believed to provide an excellent training platform (Prince and Jentsch, 2001).

ADVANTAGES

As a training device, simulation has unlimited, valuable advantages, which are explained in the following paragraphs.

Cost saving: Simulation has shown to be an effective training device by providing the required training at low cost (Moroney and Moroney, 1999). While training in the actual system has high operating and maintenance costs, simulator training saves money in terms of the costs associated with training and materials (Rolfe and Staples, 1986; Moroney and Moroney, 1999). It has been reported that flight simulators for the military operate at 5–20% of the cost of operating the actual aircraft (12% being the median cost) (Orlansky and String, 1977). In addition, research has indicated that using simulation in initial stages of training can actually reduce the number of flight hours needed in the actual aircraft to achieve proficiency. Ortiz (1994) performed an experiment in which the utilization of low-fidelity simulation was explored as a means of reducing training time in the aircraft. The results indicated that by administering initial training of maneuvers in a low-fidelity simulation, the hours spent in the actual aircraft could be significantly reduced. This reduction in actual flight time serves as additional cost savings. It has also been reported that a commercial airline can amortize the cost of a simulator in 9 months and an entire simulator facility in less than 2 yr (Moroney and Moroney, 1999). To be specific, the Boeing 767 aircraft training time costs $7000–$8000/h as opposed to an average of $400/h in a full flight simulator (Jones, Hennessy, and Deutsch, 1985). Also, consider the high costs associated with emergency training in commercial aviation, in terms of airspace utilized, ground area required for emergency landings, and so on, as well as the costs of practice fields for firing missiles for military applications (Rolfe and Staples, 1986). Such examples clearly demonstrate the cost benefits of using simulators.

The current increase in processing power and low-cost visual and graphic systems has enabled smaller companies to capitalize on simulator training (Nash, 1995). For example, consider the advancements in PC-based training, which is relatively inexpensive and has come into its own with the FAA looking closely at determining how many PC training hours should be allowed for certification purposes. This probe has been accompanied by debate over whether a PC aircraft training device (PCATD) can be effectively substituted for time in the actual aircraft. There is evidence to suggest that it can be. A study by Taylor, Lintern, Hulin, Talleur, Emanuel, and Phillips (1999) in which PCATD training was substituted for training in the actual aircraft during instrument training showed a substantial decrease in time for students to complete the flight course. Not only has there been substantial research to support the use of PCATDs in training, but many researchers have taken advantage of PCATDs to research issues such as effective instrument displays, learning processes, and aircrew coordination skills (Koonce and Bramble, 1998). Jentsch and Bowers (1998) provide a plethora of evidence supporting the validity of using PC-based technology to study aircrew coordination. PC-based flight simulators have also been used in academic contexts, serving as an aid in human factors and engineering courses (Koonce and Bramble, 1998).

Safety: Before the introduction and utilization of simulators, more accidents resulted from the practice of emergency situations than from actual emergencies (Rolfe and Staples, 1986). Simulators provide hazardous situations without worry of risk or threat to humans and the system. Simulators can provide training to inexperienced and novice individuals in a new system where performance may be crucial or pose a threat. In other words, their life may be dependent on performance in new, unfamiliar systems. For example, consider the first space shuttle landing or single-seat aircraft (Moroney and Moroney, 1999).

An increase in automation has produced an increase in complacent operators, especially in situations where there exists a low probability and frequency of system errors, problems, or malfunctions. Simulators can provide opportunities for the introduction of such an unexpected event or system error, which requires the operator to respond quickly (Moroney and Moroney, 1999). Hence, simulators can teach maneuvers and expose operators to conditions or experiences that they would otherwise be unlikely to experience in actual environments. Such experiences, even though they can be classified as infrequent events, require adequate preparation, should such an encounter occur. Such situations may include wind shear, loss of hydraulic pressure, engine loss, engine fire, exposure to wake turbulence, and clear air turbulence (Moroney and Moroney, 1999). The safety of the operator and possibly others may depend on the efficacy of such training. Thus, simulators not only enhance technical skills but also decision-making and judgment skills, especially in crucial or hazardous situations (Green, 2000).

Environmental ecology: The utilization of simulators reduces hours of operation of the operational system, which in turn reduces wear and tear on the system and its equipment. It also reduces the additional maintenance and fuel costs, the loss of revenue (while actual system is in use for training purposes), traffic congestion, and environmental problems associated with pollution and noise (i.e., low-level flying maneuvers) (Rolfe and Staples, 1986; Marohn, 1989; Cook, 1997; Moroney and Moroney, 1999). Also, the military uses simulation to develop tactics, combat management skills, and to evaluate the operational system. If these military applications were not practiced in simulation, the environment would be destroyed (i.e., damage to land associated with military missile and firing training) (Rolfe and Staples, 1986).

Simulator versus actual system: Simulators provide more in-depth, safer, less expensive and, overall, more effective training opportunities than that provided by the actual system. They provide this by allowing a training environment that incorporates instructional features, which facilitate learning and instructor intervention (Caro, 1988; Moroney and Moroney, 1999).

Simulators also have 24-h/d accessibility; void of dependency on actual system availability and usability requirements, such as aircraft traffic, airspace, and suitable weather conditions

(Rolfe and Staples, 1986; Moroney and Moroney, 1999). Simulators also provide immediate access to operating areas, i.e., a flight simulator can allow students to complete an instrument landing system (ILS) approach and then return immediately to final approach fix (FAF) for the next ILS approach without costing time or fuel (Moroney and Moroney, 1999).

The flexibility of simulators adds to their effectiveness. For example, traffic and other distractions can be eliminated from the training task. A task may be repeatedly performed in a continuous and uninterrupted sequence to promote performance precision (Cook, 1997). Furthermore, the simulated environment has a "pause" feature that allows for instructional interludes (Moroney and Moroney, 1999). Another advantage is the capacity for real-time performance measurement and feedback, adaptive training, programmed demonstrations and malfunctions, and the immediate placement of position and situation (Waag, 1978). The instructor can also demonstrate operations without concern for safety requirements or violations of regulations. For example, the instructor can deliberately permit the trainee to make a mistake or error, which may be operationally illegal, to demonstrate the following results or consequences (Moroney and Moroney, 1999).

Simulators also provide standardized scenarios to allow various operators to practice identical functions, procedures, and dynamics within identical environmental conditions. The scenarios also can be repeated to meet required performance specifications and criteria or to promote efficiency or even automated responses (overlearning of the task) (Moroney and Moroney, 1999).

Simulators also allow for data collection, consisting of performance comparisons (comparing the trainee's performance to the performance criteria and the performance of other trainees at the same level or stage of training), performance and learning diagnosis (by assessing the trainee's learning progress, the instructor can adequately target problem areas), and performance evaluation (different training approaches can be assessed by evaluating performance measurements) (Moroney and Moroney, 1999).

The enhanced transfer of training provided by simulators comes from deliberately planned and controlled deviations and manipulations of criterion or target tasks to attain accuracy and precision. The task can be further enhanced to reflect the incorporation of automated responses. Determining how the human operator can work together with automated systems is a critical issue that can best be duplicated in a simulated environment.

DISADVANTAGES

The benefits of using simulation in training do not come without drawbacks. There are certain disadvantages of simulator use and they are discussed in the following sections.

Simulator performance versus operational performance: Performance in a simulator may not necessarily reflect an individual's operational performance. Never assume that proficiency in a simulator equates to proficiency in the operational system or environment. However, it does translate into awareness of potential situations (Ray, 2000). Increased performance outcomes may be due to reduced stress levels in simulation as opposed to an actual crisis or accident. Trainees may, however, experience increased stress levels during performance evaluations, when seeking qualifications, or competing for a desired position or promotion. Still, operational performance may not be adequately reflected, since emergencies, system malfunctions, and unscheduled events are expected during training. It can also be assumed that before evaluation, the individual would have reviewed policies and procedures, which would also be nonindicative of actual operational performance (Moroney and Moroney, 1999). In addition, performance in simulators may be better than in the actual system, because factors such as fatigue, complacency, and boredom are not as prevalent in simulation (Moroney and Moroney, 1999). Simulators may impede or negate training, which may increase the training time in the operational system, such as when the trainee does not recognize the shift in responsibilities and expectations from the simulator to the operational environment (Green, 2000).

Simulator sickness: Simulator sickness is an issue that poses another problem for some operators. Simulator sickness results from discrepancies between visual and vestibular cues. Pilots many times encounter this in simulators in which the visual system (quality and field of view) is more technologically advanced and therefore disproportionate to the motion system (Burki-Cohen, Soja, and Longridge, 1998). Pilots may devise strategies to compensate for or avoid simulator sickness, which may in turn be debilitating when used in the operational system.

Instructional quality: Simulators are only as valid and valuable as the instructor, the simulator, and the data entered. That is, the performance evaluations, acceptance, and training content and usage are subject to opinions, instructions, and attitudes of operators, instructors, and management (Moroney and Moroney, 1999; Green, 2000). In other words, the quality of instruction and the individual trainee's abilities and attitudes (i.e., motivation) will have an impact on information learned in training (Rolfe and Staples, 1986). This is a topic that deserves special attention.

With the advancement in simulator technology, assumptions have been made that it is naturally accompanied by an increase in training effectiveness. This is not necessarily the case. It is the training techniques utilized, and the instructional features embedded in the simulation that ensure effective training; not the quality and fidelity of the simulator itself (Salas, Bowers, and Rhodenizer, 1998). Salas et al. (1998) suggest that there is a gap between the technological advancements in simulator capabilities and the theoretical advancements in training research. Current simulators have the ability to dramatically enhance the effectiveness of training, but efforts must be made to refocus from designing simulators to be the most technologically complex and realistic to human-centered training systems that promote learning (Salas et al., 1998). One way to do this is by employing methods that guide the design of simulation-based training. One such method is event-based approach to training (EBAT), presented by Fowlkes, Dwyer, Oser, and Salas (1998). This method "guides the design of training opportunities by systematically identifying and introducing events within training exercises that provide known opportunities to observe behaviors of interest" (Fowlkes et al., 1998, p. 210). EBAT concentrates on training objectives, exercise design and performance assessment, and keeping the links between these that are essential to effective training (Fowlkes et al., 1998).

Factors that will also affect learned information from training include any discrepancies, deviations, and misrepresented information depicted in terms of the motion, visual, and auditory cueing systems. These may impede learning and overall performance in the operational environment as trainees learn inaccurate information (Ray, 2000). Hence, the simulation must be an accurate replication of the operational system, equipment, and environment for the desired optimal transfer of training to occur.

In some cases, specifically with excessive usage, simulators have been associated with negative effects on morale and retention, as trainees are anxious to be in the operational environment: "I'm here to fly airplanes, not simulators" (Moroney and Moroney, 1999).

Initial cost: Other disadvantages of simulators as a training device include the high costs of the actual training simulators themselves, in addition to the actual test and acceptance procedure, which can take up to 3–4 months to ensure proper standards and requirements are met (Moroney and Moroney, 1999). This may also cost the customer and company time, money, and frustration (Tydeman and Kuller, 1995). Because of the high cost associated with high-fidelity simulators, researchers have investigated the option of using less expensive lower-fidelity simulators in training. Evidence suggests that low-fidelity simulators do in fact allow transfer of training in certain situations as effectively as high-fidelity simulators, and in some cases even more effectively (Koonce and Bramble, 1998). O'Neal (1997) suggests that the more complex the system being simulated (e.g., an airliner), the less effective a high-fidelity simulator will be in training. One reason for this is that some similarities between simulations and operational environments are irrelevant to transfer and can serve as distractions (Koonce and Bramble, 1998). The critical factor affecting transfer in many cases is transfer of cognitive principle, not the transfer of specific physical cues (Koonce and Bramble, 1998). As a result, students participating in initial training, which is very cognitive in nature, can benefit from a variety of low-fidelity simulators (Gibson, 2000). Currently, up to 10% of initial flight training time requirements for the procedural Instrument Flight Rules can be completed in a ground-based simulator (Macfarlane, 1997). On the other hand, recurrent or refresher training for experienced pilots needs to take place in a high-fidelity simulator (Gibson, 2000).

Fidelity can be broken into two main elements: task fidelity and instructional fidelity. Task fidelity refers to the similarity between the operational system or environment and the simulator and its missions, whereas instructional fidelity refers to the system's ability to transfer new skills to the pilot (Macfarlane, 1997). High-task fidelity is usually associated with physical fidelity and therefore high cost. Instructional fidelity is found in lower physical-fidelity simulators such as low-cost, part-task, and procedural trainers. It is still to be determined what compilation of these types of simulators is cost-effective in a training program. The question of the relationship between physical fidelity and training effectiveness has been debated for decades. Much emphasis has been put on physical fidelity when in fact its benefit has yet to be determined.

Physical fidelity is attributed to two main factors: high levels of visual detail and motion. Each of these factors has been explored by researchers and the amount to which they affect transfer of training has been questioned. In the case of visual detail, Salas, Bowers, and Rhodenizer (1998) cite research in which training in simulators with high visual scene detail did not provide better transfer than those with low scene detail, or better performance on flight skills in the aircraft. In the case of motion, Bradley and Abelson (1995) reported that they were able to fly full motion simulators at American Airlines and the Naval Air Station at Brunswick, Maine, with the motion system on and then subsequently turned off. The authors stated that even without the motion, the visual system gave convincingly persuasive impressions of motion. In addition, motion is a main factor in the high cost of simulators and many times the benefits do not justify the cost (Gawron, Dennison, and Bifferno, 2002). Also, with aviators being taught not to trust vestibular or kinesthetic cues and to rely solely on the instruments, is relying on motion in the simulator not a contradiction to this (Gawron, Dennison, and Biferno, 2002)? The question of the role of simulation fidelity in training remains. It seems obvious that physical fidelity does not translate to effective training; however, high-fidelity simulations do have a place in training and this place should be determined through training research (Salas, Bowers, and Rhodenizer, 1998). There is also a place for low-fidelity simulation in training and if the acceptable role for this can be determined, the expense associated with training could be significantly decreased.

The initial cost of a simulator training program can be reduced by effectively integrating simulators with task fidelity (high physical fidelity) and instructional fidelity (low physical fidelity) appropriately throughout training. This would likely reduce the number of high-fidelity simulators needed, by allowing less expensive, low-fidelity simulators to be substituted where they are deemed more suitable.

Also, certain simulators, specifically dome and motion-based simulators require special air-conditioned facilities, which may be costly, require additional maintenance personnel, and large available space (Moroney and Moroney, 1999).

Maintenance personnel: Another disadvantage involves the shift of maintenance personnel from the actual domain to the simulator domain. In other words, the maintenance of simulators monopolizes the maintenance personnel and their time and availability. This may prove detrimental to the operational system, its operators, and administrators, when the operational system is in a critical state or needs repair. Maintenance personnel may be preoccupied or unavailable due to simulator maintenance requirements, resulting in delay, neglect, or even incomplete or poor assessment of the operational system requirements and maintenance.

Despite the drawbacks cited here, the advantages clearly outweigh the disadvantages, optimizing the benefits-to-costs ratio as demonstrated by acceptance in various domains and regulatory agencies (Farmer, Fooij, Riemersma, Jorna, and Moraal, 1999).

APPLICABLE DOMAINS

Licensing, qualifications, and certifications received through simulator training demonstrate the degree of reliance and acceptance of simulators as a valid and effective training device (Jones, Hennessy, and Deutsch, 1985). Simulators are recognized and accepted by the following government agencies: the Federal Aviation Administration (FAA), the Department of Defense (DoD), the National Aeronautics and Space Administration (NASA), the Department of Transportation (DoT), the Department of Energy (DoE), the Nuclear Regulatory Commission (NRC), and the Bureau of Mines (BuMines) (Jones, Hennessy, and Deutsch, 1985).

Applicable domains of simulation include spacecraft, marine transportation (ships and submarines, surface and subsurface), aviation (military, commercial, and general aviation), energy systems (nuclear power and mining), ground or surface transportation (automobiles, trucks, and locomotives or trains), command and control (military, space, civil air traffic, and industrial), tactical surface warfare (direct fire, tanks, artillery, missiles, electronics, and battle), tactical strategic air warfare (ranges and air combat exercises), and health and medical care (Jones, Hennessy, and Deutsch, 1985; Marohn, 1989). All will be discussed in detail in later chapters within the application section of this book. Hence, the following discussion will be limited to major applications within specific fields.

Commercial aviation: "Within the aviation community, the effectiveness of simulators is accepted as an article of faith. Indeed, the aviation industry could not function without simulators and flight training devices (FTDs), whose existence is mandated by Federal Aviation Administration (FAA) regulations" (Moroney and Moroney, 1999). All airlines have invested heavily in flight simulators used to conduct initial and recurrent training (Taylor and Emanuel, 2000). Within the aviation industry, manufacturers, users, and regulators rely on simulators for training and testing purposes. Beyond a private pilot certification, most flight training programs utilize aircraft simulators. The FAA establishes standards and policies for the certification of civil aviation pilots. In 1954, the Federal Aviation Regulations (FARs) permitted simulators to be used for proficiency checks by air carrier pilots for all but four tasks (Caro, 1988).

Simulators are also being used to investigate, test, and evaluate the overall operational safety of the proposed Free Flight. Such research is used to identify pilot constraints on decision-making abilities and to evaluate navigational displays, proximity warning systems, pilot behavior, and traffic situations (Scallen, Smith, and Hancock, 1996).

Military: Simulators have specifically been used in the military realm for gunnery training, driver training, training artillery observers, and training maintenance staff (Nash, 1995). Other uses of simulation are to develop tactics, combat management skills, and evaluate the operational system (Rolfe and Staples, 1986). Simulations are also used to train for emergency situations such as hurricanes, fires, and chemical or hazardous material spills (Petty and Slepow, 1996).

Medical: Simulation within the medical industry primarily focuses on surgical procedures (Nash, 1995).

Driving: Driving simulators are used in human factors research, including systems engineering research, human behaviors, perceptions in specific situations, and operational features. Such research includes driver's decision-making skills (specifically left turns), head-up display requirements, warning systems, time-to-contact collision perceptions, cruise control, and safe speed requirements (specifically in dangerous areas such as tunnels) (Olofinboba, 1996; Manser and Hancock, 1996). Also included are signs and signals, route guidance, cellular phone usability and requirements, age-related driving skills, visions enhancements, and steering assistants (Olofinboba, 1996; Manser and Hancock, 1996). All these studies are aimed at reducing accident rates and human fatalities in a safe and efficient manner.

Emergency situations: Simulations are used to train the police force, military, firefighters, medical personnel, and so on, for emergency situations such as hurricanes, fires, and chemical or hazardous materials spills (Petty and Slepow, 1996).

CONCLUSION

Simulation encompasses the trainee and the equipment, systems, events, and their interactive processes (Jones, Hennessy, and Deutsch, 1985). As a "design tool, research vehicle, and training medium, they are valuable and effective in their capacity to control and assess critical aspects [of] human interactions and performance, to replicate and evaluate critical conditions that cannot otherwise be experienced without potential threat to the operational system, and more importantly human life" (Jones, Hennessy, and Deutsch, 1985, p. 56; Moroney and Moroney, 1999). Simulation has various applications, widely accepted in numerous domains, as demonstrated through qualifications or certifications in type or task. Although disadvantages exist, they are far exceeded by the benefits, in terms of costs, training acceptance and applicability, systems engineering and research, human performance assessment and research, and most importantly, safety. Overall, simulation "provides the best training, the best evaluation, and the best qualification of crew members, while providing an opportunity for those crew members to establish, modify where appropriate, and reinforce the behavior that is required" (Cook, 1997). When all factors are considered, it can be indisputably concluded that simulation most efficiently and safely elicits optimal operational skill, meeting the goals and desires of all customers, manufacturers, regulatory agencies, instructors, users, and, last but not least, the general public (Cook, 1997).

REFERENCES

Bradley, D.R. and Abelson, S.B., 1995, Desktop flight simulators: simulation fidelity and pilot performance, *Behav. Res. Methods, Instruments, Comput.,* 27(2), 152–159.

Brannick, M.T., Prince, A., Prince, C., and Salas, E., 1995, The measurement of team process, *Hum. Factors,* 37(3), 641–651.

Burki-Cohen, J., Soja, N.N., and Longridge, T., 1998, Simulator platform motion—the need revisited, *Int. J. Aviat. Psychol.,* 8(3), 293–317.

Caro, P.W., 1988, Flight training and simulation, in *Human Factors in Aviation,* Wiener, E.L. and Nagel, D.C., Eds., San Diego, CA: Academic Press.

Cook, E., 1997, Flight simulation boundaries: barriers to progress or guidelines to success? *Flight Simulation—Expanding the Boundaries: Proceedings of the Royal Aeronautical Society,* London, May 14–15.

Farmer, E., Rooij, J.V., Riemersma, J., Jorna, P., and Moraal, J., 1999, *Handbook of Simulator-Based Training,* Brookfield, VT: Ashgate Publishing.

Fowlkes, J., Dwyer, D.J., Oser, R.L., and Salas, E., 1998, Event-based approach to training (EBAT), *Int. J. Aviat. Psychol.,* 8(3), 209–221.

Gawron, V.J., Dennison, T.W., and Biferno, M.A., 2002, Mock-ups, models, simulations, and embedded testing, in *Handbook of Human Factors Testing and Evaluation,* Charlton, S.G. and O'Brien, T.G., Eds., Mahwah, NJ: Lawrence Erlbaum Associates.

Gibson, R.S., 2000, Certification of training, in *Human Factors in Certification,* Wise, J.A. and Hopkin, V.D., Eds., Mahwah, NJ: Lawrence Erlbaum Associates.

Green, M.F., 2000, Aviation instruction through flight simulation: enhancing pilots decision-making skills, *Flight Simulation—The Next Decade: Proceedings of the Royal Aeronautical Society,* London, May 10–12.

Haas, M.W., Nelson, W.T., Rapperger, D., Bolia, R., and Zacharias, G., 2001, Applying adaptive control and display characteristics to future air force crew stations, *Int. J. Aviat. Psychol.,* 11(2), 223–235.

Jentsch, F. and Bowers, C.A., 1998, Evidence for the validity of PC-based simulation in studying aircrew coordination, *Int. J. Aviat. Psychol.,* 8(3), 243–260.

Jones, E.R., Hennessy, R.T., and Deutsch, S., 1985, *Human Factors Aspects of Simulation,* Washington D.C.: National Academy Press.

Kaber, D.B. and Endsley, M.R., 1998, Team situation awareness for process control safety and performance, *Process Saf. Prog.,* 17(1), 43–48.

Koonce, J.M. and Bramble, W.J., 1998, Personal computer-based flight training devices, *Int. J. Aviat. Psychol.,* 8(3), 277–292.

Macfarlane, R., 1997, Simulation as an instructional procedure, in *Designing Instruction for Human Factors Training in Aviation,* Hunt, G.J.F., Ed., Aldershot, England: Avebury Aviation.

Manser, M.P. and Hancock, P.A., 1996, Advanced simulation technology used to reduce accident rates through a better understanding of human behaviors and human perception, in *High-Fidelity Simulation for Training, Test Support, Mission Rehearsal, and Civilian Applications: Proceedings of the International Society for Optical Engineering,* Faust, N.L., Ed., 2740, 52–59, Orlando, April 8–9.

Marohn, H.D., 1989, Benefits of flight simulation—the environmentalist's view: spring convention—flight simulation assessing the benefits and economics, *Proceedings of the Royal Aeronautical Society,* May 17–18.

Moroney, W.F. and Moroney, B.W., 1999, Flight simulation, in *Handbook of Aviation Human Factors,* Garland, D.J., Wise, J.A., and Hopkin, V.D., Eds., Mahwah, NJ: Lawrence Erlbaum Associates.

Nash, T., 1995, Test and acceptance of flight simulators: flight simulation technology, capabilities, and benefits, *Proceedings of the Royal Aeronautical Society,* London, May 17–18.

O'Neal, A.F., 1997, Design requirements for computer-based learning systems for aircraft manufacturers, in *Designing Instruction for Human Factors Training in Aviation,* Hunt, G.J.F., Ed., Aldershot, England: Avebury Aviation.

Olofinboba, O., 1996, A unique high-fidelity wrap-around simulator for human factors research applications, in *High-Fidelity Simulation for Training, Test Support, Mission Rehearsal, and Civilian Applications: Proceedings of the International Society for Optical Engineering,* Faust, N.L., Ed., 2740, 52–59, Orlando, April 8–9.

Orlansky, J. and String, J., 1977, Cost-effectiveness of flight simulator for military training (Rep. No. IDA NO. HQ 77-19470). Arlington, VA: Institute for Defense Analysis.

Ortiz, G.A., 1994, Effectiveness of PC-based flight simulation, *Int. J. Aviat. Psychol.,* 4(3), 285–291.

Petty, M.D. and Slepow, M.P., 1996, Constructive simulation for emergency management training, in *High-Fidelity Simulation for Training, Test Support, Mission Rehearsal, and Civilian Applications: Proceedings of the International Society for Optical Engineering,* Faust, N.L., Ed., 2740, 52–59, Orlando, April 8–9.

Prince, C. and Jentsch, F., 2001, Aviation crew resource management training with low-fidelity devices, in *Improving Teamwork in Organizations: Applications of Resource Management Training,* Salas, E., Bowers, C.A., and Edens, E., Eds., Mahwah, NJ: Lawrence Erlbaum Associates.

Ray, P.A., 2000, Is today's flight simulator prepared for tomorrow's requirements? Flight simulation—the next decade, *Proceedings of the Royal Aeronautical Society,* May 10–12.

Rolfe, J.M. and Staples, K.J., 1986, *Flight Simulation,* New York: Cambridge University Press.

Salas, E., Bowers, C.A., and Rhodenizer, L., 1998, It is not how much you have but how you use it: toward a rational use of simulation to support aviation training, *Int. J. Aviat. Psychol.,* 8(3), 197–208.

Salas, E., Prince, C., Baker, D., and Shrestha, L., 1995, Situation awareness in team performance: implication for measurement and training, *Hum. Factors,* 37(1), 123–136.

Scallen, S.F., Smith, K., and Hancock, P.A., 1996, Development of a simulator to investigate pilot decision making in Free Flight, in *High-Fidelity Simulation for Training, Test Support, Mission Rehearsal, and Civilian Applications: Proceedings of the International Society for Optical Engineering,* Faust, N.L., Ed., 2740, 52–59, Orlando, April 8–9.

Taylor, H.L. and Emanuel, T.W., 2000, A civil aviation view of aircrew training, in *Aircrew Training and Assessment,* O'Neil H.F. and Andrews, D.H., Eds., Mahwah, NJ: Lawrence Erlbaum Associates.

Taylor, H.L., Lintern, G., Hulin, C.L., Talleur, D.A., Emanuel, T.W., and Phillips, S.I., 1999, Transfer of training effectiveness of a personal computer aviation training device, *Int. J. Aviat. Psychol.,* 9(4), 319–335.

Tydeman, R. and Kullar, I., 1995, Test and acceptance of flight simulators, *Flight Simulation Technology, Capabilities, and Benefits: Proceedings of the Royal Aeronautical Society,* London, May 17–18.

Waag, W.L., 1978, Recent studies of simulation training effectiveness, *Proceedings of the Society of Automotive Engineers,* San Diego, November 27–30.

Weaver, J.L., Bowers, C.A., Salas, E., and Cannon-Bowers, J.A., 1995, Networked simulations: new paradigms for team performance research, *Behav. Res. Methods, Instruments and Comput.,* 27(1), 12–24.

Williams, K.W., 2002, Impact of aviation highway-in-the-sky displays on pilot situation awareness, *Hum. Factor,* 44(1), 18–27.

3 Transfer of Training

Dahai Liu, Elizabeth L. Blickensderfer,
Nikolas D. Macchiarella, and Dennis A. Vincenzi

CONTENTS

INTRODUCTION

Commercial aviation and the military have long reaped the rewards provided by the use of flight simulation to train pilots. Using simulators for training maximizes the use of operational systems for revenue producing activities, and minimizes the use of operational systems for non-revenue producing activities such as training. It also eliminates the expense of aircraft fuel and maintenance costs associated with the training, and the loss of revenue whereas the actual system is in use for training purposes (Moroney and Moroney, 1998).

Additionally, simulation can save training time. Training time-savings occur because trainers can position the trainee into the exact situation required to learn specific skills. For example, if the instructor was attempting to teach the student how to land in a crosswind, it would no longer be necessary to perform multiple takeoffs to practice crosswind landings. In this situation, the trainer can stop the simulation and place the student pilot on final approach repeatedly until he or she becomes proficient at the targeted skill.

More importantly, but much more difficult to quantify, are increases in flight training safety associated with using a simulated flight environment. Mistakes made by the student pilot in flight simulation are regrettable, but not life-threatening. The instructor and student pilot can simply stop, reset the simulator, and try the flight task again. A clear example of this benefit is found in the training of unusual attitude recovery. In actual flight training, pilots are placed into unusual attitudes (e.g., extreme degrees of pitch, roll, and yaw) for training purposes (Federal Aviation Administration, 2002). All certified pilots have faced these stressful and life-threatening situations during training and have recovered accordingly. Unfortunately, failure to recover in the real world can result in dire consequences. Flying is an inherently dangerous practice regardless of the pilot's experience level; however, through flight simulation, giving inexperienced pilots exposure to these dangerous situations without actually placing them in harms way can increase safety.

Thus, training via simulation offers numerous potential benefits. For simulation-based training to be successful, however, trainees must effectively apply learned knowledge, skills, and abilities gained from simulator training to their corresponding real-world task; in other words, transfer of training must occur.

This chapter describes the main concepts and theories pertaining to transfer of training with an emphasis on simulation-based training. To accomplish this, we first review the definition of transfer of training and discuss the factors involved. Next, we discuss research methods relating to transfer of training as well as criticisms of these methods. Finally, we propose research issues regarding transfer of training for simulation-based training environments.

TRANSFER OF TRAINING: TERMS AND CONCEPTS

The ultimate goal of training is for the trainee to transfer what was learned in training to the actual real-world setting. Transfer of training (ToT) refers to the process of applying knowledge, skills, and abilities learned from training programs to real-world situations and to the maintenance of these knowledge, skills, and abilities over time on the job (Baldwin and Ford, 1988). Transfer of training can be classified into two types: positive and negative (Chapanis, 1996).

POSITIVE TRANSFER

Positive transfer occurs when an individual *correctly* applies knowledge, skills, and abilities learned in one environment (e.g., in simulation) to a different setting (in the case of aviation, this would be real flight). Positive transfer is the goal of any type of training. In this chapter, when we refer to transfer of training, we mean positive transfer of training unless a different interpretation is indicated.

NEGATIVE TRANSFER

Negative transfer occurs when existing knowledge and skills (from previous experiences) impedes proper performance in a different task or environment. For example, a skilled typist on a QWERTY keyboard would have difficulties using, or learning how to use, a non-QWERTY keyboard such as a Dvorak keyboard.

Negative transfer develops from at least two related reasons: (1) system design changes and (2) a mismatch between a training system and the actual task. First, system design changes (e.g., controls and software menus) can create one type of negative habit transfer interference. Specifically, the task performer has experience performing the task set up in one manner and has developed a certain degree of automaticity. If a design change occurs, it is likely that the task performer will revert to performing the task according to the previous system (i.e., "habit interference"). Avoiding habit interference should be a major design goal (Chapanis, 1996). Second, if the training system procedures do not match those in the transfer environment, negative transfer is likely to occur. Consider a pilot who is trained to pull back on the yoke to lower the nose of the aircraft in a simulator. In the real world, pulling back on the yoke actually raises the nose. The pilot will likely do the same in a real-flight situation, thus endangering themselves, any passengers, and the aircraft.

In summary, negative transfer occurs when the trainee reacts to the transfer stimulus correctly as he or she has practiced and was trained, but incorrectly in relation to the real world (in this case, pulling back on the yoke thinking that this will lower the nose of the aircraft because that was what was trained, when in actuality it raises the nose).

A MODEL OF FACTORS AFFECTING THE TRANSFER OF TRAINING

A number of different authors have proposed models of training effectiveness (e.g., Cannon-Bowers et al., 1995; Colquitt et al., 2000). A full review of these models is beyond the scope of this chapter. For the purpose of this review we selected the Baldwin and Ford (1988) model of transfer of training. Baldwin and Ford (1988) conducted a review of research on transfer of training and proposed a theoretical framework of the transfer process. As shown in Figure 3.1, the model depicts transfer of training in terms of training input factors, training outcomes, and conditions of transfer. This section will review this model with an emphasis on (1) research accomplished since publication of the model and (2) research performed in simulation and aviation studies.

Training input factors: Starting with the left side of Figure 3.1, the "Training Inputs" factors include training design, trainee characteristics, and work environment. The model depicts each of these three input factors as having a direct influence on learning in the training environment. In addition, the model also connects trainee characteristics and work environment characteristics directly with the transfer performance. Thus, those factors are thought to exert a direct influence on performance in the transfer setting.

In terms of trainee characteristics, Baldwin and Ford (1988) found a number of research studies that suggest these characteristics would affect training transfer efficiency. Numerous individual differences exist, including motivation, attitudes, and ability (e.g., cognitive and physical). In an analysis specifically targeting flight simulation, Auffrey, Mirabella, and Siebold (2001) argued that goal setting, planning, motivation, and attitudes were key factors in training effectiveness.

Consider motivation, the trainee must put forth effort to learn. Therefore, a prerequisite for transfer is the trainee's motivation to successfully complete the training—to acquire the new skills and knowledge. In terms of ability, the trainee must also have the raw ability to improve his or her skills. For example, a pilot who is working on shortening his or her takeoff distance must analyze the

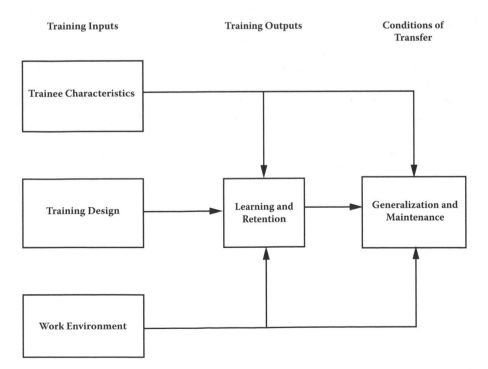

FIGURE 3.1 A model of training transfer. (Adapted from Baldwin, T., and Ford, J., *Personnel Psychol.,* 41, 63–105, 1988.)

situation and realize that he or she needs to adjust the flaps accordingly (depending upon the type of aircraft) and increase speed sufficiently to gain enough lift. The trainee must possess the cognitive ability to understand that a change in specific elements is necessary to accomplish the desired change in performance. These are just two examples of individual characteristics that relate to training effectiveness. Overall, more research is needed regarding the impact of trainee characteristics on training effectiveness.

Second, the training design or method plays a role in transfer of training. Baldwin and Ford (1988) proposed four basic principles for the design of training to facilitate transfer of training. Of particular relevance to simulation-based training are the principles of identical elements and the stimulus–response relationship. The first approach, "identical elements," dates back to the turn of the 20th century. Thorndike (1903) put forth a notion that is still held by simulator designers today. Thorndike argued that there would be transfer between the first task (simulation) and the second task (real world) if the first task contained specific component activities that were held by the second task. This approach is entirely dependent on the presence of shared identical elements (Thorndike, 1903).

Although outside the realm of flight simulation, an illustration of this principle can be found in athletics. If an individual plays softball and then tries out for the baseball team, he or she will be better off than the person who has only previously played golf. All three sports share common elements (e.g., ball, striking stick, and grass playing field). However, softball shares far more elements with baseball than golf does (e.g., number of players, bases, scoring, umpires, uniforms, fences, and dugouts). The more elements that are shared between the two environments, the better the transfer. Therefore, softball is a better form of simulation than golf for the training of baseball skills. This approach parallels the idea that simulators should duplicate the real-world situation to the greatest degree possible.

Another principle for training design can be seen in terms of "stimulus and response." In this respect, the idea is to examine the extent to which similarities exist between stimulus representation and the response demands of the training and those of the transfer task (Osgood, 1949). This perspective does not demand a duplication of elements. In contrast, the notion is that transfer of training can be obtained using training tasks and devices that do not duplicate the real world exactly, but that do maintain the correct stimulus–response relationship. Consider once again the example of athletics. Golf transfers quite well to tennis, as the golf swing (low to high) and tennis hit (low to high) are similar. Even though the sports themselves are quite different (racquets versus golf clubs and holes), the stimulus response sequence for each of the sports is quite similar.

In terms of simulation-based training, Hays et al. (1992) conducted a meta-analysis of relevant flight simulation research to identify important characteristics for simulator transfer of training. Simulator design and training context were included in the findings, and both fall under the training design section of the Baldwin and Ford (1988) model. Lathan et al. (2002) also argued that fidelity is a primary issue in simulator transfer of training effectiveness—the higher the fidelity, the better the transfer. Higher fidelity, however, does not mean "technology advance" or physical fidelity. Instead, it should be considered an indication that the simulation includes appropriate stimulus–response relationships that create a high degree of cognitive fidelity with regard to performing the simulated task. As an example, cognitive fidelity in flight simulation addresses the extent that the simulation engages the pilot in the types of cognitive activities encountered in real flight (Kaiser, 2003).

In addition to design of the simulator itself, many other variables exist in terms of training methodology (Goldstein, 1993). Regarding flight simulation, Auffrey et al. (2001) argued that instructional factors include instruction specificity, prior knowledge and experience, active use of knowledge, similarity (fidelity), practice, and elaboration methods.

The third input factor in the model is work-environment characteristics. This refers to the overall organizational support for the learner, such as supervision, sponsorship, and subsequent reward for the training and skill development. It also refers to the skill involved (i.e., task difficulty). Some tasks are easy and require little effort to transfer skills, whereas other tasks are difficult and require skills that are difficult to transfer and maintain (Blaiwes et al., 1973; Simon and Roscoe, 1984; Hays et al., 1992; Lathan et al., 2002).

The Hays et al. (1992) meta-analysis-indicated task equipment and task requirements were important factors for simulation-based training effectiveness. Lathan et al. (2002) also found that the task itself is of paramount importance. In their review regarding flight simulation, Auffrey et al. (2001) agree that the characteristics of the work environment are important factors in training transfer.

Additionally, Awoniyi et al. (2002) investigated the effect of various work environment factors on training transfer. These authors discussed the importance of the person–environment fit. Briefly, the notion is that transfer will depend on the degree of fit between a worker and the particular work environment. In other words, two workers may attend training and acquire equivalent knowledge, skills, and abilities. However, depending on the degree of person–environment fit in the organization, one worker may show a significantly higher degree of training transfer than the other. Five dimensions were studied: supervisory encouragement, resources, freedom, workload pressure, and creativity support. Results indicated that person–environment fit has a positive relationship with transfer of training and can be a moderate predictor for transfer of training.

Training outputs: The middle of the model shown in Figure 3.1, "Training Outputs," focuses on the actual outputs of training or, in other words, the amount of learning that occurred during training and the amount retained after the training program was completed. As noted, the training outputs depend on the three inputs described earlier. In turn, the amount learned during training will directly influence ultimate training transfer.

Conditions of transfer: Finally, the right side of the model, "Conditions of Transfer," refers to the posttraining environment. At this stage, the learner is back in the actual work environment. Conditions of transfer include the real-world conditions surrounding the use, generalization, and maintenance of the knowledge, skills, and abilities learned in the training program; the degree to which the learner used the knowledge, skills, and abilities in a transfer setting; and the length of time the learner retained the knowledge, skills, and abilities. Little research has been done in this area, particularly within the simulation domain. One example, however, is a study of assertiveness training for pilots (Smith-Jentsch et al., 2001). This study investigated the combined effects of trainee characteristics, team leader support, and team climate on training transfer. A multidimensional measurement of team transfer was applied. Results of their investigation showed a strong effect of transfer climate on transfer performance.

In summary, transfer of training is the combined result of input factors (characteristics of the trainee, training design, and work environment), the amount learned in training, and the conditions surrounding the transfer setting. Some of these factors are better understood than others. Simulation is one subfactor in this complex problem. Even with the best simulation available, if other variables do not exist in the appropriate manner, training will not be effective; it will not result in positive transfer. Overall, transfer of training remains a complex issue with numerous variables involved. Additional research is needed to further understand the differential impacts and the interaction effects of the variables. We now turn to a discussion of the methodologies underlying transfer of training studies.

RESEARCH METHODS

How do researchers study transfer of training? In other words, how do designers validate their simulator as a training tool? It sounds straightforward enough: simply compare performance on the job before training and after training. Unfortunately, it is not that simple, and because of the complex nature of the problem, many unknowns still exist. Indeed, transfer of training research has been inconclusive due to the differences in concepts and definitions, differences in theoretical orientations, and methodological flaws. Perhaps the greatest problem is that transfer of training is extremely difficult to measure (in terms of accurately determining whether transfer has occurred and how much has transferred). Furthermore, transfer is often measured as a product, rather than measuring it as a process (Auffrey et al., 2001).

Two major issues are involved in assessing training transfer: performance measurement and research design. A full review of these topics is beyond the scope of this chapter; however, we do offer some key terminology and issues.

TRANSFER OF TRAINING PERFORMANCE MEASUREMENT

Human performance (e.g., job performance) can be assessed in many ways. The most commonly used methods are objective performance measures and subjective judgments (Spector, 2003).

OBJECTIVE MEASURES

Objective measures are accounts of various behaviors (e.g., number of errors) or the results of job behaviors (e.g., total passengers transported). Thus, objective measures are data that objectively reflect the trainee's performance level. An obvious problem with objective measurements is that they cannot provide insight into cognitive-related aspects of performance, such as workload, situational awareness, motivation, and attitudes. These variables are vital to transfer of training assessment because they are part of the transfer of training affected factors.

SUBJECTIVE MEASURES

Another approach is to use subjective measures, which are ratings given by an expert: examples include surveys and questionnaires. Overall, Hays et al. (1992) found that these subjective performance measures were more sensitive to transfer of training effects than were objective measures. Numerous examples of subjective performance measures can be found in the training literature.

In terms of examples relating to training transfer studies, a six-item scale questionnaire was developed by Xiao (1996) to measure three aspects of training transfer (efficiency, quality, and productivity) (see also Awoniyi et al., 2002). In addition, in a study on the effect of "relapse prevention training" on the transfer of training, Burke (1997) used posttraining and follow-up surveys. In this study, trainees were taught to actively anticipate and cope with a relapse into former behaviors. The posttraining and follow-up surveys included items related to motivation to transfer, ability to transfer, training program reaction, use of transfer strategies, and use of trained skills.

SELECTING PERFORMANCE MEASURES

The selection of performance measures depends largely on the task. Indeed, it is rare for performance measures to be used in different tasks and domains without at least some modification. Training requirements are key (Hammerton, 1966). If the training purpose is to teach solely physical skills, objective measurement can be used as the primary tool. However, if cognitive training is involved, subjective performance assessment tools need to be applied to capture the cognitive skill learning and transfer. The notion of multiple measures also exists (Hammerton, 1966; Kraiger et al., 1993; Kirkpatrick, 1996). For instance, Kraiger et al. (1993) advocate separate measures for cognitive, behavioral, and attitudinal factors.

Additionally, in terms of choosing which measures of transfer are appropriate, a deeper look at the transfer process may be helpful.

Training transfer as a process: Although most transfer of training research focuses on immediate results of the training instruction, Foxon (1993) proposed that transfer does not occur immediately, but instead, occurs in a series of stages through which trainees pass. In other words, Foxon proposed a process model. The Foxon (1993) model (see Figure 3.2) fits into the "generalization and maintenance" portion of the Baldwin and Ford (1988) model in Figure 3.1. According to Foxon (1993), the degree of transfer increases progressively whereas the chance to transfer failure gets lower. Although this process model was proposed for organizational training programs, it can likely be generalized to any kind of training, including simulation training.

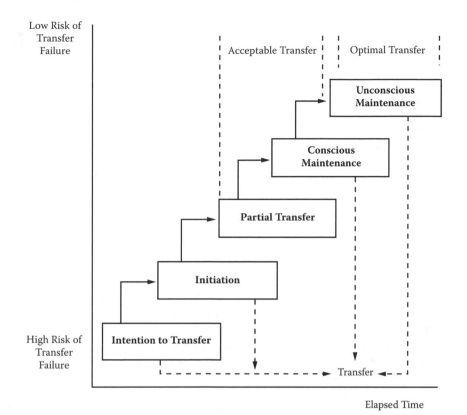

FIGURE 3.2 A model of the training transfer process. (Adapted from Foxon, M., *Aust. J. Educ. Technol.*, 9(2), 130–143, 1993.)

The Foxon (1993) model has several implications. One is for transfer of training measurements (Auffrey et al., 2001). Although traditional transfer of training measures assess one single value of transfer, the previous approach enables several points of measurements so that transfer can be estimated continuously, and other information, such as transfer speed, can also be obtained. This is similar to the notion of multiple measures of learning (e.g., Kraiger et al., 1993), but the Foxon (1993) model also emphasizes time. Combining the ideas from Kraiger et al. (1993) with the Foxon (1993) model suggests a need for multiple measures spread over multiple points in time.

Using performance measures to indicate transfer: Finally, as shown in Tables 3.1 and 3.2, Hammerton (1966), Roscoe and Williges (1980), and Taylor et al. (1999) present a number of different calculations that can be done on the performance data. These include: percent transfer (the saving of time or trials in an aircraft by using a flight simulator); transfer effective ratio (measures the efficiency of the simulation); first shot performance (how much training will be retained on first transference to the real situation); and training retained (how much training is retained on the first posttransfer trial from the simulator compared with that gained from real world).

In addition to performance measures, experimental design is another crucial issue to determine the degree of transfer of training that occurred. This will be discussed next.

EXPERIMENTAL DESIGN

Numerous training evaluation studies exist in the simulation-based training literature. Three types include: "Forward Transfer Study" (i.e., a predictive validation study); "Backward Transfer Study" (i.e., a concurrent validation study); and "Quasi-Experimental Study" (an approach similar to a construct validation study).

TABLE 3.1

Trials/Time to Transfer or Trial to Criterion (TTC)

Trials/time to transfer or trial to criterion (TTC) are the number of training trials that a subject attempted for a given task before reaching the criterion level of proficiency on that task, given the following variables:

Y_c:	The control group's number of TTC for training conducted in aircraft
Y_x:	The experimental group's number of TTC for training conducted in aircraft
X	The experimental group's number of TTC for training conducted in the simulator
F:	The mean performance on the first simulator training trial
L:	The mean performance on the last simulator training trial
T:	The mean performance on the first posttransfer trial
C:	The mean first trial performance of the real situation training
S:	The stable performance in real situation training

Forward transfer study: In the case of aviation, the classic experiment is to compare two matched groups of pilot trainees. One group (the control group) would be trained using only actual aircraft and the other (the experimental group) would receive their training via a simulator (Hays and Singer, 1989). The transfer environment is the actual aircraft. Pilot performance after training (e.g., TTC and flight technical performance) is captured, measured, and compared. This type of study is referred to as a Forward Transfer Study (Kaempf and Blackwell, 1990; Dohme, 1992; Darken and Banker, 1998), as it concurs with the transfer direction—first simulation, then the transfer environment. In some situations, however, this type of study can be expensive, time-consuming, or impossible to complete. For instance, in the occurrence of rare and dangerous events, such as engine failure, turbulence, or severe weather conditions, a forward transfer study is nearly impossible in a practical sense.

Backward transfer study: To overcome the technical difficulties inherent in forward transfer studies, researchers use the Backward Transfer Study method (Kaempf and Blackwell, 1990). In a backward transfer study (i.e., concurrent validation study), current proficient aviators perform tasks on the job and performance measures are taken. Next, the same aviators perform the tasks

TABLE 3.2

Transfer of Training Formulas

Name	Formula	Definition
Percent transfer	$\dfrac{Y_c - Y_x}{Y_c} \times 100$	Measures the saving of time or trials in aircraft training to criterion that can be achieved by use of a ground simulator
Transfer effective ratio (TER)	$\dfrac{Y_c - Y_x}{X}$	Measures the efficiency of the simulation by calculating the saving of trials per time
First shot performance (FSP)	$fsp = \dfrac{F - T}{F - L}$	Measures how much training will be retained on first transference to the real situation
Training retained (TR)	$tr = \dfrac{C - T}{C - S}$	Measures how much training is retained on the first post-transfer trial from simulator compare with that gained from real world

Source: From Taylor, H.L. et al., 1997; Taylor, H.L., Lintern, G., Hulin, C.L., Talleur, D.A., Emanuel, T.W., Jr., and Phillips, S.I., *Int. J. Aviat. Psychol.,* 9(4), 319–335, 1999; Hammerton, M., *Proceedings of the IEE Conference,* 113(11), 1881–1884, 1966.

TABLE 3.3

Index of Backward Transfer Formula (*B*)

$$B = \frac{\sum_{i=1}^{N}\left(\dfrac{A_i}{S_i}\right)}{N}$$

i = subject

N = total number of subjects

A = the mean of the subject's OPR scores for the last two trials in aircraft

S = the subject's OPR score during second simulator check ride

B less than 1 indicates that performance in the simulator was substantially below that in the aircraft.

Source: From Kaempf, G.L., and Blackwell, N.J., Transfer-of-training study of emergency touchdown maneuvers in the AH-1 flight and weapons simulator (Research Report 1561), 1990.

in the simulation. Their performance in the simulation is compared with their performance on the job. The logic of the backward transfer study method lies in the following assumption: "If the aircraft proficient aviators cannot perform the flying tasks successfully in the simulator, the poor performance is attributed to deficiencies in the simulators" (Kaempf and Blackwell, 1990). Possible simulator deficiencies include: cues that may be different from actual environment, controls that may be different from the actual environment, and the fact that flight simulators may require skills that are not required to fly aircraft (Kaempf and Blackwell, 1990).

Backward transfer studies use real pilots' performance in simulators only to predict forward transfer effectiveness for a particular simulator. If a low degree of backward transfer occurs, it implies that there are deficiencies in that simulator. Unfortunately, in the case of a high degree of backward transfer, it is not necessarily an indication of a high degree of forward transfer. It may simply mean that the pilots in the study were exemplary at getting the simulator to perform how they desired. Table 3.3 illustrates the formulas involved in backward transfer studies. Results from Kaempf and Blackwell (1990) indicate that the inexpensive backward transfer studies may be employed to predict forward transfer tasks.

Quasi-experimental study: Lintern et al. (1997) and Stewart et al. (2002) completed a quasi-experimental study (i.e., similar to construct validation studies). In this method, transfer of training is compared between one of the configurations of simulation and another configuration of the same device. Quasi-experimental study is intended to investigate the basic knowledge about transfer of training principles and theories. Potential benefits include considerable savings in experimental cost and time, provided quasi-transfer methodology can be validated as the true transfer of training.

CURVE-FITTING METHOD

Another method used to assess transfer is the curve-fitting technique. One reason to use curve fitting is that the traditional transfer of training formulas do not take prior training or experience into account. Moreover, the only data collected tends to be from immediately after one simulation exercise. Another shortcoming of traditional transfer of training formulas is that they only provide "crude" transfer by giving one global value. Also, the traditional estimates of transfer of training are not statistical tests (Damos, 1991).

In contrast, using the curve-fitting technique to assess transfer of training provides a more comprehensive measure of training transfer. In brief, the curve-fitting technique attempts to generate a learning curve for a particular task. Researchers find the best fitting equation for the data. In this way, a more exact picture of the skill acquisition process is portrayed. Thus, the researcher is examining measures of learning over time rather than one individual measure.

Curve fitting is claimed to be a major improvement for ToT estimates (Damos, 1991). Using this method, the curve equation provides estimates for rate of initial level of performance, rate of improvement, and the asymptotic level of performance for a particular group (e.g., type of training). Damos (1991) found that the curve-fitting method provided a much more detailed analysis of the data. This includes the following characteristics:

1. More insight into specific training effectiveness for differing training methods (i.e., calculating the inflection point and asymptote of the curves)
2. Transfer of training estimates without a control group
3. Statistical tests on curve parameters (to help assess differences between training interventions)

The typical steps involved in curve fitting include:

- Visual inspection of data to "guess" an equation form (i.e., a general exponential equation (Damos, 1991) $dv = c \exp(gx) + h$ where dv is the dependent variable, c, g, and h are the parameters to be fit, x is the trials block number)
- Calculating the goodness-of-fit calculations by calculating the correlations between predicted and observed value
- Performing a statistical test for each parameter

More curve-fitting techniques can be found in Spears (1985).

CRITICISMS OF TRANSFER OF TRAINING STUDIES

Valverde (1973) found that there was disparity in ToT findings. He believed that these studies were not complete ToT studies due to many missing variables. The major characteristics for these studies can be summarized with problems in the following four categories: (1) the criterion (most studies used judgmental performance measures and subjective instruments); (2) the subjects (motivation and attitude need to be considered as part of the factors in training effectiveness assessment); (3) lack of addressing the importance of the instructor; and (4) lack of addressing adequately the importance of the instructional sequence (block simulator instruction versus alternating sequence of instruction).

Although almost 30 years have passed since these finding were published, some of the comments are still valid. Blaiwes et al. (1973) summarized the previous studies on ToT and noted the following obstacles in transfer of training experiments:

1. A no-training control group often cannot be employed due to several practical issues (it is dangerous to put a student without any training in a real aircraft), so the direct measurement of amount and direction of transfer are hard to determine.
2. Performance measures are determined by training goals. Some of these goals might not be appropriate or clearly defined. Also, these measurements are mostly subjective. Developing objective measurements is extremely difficult.
3. Specifying appropriate training goals and task analysis can be difficult.
4. Difficulties of recording the desired performance measure in both simulators and real aircraft.
5. Other confounding influence factors, including tasks difficulties, trainee differences, changing crew compositions, instruction differences, and institutional differences.

Based on these findings, the authors proposed a multilevel evaluation method depending on the factors mentioned above, from simple to complex, and from qualitative to quantitative. This is similar to the notion by Kraiger et al. (1993) regarding multiple measures of learning.

SUMMARY

After reviewing the literature, a few points are quite clear. First, more work is needed to establish a systematic approach to define and quantify transfer of training. This is particularly true in aviation simulation training. Second, perhaps the most difficult issue in studying transfer of training is the existence of the multitude of variables that influence training effectiveness and, in turn, training transfer (Baldwin and Ford, 1988; Colquitt et al., 2000). Indeed, a methodical approach to testing the influence of these variables independently and in interactions with each other is essential. Additional research is needed before an exact understanding of the relative importance of the different variables is achieved. In addition, when accomplishing the studies, attention must focus on measurement—what to measure and how to measure it. Appropriate measurement is absolutely crucial. More fundamental research is needed to address the mechanism of the human learning process and the training transfer within different contexts to advance the understanding of the transfer of training.

REFERENCES

Auffrey, A.L., Mirabella, A., & Siebold, G.L., 2001, Transfer of training revisited (Report ARI-RN-2001-10), Alexandria, VA: Army Research Institute for the Behavioral and Social Sciences.

Awoniyi, E.A., Griego, O.V., & Morgan, G.A., 2002, Person-environment fit and transfer of training, *Int. J. Training Dev.,* 6(1), 25–35.

Baldwin, T., & Ford, J., 1988, Transfer of training: a review and direction for future research, *Personnel Psychol.,* 41, 63–105.

Blaiwes, A.S., Puig, J.A., & Regan, J.J., 1973, Transfer of training and the measurement of training effectiveness, *Hum. Factors,* 15(6), 523–533.

Burke, L.A., 1997, Improving positive transfer: a test of relapse prevention training on transfer outcomes, *Hum. Resour. Dev. Q.,* 8(2), 115–128.

Cannon-Bowers, J.A., Salas, E., Tannenbaum, S.I., & Mathieu, J.E., 1995, Toward theoretically based principles of training effectiveness: a model and initial empirical investigation, *Mil. Psychol.,* 7, 141–164.

Chapanis, A., 1996, *Human Factors in Systems Engineering,* New York: John Wiley & Sons.

Colquitt, J.A., LePine, J.A., & Noe, R.A., 2000, Toward an integrated theory of training motivation: a meta-analytic path analysis of 20 years of research, *J. Appl. Psychol.,* 85(5), 678–707.

Damos, D.L., 1991, Examining transfer of training using curve fitting: a second look, *Int. J. Aviat. Psychol.,* 1(1), 73–85.

Darken, R.P., & Banker, W.P., 1998, Navigating in natural environments: a virtual environment training transfer study, *Proceedings of VRAIS,* 12–19.

Dohme, J., 1992, Transfer of training and simulator qualification or myth and folklore in helicopter simulation (N93-30687), *NASA/FAA Helicopter Simulator Workshop Proceedings,* 115–121.

Federal Aviation Administration, 2002, *Private Pilot Airplane Practical Test Standards,* Oklahoma City, OK: U.S. Government Printing Office.

Foxon, M., 1993, A process approach to the transfer of training. Part 1: The impact of motivation and supervisor support on transfer maintenance, *Aust. J. Educ. Technol.,* 9(2), 130–143.

Goldstein, I.L., 1993, *Training in Organizations: Needs Assessment, Development, and Evaluation,* 3rd ed., Pacific Grove, CA: Brooks/Cole.

Hammerton, M., 1966, Factors affecting the use of simulators for training, *Proceedings of the IEE Conference,* 113(11), 1881–1884.

Hays, R.T., Jacobs, J.W., Prince, C., & Salas, E., 1992, Flight simulator training effectiveness: a meta-analysis, *Mil. Psychol.,* 4(2), 63–74.

Hays, R.T., & Singer, M.J., 1989, *Simulation Fidelity in Training System Design,* New York: Springer.

Kaempf, G.L., & Blackwell, N.J., 1990, Transfer-of-training study of emergency touchdown maneuvers in the AH-1 flight and weapons simulator (Research Report 1561), Alexandria, VA: U.S. Army Research Institute for the Behavioral and Social Sciences.

Kaiser, M.K., 2003, Flights of fancy: the art and science of flight simulation, in *Principles and Practice of Aviation Psychology,* Tsang, P.S. and Vidulich, M.A., Eds., Mahwah, NJ: Lawrence Erlbaum Associates, pp. 435–471.

Kirkpatrick, D.L., 1996, Evaluation, in *The ASTD Training and Development Handbook,* Craig, R.L., Ed., New York: McGraw-Hill.

Kraiger, K., Ford, J.K., & Salas, E., 1993, Application of cognitive, skill-based, and affective theories of learning outcomes to new methods of training evaluation, *J. Appl. Psychol.,* 78, 311–328.

Lathan, C.E., Tracey, M.R., Sebrechts, M.M., Clawson, D.M., & Higgins, G.A., 2002, Using virtual environment as training simulators: measuring transfer, in *Handbook of Virtual Environment,* Stanney, K.M., Ed., Mahwah, NJ: Lawrence Erlbaum Associates.

Lintern, G., Taylor, H.L., Koonce, J.M., Kaiser, R.H., & Morrison, G.A., 1997, Transfer and quasi-transfer effects of scene detail and visual augmentation in landing training, *Int. J. Aviat. Psychol.,* 7(2), 149–169.

Moroney, W.F., & Moroney, B.W., 1998, Flight simulation, in *Handbook of Aviation Human Factors,* Garland, D.J., Wise, J.A., & Hopkin, V.D., Eds., New York: Lawrence Erlbaum Associates.

Osgood, C.E., 1949, The similarity paradox in human learning: a resolution, *Psychol. Rev.,* 56, 132–143.

Roscoe, S.N., & Williges, B.H., 1980, Measurement of transfer of training, in *Aviation Psychology,* Roscoe, S.N., Ed., Ames, IA: Iowa State University Press, pp. 182–193.

Simon, C.W., & Roscoe, S.N., 1984, Application of a multifactor approach to transfer of training research, *Hum. Factors,* 26(5), 591–612.

Smith-Jentsch, K.A., Salas, E., & Brannick, M.T., 2001, To transfer or not to transfer? Investigating the combined effects of trainee characteristics, team leader support, and team climate, *J. Appl. Psychol.,* 86(2), 279–292.

Spears, W., 1985, Measuring of learning and transfer using curve fitting, *Hum. Factors,* 27, 251–266.

Spector, P.E., 2003, *Industrial/Organizational Psychology: Research and Practice,* 3rd ed., New York: John Wiley & Sons.

Stewart, J.E., II, Dohme, J.A., & Nullmeyer, R.T., 2002, U.S. Army initial entry otary-wing transfer of training research, *Int. J. Aviat. Psychol.,* 12(4), 359–375.

Taylor, H.L., Lintern, G., Hulin, C.L., Talleur, D.A., Emanuel, T.W., Jr., & Phillips, S.I., 1999, Transfer of training effectiveness of a personal computer aviation training device, *Int. J. Aviat. Psychol.,* 9(4), 319–335.

Thorndike, E.L., 1903, *Educational Psychology,* New York: Lemke & Buechner.

Valverde, H.H., 1973, A review of flight simulator transfer of training studies, *Hum. Factors,* 15(6), 510–523.

Xiao, J., 1996, The relationship between organizational factors and the transfer of training in the electronics industry in Shenzhen, China, *Hum Resour. Dev. Q.,* 7(1), 55–74.

4 Simulation Fidelity

Dahai Liu, Nikolas D. Macchiarella, and Dennis A. Vincenzi

CONTENTS

INTRODUCTION

With the increasing demand on training to function in highly complex situations, researchers and practitioners strive to build high-fidelity simulation devices as similar to the real situations as possible. Each year, technological advances bring simulation closer and closer to duplicating precise, authentic environments. Unfortunately, a high financial cost is associated with these highly sophisticated devices.

Simulation fidelity is one subject that has been determined to have a strong link to transfer of training. With budget limitations in mind, the issue becomes one of identifying the degree of fidelity necessary to achieve maximal transfer of training to keep the cost of the training system as low as possible. This chapter describes the main concepts and theories pertaining to simulation fidelity, and how fidelity is defined and measured. Finally, we propose a theoretical model of the relationship between fidelity and training transfer.

Simulation quality and human capabilities are critical factors that determine training effectiveness and efficiency. The key issue related to simulation quality is the "degree to which the training devices must duplicate the actual equipment" or environment. This degree of similarity is called simulation fidelity (Allen, 1986). The issue of fidelity must be addressed not only because it is quite possibly the most important factor in the assessment of simulation quality, and a key factor of simulation training transfer, but it is also a critical factor related to cost-effective simulation device design. Often simulators are not utilized because the equipment is too costly to purchase (Garrison, 1985). It is widely accepted that training devices with excessive levels of fidelity may not be cost-effective (Allen, 1986; Fortin, 1989; Roza, 2000).

Existing research in the area of flight simulation training, aviation psychology, military aviation, and many other domains has contributed greatly to the understanding of simulation. Despite this work, many questions remain unanswered. Research indicates that simulation is a valuable tool for training (Hays et al., 1992). What is not fully understood is how to make simulation more efficient, i.e., how to determine what level of fidelity is sufficient for effective transfer of training.

Despite this, fidelity or "level of detail," continues to be a major issue in simulation development (Hughes and Rolek, 2003). Due to the complex nature of simulation tasks, large numbers of objects and attributes, and random human behaviors involved, quantification of simulation fidelity becomes the most challenging aspect of fidelity measurement. Schricker, Franceschini, and Johnson (2001) concluded that the main issues regarding fidelity and how it is addressed in the literature are: (1) "No detailed, agreed-upon definition; (2) Rampant subjectivity; (3) No method of quantifying the assignment of fidelity; and (4) No detailed example of a referent."

Other major issues involve the accepted methods by which fidelity is measured. There are two major methods described in the literature for fidelity measurement. The first is through mathematical measurement that calculates the number of identical elements shared between the real world and the simulation; the greater the number of shared identical elements, the higher the simulation fidelity. This is referred to as the objective method (Gross and Freeman, 1997; Schricker et al., 2001). A second method to measure fidelity is through a trainees' performance matrix. By assessing a human's performance and then comparing it to real-world performance to measure the transfer of training, fidelity of a simulation can be measured indirectly (Parrish et al., 1983; Ferguson et al., 1985; Nemire et al., 1994; Field et al., 2002; Mania et al., 2003). We will address these methods in detail in a later section. First, a clear definition is needed to understand what is meant by "fidelity."

DEFINITION OF FIDELITY

Simulation fidelity is an umbrella term defined as the extent to which the simulation replicates the actual environment (Alessi, 1988; Gross et al., 1999). In aviation, simulation fidelity refers to the extent to which a flight training device looks, sounds, responds, and maneuvers like a real aircraft. Many simulation professionals attempt to define fidelity comprehensively, whereas others argue that fidelity is a far too nebulous idea than can even be defined. This implies that efforts of defining fidelity are currently unsuccessful (Schricker et al., 2001). Rehmann et al. (1995) investigated over 30 years of research on fidelity and found that there was no agreed-upon single definition; in fact, at least 22 different definitions can be drawn from the literature. For example, fidelity can be defined as simply as "how closely a simulation imitates reality" (Alessi, 1988), or more specifically, on different fidelity dimensions, including but not limited to equipment fidelity, environmental fidelity, psychological and cognitive fidelity, task fidelity, physical fidelity, and functional fidelity. Furthermore, Rehmann et al. (1995) found that none of these terms or definitions is applicable to overall aircraft simulation in general. This lack of a well-defined and widely accepted fidelity concept causes miscommunications between researchers and inconsistencies in their research (Roza, 2000).

Based on the previous research and a definition by Fidelity-ISG, Roza (2000) developed the following theorems regarding simulation fidelity:

1. Fidelity models are multidimensional; they involve and can be quantified using a variety of factors.
2. Fidelity is application-independent; it is an intrinsic and inherent property of a simulation model.
3. Fidelity must be quantified and qualified with respect to a referent; this means that metrics (i.e., size, weight, shape) should exist on how to determine if a simulation resembles its referent.
4. Fidelity quantification has a level of uncertainty.
5. Fidelity comparison should be based on a common referent in order to make sense. For example, comparing fidelity levels of an aircraft simulator should be drawn from the same or similar aircraft.

Seven descriptive concepts were defined to further understand and quantify fidelity: detail, resolution, error, precision, sensitivity, timing, and capacity. Specific metrics or measurements can be defined in depth for each of these concept factors.

A simulation referent is important not only to define fidelity, but also for its measurement. It can be simply described "in terms of the extent to which a representation reproduces the attributes and behaviors of a referent" (Hughes and Rolek, 2003). A referent is "an entity or collection of entities and/or conditions—together with their attributes and behaviors—present within a given operational domain" (Hughes and Rolek, 2003).

For example, in the small aircraft aviation industry, one is particularly interested in studying the single pilot performance in a Cessna 172. Thus, the cockpit of the Cessna 172 is the *reality*. The simulated cockpit would be the referent (display, radio, controls, pedals, chair, etc.); the models would be the computer-simulated models that produce this referent such as Microsoft Flight Simulator.

Roza (2000) defined a referent as "a formal specification of all knowledge about reality plus indicators to determine the uncertainty levels and quality of this knowledge to judge the confidence level of this referent data." In other words, a referent is the abstract model of the reality that is relevant to simulated tasks, and serves as a basis for measuring the simulated environment and tasks. According to Roza (2000), a referent structure consists of the following elements:

1. A referent identification section
2. A referent applicability section
3. A referent developer and validation agent
4. A referent knowledge sources section
5. A real-world structural properties section
6. A real-world parametric and behavioral data section

Roza (2000) claims that elements 2, 3, and 4 contain the indicators needed to assess the fidelity of the simulation reference, and elements 5 and 6 can be used to measure the fidelity.

By using the concept of a referent, fidelity measurement can be simplified. As Schricker et al. (2001) pointed out, if one tried to consider fidelity issues on a real-world system, it would become far too intricate. Simulations are developed to represent a certain object or group of objects in a certain domain, which can be regarded as the simulated models of a certain referent of the reality.

Fidelity can be further broken down into sub-definitions that describe detailed elements that are categorized based on the different aspects of the simulated tasks or environment. The categorization among researchers varies a great deal and no consensus has been reached. The different fidelity element categorizations depended largely on the different fidelity experiments and different simulated tasks. For example, in Zhang's (1993) study, simulation fidelity is broken down into six elements: hardware fidelity, software fidelity, fidelity for a whole tested system, fidelity of the pilot's subjective impression, simulation mission (task) fidelity, and simulation experience fidelity.

Hays and Singer (1989) identified the following three major types of variables that were believed to interact with fidelity:

1. Task-related variables, including task domain, task type, task difficulty, task frequency, task criticality, task learning difficulty, task practice requirement, and task skills, abilities, and knowledge
2. Training environment and personal variables (e.g., purpose of training, instructional principles, student population)
3. Device utilization variables that are the least understood and the most "potent" in determining training device effectiveness

TABLE 4.1

Fidelity Definitions

Word	References	Definition
Simulation fidelity	Gross et al. (1999); Alessi (1988)	Degree to which device can replicate actual environment, or how "real" the simulation appears and feels
Physical fidelity	Allen (1986)	Degree to which device looks, sounds, and feels like actual environment
Visual–audio fidelity	Rinalducci (1996)	Replication of visual and auditory stimulus
Equipment fidelity	Zhang (1993)	Replication of actual equipment hardware and software
Motion fidelity	Kaiser and Schroeder (2003)	Replication of motion cues felt in actual environment
Psychological–cognitive fidelity	Kaiser and Schroeder (2003)	Degree to which device replicates psychological and cognitive factors (i.e., communication, situational awareness)
Task fidelity	Zhang (1993); Roza (2000); Hughes and Rolek (2003)	Replication of tasks and maneuvers executed by user
Functional fidelity	Allen (1986)	How device functions, works, and provides actual stimuli as actual environment

Source: From

Table 4.1 lists a number of different aspects of fidelity and how they relate to each other as well as how researchers have attempted to describe each aspect. These definitions have been compiled from research that has focused on structuring and defining the various components of fidelity. Definitions of fidelity mainly fall within two categories: those that describe the physical experience and those that describe the psychological or cognitive experience. These two categories are briefly described in Table 4.1, and will be explored further.

PHYSICAL FIDELITY

The most commonly discussed fidelity categorization is physical fidelity (Allen, 1986; Hays and Singer, 1989; Andrews, Carroll, and Bell, 1995). Not to be confused with the broader term of simulation fidelity, this term specifically deals with the physical properties of the simulation experience. To consider high physical fidelity, the simulator must have high visual–audio fidelity, or the look, sound, feel, and, in some cases, smell of the real aircraft (Allen, 1986). Physical fidelity encompasses other definitions of fidelity such as visual–audio fidelity, equipment fidelity, and motion fidelity.

VISUAL–AUDIO FIDELITY

Visual–audio fidelity is the most frequently studied aspect of fidelity in the available literature (Rinalducci, 1996). It can be thought of as the level of visual and aural detail that the simulator displays. For example, a visually simulated airport can include several elements or artifacts that could be found when directly viewing a real-world airport. The runways, lights, hangers, control towers, ground vehicles, natural surroundings, and other airplanes could be included in the simulation. Also, communication between the control tower and pilot can also be simulated.

A low fidelity simulation would include only a few of these artifacts mentioned. For example, the low fidelity simulator may contain simply a runway and landing threshold lights, and no aural detail at all. As the simulation includes more artifacts, the level of fidelity will increase.

Technology has advanced visual fidelity, specifically, to a very high level. Although a perfect copy of the real world is beyond reach at this point, advances in satellite and aerial mapping for the purpose of simulation are producing increasingly accurate representations of the real environment and geography. For example, it is now possible to simulate and practice military operations in a computer-generated city that displays the buildings, streets, obstacles and other physical features that may be encountered in the actual battle environment. This mitigates the chance of surprises and can greatly aid in the planning and rehearsal of military operations without risking lives.

Visual–audio fidelity in flight simulation can be decomposed into two basic parts: the "what" and the "where." The "what" refers to the pilot's central vision, which is referred to as the foveal and parafoveal regions. This area includes the items the pilot is directly viewing (e.g., instruments and the windscreen). The "where" refers to visual stimulus that is in the pilot's peripheral vision. The stimuli in the peripheral vision provide the pilot with a sense of speed, motion, situational awareness, and attitude of the aircraft. Both regions of vision have been shown to be important to the control of an aircraft (Kaiser and Schroeder, 2003). Unfortunately, computer-generated graphics often lack the power to generate visual stimulus in both regions at the same time to the same degree. Thus a trade-off exists, and displays must decide what stimulus to show at what time.

As technology advances and the power of image generators improve, this confound may become a nonissue. Additionally, instrument flight requires pilots to engage and view only their instruments. Thus, there is no need for "outside" visual stimuli. In this situation, an outside visual scene may even hinder the transfer of training by distracting the pilot.

Bradley and Abelson (1995) investigated visual fidelity issues for desktop flight simulators. Although improvements in computing power and software advances have enabled high animation in visual display, the most significant factor limiting visual fidelity (quality of performance) is still the speed of frame refresh, or "frame rate." In highly detailed visual scenes, the computational demand for visual frame rate is still the bottleneck for fast visual feedback.

EQUIPMENT FIDELITY

To consider high physical fidelity, proper equipment fidelity must also be present. Equipment fidelity refers to the extent to which a simulator can emulate or replicate the equipment being used, which includes all software and hardware components of the system (Zhang, 1993). Occasionally it may become unfeasible or too costly to use actual equipment for the simulation, in which case a replica or substitute may be used in its place.

It is important, however, to maintain a certain degree of equipment fidelity for training purposes. Reed (1996) studied equipment fidelity when trying to simulate an aerial gunner station of a helicopter. During the simulation, the actual weapons system appeared to interfere with the simulation equipment, and therefore had to be replaced by a replica. Using similarly shaped and weighted equipment in combination with parts of the actual weapons system, Reed was able to preserve some equipment fidelity without endangering the training effectiveness.

MOTION FIDELITY

The role of motion fidelity is another important component of physical fidelity. It can be defined as the degree to which a simulator can reproduce the sense of motion felt by humans in the operational environment. The most advanced flight simulators have six-access motion (i.e., front, back, up, down, and side to side). The use of motion does increase the physical fidelity and realism of the simulation, but the benefits realized toward measurable transfer of training are minimal and insignificant. At best, empirical research on motion simulation has indicated that the addition of motion provides very limited benefit. For example, reproduction of the movement a pilot feels when banking for a standard turn adds to the realism experienced by the pilot, but has not been shown to improve the ability of the pilot to perform that turn in the real world.

However, the motion component of simulation has been found to be quite critical for the training of pilots for certain types of aircraft. For example, military fighter pilots often rely heavily on motion cues to perform complicated maneuvers in jet airplanes (Thomas, 2004).

Motion also has its limitations. The brain, for example, can often be tricked into sensing motion where motion does not exist. Motion, it seems, provides very little to overall training effectiveness (Garrison, 1985; Ray, 1996). It also does not reduce the real flight time necessary to reach proficiency when performing many tasks in the real world such as the turning maneuver mentioned earlier (Ray, 1996). Furthermore, Advani and Mulder (1995) argue that reproduction of motion cues with ground-based flight simulators is principally impossible due to the kinetic limitations inherent in the motion system. Simulators may be capable of reproducing the banking angle that a real aircraft may encounter in an operational setting, but they have not been able to sufficiently produce and maintain the centrifugal forces experienced when actually executing the banking maneuver in the real world.

PSYCHOLOGICAL–COGNITIVE FIDELITY

Beyond the look and feel of a simulation, there exists another component of fidelity that results in the robustness (or lack thereof) of the psychological and cognitive experience that a person receives from being in the simulator. This component is known as psychological–cognitive fidelity.

Psychological–cognitive fidelity is the extent to which psychological and cognitive factors are replicated within the simulation (Kaiser and Schroeder, 2003). The result of the degree of psychological–cognitive fidelity present within a simulation is the degree to which the user is psychologically and cognitively engaged in the same manner when compared to the degree to which the actual equipment would engage the user.

The cockpit environment is a demanding environment, requiring the pilot to constantly monitor flight systems and instrumentation, looking for failures, and maintaining a flight plan (Wickens et al., 2004). To consider a simulation with high psychological and cognitive fidelity, the simulator must require the same attentional resources from the pilot and produce similar psychological effects such as stress and workload.

Research concerned with cognitive and psychological fidelity focuses on those and other factors that affect performance. It is known that too much stress may cause critical performance decrement in flight. If, when immersed in a simulation environment, a user experiences symptoms of stress similar to those felt in the operational setting, it is generally accepted that some level of psychological–cognitive fidelity has been achieved.

OTHER FIDELITY

Task fidelity is the degree to which a simulator replicates the tasks involved in the actual environment (Zhang, 1993; Roza, 2000; Hughes and Rolek, 2003). Flight training devices must act like actual airplanes; therefore, a pilot must be able to "fly" the simulator just as he or she would fly an aircraft. This means that all tasks that need to be executed in an aircraft must be done in the same fashion when in the simulator. The extent to which these tasks are simulated may be an issue for future research.

Not all tasks may need to be replicated for all training exercises, and some may be isolated to investigate specific problems or issues. When training for cockpit communication, for example, the tasks involving communication must be exactly the same as those in the operational setting. Other tasks (e.g., stick and rudder tasks) do not need to be the same, or can be eliminated altogether, if the objective of the training does not include these tasks.

Much like task fidelity, functional fidelity is also important. Functional fidelity can be described as how the simulator reacts to the tasks and commands being executed by the pilot (Allen, 1986). Not only does the pilot have to react and fly as he or she would in a real aircraft but the simulator must also react and maneuver as a real aircraft would in an operational setting. This ensures operational correctness and accuracy, as well as adding realism and believability to the simulation. When a trainee pulls back on the yoke, for example, the simulator must react as if the aircraft were pulling up and climbing in altitude. This fidelity, along with task fidelity is essential for training effectiveness and positive transfer of training to occur.

Simulator fidelity is a complex subject that includes a number of factors. It is important to understand that these dimensions are not mutually exclusive; there is a large degree of overlap. Although expensive, high-fidelity devices are often used for advanced pilot training. However, research has shown that high fidelity may not be necessary to produce effective training results (Connolly, Blackwell, and Lester, 1989; Hays et al., 1992; Duncan and Feterle, 2000). Future research should focus on the specific knowledge to determine exact fidelity requirements. A significant related topic is that of fidelity measurement.

MEASURING FIDELITY

Although it is well accepted that fidelity is the degree of similarity between the simulation and reality, it is critical to have a detailed and precise capability to measure that fidelity. Due to the complex nature of simulated tasks, different definitions of fidelity can lead to different measures of fidelity, and thus cause inconsistency among research results. Yu (1997) points out that simulation fidelity needs to be defined on the basis of "application purpose and technical possibility." Each aspect of fidelity must be verified in a way that is both consistent and specific.

Equipment fidelity can be verified by checking whether the simulator performance is within some predetermined accuracy compared with real aircraft. In other words, visual fidelity can be measured by some consistent and specific visualization standard such as resolution.

In terms of fidelity quantification, there are several types of metrics available. Roza (2000) found all these metrics either subjective or qualitative in nature, which is not good enough for current simulation requirements. Existing fidelity metrics can be classified either as a singular metric, or a set of metrics that can be statistically combined to create a meaningful multidimensional metric.

Objective measurement of simulation fidelity attempts to compare the simulated objects with the corresponding referent or real-world environment. Due to the level of complexity involved, especially with complex simulation setup and tasking, it is nearly impossible to count and compare every single element of the simulation. To better illustrate this picture, take a look at your surroundings, either an office or a room. Imagine that your task is to count every object around you to compare every feature and detail with the simulated environment. You will have some idea of the difficulties involved in accomplishing that task.

Thus, exact measure of realism is not feasible at this time, and is considered by some to be "a goal which can never be accomplished" (Roza et al., 2001). It is practically impossible to count everything, or know everything about the reality or referent due to: (1) the high degree of uncertainty, (2) the overwhelming information involved, (3) complicated attributes and behaviors associated with the reality or referent, and (4) human limitations needed to observe and explain real-world information.

A recent report on Fidelity Definition and Metrics (FDM-ISG) attempts to specify the fidelity requirements in a formal way (Gross 1999; Roza et al., 2001). Simulation fidelity is defined as "the degree to which a model or simulation reproduces the state and behavior of a real world object or perception of a real world object, feature, condition or standard in a measurable or perceivable manner."

The importance of fidelity measurement is also addressed by the FDM-ISG (Gross et al., 1999) as "what aspect should be simulated and how to observe the simulation purpose and objectives best."

These fidelity requirements are essential for simulation system design because the fidelity requirements will ultimately affect the simulation context, purpose, and hardware and software requirements, and thus affect the trade-off results between cost and achieved transfer of training. Research on simulation has been primarily focused on hardware and software development, which is targeted at "the ultimate display" to produce the real-time simulated environment.

What is the minimum fidelity that is required to achieve the required level of transfer of training? To find the most appropriate level of fidelity needed for the simulation tasks, one still needs to be able to accurately assess the existing or proposed level of fidelity. The most common methods of fidelity measurement are mathematical modeling, research experiments, and rating methods (Schricker et al., 2001; Kaiser and Schroeder, 2003).

THE MATHEMATICAL MODEL

For years, research on fidelity quantification focused mostly on the objective mathematical formulation. Schricker et al. (2001) offers a thorough review of mathematical models on fidelity measurements.

Subjective methods: Subjective methods use expert opinions (including developers and users) to determine the degree of fidelity. Clark and Duncan proposed one of the simplest methods (Schricker et al., 2001). In this model, fidelity is measured by a binary scoring system. Simulation conditions are evaluated by either a "0" or "1," with "0" meaning that simulation does not duplicate the real-world conditions, and "1" indicating that the simulation does reproduce the real-world conditions. Averaging those ratings together provides an assessment of the overall fidelity. Although the simplicity is appealing, this method is subject to the same rating issues as any other subjective form of rating. An arbitrary judgment, or guess, can significantly affect the fidelity score.

A more advanced mathematical model is proposed by Gross and Freeman (Schricker et al., 2001). The model is based on four theorems:

I. $0 \leq F(A) \leq 1$

II. If $F(A) = 1$, then $A \equiv R$

III. $F(A) \geq F(Meta\ A)$

IV. $F(A) + F(B) = \min(F(A), F(B))$

where A and B are models of interest, $F(A)$ is the fidelity of A, *Meta A* is a model of referent (including A itself), and R is the referent of A.

The simple formula for determining the overall value of fidelity of a simulation system is as follows:

$$F_s = \Sigma F_i W_i$$

where F_i is the fidelity of each referent characteristics and F_s is the fidelity of the entire simulation system, and W_i is the relative importance rate of characteristics i. This formula, however, contradicts Theorem IV above (Schricker et al., 2001). The main reason for this contradiction is because it did not clearly define the set, operation on the set, and function.

Liu and Vincenzi (2004) modified this model definition as follows. Let set S be defined as the following: $S = \{A : A = meta_i\ R\}$ (where R is the referent of the real-world group of objects and S is the group of all possible simulation models of referent R). Then, the function of fidelity is defined on set S as $F: S \rightarrow [0,1]$. Furthermore, we define the following operations for $A \in S$ and $B \in S$, $A \oplus B = A \cup B$, (one can easily prove that $A + B$ is commutative and associative). Based on these notations, Gross and Freeman's (1997) model can be modified as follows:

I, II, and III are still true and IV becomes:

$$\min(F(A), F(B)) \leq (A \oplus B) \leq \max(F(A), F(B))$$

Gross and Freeman stated that the fidelity of any simulated system is equal to the fidelity of the individual component of the simulation of the lowest fidelity. It can be argued that this might not be the case. If we add low-fidelity components to a high-simulation model, it will certainly affect the high-fidelity components, but it should also improve the low-fidelity components if this add-on interacts with low-fidelity components. Readers who are interested in this model should refer to Schricker et al. (2001) for more details.

With models like this, we have a more comprehensive mathematical framework in place to facilitate the assessment of fidelity. Several other attempts to measure fidelity mathematically currently exist. Interested readers should refer again to Schricker et al. (2001) for more details.

FIDELITY EVALUATION FRAMEWORKS

It can be argued that although mathematical modeling is beneficial to an understanding of the concept of fidelity, it has little practical implication for actual measurements due to the complexity and uncertainty involved. Researchers are attempting to develop other alternatives to measure fidelity in the field. One way of doing this is to utilize evaluation frameworks (Roza et al., 2001; Schricker et al., 2001). Figure 4.1 illustrates a generic model of measurement framework modified from Schricker et al. (2001).

By using this framework, all simulation task-critical objects can be identified, as well as their associated behaviors and attributes for the referent. By comparing the level (percentage) of the corresponding objects from a simulation model, the fidelity can be estimated quantitatively. This framework is based on the assumption of Perato's law (20% of the elements contribute 80% of the training effects in simulation).

Roza (2000) summarized existing research on simulation fidelity, especially on fidelity characterization and quantification. Based on his study, a preliminary fidelity theory and a practical tool called Fidelity Management Process Overlay Model (FiMO) was proposed to assess and quantify simulation fidelity. After investigating the distributed simulation fidelity requirement for U.S. Department of Defense's Defense Modeling and Simulation Office (DMSO) High Level Architecture (HLA), Roza (2000) found that although HLA is well defined by the Federation Development and Execution Process (FEDEP), it focuses primarily on technological aspects and cannot answer many questions that arise regarding fidelity or fidelity quantification. A systematic and structured way is needed to efficiently characterize aspects of fidelity. FiMO is one model employed for this purpose.

This approach maps to FEDEP framework and provides a process view for characterization of fidelity issues along simulation development stages and activities. The basic framework consists of five major, iterative activities. For detailed information of this approach, readers can refer to Roza's (2000) paper. This framework is believed to have the ability to handle large amounts of fidelity data in a progressive manner.

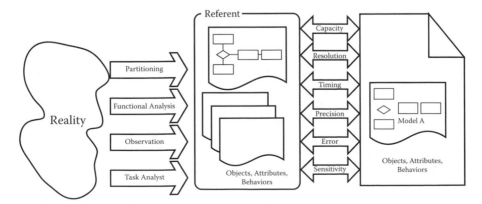

FIGURE 4.1 A conceptual illustration of measurement procedure. (Adapted from Schricker, B., Franceschini, R., and Johnson, T., "Fidelity evaluation framework", *Proceedings of the 34th Annual Simulation Symposium*, 2001.)

Bell and Freeman (1995) developed a draft Fidelity Description Requirement (FDR) they believe can be used to quantify simulation fidelity. An assessment process was proposed, and taxonomy was developed, in a hierarchical format. The top level is the simulation resource consisting of a combination of hardware and software solutions (i.e., a Cessna 172 Flight Simulator). Level 2 is the fidelity domain (i.e., physical fidelity or visual fidelity). Level 3 is the capability level, level 4 is the implementation-specific instantiations of the capability, level 5 consists of individual characteristics of an implementation, and level 6 defines the measurements for level 5. Bell and Freeman (1995) also discussed the possibility of using fuzzy logic as a means to help quantify fidelity as accurately as possible, taking into account unknowns and assumptions associated with characteristics of fidelity. This approach may be appropriate as there are a number of uncertainties involved.

Fidelity can also be measured by other indirect measurements such as by the evaluation of human performance. It is assumed that the function of fidelity is objective, i.e., for one referent; two simulation models have the same transfer of training effect if these two simulated models have the same fidelity. (Please note the opposite might not be true.) As the ultimate goal of simulation is to transfer the skills gained in training to the real-world situation and the objective measurement of fidelity is far more intriguing, the measurement of human task performance would be a good metric for any application that mainly targets transfer of training in the real world (Mania et al., 2003). Although human performance assessment alone cannot provide a quantitative assessment of simulation fidelity, it can provide a measure or indication of the relative efficiency of different simulated models for the same referent. It is more intuitive and hands-on than many other methods, and this measurement is widely accepted and used (Mania et al., 2003).

Lehmer and Chung (1999) applied Image Dynamic Measurement System (IDMS-2) to verify simulation fidelity. Measurement of delay in the visual system response time was used to assess the fidelity.

FIDELITY AND TRANSFER OF TRAINING

It is natural to assume that the higher the level of fidelity, the higher degree of transfer of training will occur. Based on the "identical elements" theory by Thorndike (1903), this notion is still strongly held by simulator designers and industries today. Thorndike argued that there would be transfer between the first task (simulation) and the second task (real world) if the first task contained specific component activities that were held by the second task. There are a number of theoretical studies (Noble, 2002) that support the notion that higher fidelity will produce higher degrees of training transfer.

The "Alessi Hypothesis" states that there is a certain point at which adding more fidelity does not transfer training at the same rate as early or beginning training (Alessi, 1988). Some proposed a U-shaped curve, whereas some theories proposed a normal curve. But according to Alessi (1988), experimental research has not provided sufficient evidence to support this high-fidelity notion as theory predicted. Some results even indicate that lower fidelity has an advantage. Alessi (1988) believed that the explanation for failing to show the high-fidelity advantage is that (1) high fidelity also means high complexity, which will require more cognitive skills, thus increasing trainee's workload, which will, in turn, impede learning; and (2) proven instructional techniques, which improve initial learning do not depend upon high-fidelity components which, in turn, tend to lower the overall fidelity of the simulation.

Alessi (1988) proposed that the relationship between learning and fidelity is nonlinear and also dependent on other factors such as the trainee experience. For different trainees, there are different learning curves, and all these curves are nonlinear and different.

According to Alessi (1988), when the level of fidelity is increased, the corresponding change in transfer of training depends largely on the trainee's characteristics and ability to respond to this increase in fidelity. For novices, initial learning is the primary focus, and for experts, who are well versed in the initial knowledge needed to perform the job or individual tasks, transfer of training related to task-specific knowledge, skills, and abilities, is essential.

Actual assessment of fidelity is extremely difficult to obtain. Alessi gave an in-depth fidelity analysis of four different types of simulation to further investigate this effect: (1) situational simulation, (2) procedural simulation, (3) process simulation, and (4) physical simulation. Four dimensions of fidelity were identified and defined for this analysis: (1) the underlying model, (2) presentation, (3) user actions, and (4) system feedback.

It was found that for different trainees and different types of simulation, the requirement for fidelity varied greatly. As an instance of procedural simulation, flight simulators need to have high fidelity of the presentation, actions, and system feedback to result in significant increases in transfer of training efficiency.

With respect to the relationship between fidelity and transfer of training, other studies have also demonstrated that the law of diminishing returns holds true. This parallels a hypothesis put forth by Roscoe in 1971, where Roscoe hypothesized that there will be diminishing returns in transfer of training as the amount of simulator training increases. Thus, the first hours of simulation training have high amounts of positive transfer of training information, and latter hours will have lower amounts of positive transfer of training information (Roscoe, 1980).

Combining these two theories (Roscoe, 1980; Alessi, 1988) we can conclude that adding more fidelity, especially in the later stages of training, produces minimal gain in transfer of training. If this is the case, increasing fidelity may not always be necessary. Fidelity is expensive, and eliminating certain key elements of fidelity that do not necessarily increase transfer of training will reduce the cost of production. The question is: Which cues can we eliminate without reducing the amount of transfer?

This issue still remains vague and less understood. To answer this question, more research is necessary. This research would need to directly compare simulation training to traditional training done in the actual aircraft or real-world environment. The main obstacle that researchers face is cost. It is extremely expensive to conduct this type of research due to the high operational costs associated with real-world systems such as commercial aircraft, combat aircraft, surface ships, submarines, and other military and civilian systems. Additional issues revolve around the possible disruption of normal training. It may be difficult to find flight schools, student pilots, or military personnel and facilities that would participate, especially because training time is already scarce, necessary, time-consuming, and expensive.

SUMMARY

It is clear that simulation can provide great benefits. The standard design approach for simulators is to incorporate the highest possible level of fidelity and hope for the best possible transfer of training outcome. This is the direct result of the belief (or assumption) that high levels of fidelity must equate to high levels of transfer of training despite the fact much evidence exists to indicate that this might not necessarily be true.

It is important to focus on the goal of simulation training, which is the transfer or translation of skills learned in one arena to another. The ever-present debate in the realm of simulation centers on how much fidelity is necessary to achieve a desired degree of training transfer. In other words, how "real" does the simulation need to be in order for the trainee to properly execute the skills learned in simulation to the real world? This question can only be answered with "it depends." As discussed previously, it depends on many factors including the individual trainees, their levels of skill, and the instructor. It also depends on the particular skills to be learned and transferred.

Low-fidelity simulators maximize the initial learning rate of novice pilots and minimize cost; whereas costly, high-fidelity simulators predict the real world in-flight performance of expert pilots (Kinkade and Wheaton, 1972; Fink and Shriver, 1978; Hays and Singer, 1989). This may be true because novice pilots may become overwhelmed by high fidelity, whereas experts will not. Initial pilot training focuses more on becoming familiar with the controls and the layout of the instruments, whereas experts will concentrate on more advanced operational aspects.

If economic constraints did not enter the picture, the question of the level of fidelity needed to obtain maximal transfer of training would not be an issue. Simulation designers would always include every possible attribute, increasing the level of fidelity as high as technology would allow. Unfortunately, financial resources are limited.

To get the most value from simulation, it is important to eliminate attributes that do not aid in the transfer of training. In other words, it has become imperative to get the most "bang for the buck." The goal is to give the trainee enough simulation fidelity to facilitate learning, without attaching costly and unnecessary simulation options and characteristics. There is no easy answer to this question at this time. Researchers in the area of human factors, psychology, computer science, engineering, and many other fields involved in the simulation industry need to work closely together to conduct systematic, multidisciplinary research to achieve maximal training benefit while controlling and minimizing cost.

REFERENCES

Advani, S.K. and Mulder, J.A., 1995, Achieving high-fideltiy motion cues in flight simulation, *AGARD FVP Symposium on Flight Simulation: Where are the Challenges,* Braunschweig, Germany.

Alessi, S.M., 1988, Fidelity in the design of instructional simulations, *J. Comp.-Based Instruction,* 15(2), 40–47.

Allen, J.A., 1986, Maintenance training simulator fidelity and individual difference in transfer of training, *Hum. Factors,* 28(5), 497–509.

Andrews, D., Carroll, L., and Bell, H., 1995, The future of selective fidelity in training devices, *Educ. Technol.,* 35, 32–36.

Bell, P.M. and Freeman, R., 1995, Qualitative and quantitative indices for simulation systems in distributed interactive simulation, *IEEE Proceedings of ISUMA-NAFIPS,* 745–748.

Bradley, D.R. and Abelson, S.B., 1995, Desktop flight simulators: simulation fidelity and pilot performance, *Behav. Res. Methods, Instruments, Comput.,* 27(2), 152–159.

Connolly, T.J., Blackwell, B.B., and Lester, L.F., 1989, A simulator–based approach to training in aeronautical decision making, *Aviat., Space Environ. Med.,* 60, 50–52.

Duncan, J.C. and Feterle, L.C., 2000, The use of personal computer-based aviation training devices to teach aircrew decision-making, teamwork, and resource management, *Proceedings of IEEE 2000 National Aerospace and Electronics Conference,* Dayton, OH, pp. 421–426.

Ferguson, S.W., Clement, W.F., Hoh, R.H., and Cleveland, W.B., 1985, Assessment of simulation fidelity using measurements of piloting technique in flight: Part II, *41st Annual Forum of the American Helicopter Society,* Ft. Worth, TX, 1–23.

Field, E.J., Armor, J.B., and Rossitto, K.F., 2002, Comparison of in-flight and ground based simulations of large aircraft flying qualities, *AIAA 2002-4800, AIAA Atmospheric Flight Mechanics Conference and Exhibit,* Monterey, CA.

Fink, C. and Shriver, E., 1978, *Simulators for Maintenance Training: Some Issues, Problems and Areas for Future Research* (Tech. Rep. No. AFHRL-TR-78-27), Lowery Air Force Base, CO: Air Force Human Resources Laboratory. *Psychology,* 46(4), 349–354.

Fortin, M., 1989, Cost/performance trade-offs in visual simulation, *Royal Aeronautical Society Conference on Flight Simulation: Assessing the Benefits and Economics,* London, pp. 19.1–19.15.

Garrison, P., 1985, *Flying Without Wings: A Flight Simulation Manual,* Blue Ridge Summit, PA: TAB Books.

Gross, D.C. and Freeman, R., 1997, Measuring fidelity differentials in HLA simulations, *Fall 1997 Simulation Interoperability Workshop.*

Gross, D.C., Pace D., Harmoon, S., and Tucker, W., 1999, Why fidelity? *Proceedings of the Spring 1999 Simulation Interoperability Workshop.*

Hays, R.T., Jacobs, J.W., Prince, C., and Salas, E., 1992, Flight simulator training effectiveness: a meta-analysis, *Mil. Psychol.,* 4(2), 63–74.

Hays, R.T. and Singer, M.J., 1989, *Simulation Fidelity in Training System Design,* New York: Springer.

Hughes, T. and Rolek, E., 2003, Fidelity and validity: issues of human behavioral representation requirements development, *Proceedings of the 2003 Winter Simulation Conference,* New Orleans, LA.

Kaiser, M.K. and Schroeder, J.A., 2003, Flights of fancy: the art and science of flight simulation, in *Principles and Practice of Aviation Psychology,* Vidulich, M.A and Tsang, P.S., Eds., Mahwah, NJ: Lawrence Erlbaum Associates, pp. 435–471.

Kinkade, R. and Wheaton, G., 1972, Training device design, in *Human Engineering Guide to Equipment Design*, Van Cott, H. and Kinkade, R., Eds., Washington D.C.: Department of Defense, pp. 668–699.

Lehmer, R.D. and Chung, W.W.Y., 1999, Image dynamic measurement system (IDMS-2) for flight simulation fidelity verification, *Am. Inst. Aeronaut. Astronaut.*, 137–143.

Liu, D. and Vincenzi, D.A., 2004, Measuring simulation fidelity: a conceptual study, *Proceedings of the 2nd Human Performance, Situation Awareness and Automation Conference (HPSAA II)*, Daytona Beach, FL, pp. 160–165.

Mania, K., Troscianko, T., Hawkes, R., and Chalmers, A., 2003, Fidelity metrics for virtual environment simulations based on spatial memory awareness states, *Presence, Teleoperators and Virtual Environments*, 12(3), 296–310.

Nemire, K., Jacoby, R.H., and Ellis, S.R., 1994, Simulation fidelity of a virtual environment display, *Hum. Factors*, 36(1), 79–93.

Noble, C., 2002, The relationship between fidelity and learning in aviation training and assessment, *J. Air Transp.*, 7(3), 34–54.

Parrish, R.V., McKissick, B.T., and Ashworth, B.R., 1983, *Comparison of Simulator Fidelity Model Predictions with In-simulator Evaluation Data* (Technical Paper 2106), Hampton, VA: NASA Langley Research Center.

Ray, P.A., 1996, Quality flight simulation cueing—why? *Proceedings of the AIAA Flight Simulation Technologies Conference*, San Diego, CA, pp. 138–147.

Reed, E.T., 1996, The aerial gunner and scanner simulator "affordable virtual reality training for aircrews," *Training-Lowering the Cost, Maintaining Fidelity: Proceedings from the Royal Aeronautical Society*, London, UK, pp. 18.1–18.15.

Rehmann, A.J., Mitman, R.D., and Reynolds, M.C., 1995, *A Handbook of Flight Simulation Fidelity Requirements for Human Factors Research* (DOT/FAA/CT-TN95/46), Wright-Patterson AFB, OH: Crew System Ergonomics Information Analysis Center.

Rinalducci, E., 1996, Characteristics of visual fidelity in the virtual environment, *Presence*, 5(3), 330–345.

Roscoe, S.N., 1980, *Aviation Psychology*, Ames, IA: Iowa State University Press.

Roza, M., 2000, Fidelity considerations for civil aviation distributed simulations, *Proceedings of the AIAA Modeling and Simulation Technologies Conference and Exhibit*, Denver, CO.

Roza, M., Voogd, J., and Jense, H., 2001, Defining, specifying and developing fidelity referents, *Proceedings of the 2001 European Simulation Interoperability Workshop*, London.

Schricker, B., Franceschini, R., and Johnson, T., 2001, Fidelity evaluation framework, *Proceedings of the IEEE 34th Annual Simulation Symposium*, Seattle, WA.

Thomas, T.G., 2004, From virtual to visual and back? *AIAA Modeling and Simulation Technologies Conference and Exhibit*, Providence, RI: AIAA Paper 2004–5146.

Thorndike, E.L., 1903, *Educational Psychology*, New York: Lemke and Buechner.

Wickens, C.D., Lee, J.D., Liu, Y., and Becker, S.E.G., 2004, *An Introduction to Human Factors Engineering*, 2nd ed., Upper Saddle River, NJ: Pearson Prentice Hall.

Yu, Zhi-gang, 1997, Inquiry into concepts of flight simulation fidelity, in *First International Conference on Nonlinear Problems in Aviation and Aerospace Proceedings*, Sivasundaram, S., Ed., USA, 679–685.

Zhang, B., 1993, How to consider simulation fidelity and validity for an engineering simulator, *Am. Inst. Aeronaut. Astronaut.*, 298–305.

5 Controls and Displays for Aviation Research Simulation

Kristen K. Liggett and Gloria L. Calhoun

CONTENTS

INTRODUCTION

This chapter will trace how controls and displays used in fast jet research simulators changed from 1970 through the present to effectively evaluate new crew station technology for Air Force fighter aircraft. The early 1970s marked the dawn of the electro-optical (E-O) era in aviation simulators. Actually, there were investigations utilizing E-O instruments as early as the 1930s. For example, in 1937, a cathode ray tube (CRT)-based E-O display called the Sperry Flightray was evaluated on a United Airlines' Flight Research Boeing (Bassett and Lyman, 1940). Over the next several decades, E-O displays were slowly integrated into predominately electro-mechanical (E-M) designs, such that pilots (private, commercial, and military) were flying cockpits that incorporated a mix of E-M and E-O instruments. Thus, the time boundaries between the E-M and E-O approaches are very vague, even though the design boundaries are clear (Nicklas, 1958). By the early 1970s, although the majority of operational aircraft contained cockpits based on E-M instruments, cockpit designers were seriously considering the design of cockpits based primarily on E-O displays. Their research during this period had a definite influence on aircraft design. For instance, the U.S. Navy's F-18 aircraft introduced in 1983 made extensive use of multifunction CRT displays.

    As part of this chapter, several research simulators will be described to illustrate the evolution of control and display technology; also, some lessons learned from the experiments carried out in these simulators will be cited. Unless otherwise stated, all of these simulators were (or are currently) at Wright-Patterson Air Force Base, Dayton, Ohio. Finally, the chapter will present changes that are anticipated in control and display technology for future simulations.

FIXED-BASED SIMULATORS

INTEGRATED INFORMATION PRESENTATION AND CONTROL SYSTEM STUDY (IIPACSS) SIMULATOR

At the start of the 1970s, the state-of-the-art in cockpit instrumentation was exemplified by the F-4 Phantom. The Phantom's two crew stations were composed of all E-M instruments, with the exception of a few single-function CRTs. However, advances in avionics were enabling the inclusion of an increasing number of computer-based functions within aircraft. If all of these additional computer-based functions had to be accessed through single-function E-M instruments, there would not be enough room in the crew station to accommodate all the required controls and displays. Moreover, it was likely that locations outside of the pilot's primary reach and vision envelope would have to be used. Thus, a new approach to the design of fighter crew stations was clearly needed. One means of preventing the pilot from becoming overloaded was to restrict the information by time-sharing controls and displays so that only the information relevant to the pilot's current task was available. This restriction led to a change in design requirements. "The requirement exists to develop an integrated control and display system that will present only essential information in a format that can be translated easily by its user into direct control inputs" (Zipoy, Premselaar, Gargett, Belyea, and Hall, 1970, p. 1). The answer was to substitute multifunction E-O displays for single-function E-M instruments. However, the question was, "How well can the operators use these new types of displays and their associated controls?"

Research in the IIPACSS simulator (Figure 5.1) arose from a need to verify that the new approach (utilizing E-O displays, which combined many of the functions of separate E-M instruments) would not degrade operator performance.

FIGURE 5.1 Integrated Information Presentation and Control System Study (IIPACSS) simulator, circa 1970. (Boeing photo produced under U.S. Air Force Contract # F33615-73-C-1201.)

Display Technology

This simulator contained one color and six monochrome CRTs, which were multifunctional in the sense that numerous menus and pictorial formats could be presented on the same device at different phases of the mission. Although an out-the-window scene was available during experiments, it was not the computer projection that we know today. It was a film taken from a camera in an aircraft that flew a particular route. The film was run backward to give the illusion that the aircraft was indeed flying the route that was preprogrammed. However, about three years later, a terrain board coupled with a camera that flew over the board provided the out-the-window scene for the pilot.

Control Technology

Besides the required throttle and flight controls, the simulator contained a great number of switches. If you examine Figure 5.1 carefully, you will see that there are 141 push-button switches in this simulator. In the early 1970s, multifunction switch technology was not available.

Representative Research

Introduction

Based on an initial evaluation of the cockpit seen in Figure 5.1, it was clear that work was needed on the design of multifunction keyboards, as well as other aspects of the cockpit such as intuitive display formats. This study (Willich and Edwards, 1975) addressed these issues. This study also incorporated the functions of the A-7D operational crew station because it had the more sophisticated avionics systems at that time. After a detailed functional analysis was performed on the A-7D, whose crew station contained primarily E-M instruments, those functions were then assigned to various multifunction displays and multifunction keyboards. The cockpit in Figure 5.1 was modified to incorporate the functions of the A-7D as well as lessons learned from the initial pilot evaluations conducted with this older, unmodified simulator. An outline of the front instrument panel of the modified cockpit appears in Figure 5.2.

The objective of this experiment was to evaluate a helmet-mounted display (HMD) versus a head-up display (HUD), different display formats for the horizontal situation display, and a newly designed multifunction keyboard. In this section, we will discuss only the results of the multifunction keyboard evaluation. (For other aspects of the study, see the Willich and Edwards, 1975 reference.) The detailed objectives relative to the keyboard were to "evaluate the utility of the multifunction keyboard in terms of matrix size, number of integrated functions, logic indenture levels, and operational suitability in accomplishing the mini mission scenarios" (Willich and Edwards, 1975, p. 67). A *mini mission* is a flight phase, for example, air-to-ground. To understand the detailed objectives, some explanation of how the multifunction keyboard was constructed is required.

Multifunction Keyboard

At the time of this study, bezel-mounted switches with legends that appeared on the display surface (most Automatic Teller Machine [ATM] designs) had not yet been envisioned. However, the mechanism used by ATMs to obtain a cash advance, in which one proceeds through multiple levels of menu logic, was employed in the following manner. To organize the over 100 switches in Figure 5.1, switches were created that had a limited number of legends—12 legends per button in this case. A 4 × 6 matrix of these switches was created, thereby allowing a total of 288 switch legends. Two identical matrix-style keyboards were placed to the left and right of the horizontal situation display (bottom-large CRT) to allow operation by either hand (Figure 5.2). The keyboard worked in the following manner: As power was applied to the multifunction keyboard, the button legends on the top row showed the names of the major systems onboard the aircraft, such as communication, navigation, sensors, etc. When one of the top row buttons was pushed, for example the communication (COMM) button, the various types of radios (ultrahigh frequency [UHF], very high frequency

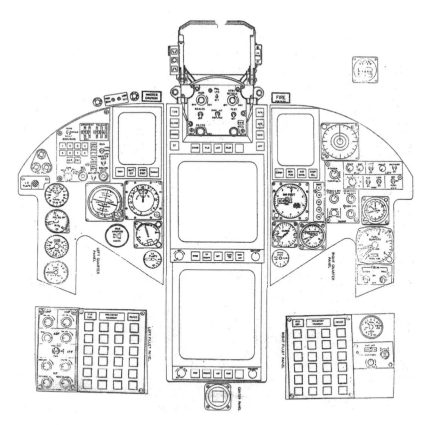

FIGURE 5.2   Modified Integrated Information Presentation and Control System Study (IIPACSS) simulator. (Boeing photo produced under U.S. Air Force Contract # F33615-73-C-1201.)

[VHF], identify friend or foe [IFF], etc.) would then appear as legends on the keyboard, and the previous legends would disappear. The pilot would then be at the second logic level. If the pilot then pushed the UHF button, the subfunctions of the UHF would be shown (third logic level), and, as before, the previous legends would disappear. Successive changes of legends on the buttons allowed the pilot to proceed through various keyboard logic levels. However, the status of the radios (e.g., the current tuned frequency of the radio) did not appear on the keyboard; the radio status was shown on the small CRTs located at the top portion of the instrument panel.

Test Procedures
All eight pilot participants were experienced in fighter or attack aircraft. Each flew three mini missions: air-to-air, air-to-ground, and instrument landing. During these mini missions, the pilots used the multifunction keyboard in normal and degraded modes (e.g., a CRT failure) to perform tasks involving the communications, navigation, sensors, and aircraft subsystems functions.

Results
An examination of the three mini missions found that there was no significant difference between normal and degraded mode performance in the air-to-air and air-to-ground mini missions. In the landing mini mission, it took significantly longer to enter a radio channel change in the degraded mode.

The pilots also filled out a questionnaire to obtain opinions on the utility of the multifunction keyboard and associated multifunction displays. Pilots felt the multifunction keyboard was very easy to operate, failures were easy to correct, and it was equally suitable for day and night use. However, they were evenly split as to the efficiency of the keyboard. Those who liked the keyboard were especially fond of its compact nature (combining several functions onto a fewer number of switches). However, those pilots who did not like the keyboard felt they could access single-function switches more quickly than going through four levels of menu logic required with the multifunction keyboard to access some functions.

Conclusions

There were two basic conclusions from the research performed in this experiment: (1) the functions of a state-of-the-art aircraft (at the time) could be successfully incorporated into a multifunction crew station; and (2) the multifunction keyboard, coupled with its corresponding CRT status displays, was a viable means of performing tasks needed to accomplish the functions. However, the optimization of the relationships between the keyboard and the corresponding CRT status displays had not yet been achieved. The pilots manipulated the switch legends on the keyboard matrix (see Figure 5.2), but the changed functions appeared on the CRTs located at the top portion of the instrument panel. As the CRTs were at a considerable distance from the multifunction keyboard, increased scanning time to verify whether the correct task had been performed was required.

Impact

This simulation was conducted as part of the U.S. Air Force's Digital Avionics Information System Program. The U.S. Navy had a similar program called the Advanced Integrated Display System Program. The research conducted by these two programs served as the basis for the E-O crew stations we see today in modern fighter aircraft.

Digital Synthesis (DIGISYN) Simulator

Display Technology

This simulator contained a HUD (but no external visual scene) and from four to six multifunction head-down CRTs, depending on the evaluation. The two CRTs in the center front panel (vertical situation display and horizontal situation display) were color, as well as the left upper CRT in some studies. The other head-down CRTs were monochrome. For some experiments, a cluster of E-M engine instruments on the upper right front panel was employed.

Besides these few E-M displays, the majority of displays were E-O, which offered a great deal of flexibility in crew station design. First, a particular format could be presented on any of the CRTs, and one evaluation focused on this advantage. Pilot performance was examined with eight arrangements of display formats depicting vertical situation, horizontal situation, and status information. The results failed to show a performance decrement across arrangements, demonstrating that this is a viable option should one of the E-O displays fail during flight (Calhoun, Herron, Reising, and Bateman, 1980).

With the flexibility afforded by computer-driven displays, the available graphics capability could also be exploited, rather than just transfer dedicated E-M display formats onto E-O surfaces. Moreover, the formats could be designed to integrate information from several dedicated E-M displays onto a single E-O display. However, to ensure that the resultant format provided information in a manner that the pilot could quickly assimilate and respond to, extensive research was required to determine which type of format and level of abstraction (e.g., alphanumeric, graphic, schematic, or pictorial) was best for the pilot's specific task. Research was also required to examine how color might best be used in computer-generated imagery, beyond the conventional sky and ground coding of the attitude director indicator (ADI) sphere and colors (green/amber/red) used in the aircraft advisory system. For several years, DIGISYN supported such display format evaluations. The section "Representative Research" provides a summary of a few studies examining the use of color coding.

Control Technology

Besides a joystick and throttle for flight control, the simulator utilized a combination of single-function controls (e.g., a telephone-style keyboard, forward of throttle on left console) as well as the multifunction control (lower left front panel). Each switch of a multifunction control addressed logic

FIGURE 5.3A   Digital synthesis (DIGISYN) simulator with projection switches, circa 1976. (U.S. Air Force photo.)

FIGURE 5.3B   Digital synthesis (DIGISYN) simulator with CRT-based bezel-mounted switches, circa 1976. (U.S. Air Force photo.)

that both determined the function of the switches and initiated the execution of those functions when the switches were selected. Obviously, if the function of a switch changed, it was important that its current function be displayed. To reflect what operation they controlled, multifunction switch legends changed, using one of two technologies available at that time: projection switches (Figure 5.3A) and CRT-based bezel-mounted switches (Figure 5.3B).

Projection switches contained a filmstrip with a series of light bulbs behind the strip. Based on the legend desired, the computer sent a signal to the appropriate light bulb, thereby lighting up the correct legend. A limitation of this technology was that only ten legends would fit on the filmstrip that was below the switch surface. Further, if a different legend was desired other than the current ten, a new filmstrip had to be created.

In CRT-based multifunction controls, the switches are adjacent to the bezel of a CRT. Thus, the switches could have as many legends as the CRT could generate, and changing a legend only involved a software modification. However, this technology also had limitations. Because of the switch depth, switches could not be mounted on the bezel itself, but rather had to be mounted outboard. Because of the distance between the switch and its corresponding legend, parallax problems could result at certain viewing angles or seat adjustments, making the association of a switch to a displayed legend ambiguous and not immediately apparent.

Several investigations examining how best to implement a multifunction control in the best manner were conducted with this simulator. More specifically, this research:

- Compared projection switch-type multifunction control to CRT bezel-mounted switches, and evaluated their location in the cockpit (Reising, 1977)
- Compared two logic design implementations, that is, branching logic for each individual aircraft system versus tailored logic that presents options that are most likely needed for the current flight phase (Herron, 1978)
- Generated design criteria for multifunction controls (e.g., how to label switches, implement switching logic, maximize the accessibility of frequently used functions, optimize switch and function assignment, and minimize hand motion; Calhoun, 1978; Calhoun and Herron, 1982)

Representative Research

Introduction
Prior to the availability of the DIGISYN simulator, the majority of research examining the utility of color coding used subjects who devoted their full attention to the color display and performed single relatively simple tasks (Christ, 1976). This research also showed that the impact of color coding is highly situation-specific and depends on a number of diverse factors such as operator task, display medium, and display environment (Krebs, Wolf, and Sandvig, 1978). DIGISYN, with color E-O displays, was an ideal platform to examine the utility of color coding on formats that were used in a somewhat peripheral manner as the highly loaded pilot also performed multiple complex tasks.

Test Procedures
Similar procedures were used in three separate experiments to examine the utility of color coding. At least 16 A-7D pilots participated in each experiment. After training, pilots flew one or more flights with each of the conditions being examined in the respective experiment. The mission tasking was designed to represent the workload present in operational flights. Pilots were required to maintain flight parameters (using the HUD as the primary flight display) as well as perform complete communications, navigation, and weapons tasks using a multifunction control and keypad. Also, pilots had to respond to information retrieval questions that required them to utilize the display format under evaluation. With the number of ongoing and intermittent tasks, pilots only had time to quickly glance at the format under evaluation to retrieve requested information. Performance on all tasks was recorded. Subjective comments were also obtained with questionnaires.

Color Formats
Three different display formats were evaluated in separate experiments examining the utility of color coding: threat format (Kopala, 1979), engine format (Calhoun and Herron, 1981), and weapons format (Aretz and Calhoun, 1982).

Threat Format
This format appeared on the color CRT directly below the HUD. Besides navigation information, symbology was presented to denote locations of aircraft (symbol "."), surface-to-air missiles ("S") and anti-aircraft artillery ("A"). Each symbol was augmented with a state designator, one of three shapes to denote friendly, unknown, or hostile. These states were color coded in one condition as green, yellow, and red, respectively. The two coding conditions (shape-coded symbology versus shape- and color-coded symbology) were tested under three different symbol density levels: 10, 20, and 30 symbols.

Engine Format
On the upper-left CRT, each of eight engine parameters was represented by a box that contained the current parameter value. Vertical rectangular bars extended from the top or bottom of the boxes, as the corresponding parameter deviated from the normal operating range midpoint. All parameters were normalized to the same range for easier interpretation. Normal, cautionary, and emergency states were indicated by shade and flash codes on the monochrome format (unfilled bar/white bar/ flashing white bar), and by color codes on the color format (green/yellow/red). Performance on retrieval of engine information was recorded for the two CRT engine formats (monochrome and color), as well as a cluster of conventional E-M instruments (fuel flow, turbine outlet temperature, RPM, oil pressure, oil quantity, and three hydraulic pressure indicators) on the right-front instrument panel. These E-M instruments operated as in conventional cockpits, with colored tape to denote operating ranges. For all three engine-format conditions, the simulation included implementation of the master caution indicator and corresponding messages on failed parameters.

Weapons Format
In three of four experimental conditions evaluated, the upper-left CRT presented information pertaining to all the weapons onboard the aircraft, as well as information pertaining to the weapon option currently selected. The format consisted of a white planform against a darker background. Shapes on the planform presented the weapons onboard, and a different shape was used for each type of weapons, one shape for each of six different types. The station from which the selected weapons would be delivered was indicated by the location of the symbols on the planform. Line/ flash (monochrome) or shade (color) coding were used to code the status of each selected weapon. This included weapons selection status, master arm switch activation, drop mode, interval, weapon fuzing, release status, and presence of a hung bomb. Besides the monochrome-coded and color-coded pictorial formats, an alphanumeric format was also evaluated that presented information on the CRT used in the multifunction control. In a fourth condition, both the alphanumeric and color pictorial format were presented.

Results
In the experiment that utilized a threat format, the results showed a 40% increase in time to identify friendly, unknown, and hostile symbols when monochrome shape-coding was used, compared to redundant color-coding. The effectiveness of redundant color-coding became more pronounced as the symbol density of the threat format increased. Performance with the monochrome-coded pictorial weapons format was also found to be significantly worse than the color pictorial format. Moreover, the monochrome format was also worse than the alphanumeric format and the combined alphanumeric and color pictorial format. The subjective data showed pilot preference for the combined format. One pilot commented that the pictorial format helped one acquire situation awareness with a quick glance, with the alphanumeric information as a backup if there was any confusion. Different results were obtained with the engine format. There were no significant performance differences between the monochrome and color CRT formats. With regard to having the engine information integrated onto a single format versus the conventional array of E-M instruments, both CRT formats were superior as measured by pilots' speed and accuracy in identifying failed engine parameters.

Conclusions

The results from these experiments concur with the literature review provided by Reising and Calhoun (1982). Color coding resulted in performance improvements when the format was unformatted, highly dense, involved a search for relevant information, and had a logical relationship between color and the tasks. Both the threat and weapons formats can be viewed as dense and unformatted (e.g., 30 threat symbols at some levels and weapons information changed depending on weapon option). Both formats also involved an active search for information, either to find a particular threat or determine a parameter of a weapon store. The color coding also had a relationship to the task (e.g., red for hostile threat and hung bomb). The engine format, in contrast, was a simple display with the information clearly expressed in histograms. The location of a specific parameter was constant: the corresponding box at the center of the display. Additionally, the master caution alerting system served as an additional cue of abnormal states. Thus, monochrome codes were sufficient for the E-O format presenting engine information; color coding did not show a payoff.

Impact

The DIGISYN can be viewed as one of the earliest test beds primarily based on multifunction technology; the cockpit featured a multifunction control and the majority of displays were E-O. Thus, this simulator was ideal for research focused on exploiting the advantages of computer-based controls and displays. As a result of the numerous experiments that were conducted over many years, the utility of multifunction controls and integrated formats on multifunction displays was demonstrated. Many design guidelines were identified in the process as well. Without question, the research conducted with the DIGISYN was a strong contributor to the glass-cockpit crew station designs operational today.

MICROPROCESSOR APPLICATIONS FOR GRAPHICS
AND INTERACTIVE COMMUNICATION (MAGIC) SIMULATOR

The MAGIC simulator was employed to conduct part-task pilot-in-the-loop research studies investigating pilot–vehicle interfaces for cockpit applications (Figure 5.4). The simulator was a single-seat fighter shell. Six computers were used to support the simulation: three personal computers (PCs) and three graphics workstations. The fact that MAGIC relied on PCs for its operation demonstrates the low-cost aspect of this type of simulator. The cockpit was outfitted with various off-the-shelf

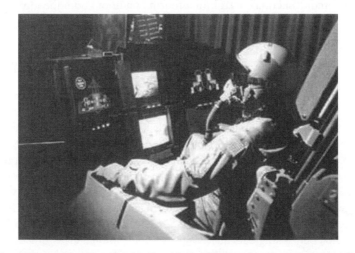

FIGURE 5.4 Microprocessor Applications for Graphics and Interactive Communication (MAGIC) simulator, circa 1985. (U.S. Air Force photo.)

products over the years for the purpose of comparing different controls and displays. Studies included the use of various HUD symbology sets to recover from unusual attitudes (Reising, Zenyuh, and Barthelemy, 1988), and pathway-in-the-sky HUD symbology for complex, curved approaches and landings (Reising, Liggett, Solz, and Hartsock, 1995). Additional studies (see the section "Representative Research") compared the use of three-dimensional (3-D) joysticks, touch screens, and speech recognition to designate targets.

Display Technology

MAGIC contained five color CRTs, which provided dynamic graphics capability. Typical displays for the head-down CRTs were system status formats, computerized checklists, radar sensor displays, and digital images from laser disks. There was no out-the-window visual scene, so subjects used the top-most monitor to view HUD symbology. The center CRT, typically containing a moving map display, could be exchanged with a 3-D display that pilots could use to view images with liquid crystal display (LCD) shutter glasses.

Control Technology

An F-16 side-mounted limited-displacement control stick was used to fly the F-16 aeromodel for the flight tasks. The stick also contained a weapon's release button, a trigger, and a pitch-trim switch. An A-7 aircraft throttle was also employed, and it included speed brakes and communications switches.

The cockpit also contained three banks of four programmable display push-buttons each. These were pixel-addressable light-emitting diode displays capable of displaying alphanumeric or pictorial information. There was also a bank of four multicolor switches below the topmost monitor. Three of the CRTs housed touch screen overlays, which were used as control interfaces to change the graphics on the screen. MAGIC also contained various speech recognition systems, again used as a control interface to change displays for the pilot. Other control devices included a magnetic tracker and an ultrasonic tracker attached to the pilot's glove to manipulate cursor control in 3-D space.

Voice Systems

Over the years, MAGIC hosted different speech recognition systems, each with its own strengths and weaknesses. It was this observation of various systems that led to a unique study geared at increasing the recognition accuracy of state-of-the-art speech system of that time (Barry, Liggett, Williamson, and Reising, 1992). The idea was to combine the strengths of each of three individual systems (two working in isolated mode and one in connected-speech mode) to increase recognition accuracy in the following manner. When a person spoke a word, all three systems reported a best guess word, a second choice word, and a distance score for each of the two words reported. A "majority rules" algorithm was implemented, which determined the word recognized as a best guess by the majority of the three systems. If there was no majority, the second choice words were added to the set of words, and a majority was looked for again. Finally, if there was still no majority, the response with the lowest distance score was reported. Using this algorithm, word recognition accuracy increased from 92.99% (the average of the three systems' individual accuracies) to 99.43% (the accuracy using the "majority rules" algorithm).

Representative Research

Introduction

One series of experiments conducted in MAGIC evaluated methods for designating targets residing in a stereoscopic 3-D volume. This research was published in several articles (Barthelemy, Reising, and Hartsock, 1991; Liggett, Reising, Beam, and Hartsock, 1993; Reising, Liggett, Rate, and Hartsock, 1992; and Solz, Reising, Liggett, Lohmeyer, and Hartsock, 1994). Three different cursor-control devices were used to designate targets. These included a three-axis joystick, an ultrasonic tracking device, and a voice control system. The ultrasonic tracking device was attached to a glove, and participants moved the cursor using this device by pointing to the target of interest. Because this type of task requires both gross and precise positioning, two aiding techniques were implemented. One was simple in that a color change of the target was instituted when the cursor penetrated the target area, informing the participants that the cursor was indeed in the same physical space as the target. The other aiding algorithm, referred to as *enhanced aiding,* used a mathematical algorithm to compute the distance from the cursor to the target closest to it as it traversed the 3-D space. Once this distance was computed, the closest target was highlighted, thus eliminating the need for precise positioning (Osga, 1991). The algorithm continuously computed the distance between the cursor and all targets in the depth volume. The 3-D volume within which targets and the cursor interacted extended from 7 in. in front of the physical display surface to 15 in. behind the physical display surface. Participant performance differences based on two target densities were also investigated.

Results

Results showed that the hand tracker provided the best performance with respect to total target designation time. The enhanced aiding was best in terms of both target designation time and accuracy. A speed–accuracy trade-off was observed when the density variable was analyzed; the low-density condition provided faster total target designation times, but the high-density condition had fewer errors.

Impact

This cockpit provided a consistent, uniform experimental environment for conducting a number of part-task evaluations. Consistency is especially important in stereographic evaluations as the distance between a participant's eyes and the display affects image disparity and, therefore, perceived stereographic effect. Also, the versatility of the cockpit supported the easy integration of the various control devices.

These types of evaluations made researchers investigate alternatives to traditional control and display devices for cockpit tasks that were becoming more challenging as information being presented on the traditional two-dimensional (2-D) displays increased. As such, pilots' visual processing capabilities were being overloaded, and 3-D displays offered a potential solution to this problem. However, introducing this type of display also introduces control challenges. This simulator facilitated the evaluation of numerous control techniques that may compensate for new control issues associated with the incorporation of 3-D displays in future cockpits.

Panoramic Cockpit Control and Display System (PCCADS) Simulator

During the second half of the 1980s, the continued maturation of larger and larger flat-panel displays (e.g., LCDs) started researchers thinking about the design of a cockpit in which the whole front panel would be a single display. As with any new technology, many questions arose, such as "What is the best way to optimize the design of the crew station when operators can place display formats wherever they wish?" In addition, new display formats could extend across either the entire or a part of the display such as a half, a third, etc. Also, improvements in HMDs warranted investigation of how they would interact with the new displays available with the single instrument panel. The PCCADS research simulator was developed to evaluate the potential improvements in mission effectiveness by providing a large color display area and the effectiveness of including an HMD and a helmet-mounted sight (HMS) in the cockpit (Figure 5.5).

Display Technology

The HMD provided airspeed, altitude, attitude, heading, and weapon status cues. It also portrayed a line of sight (LOS) for radar, and one for a weapon seeker. This was accomplished with the use of a magnetic head-tracker. The tracker-head position data and status information were used to point the simulated radar antenna or the simulated weapon seeker.

FIGURE 5.5   Panoramic Cockpit Control and Display System (PCCADS) simulator, circa 1988. (U.S. Air Force photo.)

The head-down portion of the simulator was unique in that it was one large display (18 × 24 in.) containing an integrated picture of mission-essential information. This also allowed for the rapid reconfiguration of numerous head-down configurations. For example, via software, the head-down display could be configured to look like an F-15E or an F-16 cockpit instrument panel.

PCCADS employed a projection system to show a realistic out-the-window scene (37° horizontal by 27° vertical field of view [FOV]), driven by a state-of-the-art graphics generator.

Control Technology

The simulator employed a touch-sensitive overlay in order to manipulate switches displayed, as well as position display formats in various locations, on the head-down display. Speech recognition and control were other options for interaction. An F-15E stick and throttle, along with their additional switches and buttons, provided "HOTAS" functionality, that is, function selection while keeping the pilots' "hands on throttle and stick."

Representative Research

Introduction

The research discussed in this section dealt with one of the basic aspects of flying, that is, maintaining flight safety when there is no dedicated head-down primary attitude indicator (AI). At the time this research was conducted, there was a definite desire to provide the pilot with as much mission-related information as possible. There was a second idea that the HUD could be used as the primary flight reference display and be substituted for a head-down primary AI. However, there was a concern that loss of attitude awareness (a potential flight safety problem) could result.

The Evolution of the Background Attitude Indicator

With limited panel space, one design solution was to decrease the size of the ADI and move it out of the primary viewing area, with pilots employing the HUD as the primary flight display. Researchers at Lockheed Fort Worth (Spengler, 1988) evaluated an alternate approach. They created a background attitude indicator (BAI) format designed with the goal of replacing the conventional dedicated head-down ADI, while maintaining flight safety. The BAI uses a 3/4 in. electronic border around the outer edge of a head-down display format. The evolution of this concept is illustrated in Figure 5.6, and its implementation is shown in Figure 5.7.

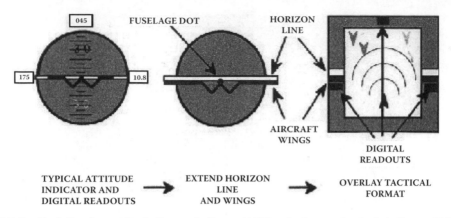

FIGURE 5.6 Evolution from attitude director indicator (ADI) to background attitude indicator (BAI).

In Figure 5.7, three display formats are shown on a front panel, the central rectangular portion of each presenting mission-related information. The background border extended across all three displays and presented a single attitude format.

The attitude information, in essence, framed the mission-essential display format and acted as one large AI. The BAI consisted of a white horizon line with blue above it to represent positive pitch, and brown below it to represent negative pitch. This display worked very well for detecting deviations in roll, but was less successful in showing deviations in pitch because, once the horizon line left the pilot's FOV, the only attitude information present in the BAI was solid blue (sky) or brown (ground). Because the concept was effective in showing roll deviations but lacking in the pitch axis, enhancing the pitch axis became the focus of the work done in this simulator.

PCCADS BAI Research: Part 1

The initial work began by enhancing the pitch cues for a BAI, which framed one display format only (as opposed to framing three display formats as in the original Lockheed work; Liggett, Reising, and

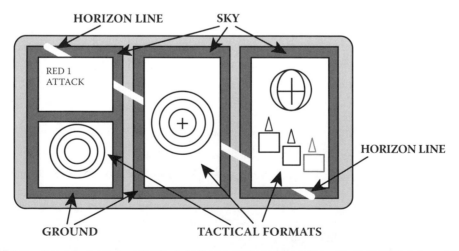

FIGURE 5.7 Spengler background attitude indicator. (Adapted from Spengler, R. P. 1988. *Advanced Fighter Cockpit* (Tech. Rep. ERR-FW-2936). Fort Worth, TX: General Dynamics.)

Hartsock, 1992). Eight variations of the BAI were evaluated, and each contained the following common elements (Figure 5.8):

1. Digital readouts of airspeed, altitude, and heading
2. Wing reference lines to provide an attitude reference (extensions of the normal miniature aircraft wings)
3. Ghost horizon (a dashed white line that appeared when the true horizon left the pilot's FOV, and that indicated the direction of the true horizon)

This configuration was tested alone, as well as with the additions of color shading (the lightest shade of blue or brown appeared at the horizon and became gradually darker as positive or negative pitch increased to 90°), color patterns (a vertical wedge with the thinnest portion at the horizon and the thickest portion at the zenith or nadir), and pitch lines with numbers. These design features were compared individually, in combinations of two, and with all three present. To determine if effective pitch information was being portrayed, the PCCADS study simulated the task of recovering from unusual attitudes. This task is often used to determine if adequate pitch information is present, as it is a key factor in a successful recovery.

Results of BAI Part 1

Results showed that the combination of color shading and color patterns was the format that had the quickest initial stick input time. When using this format, the pilots moved the control stick to begin their recoveries more quickly than when using any other format. This measure of initial stick input time related to the interpretability of the format because the pilots looked at the format, determined their attitude via the cues on the BAI, and began their recovery as quickly as possible.

PCCADS BAI Research: Part 2

Follow-on research (Reising, Liggett, and Hartsock, 1995) was conducted to evaluate the use of color shading and patterns to portray pitch information when the BAI extended across three horizontally adjacent head-down formats (the display configuration employed by Lockheed). The procedures and pilot tasking were similar to the first study. There were, however, two different mechanizations of the BAI: Triplets and Global. The Triplets format consisted of each of the three displays presenting individual, identical attitude information. Each display acted as a single, independent AI. Because the pilot could be focusing on the information from any of the three display formats at

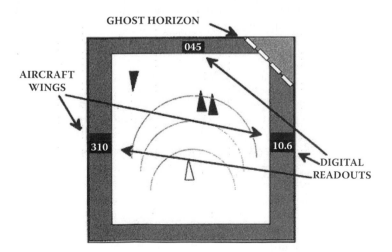

FIGURE 5.8   Digital readouts, wings, and ghost horizon (plane is in a 45° roll, negative pitch).

a given time, it was thought that being able to interpret the aircraft's attitude from using just the information from that specific BAI may be beneficial. The Global format consisted of all three horizontally adjacent BAIs acting as one large AI as in the original Lockheed study. It was anticipated that using the global BAI would be similar to seeing the outside world in its entirety and thus provide a benefit to the pilot. The Triplets and the Global formats had the same common elements of digital readouts, wing reference lines, a ghost horizon, and sky pointers. The pitch cues used were of two styles: (1) color shading and color patterns (the best format from the previous research), and (2) color shading, color patterns, and pitch lines with numbers. Although the second format was not considered the most beneficial from the previous research, the pilots expressed a unanimous preference for the BAI format that included pitch lines and numbers.

Results of BAI Part 2

Objective results were inconclusive; however, subjective results revealed that the pilots highly favored the Global format that provided color shading, color patterns, and pitch lines with number references. Thirteen of sixteen subjects ranked this type of format highest. The global aspect tended to give the pilots excellent peripheral bank cues; the combination of shaded patterns and pitch lines with numbers gave both qualitative and quantitative pitch reference, as well as pitch rate information. The Triplet format was rated low because the individual formats tended to distract the pilot with each BAI moving separately and displaying identical yet independent attitude information. The pilots were inclined to use only the center display for attitude information and completely ignore the two outboard displays.

Conclusions

Based on the results of these simulation studies, BAIs appear to be a viable means of enabling the pilot to recover from unusual attitudes. Single BAIs work best with visual cues (such as color shading and color patterns) that create a flow pattern to facilitate pilot detection of motion while not requiring the pilot to focus on a specific readout. When using multiple BAIs, pilots preferred having a global BAI that uses a combination of shaded patterns and pitch lines. The pitch lines with numbers allowed the pilot to make an exact, quantitative assessment of attitude, and the color shades and wedge width gave the pilot "quick glance" qualitative orientation information.

Impact

This research demonstrated the feasibility of a new and innovative display format that would not be possible without the inclusion of a large CRT in the cockpit. Because of the CRT's large surface area, the display formats can be configured in nontraditional ways. The trend of duplicating the E-M instrumentation with an E-O display format may finally disappear as a paradigm shift takes place, and the full potential of large E-O displays becomes apparent.

Helmet-Mounted Oculometer Facility (HMOF) Simulator

This simulator was established to capitalize on the unique capability for unobtrusive and accurate monitoring of eye and helmet positions of Honeywell's HMOF. Besides this oculometer system, the single-seat simulator (A-7 geometry) contained various controls and displays to support research that was more basic in nature. Test participants were not pilots, and the tasks they performed were designed to represent cockpit workload demands rather than simulate actual piloting tasks.

One line of research in this simulator focused on determining whether eye and head measures were valuable objective indicators of the effectiveness of attention cues and control and display design. Parameters of eye and head movements (e.g., sequence and latencies) were examined in comparison to the conventional performance index, manual reaction time, as a function of several factors: attention cue modality, tasks, attention allocation between tasks, and information location (Calhoun, Arbak, and Janson, 1985). One of the cue modalities evaluated was the application of

3-D auditory signals (Calhoun and Janson, 1990). Results suggested that these relatively unobtrusive measures may be valuable indices for evaluating candidate crew station designs by detecting a pilot's awareness of cues and changes in information presented.

Another line of research evaluated the application of the operator's LOS as an alternative control. With such control, the computer initiated a predefined action once it received an input based on the operator's point of gaze. Use of eye control eliminated the need for a selective manual response by substituting the natural movement of the eye that was inherent to the visual task. Thus, in cockpit applications, pilots would be afforded a useful hands-free, head-up control mechanism. Research in this facility examined the spatial and temporal parameters for implementing the eye-control algorithm and quantified the efficiency of eye control compared to other control mechanisms (Calhoun, Janson, and Arbak, 1986).

Display Technology

In its basic configuration, the simulator contained two monitors. The upper centrally located monochrome monitor (approximately 10 × 12 cm) presented symbology for a pursuit tracking task that could be varied in difficulty level. A color monitor (approximately 20 × 30 cm) was located below the front switch panel. This simulator had no external visual scene. During testing, the cockpit was darkened by a light-tight curtain that surrounded the simulator.

Control Technology

The right-console joystick was used for the participants' inputs to the tracking task. The stick was fitted with four switches, two of which were thumb-actuated push-buttons. A pressure-sensitive 12.5 × 12.5 mm switch plate was mounted on the left console. The front switch panel contained seven dedicated switches. These momentary switches measured 14 × 20 mm. The middle switch subtended a visual angle of 1.2° × 1.7°. The switches were labeled with black numerals. For some experiments, control based on eye LOS was activated.

Eye and Head Monitor

The participant's eye was illuminated by a halogen lamp filtered to pass near-infrared light. This light was collimated and reflected from a small coating on a parabolic helmet visor into the right eye. Some light was reflected from the cornea, and a portion of the light that entered the pupil was reflected by the retina and passed out of the eye through the pupil, and was scanned by a miniature charge-coupled device (CCD) video camera. As the eye rotated about its center of rotation to look around the visual field, the corneal reflection moved differentially with respect to the pupil. Thus, eye direction could be determined from the relative positions of the center of the pupil and the center of the corneal reflection. At extreme angles of fixation, eye direction was determined from the shape of the pupil. A magnetic HMS provided accurate helmet position and attitude determination in six degrees of freedom with respect to a fixed coordinate system. The HMD utilized a transmitter mounted behind and above the helmet to create a magnetic field around the cockpit and a helmet-mounted receiver that responded to movement through the field with varying output voltages. A computer calculated helmet position and rotation based on these voltages. These data were combined with eye-angle data to determine eye LOS with respect to a fixed coordinate system.

Representative Research

Introduction
In that the visual system is the primary channel for pilots to acquire information, and eye muscles are extremely fast, it is advantageous to have the direction of eye gaze also serve as a control input. In other words, if the pilot is looking at a target or button, it is more efficient to use the pilot's gaze to

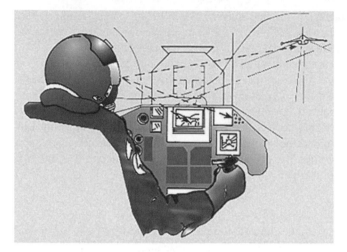

FIGURE 5.9   Illustration of cockpit application of eye control.

aim a weapon or select a switch (Figure 5.9). One approach to implementing gaze-based control is to combine LOS data with LOS dwell-time criteria. The operator selects an item on a display simply by looking at it for the criterion time. Using dwell time to initiate the control action is particularly useful if the operator's gaze is only being utilized to call up additional data. In this manner, the operator's sequential review of a series of icons can be made more rapidly, with detailed information popping up, as the gaze briefly pauses on each icon. Typically, required dwell times ranged from 30 to 250 ms. Longer dwell times tend to mitigate the speed advantage of gaze-based control. However, shorter dwell times increased the likelihood of a Midas touch, with commands activating wherever the operator gazes.

One solution was to require a consent response such that gaze-based control was similar to the operation of a computer mouse and button press. The gaze (or mouse) indicated the response option on a display, and the consent (or button press) triggered the control action. This mechanism was evaluated in an experiment in which the participants selected discrete switches on the simulator's front panel while manually tracking a target (Calhoun, Janson, and Arbak, 1986). In two of the three control methods, participants directed their gaze at the switch indicated by an auditory cue and then made a consent input (either a manual response via a joystick button or a verbal response). In a third condition, participants selected the switches with their left hand.

Procedures
Six participants were randomly assigned to a sequence of the three switching methods. The order of the switching methods was such that, across participants, each method was preceded equally often by each of the other methods. In the conventional manual method, participants selected the cued switch with their left hand. The switch was illuminated during switch closure. Between switch selections, participants were required to keep their left hand on the left console switch plate, and the position of this switch was recorded continuously throughout the run. In the two eye-control methods, participants directed their gaze at the cued switch. The participants' resulting eye LOS was computed at a rate of 60 Hz. When the system detected an eye LOS within 2.54 cm of the center of a switch for two of three consecutive samples (at least 33.4 ms), that switch was illuminated as feedback to the participant. The switch remained illuminated until (1) another switch was selected, (2) a five-second time-out interval had expired, or (3) a consent response was made. Thus, the operator could make the consent response while not looking at the switch (e.g., return attention to the tracking task). In one eye-control method, participants manually closed a push-button on the joystick for the consent response. In the second eye-control method, the consent consisted

of uttering the word "Go" into the microphone. The participant then heard either the word "Go" or a beep through the intercom to provide feedback as to whether the speech system successfully recognized the utterance or not.

In each five-minute run, an auditory cue ("one," "two,"..., "six") corresponding to the switches numbered 1 through 6 was presented 42 times while the participant was completing a tracking task (manual inputs on a joystick to overlay a dot on a continuously moving cursor). Eight five-minute runs constituted a session. Sessions were conducted with each method until tracking error and switching-time performance met training criteria. Switching time and accuracy data from the final four runs for each of six participants per switching method were analyzed (over 3000 switching trials).

Results

Switch activations that were not completed (i.e., switch not selected or consent not made) or completed incorrectly were dropped. The remaining data for accurate switch selections (96% of the trials) showed that it took less than a tenth of a second longer for the participants to select these switches with their eye LOS and push a button on the joystick (manual consent), than when using their left hand. This lack of a significant difference in average selection time indicates that eye control is a practical method for activating switches mounted in the central FOV, and that eye-control switching is a feasible alternative to manual switching, especially when it is desirable to keep the hands on the left and right console controls.

The results also showed that average switching time was significantly longer with the eye and voice consent method (2.83 seconds), than with the eye and manual consent method (1.78 seconds) or the manual method (1.72 seconds). It is important to note, for the eye and voice consent method, that the time required for the voice system to recognize an utterance and transmit the results to the computer made up a component of the total switching time (0.92 seconds). Subtraction of the equipment-induced response lag from each eye and voice consent switching time and examination of these data indicated that the differences in mean times for the three switching methods were not significant.

Conclusions

The very small difference in selection time between the eye and manual consent method and the manual method indicated that eye-controlled switching is a feasible alternative to manual switching. The longer switching time with eye control and voice consent illustrated the importance of examining the total switching time, from the beginning of the switching task to the closing of the consent switch, when comparing control mechanisms. The delay introduced by the equipment components and by the duration of the utterance resulted in a corresponding inflation in overall switching time.

Impact

The HMOF was unique, as all the research conducted on this simulator was geared toward exploiting the capabilities afforded by a single technology—LOS tracking. Additionally, the research conducted using this simulator illustrates how a representative scenario and task environment can be utilized iteratively to identify optimal settings for the numerous parameters involved in a new concept. Ideally, the implementation of any new control and display approach should be fine tuned with such a research test bed before evaluation in a higher-fidelity simulation. Research with this simulator also marked a significant change in control technology, switching from comparing alternative candidate approaches (e.g., manual versus speech) to an approach that integrates two or more technologies such that they are used together to perform a task. In this instance, the controls were mapped to different subcomponents of a task. The operator used eye gaze to designate a desired function and either a generic button or voice command for a consent response, commanding the system to execute the designated function. The use of both technologies capitalizes on the ability of eye gaze to rapidly designate a position on 2-D surfaces and a button press or voice command to quickly initiate an action.

Synthetic Interface Research for UAV Systems (SIRUS) Simulator

Unmanned air vehicles (UAVs) have become key to aerospace intelligence, surveillance, and reconnaissance operations. More recently, their role has been expanded into search and rescue, chemical and biological detection, communication relays, and various combat operations. Currently, many UAVs are remotely operated as multiple task telerobotic control systems via stick-and-throttle manipulations. However, the physical separation of the crew from the aircraft makes this control challenging, as ground-based operators do not receive the rich stream of multisensory information that onboard pilots receive regarding the surrounding environment, and the information that is received is often delayed or degraded due to limitations in communications. The SIRUS ground control station simulator (Figure 5.10) was established to support research that evaluates the potential value of multisensory interfaces for improving control station operations where the UAV is under direct telerobotic control.

This simulator consists of two operator stations. The Air Vehicle Operator (AVO) sits at the left workstation and controls UAV flight, manages subsystems, and handles external communications. From the right workstation, the Sensor Operator (SO) is responsible for locating and identifying targets by controlling cameras mounted on the UAV. Using this simulator, the validity of novel concepts is tested by having participants employ the technology while completing representative control operations. To date, research has addressed visual display enhancements (Draper, Geiselman, Lu, Roe, and Haas, 2000), head-coupled head-mounted display applications (Draper, Ruff, Fontejon, and Napier, 2002), haptic vibration alerts (Draper, Ruff, Repperger, and Lu, 2000), tactile system alerts (Calhoun, Draper, Ruff, Fontejon, and Guilfoos, 2003), and voice-based control (Draper, Calhoun, Ruff, Williamson, and Barry, 2003).

Display Technology

Each station has an upper and a head-level 17-in. color CRT display, as well as two 10-in. head-down color displays. The upper CRT of both stations generally displays a bird's-eye area map (fixed, north up) with overlaid symbology identifying such things as current UAV location, mission waypoints,

FIGURE 5.10   Synthetic Interface Research for UAV Systems (SIRUS) simulator, circa 1998 (U.S. Air Force photo.)

and current sensor footprint. The head-level CRTs (i.e., camera display) present simulated video imagery from the cameras mounted on the UAV. HUD symbology is overlaid on the AVO's camera display, whereas sensor-specific data are overlaid on the SO's camera display. The four smaller head-down displays present detailed subsystem and communication information. This simulator has no external visual scene.

Control Technology

Both stations have right-hand and left-hand joysticks, as well as two left-hand levers. At the AVO's station, the joystick and throttle are used to control the UAV's flight path and speed. At the SO's station, the right-hand joystick controls the gimbaled camera position, and the left-hand joystick controls camera zoom factor. Each station also has a trackball and a QWERTY-type alphanumeric keyboard with a horizontal row of function keys on top.

Representative Research

Introduction

Current UAV missions require a high degree of crew coordination to successfully locate and identify ground targets. For example, the AVO's camera display can be configured to look at large FOV imagery from the gimbaled camera controlled by the SO, whereas the SO views higher-resolution (smaller-FOV) imagery from the same camera to facilitate individual target identification. Thus, while the SO is zoomed in on a particular area, the AVO can spot potential targets that lie outside the SO's instantaneous FOV. Currently, this target information is communicated verbally between the operators, but this is complicated because each operator is using a different frame of reference (earth- versus sensor-referenced). The pilot views the target in cardinal directions: north, south, east, and west. The SO then has to map these directions to where the camera is currently pointing with respect to the direction the UAV is flying. The operators need a common frame of reference to help communicate target information.

This study (Draper, Geiselman, Lu, Roe, and Haas, 2000) evaluated the following four display concepts (Figure 5.11) superimposed on the SO's camera-view display:

- Baseline: This provided no added symbology.
- Floating Compass Rose: This provided a constant reference to real-world cardinal headings (N, S, E, W), regardless of air vehicle or camera orientation.
- Locator line/Telestrator: Via a cursor/track ball, the AVO designated a target location on the AVO's (10° FOV) display, resulting in a locator line being presented on the SO's (1° FOV) display, indicating the direction and angular distance the camera's LOS should traverse in order to overlay it on the target.
- Combined locator line/telestrator and Floating Compass Rose (N, S, E, W)

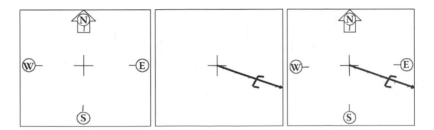

FIGURE 5.11   Three display concepts for target search and localization by the Sensor Operator (SO) of a UAV ground control station.

Procedures

Twelve participants acted as SOs, and four rated pilots were trained to serve as AVOs. The AVO directed the SO to a ground-target area. The SO's task was to maneuver the camera aimsight reticle onto the target and designate it. Targets initially appeared either within the AVO head-level display (near condition: 5° radial distance from center) or outside the display (far condition: 20° radial distance). The far condition required the AVO to initially utilize the upper (map) display to instruct the SO to maneuver the camera to the local area.

Results

The results indicated that target designation time was significantly reduced for conditions that utilized the locator line (alone or with the Compass Rose) for both near and far targets. Time to designate targets was reduced by an average of almost 50%. There was also less verbal communication when the locator line was used, freeing the audio channel for other tasks.

Conclusions

The locator line expedited transfer of target location information between the UAV operators (AVO and SO). The locator line concept was based on the effective use of similar symbology on aircraft HUDs and HMDs. Thus, an interface concept that was found useful for manned crew stations was found to be useful also for unmanned aircraft control. For both applications, the locator line concept may have additional utility for potential targets identified by sources external to the crew.

Impact

To date, research with this simulator has demonstrated potential for reducing workload and improving operator situation awareness and task performance. It has also shown that technology proven useful for other complex control applications may not be useful for UAV control. For instance, it was thought that HMD technology would enhance the SO's wide-area searches and spatial orientation, as it has done for some manned aircraft applications. However, the results of a series of studies showed that there must be a fundamental limitation of head-coupled control for performing teleoperated search tasks. Use of the joystick and workstation display resulted in better performance on all measures compared to several HMD configurations evaluated (Calhoun, Draper, and Ruff, 2003). These findings illustrate that it is critical to test candidate interfaces for UAV control in representative ground control station simulators.

As the role of UAVs increases in civilian and military operations, there will be a growing need for research simulators to identify means of improving the operator's presence in the remote environment under stick-and-throttle control. Moreover, as more autonomous UAVs are developed, multi-UAV task environment simulators will be needed to address technologies that will assist UAV operators in supervising multiple UAVs at the same time.

MOTION-BASED SIMULATORS

The simulators discussed thus far are all fixed-based simulators, that is, they do not move. However, as aircraft become more and more agile, there are many human factors issues that need to be considered for cockpit design. Because of this, motion-based simulators provide a means for exploring human-related issues prior to costlier flight test options. Motion-based simulators are used primarily for demonstration and training. Some are used for gravity (G)-tolerance testing, such as centrifuges. However, there has been little control or display research conducted in motion-based simulators to date. This is unfortunate because motion environments, especially high-acceleration ones, have numerous physiological and psychological consequences that could impact the utility of controls and displays. For instance, under high acceleration, it is difficult to move the arm or hand to select functions on the front panel. Hence, the effects of acceleration on the utility of eye gaze and speech-based control would be of interest as viable alternative controls. High acceleration is also known to affect color vision. In fact, research was conducted in a one-motion-based simulator to evaluate this effect. This simulator and research will be described in the next section.

DYNAMIC ENVIRONMENTAL SIMULATOR (DES)

The DES centrifuge provided multiaxis G exposures in a gimbaled cab (Figure 5.12). It exposed participants up to a maximum of 9Gs, and could combine accelerations (Gx + Gy + Gz). A variety of physiological and experimental measurements could be collected during simulation testing. These included heart rate, skin response, eye blink rate, blood flow, head movement, and G-exposure data. There was also closed-circuit video and audio available for data recording purposes. The DES was used to test personal protective equipment, helmet-mounted systems, and cockpit systems. It supported both sustained acceleration and spatial disorientation research. After modification, the DES allowed closed-loop motion-based studies. So, in addition to the previously mentioned collectable data parameters, pilot flight performance metrics could be collected and analyzed.

Display Technology

The cab contained a domed visual scene provided by a front projection system. It displayed a 180° horizontal by 160° vertical out-the-window FOV. Also, HUD symbology could be projected onto the out-the-window scene for HUD symbology evaluations. The head-down display contained one 23-in. diagonal LCD, and the format presented on this display could be changed via software to represent a number of head-down instrument panels. (e.g., an F-18 head-down suite). Later studies will incorporated an HMD and head tracker to determine the effects of helmet slippage on mission performance under high Gs.

Control Technology

The cab contained an F-16 control stick and throttle that was used by participants to fly an F-16 aeromodel. As with many of the simulators described, this system could be switched with other aero-models, sticks, and throttles.

FIGURE 5.12 Dynamic Environmental Simulator (DES), circa 1969. (U.S. Air Force photo.)

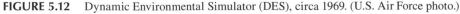

Representative Research

Introduction

One of the biggest advances in head-down information presentation has been the addition of color to the displays. Pilots can rely on known color schemes to determine the meaning of specific objects on a display (e.g., green = good, red = bad) and can learn new color schemes for displays use. Color has been shown to improve pilot performance and reduce workload. However, when pilots are pulling high Gs or sustaining acceleration, the blood pressure in the eye is reduced, and this may cause changes in color vision. Four experiments were conducted in the DES to help determine the effects of sustained acceleration on color vision (Chelette, Allnutt, Tripp, Esken, Bolia, and Post, 1999). A few will be summarized in the following text.

Background

To get an idea of what actually happens to color vision under high Gs, a preliminary study was conducted in which participants with normal color vision viewed a color map as the G profile ramped up from the baseline (1.4G) at a rate of 0.1G per second until the participants experienced almost complete blackout. Participants were to report what they saw during this process. A number of participants said that the river (a cyan color) faded away first, then the yellow and green of the terrain faded together, and finally the red and dark blues faded to black. This observation led to numerous studies conducted in the DES to explore visual contrast sensitivity, night vision, and visual acuity under Gs.

Luminance Study

Four colors (red, green, blue, and yellow) at various luminance levels were tested in the following manner. A grid display was developed that contained four rows of digits in various colors; one color per row. The columns had varying luminance contrast ratios. For instance, each column had the same luminance contrast ratio with its background, regardless of the digit color. Participants were subjected to a G profile that progressed from the baseline to near blackout at a slow onset rate. Results showed that digits were recognized longer when they had greater luminance contrast ratios with their backgrounds than digits with lesser luminance contrast ratios with their backgrounds.

Color Identification Study

The objective was to determine if participants could identify colors at high Gs. The study employed five colors (red, green, blue, yellow, and grey), at three contrast ratios to represent dark viewing, daylight viewing, and twilight conditions. Six G levels were tested from 1G–9G (1.0, 7.0, 7.5, 8.0, 8.5, and 9.0). Results showed that there were no significant differences in terms of reaction time and accuracy between the colors, the contrast ratios, or the G levels. However, one participant had a large number of errors with the color yellow. Therefore, even though it does not appear that most participants have a hard time distinguishing colors under G, this study showed how an undetected color perception deficit of a particular participant may become evident at high Gs.

Color Discrimination Study

The objective was to determine if colors could be discriminated under high Gs when the task involved mathematical judgment and choice. This task was more representative of a pilot task in that the display contained seven targets, four of one color and three of another. The participants' task was to simply press a button that indicated the color of the most number of targets. For this study, contrast ratio was held constant, and four G levels were used (1.0, 7.0, 8.0, and 9.0). Although the overall error rate was below 10%, trends showed that there were more errors in this task than in the previous ones, and the majority of errors occurred at 9Gs. The most common errors encountered were not being able to discriminate between yellow and green (yellow was commonly mistaken for green), and between grey and blue (grey was commonly mistaken for blue).

Conclusions

On the basis of results of the reported studies, colors with similar luminance contrast ratios should not be used on the same display because they may fade together during high-G maneuvering. These types of studies may be instrumental in detecting color deficiencies for pilots who intend to fly high-G aircraft. Also, under high-G conditions, pilots may be prone to not being able to discriminate between yellow and green. Given that green is commonly used to represent friendly objects, this may compromise pilot performance if they cannot discriminate between friendly and unknown entities.

Impact

A motion-based simulator like the DES is the perfect avenue for conducting many types of control and display research in which pilots can fly high-G profiles in a realistic manner with closed-loop control. For example, studies like these can produce display design guidance for color displays in high-G aircraft and can help determine color vision screening recommendations.

IN-FLIGHT SIMULATORS

Although the motion-based simulator described in the previous section allows for testing in some aspects of the flight regime (e.g., acceleration), there are many other aspects that can only be examined in flight. The purpose of in-flight simulators is to get as close as possible to the environment in which the crew station technology will ultimately be employed. A few will be discussed in the following sections.

VARIABLE IN-FLIGHT STABILITY TEST AIRCRAFT (VISTA) LOCKHEED NF-16D FIGHTER AIRCRAFT

VISTA (Figure 5.13) is an F-16D flight test vehicle in which the front seat serves as an evaluation cockpit, and the rear seat serves as a safety cockpit. It has been used to conduct a variety of airborne simulations to evaluate flying qualities, flight controls, and control and display issues. A recent study evaluating HMD symbology in VISTA is described in this section.

Representative Research

Introduction

HMDs can provide an important function in future aircraft—off-boresight targeting. This capability highlights a major difference between HMDs and HUDs. HUDs are mounted to the instrument panel of the cockpit and can provide on-boresight information only. On-boresight refers to the visual area the pilot sees when looking down the longitudinal axis of the aircraft (i.e., looking straight ahead). HMDs are mounted to the pilot's head, and can provide on-boresight as well as off-boresight information. Off-boresight refers to all other visual areas the pilot views (i.e., not looking straight ahead).

FIGURE 5.13 Variable In-Flight Stability Test Aircraft (VISTA). (U.S. Air Force photo.)

Some of the challenges with integrating HMDs in the cockpit are determining how to present information, and what information needs to be presented to the pilot not only at various phases of the mission but also at various head positions. This study (Jenkins, Thurling, Havig, & Geiselman, 2002) focused on determining the best off-boresight HMD symbology for targeting, as well as attitude maintenance during realistic air-to-air and air-to-ground target acquisition scenarios. Unusual attitude recovery performance was also examined.

Symbology Sets

The off-boresight symbology sets tested included a nondistributed flight reference (NDFR) format and a visually coupled acquisition and targeting system (VCATS) format. The NDFR allows ownship status information to always be available on the HMD regardless of where the pilot is looking. It includes both digital and analog information. The digital information includes airspeed, altitude, and heading. The analog information is portrayed with the arced portion of the display. Attitude is interpreted by comparing the position and length of the arc with the aircraft symbol (Figure 5.14).

VCATS (Figure 5.15) was designed as a high-altitude ownship attitude reference. It includes a horizon line split by an aircraft symbol representing climb/dive angle. The horizon line on this symbology set rotates as does the standard ADI and HUD horizon line. The VCATS horizon line also changes shape as climb/dive angle increases or decreases. For instance, when climb/dive angle is negative, the line becomes dashed and portrays a chevron-type symbol. Digital readouts of airspeed, heading, and altitude are presented around the outer boundaries of the HMD FOV.

The military standard 1787 HUD (Mil-Std HUD) symbology was present on the HUD for the air-to-air and air-to-ground tasks, and on the HMD in virtual HUD mode during the unusual attitude recovery tasks when pilots looked on-boresight. The reason the on-boresight symbology was presented on the HMD for this task was that the pilot-subjects wore leather visors to prevent themselves from seeing the outside world as the evaluation pilot flew the aircraft into the unusual attitude. These visors also prevented them from seeing the HUD. Thus, the virtual HUD on the HMD was utilized for this task. This symbology included a climb/dive ladder, a moving horizon line, fixed aircraft reference, bank scale, clocks to represent airspeed and altitude, and a heading tape (Figure 5.16).

Procedures

Participants evaluated the various HMD formats for a total of 11.7 flight hours. Test points were flown from the front cockpit by the evaluation pilot. The safety pilot in the rear cockpit set up the HMD configurations, performed routine F-16 flight procedures, and monitored the safety of the

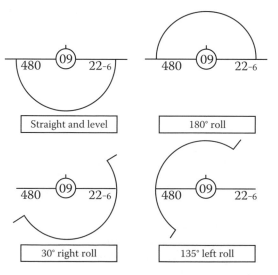

FIGURE 5.14 Nondistributed flight reference (NDFR) symbology.

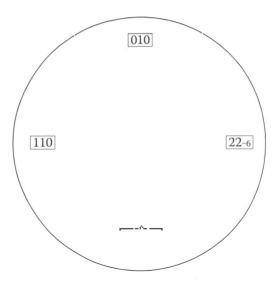

FIGURE 5.15 Visually coupled acquisition and targeting system (VCATS) symbology.

flights. Pilots became familiar with the symbology in the ground simulation mode, which is basically a fixed-base simulator that happens to be the cockpit of a real aircraft. For the air-to-air and air-to-ground tasks, pilots flew with the standard HUD symbology on the HUD when they were looking on-boresight, and either nothing, the NDFR, or VCATS symbology on the HMD when they looked off-boresight. For the unusual attitude recovery task, pilots were looking off-boresight when the task began, and they flew with the standard HUD symbology on the HMD when looking on-boresight, and either nothing, the NDFR, or VCATS symbology on the HMD when looking off-boresight.

Results
For the unusual attitude recovery task, pilots performed 37% faster in initiating a correct input with the NDFR format than with the Mil-Std HUD format. Pilots also performed 18% faster with the NDFR than VCATS for the same measure. For the air-to-ground task, both the NDFR and the

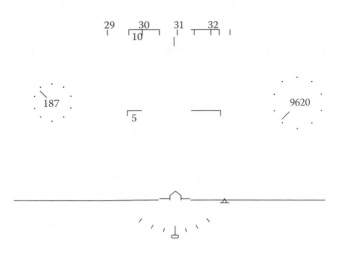

FIGURE 5.16 Standard head-up display (HUD) symbology.

Mil-Std HUD provided an adequate or desired amount of off-boresight search time, with the NDFR allowing the highest percentage (longer search times mean that the off-boresight symbology provided adequate information for the pilots to maintain safe flight without having to return attention to the on-boresight flight display). For the air-to-air task, the NDFR format allowed pilots to achieve the highest percentage of off-boresight search time while still maintaining aircraft parameters. Although the VCATS symbology also provided an adequate amount of off-boresight search time, one of the pilots' primary task performance metrics was degraded when pilots used VCATS for off-boresight searching.

Conclusions

This study shows the advantages of using off-boresight attitude symbology not only for air-to-air and air-to-ground target acquisition tasks but also for recovering from unusual attitudes.

Impact

HMDs are the wave of the future. Not only are they slated for the newest fighter aircraft, many older models will be retrofitted with some type of HMD for increased mission performance. Just as with all new technologies that are incorporated into the cockpit, thorough testing must be conducted to determine the applicability of the technology not only for its intended purpose but for all aspects of flight. Using an in-flight simulator such as VISTA provides a realistic environment to conduct such technology testing. Making this type of simulation available can lower the risk of integrating new technologies by conducting proof-of-concept testing and solving integration issues.

Total In-Flight Simulator (TIFS) NC-131H Transport Aircraft

The purpose of TIFS (Figure 5.17) is to perform airborne simulations of new or existing aircraft to evaluate flying qualities, flight control characteristics, human factors concerns, or other issues of interest. This simulator allows for the variation of numerous parameters in-flight, such as aircraft flight characteristics, controller feel characteristics, and HUD formats. Also, the cockpit can be reconfigured to represent other aircraft. The front seat serves as the evaluation cockpit and the rear seat serves as the safety cockpit. The HUD and head-down displays are driven by a programmable display generator, which allows for quick changes to display formats. The method for aircraft control is also variable; control sticks, wheels, and throttles are easily interchanged in the evaluation cockpit.

FIGURE 5.17   Total In-Flight Simulator (TIFS). (U.S. Air Force photo.)

Representative Research

The TIFS aircraft has evaluated a number of control and display configurations for different aircraft, for example, the "glass" version of the Air Force's C-141 transport aircraft, called the Control/Display System (CDS). The objective of this study was to test the adequacy of the LCDs that replaced the E-M primary flight displays (ADI and horizontal situation indicator). The pilots performed tasks such as unusual attitude recovery and instrument system landing approaches. "The objective and subjective flight test data showed that performance, pilot workload, spatial orientation, and air crew acceptance using the proposed CDS display format were improved or no worse than commensurate with, that obtained using the current C-141 instrument format, in almost every instance of analysis" (Gawron and Bailey, 1995, p. 84).

The aircraft has also been used by NASA (National Aeronautics and Space Administration) to test the Synthetic Vision System (SVS), which was a key part of the High-Speed Research Program. "The SVS project develops synthetic vision technologies with practical applications to eliminate low visibility conditions as a causal factor in civil aircraft accidents" (Wilshire, Latorella, and Glaab, 2000, p. 376). As part of the flight testing of the SVS technologies, the TIFS crew station was configured with displays showing different views of the outside world that would aid the pilot and aircraft landing during poor visibility conditions. The results showed that, whereas some features (such as ground texturing) were beneficial, others (such as minimized display formats) did not aid in the landing task.

Impact

The two studies just discussed serve to illustrate the versatility of the TIFS aircraft in evaluating different control and display configurations. The real advantage of TIFS is its ability, over two decades, to reconfigure itself to evaluate everything from transport cockpit displays such as in the C-141, to handling qualities of the space shuttle.

NASA's OV-10

Although not designed initially to be an in-flight simulator, the OV-10 has been used extensively to test spatial audio and speech recognition technologies. The OV-10A aircraft is a twin-engine, two-crew-member, tandem-seating turboprop aircraft (Figure 5.18).

FIGURE 5.18   OV-10A aircraft. (U.S. Air Force photo.)

Display Technology

The displays in the backseat are dependent on the research taking place at the time of flight. For instance, during a speech recognition study, a monochrome monitor was installed that displayed words the participants were to say into a microphone.

Control Technology

There was a keyboard in the backseat, as well as a push-to-talk switch, an acoustic microphone, and a noise-canceling boom microphone for the speech recognition studies.

Representative Research

Introduction

Speech recognition has long been advocated as a natural and intuitive method by which humans could potentially communicate with complex systems. Recent work in the area of robust speech recognition, in addition to advances in computational speed and signal-processing techniques, has resulted in significant increases in recognition accuracy, spawning a renewed interest in the application of this technology. Just recently, speech recognition systems have advanced to the point where 99% accuracy in a laboratory environment is commonplace. This high accuracy is key to acceptance of the technology by the user community.

The demands on military pilots are extremely high because of the very dynamic environment within which they operate. The pilot has only a limited capability to effectively manage available onboard and offboard information sources using just hands and eyes. Because workload is high, and the ability to maintain situational awareness is imperative for mission success, voice control is ideal for military cockpit applications. For these reasons, researchers have been evaluating the use of speech recognition technology to augment the pilot's ability to control and display information.

The potential use of automated speech recognition technology as a natural, alternative method for the management of aircraft subsystems has been studied by both the Air Force and Navy for over 10 years. But, because recognition accuracies had not attained acceptable levels for use in the cockpit, this technology has not yet become operational. Now that speech recognition performance is adequate and reliable, it is an optimal time to verify that performance would not deteriorate in the operational flight environment due to high noise, acceleration, or vibration.

The objective of this experiment (Williamson, Barry, and Liggett, 1996) was to measure word recognition accuracy of the ITT VRS-1290 speech recognition system in an OV-10A test aircraft both on the ground and in 1G and 3G flight conditions. A secondary objective was the compilation of a speech database that could be used to test other speech recognition systems.

Test Procedures

Sixteen participants were involved in this study. All participants were tested in the laboratory, in the hangar (sitting in the aircraft cockpit with no engines running), and in flight. During flight, participants experienced a 1G data collection session (referred to as 1G1), followed by a 3G data collection session, and then another 1G data collection session (referred to as 1G2) to test for possible fatigue effects.

The study was divided into two separate sessions. The first session consisted of generating the participants' templates in a laboratory setting and collecting some baseline performance data. Participants were briefed on the nature of the experiment, and template enrollment was performed. A system identical to the one in the aircraft was used as the ground support system for template generation. The participants used the same helmet and boom-mounted microphone that was used in the aircraft. Template training involved the participants' speaking a number of sample utterances. Once template generation was completed, a recognition test followed that consisted of reciting the utterances to collect baseline recognition data.

The first aircraft test session was performed in the hangar to provide a baseline (the aircraft in quiet conditions). This consisted of each participant speaking the 91 test utterances twice, for a total of 182 utterances. During both ground and airborne testing, participants needed little or no assistance from the pilot of the aircraft. The participants sat in the rear seat of the OV-10A and were prompted with a number of phrases to speak. All prompts appeared on a 5-in. × 7-in. monochromatic LCD in the instrument panel directly in front of the participants. Their only cockpit task was to reply to the prompts. Close coordination was required, however, between the pilot and participants while the 3G maneuvers were being performed as the pilot had to execute a specific maneuver in order to keep the aircraft in a 3G state.

Results

Three comparisons of word recognition accuracy were of primary interest:

1. Ground (lab + hangar) versus air (1G1 + 3G + 1G2)
2. 1G (1G1 + 1G2) versus 3G
3. 1G1 versus 1G2

Orthogonal comparisons were done for each of these scenarios. However, no significant differences were found (Figure 5.19).

Conclusions

Results showed that the ITT VRS-1290 Voice Recognizer/Synthesizer system performed very well, achieving over 97% accuracy over all flight conditions. The concept of speech recognition in the fighter cockpit is very promising. Any technology that enables a pilot to stay head-up and hands-on will greatly improve flight safety and situational awareness.

Impact

This flight test represented one of the most extensive in-flight evaluations of a speech recognition system ever performed. Over 5,100 utterances comprising more than 25,000 words or phrases were spoken by the twelve participants during the flight (four of the sixteen participants' flight test data was not useable). This number combined with the two ground conditions resulted in a test of over 51,000 words and phrases. The audio database of digital audio tape (DAT) recordings has been transferred onto CD-ROM and has been used to facilitate laboratory testing of other speech recognition systems. The DAT recordings have proved to be extremely valuable because many new voice

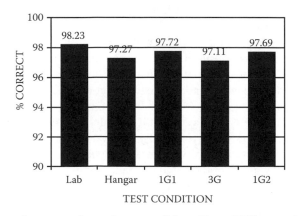

FIGURE 5.19 Mean word accuracy for each test condition. (From Williamson, D. T., Barry, T. P., and Liggett, K. K. 1996. Flight test performance optimization of ITT VRS-1290 speech recognition system. *Audio Effectiveness in Aviation: Proceedings of the Aerospace Medical Panel Symposium.*)

recognition systems have been produced after this study was conducted. With this database, new systems can be tested against speech recorded in an extremely harsh environment (the participants' crew station was directly in line with the noisy engines) without requiring additional flight tests. The CD-ROM database has been made available for distribution to the speech recognition research community. Finally, the example study illustrates the importance of flight-testing controls and displays in the environment in which they will be used. The OV-10, as well as the in-flight simulators discussed in this section, is invaluable as risk-reduction vehicles for ensuring that the control and display technology can be integrated into the airborne environment.

THE FUTURE OF DISPLAYS AND CONTROLS TECHNOLOGY FOR SIMULATION

FUTURE DISPLAYS

As technology advances, the various types and capabilities of displays available for use in simulation increase. Graphics generators are providing more realistic imagery, and HMDs are becoming more popular with higher resolution and larger FOVs. Also, no longer is one restricted to visual displays; multisensory displays are becoming more popular. The following sections describe some of these new display technologies for simulators.

Visual Displays

Infinity Cube™
The Electro Visual Engineering's Infinity Cube™ is a state-of-the-art visual display system that has been integrated with a single-seat fighter cockpit simulator to create a realistic flight environment. The out-the-window scene presents collimated imagery (focused at optical infinity), which allows for a real-world feel by giving out-the-window objects the correct size, altitude, and visual cues (Eicher, 2001). The visual scene is ideally suited to conducting research that involves the use of night-vision goggles or HMDs because images from these devices are collimated as well.

The Cube provides a full-color collimated out-the-window visual scene, supporting a wide FOV (−100° to +100° horizontal by −30° to +90° vertical) to the pilot. The Infinity Cube uses four displays, one each on the front, top, left, and right of the simulator. A hybrid system including both inertial and ultrasonic sensing technologies is used to track helmet position because the metal framework housing the displays complicates the use of a magnetic head tracker.

Retinal Scanning Display (RSD)
Traditional HMDs use an image source to project a picture on a piece of glass that resides in front of the user's eyes. Similar to using an HUD, pilots look through the glass to obtain information while simultaneously viewing the real world. In contrast, the RSD is a head-mounted display or an HMD that eliminates the piece of glass by using a scanning beam that actually "paints" or projects images directly on the retina of the eye. Although this may sound a bit risky, these systems meet safety rules set by the American National Standards Association and the International Electrotechnical Committee (Lake, 2001).

The advantage of this type of display is that it provides head-up and hands-free information and control in full color with daylight readability in a variety of ambient settings. The RSD is based on open standards, so it can receive television signals and graphics formats that can be displayed on an 800 pixel wide by 600 pixel high image. With the advent of wearable computers, this type of HMD is not only suited for military applications (such as for cockpits, command and control centers, soldiers, etc.) but is finding uses in a variety of nonmilitary situations including firefighters viewing floor plans during a rescue, technicians viewing manuals during a repair, drivers viewing moving maps during a trip, or surgeons viewing patient's vital statistics during surgery.

Audio Displays

In addition to visual displays, audio displays are becoming more and more popular in aircraft simulators. More recently, attention has shifted to localized audio (commonly referred to as 3-D audio), which are tones or cues presented at a fixed position in the external environment of the listener. This is accomplished with the use of localization systems that utilize digital signal processing technologies to encode real-time directional information for presentation over headphones. Head tracking is used to position the tone relative to the listener's external environment regardless of head position. The tone placement can vary in azimuth (left and right), elevation (up and down), and range (distance from the listener). Research in the DES (discussed in the section "Motion-Based Simulators") has shown that pilots' ability to localize virtual auditory tones is relatively unchanged (no significant increase in localization error) up to approximately 5.5 +Gz, but begins to deteriorate at 7.0 +Gz (Nelson, Bolia, McKinley, Chelette, Tripp, and Esken, 1998).

There are numerous applications of this technology in the cockpit. The addition of localized audio to visual displays has been shown to significantly reduce the time required to search and detect targets as compared to the time taken for visual-only displays (with 50 distractors, target identification time averaged 15.8 seconds with visual-only compared to 1.5 seconds with visual plus localized audio; Simpson, Bolia, McKinley, and Brungart, 2002). Also, localized audio cues in simulators have been shown to effectively redirect gaze (Perrott, Cisneros, McKinley, and D'Angelo, 1996), and have been used to enhance pilots' spatial orientation (Endsley and Rosiles, 1995).

Tactile Displays

Tactile displays show promise as efficient methods for portraying information to pilots, especially those who are visually saturated. Tactile systems include anything from basic stick shakers to vibrating wrist bands, to full vests that employ an array of tactors. The Tactile Situation Awareness System (TSAS), one of the most well-known candidate tactile displays, is an example of the latter. TSAS incorporates a number of pneumatic and E-M tactors that vibrate in specific areas on the user's torso to convey various types of information. In a fixed-wing aircraft application, TSAS can be used to present attitude information by using the various tactors to represent the horizon. For example, as the pilot maneuvers the aircraft, tactors vibrate to indicate where the horizon is with respect to the aircraft. So if the pilot performs a loop, the tactile sensation experienced by pilots would be a vibration that moves up their back as the plane climbs, presents on their shoulders when the plane is inverted, and then comes down the front of their vest as the loop continues. In a rotary-wing aircraft application, TSAS has been shown to improve hover capability by providing significantly increased total time on target (Raj, Kass, and Perry, 2000). TSAS has also been shown to be effective for a number of applications including augmenting visual display information for high altitude, high opening parachute operations in the air, and navigating on the ground for U.S. military Special Forces (Chiasson, McGrath, and Rupert, 2002). Along those same lines, researchers at TNO Human Factors in the Netherlands have been investigating the use of a vibro-tactile vest for human computer interactions, and have provided some guidelines for its incorporation into many interfaces (van Erp, 2002).

Wrist tactors are a simpler form of the tactile vest. Basically, one vibro-tactor is incorporated into a wristband to portray information in a variety of applications. These include enhanced situation awareness for altered-gravity environments (Traylor and Tan, 2002), alerting pilots of automation interventions (Sarter, 2000), and for operators detecting faults in a multitask environment (Calhoun, Draper, Ruff, and Fontejon, 2002).

Summary

The future holds much promise for the efficient display of information. Visual displays, once the only way to convey important data, will be complemented and augmented with multisensory displays. These auditory and tactile displays can provide much-needed attentional guidance in environments that are overtasking the visual channel. This trend is true in the aviation environment, as well as in other areas such as medical applications, automobile applications, and virtual reality applications for entertainment. Before their application in operational environments, advance displays such as the ones just described need to undergo evaluation in research simulators.

FUTURE CONTROLS

In aviation, head-down glances can cause disorientation and vertigo and distract from attending to primary flight tasks. Therefore, it is anticipated that future aviation research simulators will continue to explore the use of hands-free, head-up control technologies. Such technologies will include speech control and the use of head and/or eye LOS as a control input. Speech-based control is a very mature technology, and use of "macro" speech commands can replace numerous selections on a head-down multifunction keyboard. Control based on head-aiming is also a very mature technology, although its application in the operational environment is more involved. For eye LOS control, efforts are under way to explore how eye tracking optics might be integrated into HMD systems, and how best to track the eye under varying illumination conditions and at more extreme look angles (e.g., +40° azimuth and elevation) where it is difficult to maintain track of the eye due to eyelid occlusion of the pupil.

There are additional novel head-up control technologies that, with further research and development, may prove promising for control operations in aviation and other complex systems (McMillan, Eggleston, and Anderson, 1997). Each of these is described briefly in the following sections.

Gesture-Based Control

There are a variety of sensing techniques (optical, magnetic, and ultrasonic) to read body movements directly (Sturman and Zeltzer, 1994). Because the operator's body and hands can be involved in other activities, gesture-based control may best involve detecting defined movements of the face or lips. In one implementation, a headset boom located in front of the speaker's lips contains an ultrasonic signal transmitter and receiver. A piezoelectric material and a 40 KHz oscillator are used to create a continuous wave ultrasonic signal (Jennings and Ruck, 1995). The transmitted signal is reflected off the speaker's mouth, creating a standing wave that changes with movements in the speaker's lips. The magnitude of the received signal is processed to produce a low frequency output signal that can be analyzed to produce lip motion templates.

In one candidate application of lip motion measurement, lip movements are processed during speech inputs to provide lip reading. An experiment using an ultrasonic lip motion detector in a speaker-dependent, isolated word-recognition task demonstrated that the combination of ultrasonic and acoustic recognizers enhances speech recognition in noisy environments (Jennings and Ruck, 1995). An alternate application approach would be to translate symbolic lip gestures into commands that are used as control inputs.

Electromyographic (EMG)-Based Control

Electrodes positioned on the surface of skin can detect the asynchronous firing of hundreds of groups of muscle fibers. EMG-based control is based on these electrical signals that accompany muscle contractions, rather than the movement produced by contractions for control. Most commonly, the electrical signals are compared to a threshold value to derive a binary control input; a value above threshold initiates one control action and a value below threshold initiates another (Nelson, Hettinger, Cunningham, Roe, Lu, Haas, Dennis, Pick, Junker, and Berg, 1996). For instance, in one concept demonstration, operators raised an eyebrow or clenched the jaw to make control inputs (enter and tab, respectively) for a task presented on an HMD (Junker, Berg, Schneider, and McMillan, 1995). Semidry electrodes integrated into the display assembly detected the changing electrical activity produced by these subtle gestures, and employed these signals to sequence through procedures.

Electroencephalographic (EEG)-Based Control

Electrodes positioned over specific areas of the scalp can provide the necessary signals to implement EEG-based control. This type of control translates the electrical activity of the brain into a control signal. In one approach, EEG patterns are brought under conscious voluntary control with training and biofeedback (Nasman, Calhoun, and McMillan, 1997). A more applicable approach harnesses naturally occurring brain rhythms, patterns, and responses that correspond to human sensory processing, cognitive activity, or motor control (Farwell and Donchin, 1984). One example employs the brain's steady-state visual evoked response (SSVER). The SSVER is typically generated by a luminance-modulated (flickering) stimulus. It is characterized by increased power at the frequency of that stimulus. To implement this control, the luminance of selectable items on a computer display is modulated at different frequencies. The system monitors the brain's electrical activity for an SSVER at each frequency while the operator fixates on the desired flickering item. A selection occurs if the system detects an SSVER at the frequency of a particular item. Thus, the operator's choice (gaze point) between selectable items is identified by detecting which frequency is dominant in the visually evoked brain activity (Middendorf, McMillan, Calhoun, and Jones, 1999). Although detection of these responses is easily accomplished with inexpensive components, optimization of this alternative control requires minimizing the time required for signal processing, developing easily donned electrodes, and minimizing the distraction produced by flashing display items.

Summary

Controls in future simulators are likely to be multifunctional and designed to enable the operator to attend to primary tasks, while minimizing overall workload. In the case of aviation, this means control technologies that enable pilots to keep their hands on the stick and throttle and their heads up, out of the cockpit. Additionally, there will be more frequent use of multimodal (employing more than one sense) controls for a variety of reasons (Calhoun and McMillan, 1998; Hatfield, Jenkins, Jennings, and Calhoun, 1996). One is that mapping several control modalities to a single control action provides the operator with increased flexibility so that (a) the operator can exercise individual preferences, (b) a temporary task or environmental condition may deem one controller more efficient than another, and (c) if one control device malfunctions, the operator can use a different control. A multimodal approach is also useful when two or more controls are integrated so that they can be joined together to perform a task. There are at least three integration approaches:

- Having one control technology improve the performance of another technology (e.g., eye LOS can enhance speech processing by restricting the vocabulary search to the most likely commands associated with the current gaze point)
- Two or more technologies used in parallel to increase the reliability of the control action (e.g., augmenting acoustic signals with lip movement data to improve speech recognition in high noise conditions)
- Mapping controls to different task components (e.g., eye LOS designates a desired control function, and a purposeful facial muscle signal serves as a consent response)

Additionally, it is likely that controls in future simulations will be adaptive depending on several potential triggers. This will be explained more in the following section.

PILOT AIDING SYSTEM

With the increasing sophistication of computer technology, manned aircraft capabilities have increased, complicating crew station operation. Moreover, autonomous aircraft control is now more plausible. Soon, a combination of semiautonomous and fully autonomous UAVs will augment manned forces. In order to enable efficient aircraft control, a significant amount of automation will be required, especially when coupled with the desire, in the case of UAVs, to move from a situation where a number of operators control one vehicle to where one operator controls a number of vehicles. A key factor in having the operator interact with the vehicles at different levels of automation is the philosophy used in building the automation.

The philosophy now being advocated is human-centered automation (Billings, 1991), which starts with the operator as the heart of the system and then incorporates the automation. From the operators' point of view, automation is designed as it should be—to augment or assist an operator to make up for limitations (Wickens, 1992). Although this automation philosophy is consistent with that of earlier years, the implementation is much more difficult because of the increased sophistication of avionics systems. In the case of the UAV, the avionics will be partly contained in the flying platform and partly incorporated into the operator's console, in both airborne or ground-based systems. On the other hand, because of present-day advances in computers and software, the resulting product can be much closer to a true team. Operator–machine relationships are being created that emulate those occurring between two crew members based on mutual support and assistance. A major component in achieving this mutual support and assistance is through software called "associate systems." "Associate systems are computer-based aiding systems that are intended to operate as an associate to the human user" (Geddes, 1997, p. 221). Geddes goes on to list three very important rules for associate systems and their relationship with the human operator:

- Mixed initiative: Both the human operator and the decision aid can take action.
- Bounded discretion: The human operator is in charge.
- Domain competency: The decision aid has broad competency, but may have less expertise than the human operator.

Because of the mixed initiative aspects of an associate system, function allocation has to be looked at in an entirely new light. The idea of function allocation has been around since the 1950s (Fitts, 1951), and had as its basic premise that the role of operator and the machine (computer) would stay relatively constant during the operation of the system. However, this premise does not hold for modern systems as they contain associate systems (which can have varying levels of automation) and, therefore, static function allocation is no longer applicable (Hancock and Scallen, 1996). Rather, dynamic function allocation is a key feature of associate systems with varying levels of automation.

Another way to understand how the operator and electronic crew member will interact is to show how the relationship between the human and the machine changes as a function of organizational structure. Taylor (1993) illustrates this changing relationship in Figure 5.20. This figure shows a summarization of different control philosophies (specifically manual, supervisory, and cooperative) depicting the various interactions between the operator and the automation. The portion of the chart labeled "Cooperative Functionings" indicates how the operator and automation would work together in an associate system. In manual control (Figure 5.20a), the human specifies the goals and functions to be accomplished, and the machine carries out the tasks. In the next level, supervisory control (Figure 5.20b), the human still specifies the goals but the machine carries out both the tasks and functions. In cooperative functioning (Figure 5.20c), the human and machine interact at all levels, and either can perform the goals, functions, and tasks. It is through this dynamic sharing of authority that the operator and the associate can begin to operate as a team. But to function effectively as a team, both parties must trust each other. As it is not clear how the associate

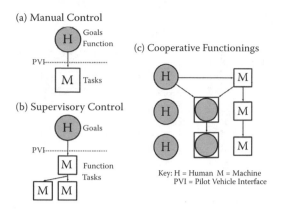

FIGURE 5.20   Systems authority concepts. (From Taylor, R. 1993. Human factors of mission planning systems: Theory and concepts. *AGARD LS 192 New Advances in Mission Planning and Rehearsal Systems*, 2-1–2-22.)

could or could not trust the human operator, the crucial aspect of teambuilding is that the operator must be able to trust the associate.

One means of establishing operator trust in the associate is to allow the operator to decide how much authority or levels of autonomy (LOA) to give the associate. "LOA defines a small set ('levels') of system configurations, each configuration specifying the degree of automation or autonomy (an 'operational relationship') at which each particular subfunction performs. The pilot sets or resets the LOA to a particular level as a consequence of mission planning, anticipated contingencies, or inflight needs" (Krobusek, Boys, and Palko, 1988, p. 124). One question that must be answered is how many levels of automation should be assigned to the associate. A number of researchers have examined this issue. They suggest as many as ten (Sheridan, 1980) and as few as five (Endsley, 1996) levels. An associate with five levels of automation is shown in Figure 5.21. This model allows for complete autonomy for either the operator or the associate with three levels of authority sharing in between. In levels 3 and 4, "AI" is an abbreviation for artificial intelligence.

Using these levels, the operators could establish a contract with the associate in the premission phase. They could, through a dialogue at a computer workstation, define what autonomy they wish the associate to have in terms of flight phase and system function. As an example, weapon consent would always remain exclusively the operator's task, but reconfiguration of the UAV's flight control surfaces to get the best flight performance in the event of battle damage would be the exclusive

		Roles	
Level of Automation		Human	System
None	1	Decide, Act	———
Decision Support	2	Decide, Act	Suggest
Consentual AI	3	Concur	Decide, Act
Monitored AI	4	Veto	Decide, Act
Full Automation	5	———	Decide, Act

FIGURE 5.21   Levels of control and automation. (From Endsley, M. R. 1996. Automation and situational awareness. In Parasuraman, R., and Mouloua, M. (Eds.), *Automation and Human Performance: Theory and Applications* (pp. 163–181). Mahwah, NJ: Lawrence Erlbaum Associates.)

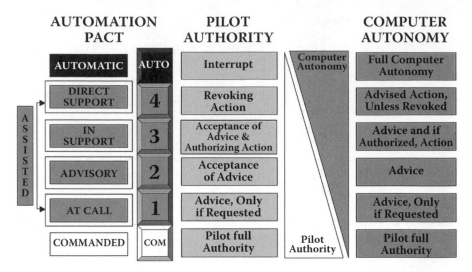

FIGURE 5.22   Pilot authorization and control of tasks (PACT) levels of pilot authority and contractual auton-omy. (From Taylor, R., Brown, L, and Dickson, B. 2002. From safety net to augmented cognition: Using flexible autonomy levels for on-line cognitive assistance and automation. *Proceedings of the RTO HFM Symposium on Spatial Disorientation in Military Vehicles: Causes, Consequences, and Cures,* RTO-MP-086, pp. 27–8.)

task of the associate. One architecture (Figure 5.22) illustrating how contracts can be established between the operator and the associate at various levels of autonomy is called the *pilot authoriza-tion and control of tasks* (PACT).

> PACT is based on the idea of contractual autonomy.... The contract defines the nature of the opera-tional relationship between the pilot and the computer aiding during cooperative performance of func-tions and tasks. Autonomy is limited by a set of contracts, or binding agreements, made between the pilot and the computer automation system governing and bounding the performance of tasks. Through PACT contracts, the pilot retains authority and executive control, while delegating responsibility for the performance of the tasks to the computer. (Taylor, Brown, and Dickson, 2002, P. 8)

CONCLUSION

The operator of future systems, whether a pilot in a manned aircraft or an operator in a UAV console, will be tightly coupled with aiding software. This software will have various levels of authority and adaptiveness that will allow the building of a very close-knit and efficient operator–computer team.

SUMMARY

Prior to the 1970s, controls and displays in aircraft research simulators tended to replicate the opera-tional approach; each control and display device performed a dedicated function. However, with the advent of E-O devices and computer-based systems, a crew station revolution began and interfaces were implemented that integrated multiple functions onto fewer control and display devices. Multi-function displays presented information that used to be on one or more analog displays. Adding switches to the joystick and throttle enabled pilots to control multiple functions while keeping their hands on throttle and stick. Plus, the number of functions that could be controlled by a single multi-function keyboard was only limited by the workload involved in navigating multiple pages to access functions several levels deep in the menu structure. Still, these controls and displays required some "head down" time in the cockpit.

In the 1980s and 1990s, simulation research shifted to exploiting this digital technology and exploring how it could be used in innovative ways. Rather than merely duplicate conventional formats on multifunction displays, the use of color, pictorial representation, and 3-D displays were explored for facilitating information acquisition. In addition, head-mounted displays driven by head position had the advantage of allowing pilots to control the aircraft while keeping their "eyes out of the cockpit." Simpler, less-cumbersome control technologies were also evaluated including use of speech commands and head and/or eye gaze.

More recently, research has started to evaluate controls and displays that will tap the pilots' biosignals to an even greater extent. Anticipated future displays include retinal presentations and alternative modalities, including tactile displays and spatial audio displays. Novel controls include interfaces based on gesture input and biopotential signals from muscles or the brain. These technologies all promote head-up, hands-free control and display. However, aside from voice-based systems, these technologies are still immature and have either limited bandwidth or integration hurdles to be solved with further development and simulation evaluation.

The 21st century marks a shift to a human-centered control/display design approach. The pilot's requirements are paramount, and as a result, attention has shifted to what control/display options best fulfill them. Multimodal approaches are also stressed, in order not to overload any single modality of the pilot. Along with this increased focus on the pilot, the role in which the computer can offer assistance is under careful scrutiny. Automation is a key design parameter and involves determining in simulation research how functions should be dynamically allocated between the pilot and the computer and what authorization procedures should be in effect.

Although this chapter's treatment of the evolution of controls and displays focused on research simulators for Air Force cockpits and UAV operator consoles, similar trends are evident in other domains, such as nuclear power plants and telephone network stations. This is because the impetus of this evolution, that is, the capabilities of computer-based systems, provides an excellent opportunity to improve how information is controlled and displayed in any complex workstation. Additionally, this chapter illustrates the importance of research simulation. Iterative use of a representative task environment in research should be employed to optimize the implementation parameters of candidate controls and displays. However, it is important to also evaluate candidate interfaces in a high-fidelity simulator that is similar to the operational environment. Ultimately, testing in the actual application environment is ideal because that is the true validation of the design. However, whatever the testing environment, simulators will play a key role in the advancement of control and display technology for efficient operator–workstation teams.

ACKNOWLEDGMENT

The authors would like to acknowledge Dr. John M. Reising who spearheaded much of the fixed-based simulator research reported herein. It is due to his expertise in this area that this chapter was initiated, and we are grateful for both his significant contributions to it, as well as to his valuable insight.

REFERENCES

Aretz, A. J., & Calhoun, G. L. 1982. Computer generated pictorial stores management displays for fighter aircraft. *Proceedings of the Human Factors Society 26th Annual Meeting,* 455–459.

Barry, T. P., Liggett, K. K., Williamson, D. T., & Reising, J. M. 1992. Enhanced recognition accuracy with the simultaneous use of three automated speech recognition systems. *Proceedings of the Human Factors Society 36th Annual Meeting,* 288–292.

Barthelemy, K. K., Reising, J. M., & Hartsock, D. C. 1991. Target designation in a perspective view, 3-D map using a joystick, hand tracker, or voice. *Proceedings of the Human Factors Society 35th Annual Meeting,* 97–101.

Bassett, P, & Lyman, J. 1940, July. The flightray, a multiple indicator. *Sperryscope,* p. 10.

Billings, C. 1991. *Human centered automation* (NASA Technical Memorandum 103885). Moffett Field, CA: Ames Research Center.

Calhoun, G. L. 1978. Control logic design criteria for multifunction switching devices. *Proceedings of the Human Factors Society 22nd Annual Meeting,* 383–387.

Calhoun, G. L., Arbak, C. J., & Janson, W. P. 1985. Eye and head response to an attention cue in a dual task paradigm. *Proceedings of the Human Factors Society 29th Annual Meeting,* 1125–1129.

Calhoun, G. L., Draper, M. H., & Ruff, H. A. 2003. Multi-sensory interface concepts for teleoperated unmanned air vehicle (UAV) systems. *Proceedings of the 12th International Symposium on Aviation Psychology,* 190–195.

Calhoun, G. L., Draper, M. H., Ruff, H. A., & Fontejon, J. V. 2002. Utility of a tactile display for cueing faults. *Proceedings of the Human Factors and Ergonomics Society 46th Annual Meeting,* 2144–2148.

Calhoun, G. L., Draper, M. H., Ruff, H. A., Fontejon, J. V., & Guilfoos, B. J. 2003. Evaluation of tactile alerts for control station operation. *Proceedings of the Human Factors and Ergonomics Society 47th Annual Meeting,* 2118–2122.

Calhoun, G. L., & Herron, E. L. 1981. Computer generated cockpit engine displays. *Proceedings of the Human Factors Society 25th Annual Meeting,* 127–131.

Calhoun, G. L., & Herron, E. L. 1982. Pilot-machine interface considerations for advanced avionics systems. *AGARD 43rd Symposium of the Avionics Panel on Advanced Avionics and the Military Aircraft Man/ Machine Interface,* 24, 1–7.

Calhoun, G. L., Herron, E. L., Reising, J. M., & Bateman, R. P. 1980. *Evaluation of factors unique to multi-function controls/displays devices* (Rep. No. AFWAL-TR-80-3131). Wright-Patterson Air Force Base, OH: Air Force Wright Aeronautical Laboratories.

Calhoun, G. L., & Janson, W. P. 1990. Eye and head response as indicators of attention cue effectiveness. *Proceedings of the Human Factors Society 34th Annual Meeting,* 1–5.

Calhoun, G. L., Janson, W. P., & Arbak, C. J. 1986. Use of eye control to select switches. *Proceedings of the Human Factors Society 30th Annual Meeting,* 154–158.

Calhoun, G. L., & McMillan, G. R. 1998. Hands-free input devices for wearable computers. *HICS 4th Annual Symposium on Human Interaction with Complex Systems,* 118–123.

Chelette, T., Allnutt, R., Tripp, L., Esken, R., Bolia, S., & Post, D. 1999. Polychromatic percepts during hyper-gravity. *Journal of Gravitational Physiology,* 6(1), 13–4.

Chiasson, J., McGrath, B. J., & Rupert, A. H. 2002. Enhanced situation awareness in sea, air and land environments. *Proceedings of the RTO HFM Symposium on Spatial Disorientation in Military Vehicles: Causes, Consequences, and Cures,* 32-1–32-10.

Christ, R. E. 1976. *Analysis of Color and its Effectiveness.* Paper presented at the Naval Air Test Center Third Advanced Aircrew Display Symposium, Patuxent River, MD.

Draper, M. H., Calhoun, G. L., Ruff, H. A., Williamson, D. T., & Barry, T. P. 2003. Manual versus speech input for unmanned aerial vehicle control station operations. *Proceedings of the Human Factors and Ergonomics Society 47th Annual Meeting.*

Draper, M. H., Geiselman, E. E., Lu, L. G., Roe, M. M., & Haas, M. W. 2000. Display concepts supporting crew communication of target location in unmanned air vehicles. *Proceedings of the Human Factors and Ergonomics Society 44th Annual Meeting,* 385–388.

Draper, M. H., Ruff, H. A., Fontejon, J. V., & Napier, S. 2002. The effects of head-coupled control and head-mounted displays (HMDs) on large-area search tasks. *Proceedings of the Human Factors and Ergonomics Society 46th Annual Meeting,* 2139–2143.

Draper, M. H., Ruff, H. A., Repperger, D. W., & Lu, L. G. 2000. Multi-sensory interface concepts supporting turbulence detection by UAV controllers. *Proceedings of the Human Performance, Situation Awareness and Automation Conference,* 107–112.

Eicher, J. A. 2001. Infinity Cube™ Display System. *NASA Tech Briefs.* Retrieved May 22, 2008 from http:// findarticles.com/p/articles/mi_ga3957/15_200103/ai_n8947789.

Endsley, M. R. 1996. Automation and situational awareness. In Parasuraman, R., & Mouloua, M. (Eds.), *Automation and human performance: theory and applications* (pp. 163–181). Mahwah, NJ: Lawrence Erlbaum Associates.

Endsley, M. R., & Rosiles, S. A. 1995. Auditory localization for spatial orientation. *Journal of Vestibular Research,* 5(6), 473–485.

Farwell, L. A., & Donchin, E. 1984. Talking off the top of your head: Toward a mental prosthesis utilizing event-related brain potentials. *Electroencephalography and Clinical Neurophysiology,* 70, 510–523.

Fitts, P. M. 1951. *Human engineering for an effective air-navigation and traffic-control system.* Washington D.C.: National Research Council.

Gawron, V. J., & Bailey, R. E. 1995. In-flight evaluation of the C-141 all-glass cockpit. *Proceedings of the 8th International Symposium on Aviation Psychology,* 80–85.

Geddes, N. 1997. Associate systems: a framework for human-machine cooperation. In Smith, M., Salvendy, G., & Koubek, R. (Eds.), *Designing of computing systems: Social and ergonomic considerations.* Amsterdam: Elsevier.

Hancock, P. A., & Scallen, S. F. 1996. The future of function allocation. *Ergonomics In Design,* Q4, 24–29.

Hatfield, F., Jenkins, E. A., Jennings, M. W., & Calhoun, G. L. 1996. Principles and guidelines for the design of eye/voice interaction dialogs. *HICS 3rd Annual Symposium on Human Interaction with Complex Systems,* 10–19.

Herron, E. L. 1978. Two types of system control with an interactive display device. *Proceedings of the 1978 International Symposium and Exhibition of the Society for Information Display,* 84–85.

Jenkins, J. C., Thurling, A. J., Havig, P. R., & Geiselman, E. E. 2002. Flight evaluation of the non-distributed flight reference off-boresight helmet-mounted display symbology. In Lewandowski, R. J., Haworth, L. A., & Girolamo, H. J. (Eds.) *Proceedings of SPIE Helmet-Mounted Displays VII,* Vol 4711, 341–355.

Jennings, D. L., & Ruck, D. W. 1995. Enhancing automatic speech recognition with an ultrasonic lip motion detector. *Proceedings of the IEEE International Conference on Acoustics, Speech and Signal Processing,* 868–871.

Junker, A., Berg, C., Schneider, P., & McMillan, G. 1995. *Evaluation of the CyberLink interface as an alternative human operator controller* (US Air Force Technical Rep. AL/CF-TR-1995-0011). Wright-Patterson Air Force Base, OH: Armstrong Laboratory.

Kopala, C. J. 1979. The use of color-coded symbols in a highly dense situation display. *Proceedings of the 23rd Human Factors Society Annual Meeting,* 397–401.

Krebs, M. J., Wolf, J. D., & Sandvig, J. H. 1978. *Color display design guide* (Rep. ONR-CR213-136-2F). Arlington VA, Office of Naval Research.

Krobusek, R. D., Boys, R. M., & Palko, K. D. 1988. *Levels of autonomy in a tactical electronic crewmember. Proceedings of The Human—Electronic Crew: Can They Work Together?,* (Tech. Rep. WRDC-TR-89-7008). 124–132 Wright-Patterson Air Force Base, OH: Cockpit Integration Directorate.

Lake, M. 2001. How it Works: Retinal Displays Add a Second Data Layer. Retrieved May 23, 2008, from http://www.telesensory.com/text/ny_times_apr_26_01_rsd.html.

Liggett, K. K., Reising, J. M., Beam, D. J., & Hartsock, D. C. 1993. The use of aiding techniques and continuous cursor controllers to designate targets in 3-D space. *Proceedings of the Human Factors Society 37th Annual Meeting,* 11–15.

Liggett, K. K., Reising, J. M., & Hartsock, D. C. 1992. The use of a background attitude indicator to recover from unusual attitudes. *Proceedings of the Human Factors Society 36th Annual Meeting,* 43–47.

McMillan, G. R., Eggleston, R. G., & Anderson, T. R. 1997. Nonconventional controls. In Salvendy, G. (Ed.), *Handbook of human factors and ergonomics* (2nd ed., 729–771). New York: John Wiley and Sons.

Middendorf, M. S., McMillan, G. R., Calhoun, G. L., & Jones, K. S. 1999. EEG-based control of virtual buttons. *Proceedings of the 43rd Annual Meeting of the Human Factors and Ergonomics Society,* 942–946.

Nasman, V. T., Calhoun, G. L., & McMillan, G. R. 1997. Brain-actuated control and HMDs. In Melzer, J., & Moffitt, K. (Eds.), *Head-mounted displays: Designing for the user* (285–310). New York: McGraw-Hill.

Nelson, W. T., Bolia, R. S., McKinley, R. L., Chelette, T. L., Tripp, L. D., & Esken, R. L. 1998. Localization of virtual auditory cues in a high +Gz environment. *Proceedings of the Human Factors and Ergonomics Society 42nd Annual Meeting,* 97–101.

Nelson, W. T., Hettinger, L. J., Cunningham, J. A., Roe, M. M., Lu, L. G., Haas, M. W., Dennis, L. B., Pick, H. L., Junker, A., & Berg, C. B. 1996. Brain-body-actuated control: Assessment of an alternative control technology for virtual environments. *Proceedings of the 1996 IMAGE Conference,* 225–232.

Nicklas, D. 1958. *A history of aircraft cockpit instrumentation 1903–1946* (Tech. Rep. No. 57–301). Wright-Patterson Air Force Base, OH: Wright Air Development Center.

Osga, G. A. 1991. Using enlarged target area and constant visual feedback to aid cursor pointing tasks. *Proceedings of the Human Factors Society 35th Annual Meeting,* 369–373.

Perrott, D. R., Cisneros, J., McKinley, R. L., & D'Angelo, W. R. 1996. Aurally aided visual search under virtual and free-field listening conditions. *Human Factors,* 38, 702–715.

Raj, A. K., Kass, S. J., & Perry, J. F. 2000. Vibrotactile displays for improving spatial awareness. *Proceedings of the IEA 2000/HFES 2000 Congress,* 1-181–1-184.

Reising, J. M. 1977. Multifunction keyboard configurations for single-seat, air-to-ground fighter cockpits. *Proceedings of the Human Factors Society 21st Annual Meeting,* 363–366.

Reising, J. M., & Calhoun, G. L. 1982. Color display formats in the cockpit: who needs them? *Proceedings of the Human Factors Society 27th Annual Meeting,* 446–450.

Reising, J. M., Liggett, K. K., & Hartsock, D. C. 1995. New flight display formats. *Proceedings of the 8th International Symposium On Aviation Psychology,* 86–91.

Reising, J. M., Liggett, K. K., Rate, C., & Hartsock, D. C. 1992. 3-D target designation using two control devices and an aiding technique. *Proceedings of SPIE Electronics Imaging Symposium,* 146–154.

Reising, J. M., Liggett, K. K., Solz, T. J., & Hartsock, D. C. 1995. A comparison of two head up display formats used to fly curved instrument approaches. *Proceedings of the Human Factors and Ergonomics Society 39th Annual Meeting,* 1–5.

Reising, J. M., Zenyuh, J. P., & Barthelemy, K. K. 1988. Head-up display symbology for unusual attitude recovery. *Proceedings of the National Aerospace and Electronics Conference,* 926–930.

Sarter, N. B. 2000. The need for multisensory interfaces in support of effective attention allocation in highly dynamic event-driven domains: The case of cockpit automation. *The International Journal of Aviation Psychology,* 10(3), 231–245.

Sheridan, T. B. 1980, October. Computer control and human alienation. *Technology Review,* 61–73.

Simpson, B. D., Bolia, R. S., McKinley, R. L., & Brungart, D. S. 2002. Sound localization with hearing protectors: performance and head motion analysis in visual search task. *Proceedings of the Human Factors and Ergonomics Society 46th Annual Meeting,* 1618–1622.

Solz, T. J., Reising, J. M., Liggett, K. K., Lohmeyer, T., & Hartsock, D. C. 1994. The use of aiding techniques and varying depth volumes to designate targets in 3-D space. *Proceedings of the Human Factors Society 38th Annual Meeting,* 1–5.

Spengler, R. P. 1988. *Advanced fighter cockpit* (Tech. Rep. ERR-FW-2936). Fort Worth, TX: General Dynamics.

Sturman, D. J., & Zeltzer, D. 1994. A survey of glove-based input. *IEEE Computer Graphics and Applications,* 23, 30–39.

Taylor, R. 1993. Human factors of mission planning systems: Theory and concepts. *AGARD LS 192 New Advances in Mission Planning and Rehearsal Systems,* 2-1–2-22.

Taylor, R., Brown, L, & Dickson, B. 2002. From safety net to augmented cognition: Using flexible autonomy levels for on-line cognitive assistance and automation. *Proceedings of the RTO HFM Symposium on Spatial Disorientation in Military Vehicles: Causes, Consequences, and Cures,* RTO-MP-086, 27-1–27-22.

Traylor, R., & Tan, H. Z. (2002). Development of a wearable haptic display for situation awareness in altered-gravity environment: Some initial findings. *Proceedings of the 10th Symposium on Haptic Interfaces for Virtual Environments and Teleoperator Systems,* 159–164.

van Erp, J. B. 2002. Guidelines for the use of vibro-tactile displays in human computer interaction. *EuroHaptics 2002.*

Wickens, C. 1992. *Engineering Psychology and Human Performance* (2nd ed.). New York: HarperCollins.

Williamson, D. T., Barry, T. P., & Liggett, K. K. 1996. Flight test performance optimization of ITT VRS-1290 speech recognition system. *Audio Effectiveness in Aviation: Proceedings of the Aerospace Medical Panel Symposium.*

Willich, W., & Edwards, R. E. 1975. *Analysis and flight simulator evaluation of an advanced fighter cockpit configuration* (Tech. Rep. AFAL-TR-75-36). Wright-Patterson Air Force Base, OH: Air Force Avionics Laboratory.

Wilshire, K. F., Latorella, K. A., & Glaab, L. J. 2000. NASA Langley crew systems contributions to aviation safety technology: Results of studies to date. *Proceedings of the IEA 2000/HFES 2000 Congress,* Vol. 4, 376–379.

Zipoy, D. R., Premselaar, S. J., Gargett, R. E., Belyea, I. L., & Hall, H. J. 1970. *Integrated information presentation and control systems study, Vol. 1: system development concepts* (Tech. Rep. AFFDL-TR-70-79, Vol. 1). Wright-Patterson Air Force Base, OH: Air Force Flight Dynamics Laboratory.

6 Simulation Sickness

Kay M. Stanney and Robert S. Kennedy

CONTENTS

INTRODUCTION

Simulator systems afford ecologically valid training that allows for training curricula to be explicitly represented and contextually relevant. Such systems can be expressly designed to consolidate prior knowledge gained in the classroom and via other instructional media, to allow for elaboration and reflection of learned information, to enhance higher-order problem-solving skills, and to facilitate assimilation of knowledge in long-term memory (Cohn et al., 2007; Gibson, 1979; Lave and Wenger, 1990; Spiro, Coulson, Feltovich, and Anders, 1988). These systems can also provide a range of assessment methods, including precise real-time performance measurement, assessment, and diagnosis, as well as scenario replay for after action review (AAR; Brooks Rose, Attree, and Elliot-Square, 2002; Dalgarno and Harper, 2003; Gaggioli, 2001). There are, however, limitations of such training systems in the form of adverse effects associated with motion sickness and lingering aftereffects, which may lead to negative training, increased dropout rates, and shorter-duration exposures.

In today's simulator systems, trainees can be immersed in an experience characterized by suboptimal visual resolution, inadequate sound spatialization, encumbering interactive devices, and misregistration of tracking information (Stanney, Salvendy, et al., 1998). These technological shortcomings may engender adverse physiological effects and pose usability concerns that need to be considered when determining how best to design and use interactive training technology. More specifically, simulator systems can be hampered by trainee-related factors such as intense malaise, high attrition rates, limited exposure durations, possibility for rejection of the system, possible decrements in human performance, and unequal opportunities for use.

Although the exact causes of these problems remain elusive, they are thought to be a result of system design (e.g., scene content, user control strategies), and technological deficiencies (e.g., lag, distortions, limited sensorial cues), as well as individual susceptibility (see review of factors by

Kolasinski [1995] and Stanney, Salvendy, et al. [1998]). The most widely accepted theory is that mismatches (due to system design issues or technological deficiencies) between the sensorial stimulation provided by a simulator and the stimulation expected due to real-world experiences (recorded in established neural pathways) are the primary cause of motion sickness (a.k.a. Sensory Conflict Theory; Reason, 1970, 1978; Reason and Brand, 1975). The resulting motion sickness is associated with a host of related problems, including vomiting (about 1%), nausea, disorientation, and oculomotor problems, as well as sleepiness (i.e., sopite syndrome), and visual flashbacks. These effects can be quite pervasive. For example, approximately 80–95% of those exposed to a virtual environment (VE) simulator report some level of symptomatology following exposure, which may be as minor as a headache or as severe as vomiting or intense vertigo (Stanney, Salvendy, et al., 1998). More troubling, the problems do not stop immediately upon cessation of exposure, as simulator exposure has been associated with lingering aftereffects (Stanney and Kennedy, 1998), which can render an individual ill equipped to operate in their normal environment for a period of time after exposure. List 1 provides a synopsis of the extent and severity of the adverse effects associated with simulator exposure that have been reported in the literature.

Based on the studies summarized in List 1, the most conservative predictions would be that at least 5% of all trainees will not be able to tolerate prolonged use of current simulator systems and that a substantial proportion would experience some level of adverse effects. Further, females, younger individuals, and those highly susceptible to motion sickness may be particularly bothered by simulator exposure. Although the data is sparse, older persons may be even more susceptible than young adults (Kennedy, 2000). In addition to the problems described in List 1, the consequences associated with such adverse effects may also include unequal opportunities for simulator training accessibility among the moderate to highly motion sickness susceptible population (Stanney, Kingdon, and Kennedy, 2002), decreased trainee acceptance and use of simulator training systems (Biocca, 1992), decreased human performance (Kolasinski, 1995; Lawson et al., 2002; Stanney, Kingdon, and Kennedy, 2002), and the acquisition of improper behaviors (e.g., reduction of rotational movements to quell side effects; Kennedy, Hettinger, and Lilienthal, 1990).

List 1: Problems Associated with Exposure to Simulator Systems

- Simulator system exposure can cause people to vomit (about 1.5%), and approximately three-quarters of those exposed tend to experience some level of nausea, disorientation, and oculomotor problems (Cobb, Nichols, Ramsey, and Wilson 1999; DiZio and Lackner, 1997; Howarth and Finch, 1999; Lawson, Graeber, Mead, and Muth, 2002; Regan and Price, 1994; Singer, Ehrlich, and Allen, 1998; Stanney, Kingdon, Graeber, and Kennedy, 2002; Stanney, Salvendy, et al., 1998; Wilson, Nichols, and Haldane, 1997; Wilson, Nichols, and Ramsey, 1995).
- With prolonged (>45 min) exposure, oculomotor problems may become more pronounced, whereas nausea and disorientation level off (Stanney, Kingdon, Graeber, and Kennedy, 2002).
- 80–95% of individuals interacting with a head-mounted display (HMD) simulator system report some level of side effects, with 5–50% experiencing symptoms severe enough to end participation, approximately 50% of those dropouts occurring in the first 20 min and nearly 75% by 30 min (Cobb et al., 1999; DiZio and Lackner, 1997; Howarth and Finch, 1999; Regan and Price, 1994; Singer et al., 1998; Stanney, Kennedy, and Kingdon, 2002; Stanney, Kingdon, Graeber, and Kennedy, 2002; Stanney, Lanham, Kennedy, and Breaux, 1999; Wilson et al., 1995; Wilson et al., 1997).
- Before the age of 2, children appear to be immune to motion sickness, after which time susceptibility increases until about the age of 12, at which point it declines again (Money, 1970). Those over 25 years are thought to be about half as susceptible as they were at 18 years of age (Mirabile, 1990).

- Females exposed to simulator systems can be expected to be more susceptible to motion sickness than males and to experience higher levels of oculomotor and disorientation symptoms as compared to males (Graeber, 2001; Stanney, Kingdon, Graeber, and Kennedy, 2002). In general, females tend to adapt more slowly to nauseogenic stimulation (McFarland, 1953; Mirabile, 1990; Reason and Brand, 1975).
- Individuals susceptible to motion sickness can be expected to experience more than twice the level of adverse effects to simulator exposure as compared to nonsusceptible individuals (Stanney, Kingdon, Graeber, and Kennedy, 2002).
- Individuals exposed to simulator systems can be expected to experience lowered arousal (e.g., drowsiness, fatigue) following exposure (Lawson et al., 2002; Stanney, Kingdon, Graeber, and Kennedy, 2002).
- Flashbacks (i.e., visual illusion of movement or false sensations of movement when not in the simulator) can be expected to occur quite regularly to those exposed to a simulator system (Lawson et al., 2002; Stanney, Kingdon, Graeber, and Kennedy, 2002).
- Prolonged aftereffects can be expected following simulator exposure, with symptoms potentially lasting more than 24 hours (Baltzley, Kennedy, Berbaum, Lilienthal, and Gower, 1989; Stanney and Kennedy, 1998; Stanny, Kingdon, Graeber, and Kinnedy, 2002; Stanney, Kingdon, and Kennedy, 2002).

INDIVIDUAL SUSCEPTIBILITY AND STIMULUS INTENSITY

The fundamental question is, Can an understanding of human physiological responses to simulator training technology be developed such that design guidelines and usage protocols can be devised that render such systems safe and effective to use? Research conducted over the past several decades has made tremendous gains in this regard (Chinn and Smith, 1953; Crampton, 1990; DiZio and Lackner, 1997, 2002; Howarth and Finch, 1999; Kennedy and Fowlkes, 1992; Lawson et al., 2002; McCauley and Sharkey, 1992; McNally and Stuart, 1942; Reason, 1970, 1978; Reason and Brand, 1975; Sjoberg, 1929; Stanney et al., 1998; Tyler and Bard, 1949; Welch, 2002; Wendt, 1968).

These researchers set out to achieve a number of challenging objectives, including developing tools to measure the adverse effects of simulator exposure (Kennedy and Stanney, 1996; Stanney, Kennedy, Drexler, and Harm, 1999), examining the psychometrics of motion sickness (Kennedy, Stanney, and Dunlap, 2000; Kingdon, Stanney, and Kennedy, 2001; Stanney and Kennedy, 1997a, 1997b; Stanney, Kingdon, Nahmens, and Kennedy, 2003; Stanney, Lanham, et al., 1999), developing usage protocols (Stanney, Kennedy, and Kingdon, 2002) and screening tools (Kennedy, Lane, Stanney, Lanham, and Kingdon, 2001), investigating system-related issues that influence motion sickness (Stanney and Hash, 1998; Stanney, Kingdon, Graeber, and Kennedy, 2002; Stanney, Salvendy, et al., 1998), and examining the efficacy of readaptation mechanisms for recalibrating those exposed to simulator systems (Stanney, Champney, et al., 2007; Smither, Mouloua, and Kennedy, 2003), as well as examining the influences of motion sickness on human performance (Kennedy, French, Ordy, and Clark, 2003; Stanney, Kingdon, and Kennedy, 2001), among other related pursuits.

These studies have lead to the understanding that the response to simulator exposure varies directly with the capacity of the individual exposed (e.g., susceptibility, experience), dose (i.e., stimulus intensity), and exposure duration (Kennedy, Stanney, and Dunlap, 2000). This indicates that through effective usage protocols that address the screening of individuals, strength of the simulator stimulus, and usage instructions, the problems associated with simulator technology can be minimized.

From the individual susceptibility perspective, age, gender, prior experience, individual factors (e.g., unstable binocular vision; individual variations in interpupillary distance [IPD]; susceptibility to photic seizures and migraines), drug or alcohol consumption, health status, and ability to adapt to novel sensory environments (see List 2) are all thought to contribute to the extent of symptoms experienced (Kennedy Dunlap, and Fowlkes, 1990; Kolasinski, 1995; McFarland, 1953; Mirabile, 1990; Reason and Brand, 1975; Stanney, Kennedy, and Kingdon, 2002; Stanney, Salvendy, et al., 1998).

LIST 2: FACTORS AFFECTING THE CAPACITY TO RESIST ADVERSE EFFECTS OF SIMULATOR EXPOSURE

- *Age.* Expect little motion sickness in those under age 2, greatest susceptibility to motion sickness between the ages of 2 and 12, and motion sickness to decline after 12 years, with those over 25 years being about half as susceptible as they were at 18 years of age.
- *Gender.* Expect females to be more susceptible than males (perhaps as much as three times more susceptible).
- *Anthropometrics.* Consider setting simulator stimulus intensity in proportion to body weight/stature.
- *Individual susceptibility.* Expect individuals to differ greatly in motion sickness susceptibility and use the Motion History Questionnaire (MHQ; Kennedy and Graybiel, 1965; Kennedy, Lane, Grizzard, Stanney, Kingdon, and Lanham, 2001) or another instrument to gauge the susceptibility of the target trainee population.
- *Drug or alcohol consumption.* Limit simulator exposure to those individuals who have not recently consumed drugs or alcohol.
- *Rest.* Encourage individuals to be well rested before commencing simulator exposure.
- *Ailments.* Discourage those with cold, flu, or other ailments (e.g., headache, diplopia, blurred vision, sore eyes, or eyestrain) from participating in simulator exposure. Also, those susceptible to photic seizures and migraines, as well as individuals with preexisting binocular anomalies should avoid exposure.
- *Clinical trainee groups.* Become informed and sensitive to the vulnerabilities of these trainee groups (e.g., unique psychological, cognitive, and functional characteristics). Also, those displaying comorbid features of various psychotic, bipolar, paranoid, substance abuse, claustrophobic, or other disorders where reality testing and identity problems are evident, should avoid exposure.

Although considerable research into the causes of seasickness, motion sickness, simulator sickness, space sickness, and cybersickness has been ongoing for decades (Chinn and Smith, 1953; Crampton, 1990; Kennedy and Fowlkes, 1992; McCauley and Sharkey, 1992; McNally and Stuart, 1942; Reason, 1970, 1978; Reason and Brand, 1975; Sjoberg, 1929; Stanney, Salvendy, et al., 1998; Tyler and Bard, 1949; Wendt, 1968), there are currently few, if any, efforts focusing on the development of means of reducing adverse effects by "acclimating" trainees to the simulator stimulus (but see Graeber, 2001a; or Smither, Mouloua, and Kennedy, 2003). Yet, stimulus–response studies, such as the classical conditioning studies of Pavlov (1928), offer a potential paradigm through which to realize such acclimation.

There is, however, a lack of understanding about the factors that drive simulator stimulus intensity such that this knowledge can be used to develop simulator usage protocols that will minimize adverse effects. In fact, current usage of simulator technology generally treats trainees as if they are immune to motion sickness or possess low motion sickness susceptibility, and are capable of rapid acclimation to novel sensory environments. This is not the case, as evidenced by the intensity and extent of side effects described in List 1.

Research that is focused on developing an understanding of the system design, technological, and individual drivers of adverse effects associated with simulator exposure can be used to make predictions on stimulus intensity (see List 3). As described in List 3, there are a number of diverse factors influencing stimulus intensity. By developing an understanding of these factors, means of acclimating trainees to a simulator stimulus can potentially be identified.

TACKLING THE PROBLEM

The summary in List 3 suggests that the intensity of a simulator stimulus could be reduced by short-ening exposure duration, maintaining an intersession interval of 2–5 days, and reducing the degrees of freedom (DOF) of trainee movement control—particularly avoiding rotational movements and simplifying visual scenes. List 3 further suggests that the exact conditioning strategy that will be most effective may depend on individual susceptibility. If these tactics are coupled with condition-ing approaches, reductions in adverse effects and associated dropout rates should result. Although the technological factors within any given system can produce varying adverse effects, system developers should ensure that the guidelines in List 4 are followed to minimize stimulus strength (Stanney, Kennedy, and Kingdon, 2002).

Focusing on the parameters in List 4, system developers should identify the primary factors that induce adverse effects in their system. As can be seen from the various studies reported herein (see also Stanney et al., 1998), the manner in which individual software and hardware components can be integrated varies greatly. Thus, the steps in List 5 can be used to establish the stimulus intensity of a simulator.

LIST 3: FACTORS INFLUENCING SIMULATOR STIMULUS INTENSITY

- Adverse effects associated with simulator exposure are positively correlated with exposure duration (Kennedy, Stanney, and Dunlap, 2000). Lanham (2000) has shown that sickness increases linearly at a rate of 23% per 15 min. Dropouts occur in as little as 15 min of expo-sure (Cobb et al., 1999; DiZio and Lackner, 1997; Howarth and Finch, 1999; Regan and Price, 1994; Singer et al., 1998; Stanney, Kingdon, Graeber, and Kennedy, 2002; Stanney, Kingdon, and Kennedy, 2002; Stanney, Lanham et al., 1999; Wilson et al., 1995; Wilson et al., 1997).
- Simulator studies have indicated that intersession intervals of 2–5 days are effective in mitigating adverse effects, whereas intervals less than or greater than 2–5 days are ineffective in reducing symptomatology (Kennedy, Lane, Berbaum, and Lilienthal, 1993; Watson, 1998).
- In vection drums, repeated exposure intervals within a session less than 2 hours appear to heighten adverse effects upon reentry (Graeber, 2001a).
- As the amount of trainee movement control in terms of DOF and head tracking increases, so does the level of nausea experienced (So and Lo, 1999; Stanney and Hash, 1998; Stan-ney, Kingdon, Graeber, and Kennedy, 2002). Complete trainee movement control (6 DOF) can be expected to lead to 2.5 times more dropouts than streamlined control (3 DOF).
- The rate of visual flow (i.e., visual scene complexity) may influence the incidence and, more so, the severity of motion sickness experienced by an individual (Kennedy and Fowlkes, 1992; McCauley and Sharkey, 1992). Complex visual scenes may be more nauseogenic than simple scenes, with complex scenes possibly resulting in 1.5 times more emetic responses. However, scene complexity does not appear to affect dropout rates (Dichgans and Brandt, 1978; Kennedy, Berbaum, Dunlap, and Hettinger, 1996; Stanney, Kingdon, Graeber, and Kennedy, 2002). Such effects may be exacerbated by a large field of view (FOV; Kennedy and Fowlkes, 1992), high spatial frequency content (Dichgans and Brandt, 1978), and visual simulation of action motion (i.e., vection [Kennedy, Berbaum, et al., 1996]).
- Various technological factors thought to influence how provocative a simulator is include system consistency (Uliano, Kennedy, and Lambert, 1986); lag (So and Griffin, 1995); update rate (So and Griffin, 1995); mismatched IPD (Mon-Williams, Rushton, and Wann, 1995); and unimodal and intersensorial distortions (both temporal and spatial [Welch, 1978]).

- Individual factors thought to contribute to an individual's motion sickness susceptibility include age, gender, prior experience, individual factors (e.g., unstable binocular vision, individual variations in IPD, susceptibility to photic seizures and migraines), drug or alcohol consumption, health status, and ability to adapt to novel sensory environments (Kennedy, Dunlap, and Fowlkes, 1990; Kolasinski, 1995; McFarland, 1953; Mirabile, 1990; Reason and Brand, 1975; Stanney, Kennedy, and Kingdon, 2002; Stanney, Salvendy, et al., 1998).
- Individuals who have experienced an emetic response associated with carnival rides can be expected to experience more than twice the level of adverse effects to simulator exposure as compared to those who do not experience such emesis (Stanney, Kingdon, Graeber, and Kennedy, 2002).
- Individuals with higher preexposure drowsiness will be more likely to experience drowsiness following exposure, and those exposed for 60 min or longer can be expected to experience more than twice the level of drowsiness as compared to those exposed for a shorter duration (Lawson et al., 2002; Stanney, Kingdon, Graeber, and Kennedy, 2002).
- As drowsiness increases, one can expect a greater severity of flashbacks (Lawson et al., 2002; Stanney, Kingdon, Graeber, and Kennedy, 2002).
- Body mass index (BMI) does not seem to be related to motion sickness symptoms. However, those with a higher BMI may be less prone to experience an emetic response (Stanney, Kingdon, Graeber, and Kennedy, 2002).

LIST 4: ADDRESSING SYSTEM FACTORS THAT INFLUENCE THE STRENGTH OF A SIMULATOR STIMULUS

- Ensure that any system lags/latencies are stable; variable lags/latencies can be debilitating.
- Minimize display/phase lags (i.e., end-to-end tracking latency between head motion and resulting update of the display).
- Optimize frame rates.
- Provide adjustable IPD.
- When a large FOV is used, determine if it drives high levels of vection (i.e., perceived self-motion).
- If high levels of vection are found and they lead to high levels of sickness, then reduce the spatial frequency content of visual scenes.
- Provide multimodal feedback that minimizes sensory conflicts (i.e., provide visual, auditory, and haptic/kinesthetic feedback appropriate for the situation being simulated).

LIST 5: STEPS TO QUANTIFYING SIMULATOR STIMULUS INTENSITY

- Get an initial estimate. Talk with target trainees (not developers) of the system, and determine the level of adverse effects they experience.
- Watch trainees during and after exposure, and note comments and behaviors.
- Try the system yourself. Particularly, if you are susceptible to motion sickness, obtain a first-hand assessment of the adverse effects.
- Measure the dropout rate. If most people can stay in for an hour without developing symptoms, then the system is likely to be benign; if most people drop out within 10 min, then the system is probably in need of redesign.
- Use simple rating scales to assess sickness (Kennedy, Lane, Berbaum, and Lilienthal, 1993), and visual, proprioceptive, and postural measures to assess aftereffects (Kennedy, Stanney, Compton, Drexler, and Jones, 1999).
- Determine how the system under evaluation compares to other simulator systems.
- Summarize the severity of the problem, specify required interventions (e.g., warnings, instructions), and set expectations for use (e.g., target exposure duration, intersession intervals).
- Expect dropouts. With a high intensity simulator stimulus, drop-out rates can be high.

USAGE PROTOCOL

Integrating the issues reviewed earlier, List 6 provides a systematic simulator usage protocol that can be used by system developers and system administrators to minimize risks to trainees exposed to simulator systems (see also Naval Training Systems Center, 1989):

List 6: Simulator System Usage Protocol

- Review information in List 2, and identify the individual capacity of the target trainee population to resist adverse effects of simulator exposure.
- Consider the factors in List 3 and, following the guidelines in List 4, design simulator stimulus to minimize adverse effects.
- Following the guidelines in List 5, quantify the simulator stimulus intensity of the target system.
- Provide warnings for those with severe susceptibility to motion sickness, seizures, migraines, cold, flu, or other ailments (see List 2).
- Educate trainees as to the potential risks of VE exposure. Inform trainees of the insidious effects they may experience during exposure, including nausea, malaise, disorientation, headache, dizziness, vertigo, eyestrain, drowsiness, fatigue, pallor, sweating, increased salivation, and vomiting.
- Educate trainees as to the potential adverse aftereffects of simulator exposure (see List 1). Inform trainees that they may experience visual disturbances, visual flashbacks, as well as unstable locomotor and postural control for prolonged periods following exposure. Relating these experiences to excessive alcohol consumption may prove instructional.
- Educate and inform trainees that if they start to feel ill, they should terminate their simulator exposure because extended exposure is known to exacerbate adverse effects (Kennedy, Stanney, and Dunlap, 2000).
- Prepare trainees for their transition to the simulator by informing them that there will be an adjustment period.
- Adjust environmental conditions. Provide adequate airflow and comfortable thermal conditions (Konz, 1997). Sweating often precedes an emetic response, thus proper airflow can enhance trainee comfort. In addition, extraneous noise should be eliminated, as it can exacerbate ill effects.
- Adjust equipment to minimize fatigue. Fatigue can exacerbate the adverse effects of simulator exposure. To minimize fatigue, ensure all equipment is comfortable and properly adjusted for fit.
- Limit initial exposures. For strong simulator stimuli, limit initial exposures to a short duration (e.g., 10 min or less) and allow an intersession recovery period of 2–5 days.
- Avoid provocative movements. For strong simulator stimuli, warn trainees to avoid movements requiring high rates of linear or rotational acceleration and extraordinary maneuvers (e.g., flying backward) during initial interaction (McCauley and Sharkey, 1992).
- Monitor trainees. Throughout simulator exposure, an attendant should be available at all times to monitor trainees' behavior and ensure their well-being.
- Look for red flags. Indicators of impending trouble include excessive sweating, verbal frustration, lack of movement within the environment for a significant amount of time, and less overall movement (e.g., restricting head movement). Trainees demonstrating any of these behaviors should be observed closely, as they may experience an emetic response. Extra care should be taken with these individuals following exposure. (It is beneficial to have a plastic bag or garbage can located near trainees in the event of an abrupt emetic response.)
- Set criteria for terminating exposure. Exposure should be terminated immediately if trainees verbally complain of symptoms and acknowledge they are no longer able to continue.

Also, to avoid an emetic response, if telltale signs are observed (i.e., sweating, increased salivation), exposure should be terminated. Some individuals may be unsteady following exposure. These individuals may need assistance when initially standing up afterward.

- After exposure, the well-being of trainees should be assessed (debriefing). Measurements of their hand–eye coordination and postural stability should be taken. Similar to field sobriety tests, these can include measurements of balance (e.g., standing on one foot, walking an imaginary line, leaning backward with eyes closed); coordination (e.g., alternate hand clapping and finger-to-nose touch while the eyes are closed); and eye nystagmus (e.g., follow a pen light with the eyes, without moving the head). Do not allow individuals who fail these tests to conduct high-risk activities until they have recovered (e.g., have someone drive them home).
- Set criteria for releasing trainees. Specify the amount of time after exposure that trainees must remain on premises before driving or participating in other such high-risk activities. In our lab, a two-to-one ratio was used; following exposure, trainees had to remain in the laboratory for twice the duration of exposure to allow recovery.
- Call trainees the next day or have them call to report any prolonged adverse effects (follow-up).

CONCLUSIONS

To minimize the risks associated with exposure to training simulators, system developers and system administrators should identify the capacity of the target trainee population to resist the adverse effects of exposure, quantify and minimize simulator stimulus intensity, and follow a systematic simulator system usage protocol. This protocol should focus on warning, educating, and preparing trainees; setting appropriate environmental and equipment conditions; limiting initial exposure duration; monitoring trainees while looking for red flags, and setting criteria for terminating exposure, debriefing, and release (e.g., persons who appear sick may indeed be sick! Look for characteristic signs). Adopting such a protocol can minimize the risk factors associated with simulator exposure, thereby enhancing the safety of trainees, while limiting the liability of system developers and administrators.

ACKNOWLEDGMENTS

This material is based on work supported in part by the Office of Naval Research (ONR) under grant number N000149810642, the National Science Foundation (NSF) under grant numbers DMI9561266 and IRI-9624968, and the National Aeronautics and Space Administration (NASA) under grant numbers NAS9-19482 and NAS9-19453. Any opinions, findings, and conclusions or recommendations expressed in this chapter are those of the authors and do not necessarily reflect the views or the endorsement of the ONR, NSF, or NASA.

REFERENCES

Baltzley, D. R., Kennedy, R. S., Berbaum, K. S., Lilienthal, M. G., & Gower, D. W. 1989. The time course of postflight simulator sickness symptoms. *Aviation, Space, and Environmental Medicine*, 60(11), 1043–1048.
Biocca, F. 1992. Will simulation sickness slow down the diffusion of virtual environment technology? *Presence: Teleoperators and Virtual Environments*, 1(3), 334–343.
Brooks, B. M., Rose, F. D., Attree, E. A., & Elliot-Square, A. 2002. An evaluation of the efficacy of training people with learning disabilities in a virtual environment. *Disability and Rehabilitation*, 24(11–12), 622–626.
Chinn, H. I., & Smith, P. K. 1953. Motion sickness. *Pharmacological Review*, 7, 33–82.
Cobb, S. V. G., Nichols, S., Ramsey, A. D., & Wilson, J. R. 1999. Virtual Reality-Induced Symptoms and Effects (VRISE). *Presence: Teleoperators and Virtual Environments*, 8(2), pp. 169–186.

Champney, R., Stanney, K. M., Hash, P., Malone, L., Kennedy, R. S., & Compton, D. (2007). Recovery from virtual environment exposure: Expected time-course of symptoms and potential readaption mechanisms. *Human Factors,* 49(3), 491–506.

Cohn, J. V., Stanney, K. M., Milham, L. M., Jones, D. L., Hale, K. S., Darken, R. P., & Sullivan, J. A. (2007). Training evaluation of virtual environments. In E. L. Baker, J. Dickieson, W. Wulfeck, & H. O'Neil (Eds.), *Assessment of problem solving using simulations* (pp. 81–105). Mahwah, NJ: Lawrence Erlbaum.

Crampton, G. H. (Ed.) 1990. *Motion & space sickness.* Boca Raton, FL: CRC Press.

Dalgarno, B., & Harper, J. 2003. 3D environments for spatial learning: The importance of learning task design. In Crisp, G., Thiele, D., Scholten, I., Barker, S., & Baron, J. (Eds.), *Interact, Integrate, Impact—Proceedings of the 20th Annual Conference of the Australian Society for Computers in Learning in Tertiary Education,* (pp. 142–151). New South Wales, Australia: Ascilite. Accessed 9/8/06.

Dichgans, J., & Brandt, T. 1978. Visual-vestibular interaction: Effects on self-motion perception and postural control. In Held, R., Leibowitz, H. W., & Teuber, H. L. (Eds.), *Handbook of sensory physiology, Vol. VIII: Perception* (pp. 756–804). Heidelberg: Springer-Verlag.

DiZio, P., & Lackner, J. R. 1997. Circumventing side effects of immersive virtual environments. In Smith, M., Salvendy, G., & Koubek, R. (Eds.), *Design of computing systems: Social and ergonomic considerations* (pp. 893–896). Amsterdam, Netherlands: Elsevier Science Publishers, San Francisco, CA, August 24–29.

DiZio, P., & Lackner, J. R. 2002. Proprioceptive adaptation and aftereffects. In Stanney, K. M. (Ed.), *Handbook of virtual environments: Design, implementation, and applications* (pp. 791–806). Mahwah, NJ: Lawrence Erlbaum Associates.

Gaggioli, A. 2001. Using virtual reality in experimental psychology. In Riva, G., & Galimberti, C. (Eds.), *Towards cyberpsychology: Mind, cognition, and society in the Internet Age* (pp. 157–174). Amsterdam, Netherlands: IOS Press.

Gibson, J. J. 1979. *The ecological approach to visual perception.* Boston: Houghton Mifflin.

Graeber, D. A. 2001. *Use of incremental adaptation and habituation regimens for mitigating optokinetic side effects.* Unpublished doctoral dissertation, University of Central Florida.

Howarth, P. A., & Finch, M. 1999. The nauseogenicity of two methods of navigating within a virtual environment. *Applied Ergonomics,* 30, 39–45.

Kennedy, R. S. 2000, September. *Virtual environments and the aging process.* Paper presented at NIDCD-NHTSA Workshop on Vehicular Driving Performance in Vestibular-Impaired Individuals, Washington D.C.

Kennedy, R. S., Berbaum, K. S., Dunlap, W. P., & Hettinger, L. J. 1996. Developing automated methods to quantify the visual stimulus for cybersickness. *Proceedings of the Human Factors and Ergonomics Society 40th Annual Meeting* (pp. 1126–1130). Santa Monica, CA: Human Factors and Ergonomics Society.

Kennedy, R. S., Dunlap, W. P., & Fowlkes, J. E. 1990. Prediction of motion sickness susceptibility: A taxonomy and evaluation of relative predictor potential. In Crampton, G. H. (Ed.), *Motion and space sickness* (pp. 179–215). Boca Raton, FL: CRC Press.

Kennedy, R. S., & Fowlkes, J. E. 1992. Simulator sickness is polygenic and polysymptomatic: Implications for research. *International Journal of Aviation Psychology,* 2(1), 23–38.

Kennedy, R. S., French, J., Ordy, J. M., & Clark, J. 2003. *Visually induced motion sickness, cognitive performance, saliva melatonin, and cortisol.* Paper accepted for presentation at the Society for Neuroscience 33rd Annual Meeting, November 8–12, New Orleans, LA.

Kennedy, R. S., & Graybiel, A. 1965. *The Dial test: A standardized procedure for the experimental production of canal sickness symptomatology in a rotating environment* (Rep. No. 113, NSAM 930). Pensacola, FL: Naval School of Aerospace Medicine.

Kennedy, R. S., Hettinger, L. J., & Lilienthal, M. G. 1990. Simulator sickness. In Crampton, G. H. (Ed.), *Motion and space sickness* (pp. 247–262). Boca Raton, FL: CRC Press.

Kennedy, R. S., Lane, N. E., Berbaum, K. S., & Lilienthal, M. G. 1993. Simulator sickness questionnaire: An enhanced method for quantifying simulator sickness. *International Journal of Aviation Psychology,* 3(3), 203–220.

Kennedy, R. S., Lane, N. E., Grizzard, M. C., Stanney, K. M., Kingdon, K., & Lanham, S. 2001. Use of a motion history questionnaire to predict simulator sickness. *Proceedings of the Sixth Driving Simulation Conference- DSC2001* (pp. 79–89). France: INRETS/Renault.

Kennedy, R. S., Lane, N. E., Stanney, K. M., Lanham, D. S., & Kingdon, K. 2001. Use of a motion experience questionnaire to predict simulator sickness. *Usability evaluation and interface design: Cognitive engineering, intelligent agents and virtual reality* (pp. 1061–1065). Mahwah, NJ: Lawrence Erlbaum Associates.

Kennedy, R. S., & Stanney, K. M. 1996. Postural instability induced by virtual reality exposure: Development of a certification protocol. *International Journal of Human-Computer Interaction*, 8(1), 25–47.

Kennedy, R. S., Stanney, K. M., Compton, D. E., Drexler, J. M., & Jones, M. B. 1999. *Virtual environment adaptation assessment test battery* (Phase II Final Report, Contract No. NAS9-97022). Houston, TX: NASA Lyndon B. Johnson Space Center.

Kennedy, R. S., Stanney, K. M., & Dunlap, W. P. 2000. Duration and exposure to virtual environments: Sickness curves during and across sessions. *Presence: Teleoperators and Virtual Environments*, 9(5), 463–472.

Kingdon, K., Stanney, K. M., & Kennedy, R. S. 2001. Extreme responses to virtual environment exposure. *The 45th Annual Human Factors and Ergonomics Society Meeting* (pp. 1906–1910). Minneapolis/ St. Paul, MN, October 8–12, 2001.

Kolasinski, E. M. 1995. *Simulator sickness in virtual environments* (ARI Technical Report 1027). Alexandria, VA: U.S. Army Research Institute for the Behavioral and Social Sciences.

Konz, S. 1997. Toxicology and thermal discomfort. In Salvendy, G. (Ed.), *Handbook of human factors and ergonomics* (2nd ed., pp. 891–908). New York: John Wiley and Sons.

Lanham, S. 2000. *The effects of motion on performance, presence, and sickness in a virtual environment.* Masters thesis, University of Central Florida.

Lave, J., & Wenger, E. 1990. *Situated learning: Legitimate peripheral participation.* Cambridge, UK: Cambridge University Press.

Lawson, B. D., Graeber, D. A., Mead, A. M., & Muth, E. R. 2002. Signs and symptoms of human syndromes associated with synthetic experiences. In Stanney, K. M. (Ed.), *Handbook of virtual environments: design, implementation, and applications* (pp. 791–806). Mahwah: NJ: Lawrence Erlbaum Associates.

McCauley, M. E., & Sharkey, T. J. 1992. Cybersickness: perception of self-motion in virtual environments. *Presence: Teleoperators and Virtual Environments*, 1(3), 311–318.

McFarland, R. A. 1953. *Human factors in air transportation: Occupational health and safety.* New York: McGraw-Hill.

McNally, W. J., & Stuart, E. A. 1942. Physiology of the labyrinth reviewed in relation to seasickness and other forms of motion sickness. *War Medicine*, 2, 683–771.

Mirabile, C. S. 1990. Motion sickness susceptibility and behavior. In Crampton, G. H. (Ed.), *Motion and space sickness* (pp. 391–410). Boca Raton, FL: CRC Press.

Money, K. E. 1970. Motion sickness. *Psychological Reviews*, 50(1), 1–39.

Mon-Williams, M., Rushton, S., & Wann, J. P. 1995. Binocular vision in stereoscopic virtual-reality systems. *Society for Information Display International Symposium Digest of Technical Papers*, 25, 361–363.

Naval Training Systems Center (NTSC). 1989, October. *Simulator Sickness Field Manual: MOD 4.* Orlando, FL: Naval Training Systems Center, Human Factors Laboratory.

Pavlov, I. P. 1928. *Lectures on conditioned reflexes* (Translated by Gantt, W. H.). New York: International.

Reason, J. T. 1970. Motion sickness: A special case of sensory rearrangement. *Advancement in Science*, 26, 386–393.

Reason, J. T. 1978. Motion sickness adaptation: A neural mismatch model. *Journal of the Royal Society of Medicine*, 71, 819–829.

Reason, J. T., & Brand, J. J. 1975. *Motion sickness.* New York: Academic Press.

Regan, E. C., & Price, K. R. 1994. The frequency of occurrence and severity of side-effects of immersion virtual reality. *Aviation, Space, and Environmental Medicine*, 65, 527–530.

Singer, M. J., Ehrlich, J. A., & Allen, R. C. 1998. Virtual environment sickness. Adaptation to and recover from a search task. *Proceedings of the 42nd Annual Human Factors and Ergonomics Society Meeting* (pp. 1506–1510). Chicago, IL, October 5–9.

Sjoberg, A. A. 1929. Experimental studies of the eliciting mechanism of sea sickness. *Acta Oto-Laryngolica*, 13, 343–347.

Smither, J. A., Mouloua, M., & Kennedy, R. S. 2003. *Reducing symptomatology of visually-induced motion sickness through perceptual training.* Manuscript submitted for publication.

So, R. H., & Griffin, M. J. 1995. Effects of lags on human operator transfer functions with head-coupled systems. *Aviation, Space, and Environmental Medicine*, 66, 550–556.

So, R. H. Y., & Lo, W. T. 1999. Cybersickness: An experimental study to isolate the effects of rotational scene oscillations. In *Proceedings of the IEEE Virtual Reality Conference* (pp. 237–241). Los Alamitos, CA: IEEE Computer Society.

Spiro, R. J., Coulson, R. L., Feltovich, P. J., & Anderson, D. 1988. Cognitive flexibility theory: Advanced knowledge acquisition in ill-structured domains. In Patel, V. (Ed.), *Proceedings of the 10th Annual Conference of the Cognitive Science Society.* Hillsdale, NJ: Lawrence Erlbaum.

Stanney, K. M., & Hash, P. 1998. Locus of user-initiated control in virtual environments: Influences on cybersickness. *Presence: Teleoperators and Virtual Environments, 7*(5), 447–459.

Stanney, K. M., & Kennedy, R. S. 1997a. Cybersickness is not simulator sickness. *Proceedings of the 41st Annual Human Factors and Ergonomics Society Meeting* (pp. 1138–1142). Albuquerque, NM, September 22–26.

Stanney, K. M., & Kennedy, R. S. 1997b. The psychometrics of cybersickness. *Communications of the ACM, 40*(8), 67–68.

Stanney, K. M., & Kennedy, R. S. 1998. Aftereffects from virtual environment exposure: How long do they last? *Proceedings of the 42nd Annual Human Factors and Ergonomics Society Meeting* (pp. 1476–1480). Chicago, IL, October 5–9.

Stanney, K. M., Kennedy, R. S., Drexler, J. M., & Harm, D. L. 1999. Motion sickness and proprioceptive aftereffects following virtual environment exposure. *Applied Ergonomics, 30,* 27–38.

Stanney, K. M., Kennedy, R. S., & Kingdon, K. 2002. Virtual environments usage protocols. In Stanney, K. M. (Ed.), *Handbook of virtual environments: Design, implementation, and applications* (pp. 721–730). Mahwah, NJ: Lawrence Erlbaum Associates.

Stanney, K. M., Kingdon, K., Graeber, D., & Kennedy, R. S. 2002. Human performance in immersive virtual environments: Effects of duration, user control, and scene complexity. *Human Performance, 15*(4), 339–366.

Stanney, K. M., Kingdon, K., & Kennedy, R. S. 2001. Human performance in virtual environments: Examining user control techniques. In Smith, M. J., Salvendy, G., Harris, D., & Koubek, R. J. (Eds.), *Usability evaluation and interface design: Cognitive engineering, intelligent agents and virtual reality* (Vol. 1 of the Proceedings of HCI International 2001, pp. 1051–1055). Mahwah, NJ: Lawrence Erlbaum.

Stanney, K. M., Kingdon, K., & Kennedy, R. S. 2002. Dropouts and aftereffects: Examining general accessibility to virtual environment technology. *The 46th Annual Human Factors and Ergonomics Society Meeting* (pp. 2114–2118). Baltimore, MD, September 29–October 4, 2002.

Stanney, K. M., Kingdon, K., Nahmens, I., & Kennedy, R. S. 2003. What to expect from immersive virtual environment exposure: Influences of gender, body mass index, and past experience. *Human Factors, 45*(3), 504–522.

Stanney, K. M., Lanham, S., Kennedy, R. S., & Breaux, R. B. 1999. Virtual environment exposure drop-out thresholds. *The 43rd Annual Human Factors and Ergonomics Society Meeting* (pp. 1223–1227). Houston, TX, September 27–October 1, 1999.

Stanney, K. M., Salvendy, G., Deisinger, J., DiZio, P., Ellis, S., Ellison, E., Fogleman, G., Gallimore, J., Hettinger, L., Kennedy, R., Lackner, J., Lawson, B., Maida, J., Mead, A., Mon-Williams, M., Newman, D., Piantanida, T., Reeves, L., Riedel, O., Singer, M., Stoffregen, T., Wann, J., Welch, R., Wilson, J., & Witmer, B. 1998. Aftereffects and sense of presence in virtual environments: Formulation of a research and development agenda. Report sponsored by the Life Sciences Division at NASA Headquarters. *International Journal of Human-Computer Interaction, 10*(2), 135–187.

Tyler, D. B., & Bard, P. 1949. Motion sickness. *Physiological Review, 29,* 311–369.

Uliano, K. C., Kennedy, R. S., & Lambert, E. Y. 1986. Asynchronous visual delays and the development of simulator sickness. *Proceedings of the Human Factors Society 30th Annual Meeting* (pp. 422–426). Dayton, OH: Human Factors Society.

Watson, G. S. 1998. The effectiveness of a simulator screening session to facilitate simulator sickness adaptation for high-intensity driving scenarios. *Proceedings of the 1998 IMAGE Conference,* The IMAGE Society, Chandler, AZ.

Welch, R. B. 1978. *Perceptual modification: Adapting to altered sensory environments.* New York: Academic Press.

Welch, R. B. 2002. Adapting to virtual environments. In Stanney, K. M. (Ed.), *Handbook of virtual environments: Design, implementation, and applications.* Mahwah: NJ: Lawrence Erlbaum Associates.

Wendt, G. R. 1968. *Experiences with research on motion sickness* (NASA Special Publication No. SP-187). Pensacola, FL: Fourth Symposium on the Role of Vestibular Organs in Space Exploration.

Wilson, J. R., Nichols, S., & Haldane, C. 1997. Presence and side effects: Complementary or contradictory? In Smith, M., Salvendy, G., & Koubek, R. (Eds.), *Design of computing systems: Social and ergonomic considerations* (pp. 889–892). Amsterdam, Netherlands: Elsevier Science Publishers, San Francisco, CA, August 24–29.

Wilson, J. R., Nichols, S. C., & Ramsey, A. D. 1995. Virtual reality health and safety: Facts, speculation and myths. *VR News, 4,* 20–24.

7 Simulation-Based Situation Awareness Training

Laura D. Strater and Cheryl A. Bolstad

CONTENTS

INTRODUCTION

The term situation awareness (SA) has been around since World War II. Although originally associated with military pilots, over the last several years it has emerged as a field of research in its own right and is now being examined in other domains, such as army operations, air traffic control (ATC), nuclear power plant operation, and medical applications (Bolstad, Riley, Jones, and Endsley, 2002; Collier and Folleso, 1995; Endsley, 1995a; Gaba, Howard, and Small, 1995; Sollenberger and Stein, 1995; Wright, Taekman, and Endsley, 2004). At its core, SA involves being aware of what is happening around oneself to understand how information, events, and one's own actions will affect one's goals and objectives, both now and in the near future. In fact, SA is employed regularly in the complex and dynamic tasks typical of everyday life, such as driving a car, crossing the street, or juggling items on a busy schedule. It is especially critical in work domains where the information flow can be quite high and poor decisions may lead to serious consequences (e.g., piloting an airplane, functioning as a soldier, or treating critically ill or injured patients).

As much of the study of SA has focused on those fields of endeavor where the consequences of poor SA can be quite severe, simulations have proved to be a valuable resource for both basic and applied research in these fields. Through simulations, one can safely and objectively investigate SA in many complex and critical tasks. Although SA is of great interest as a basic research topic, its applicability to realistic, everyday, yet critical tasks means that it is also of significant relevance in more applied work. This application-inspired perspective has initiated a process that begins with basic research on the nature of SA within a given field of investigation. Thus, much of the basic research has been driven by a desire to improve SA, and subsequently, performance. The research can then be used for developing objective measures that can guide the design and development of equipment, information displays, or training programs aimed at improving SA.

Operationally valid simulations provide an excellent vehicle to support these research and design efforts, particularly for training programs aimed at enhancing SA. Accordingly, the aim in this chapter is to describe how simulations can be employed throughout the process life cycle of training, design, and evaluation. We first provide some background information on the SA construct and the use of simulations in SA research, measurement, and training. We then introduce our structured SA-oriented training development process, including a discussion on basic research and development of measures. We illustrate the application of this process with details from one of our research projects aimed at developing simulation-based SA training for infantry platoon leaders.

SIMULATIONS IN SA RESEARCH, MEASUREMENT, AND TRAINING

Endsley (1995a) formally defines SA as "... the perception of the elements in the environment within a volume of time and space, the comprehension of their meaning and the projection of their status in the near future" (p. 36). This definition encompasses several concepts that are important in understanding the SA construct. First, SA comprises three levels: perception, comprehension, and projection. Level 1 SA, *perception,* involves detecting relevant cues through a variety of ways, including direct observation of the environment or indirect observation by means such as verbal or nonverbal communications and information displays. Level 2 SA, *comprehension,* involves integrating information to understand how it will affect the individual's goals and objectives. This includes developing a comprehensive picture of the world, or of that portion of the world of concern to the individual. Level 3 SA, *projection,* involves extrapolating this information forward in time to determine how it will affect future states of the operational environment. Level 3 SA combines what individuals know about the current situation with their mental models or schemata of similar events to predict what might happen next. For instance, a driver approaching a red light might predict that ignoring the light and proceeding into the intersection would result in a car accident. Thus, mental models help ease the cognitive workload required to develop Level 2 and Level 3 SA.

SA also involves both a temporal and spatial component. Time is an important concept because SA is a dynamic construct, changing at a tempo dictated by the actions of individuals, task characteristics, and the surrounding environment. As new inputs enter the system, the individual incorporates them into this mental representation, making changes as necessary in plans and actions to achieve the desired goals. SA also involves knowledge about the activities and events occurring at a specific location of interest to the individual. Thus, the concept of SA includes perception, comprehension, and projection of situational information, as well as temporal and spatial components.

SIMULATIONS IN SA RESEARCH

There are several reasons for the recent interest in SA as the focus of research efforts. First, it has tremendous relevance to everyday life as it forms the basis for decision making and action. Another reason is that we live in the "information age." In many workplaces, this has meant a huge increase in systems, displays, and technologies. The problem in this environment is no longer lack of information but finding, within the volumes of data available, those precise bits of information that are needed to make an informed, reasoned decision. A widening gap exists between the large volume of data being produced and disseminated and the individual's ability to find the right, disparate bits and process them together to arrive at the actual information being sought. If we examine research on aviation accidents and performance under demanding battlefield conditions, we see that operators have no difficulty physically performing their tasks or choosing the correct action once they understand the situation, but they struggle with developing and maintaining an understanding of the situation (Brezovic, Klein, Calderwood, and Thordsen, 1987; Jones and Endsley, 1996). For this reason, researchers are interested in understanding, evaluating, and improving SA.

However, because of the dynamic and complex operational environments in which it is studied and the inherent dangers that may result from poor decisions that are based on it, SA is often difficult to study in the "wild." Combat settings provide an excellent example of an environment in which information flows very rapidly and combatants must make instantaneous decisions and take action based on incomplete or misleading data. Although combat settings provide a rich domain for the investigation of SA, the criticality of the decisions and the pace, rigors, and hazards of the environment make field investigations problematic. Thus, simulations have done much to advance the study of SA in both basic and applied research because they provide a cost-effective, minimal-risk vehicle for scientific investigation and objective measurement of the construct. Simulations provide a useful medium for studying the formation and development of SA. Specifically, in a simulation setting, SA can be investigated in a controlled environment that provides the needed complexity and dynamicism for its development with minimal risk to the study participants—and researchers!

SIMULATIONS IN SA MEASUREMENT

Simulations are useful not only for studying SA but also for measuring it. Through simulations, one can safely and objectively measure SA in many complex and critical tasks. Although multiple measurements of SA have been developed (Endsley and Garland, 2000), many of the most widely used measurements are subjective, indirect, or performance-based. Such measurements offer tremendous advantages in terms of ease of use and lack of obtrusiveness. However, they often have limited sensitivity to qualitative differences in comparison studies, such as investigating the relative merits of competing design concepts or evaluating the effect of an experimental treatment. Additionally, many users are biased toward familiar concepts and ideas, leading subjective or performance-based measurements to be skewed in favor of familiarity, as opposed to innovation.

The simulated environment allows for objective measurement of SA, which is seldom possible in the real world. Objective measurements provide detailed information that cannot be gained from subjective ones, including a true indication of what the individual has perceived, what they understand about that information, and what they believe is likely to happen because of it. Thus, objective measurements can assess an individual's SA across all three levels, and not just how well they performed on a task or how well they believe they did.

SIMULATIONS IN SA TRAINING

In addition to providing a rich environment for SA research and measurement, simulations can also be used as the "delivery" vehicle for training programs, that is, simulations are also useful in implementing training programs that are geared to enhancing SA. In a simulated environment, events and actions can be carefully scripted to target the desired learning objectives in a systematic manner.

In a simulation, instructors can ensure that each lesson builds on prior lessons and prepares the trainee for upcoming lessons. Once the participant has been trained, the simulated environment can also be used to evaluate the training program's effectiveness.

Simulations provide more than just a controlled environment for training SA. They also have the capability to provide feedback to the participant and researcher as well as allow for the comparison of an individual's performance against "ground truth." During training, it is essential to give trainees an idea of how they are doing and where they need to improve. In addition, simulations mimic the real world, providing task realism to increase the possibility of transfer of training. Further, simulations provide greater and less complex evaluation capabilities than real-world training opportunities. Many simulations even have built-in data recording capabilities to aid evaluation and feedback processes. Finally, simulations are not only cost-effective compared to the real world, they are appealing to users as well. Many simulations provide a game-like interface, which is very motivating to young adults.

As evident from the previous discussion, simulation-based training offers many advantages over traditional classroom instruction. Yet, this begs the question *"Why train SA?"* There are several reasons for the recent interest in training programs targeted at enhancing trainees' SA. First, as discussed earlier in this chapter, SA forms the basis for good decision making and performance in many domains, and lack of it can have dangerous consequences. For example, human error remains the leading cause of transportation accidents. In fact, human error was found to be the cause of 87% of all highway accidents (U.S. Bureau of Transportation, 1997). In general aviation, pilot error was found to be a "broad cause or factor" in 84% of all general aviation accidents and 90.6% of all fatal accidents (Trollip and Jensen, 1991). Many of these human errors can be attributed to poor SA. For example, a study of aviation accidents among major air carriers found that 88% of those involving human error could be attributed to problems with SA (Endsley, 1995c). Therefore, it follows that good SA is a necessary condition for good decision making, and the lack of it can adversely affect outcomes. Thus, the development and validation of methods aimed at training and improving SA is of great interest.

In addition, significant individual differences exist in the degree to which people are able to detect and assimilate information to form a coherent and complete picture of the situation. Although this issue has not been studied in detail across a broad spectrum of domains, as great as a tenfold difference in SA abilities has been found among trained aviators (Endsley and Bolstad, 1994), and anecdotal evidence suggests such differences might exist in other domains as well. A number of factors are likely to contribute to individual differences in SA ability (Endsley et al., 2000). Some may involve basic capability differences such as pattern-matching skills, perceptual speed, spatial ability, and attention sharing. However, significant advantages in SA can be gained through training and experience within the relevant domain. These allow individuals to develop mental models and memory stores that provide rapid real-time pattern matching to perceived information to form the highest levels of SA. Under the strain of high workload conditions, these capabilities are decisive in the individual's ability to gain and maintain SA.

Because an individual's understanding of the situation can never be fully complete, it is important that training programs seeking to enhance SA prepare the trainee to encounter novel and complex events. Simulations provide the opportunity to encounter a broader range of situations and events than would normally be seen in the same time period, thus increasing the trainee's access to mental models of the operational world. Mental models provide a framework that helps the trainee to gain an understanding of the situation more quickly, but training must emphasize determining how well the current situation fits the mental model, thus helping the trainee analyze the situation to determine the critical cues.

Although there have been several programs designed to train SA in nonsimulated environments (Artman, 1999; Endsley and Robertson, 2000a/b), simulator training can capitalize on the dynamic information needs associated with maintaining and developing SA. Many studies have used simulations to measure or evaluate SA as part of their research objectives (Bolstad, Endsley, Howell, and

Costello, 2002; Stark, Comstock, Prinzel, Burdette, and Scerbo, 2001). However, there are far fewer studies that have used simulations as a vehicle for training SA. One reason for this lack of research is the difficulty involved in training a complex and multifaceted construct such as SA. Some studies that have attempted to train SA address only a single component such as pattern recognition (Kass, Herschler, and Companion, 1991) or attention allocation (Tlauka, Stanton, and McKenna, 2000), but developing and maintaining SA is more complex than these skills alone. Therefore, we propose a structured SA-oriented training development process aimed at ensuring that training focuses on the information, skills, and behaviors associated with the development of SA within a domain.

STRUCTURED SA-ORIENTED TRAINING DEVELOPMENT PROCESS

Because the field of SA is relatively new, there are no long-established, standard procedures for developing training programs to improve trainees' SA. Here, we offer the outline of a process that we have used, in various ways, to develop SA training programs for multiple environments (see Figure 7.1). This process can be followed to develop training programs that target the skills and knowledge bases involved in the development of superior SA. We illustrate the six steps in the SA-oriented training development process with an example from our own research, describing the development of a training program to enhance the SA of new infantry platoon leaders who are generally inexperienced officers but lead combat troops. Simulations played a critical role in administering and evaluating this training program.

STEP 1: IDENTIFY DOMAIN-SPECIFIC SA REQUIREMENTS

SA is highly domain-specific; by this we mean that the knowledge and skills necessary to develop superior SA in one domain are generally very different from those in another. Therefore, the first step in developing an SA training program is to conduct some form of requirements analysis to identify the domain-specific dynamic information requirements (i.e., the SA needs) for the position of interest. This analysis guides the development of the training program by focusing attention on those aspects of the situation that are necessary for information dominance in the field. Although this type of research rarely employs simulations, it has been included here because it provides critical information about the nature of SA within the domain as well as the information that will be used to develop domain-specific objective SA measures.

An SA requirements analysis usually employs a combination of cognitive engineering procedures. Expert elicitation, observation of operator task performance, verbal protocols, formal questionnaires, and analysis of written materials and documentation (i.e., training manuals

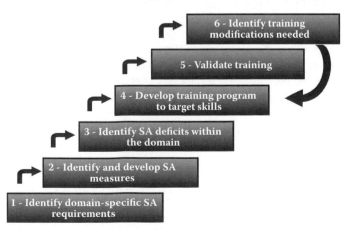

FIGURE 7.1   Structured process for developing an SA-oriented training program.

and checklists) have formed the basis for these analyses. To date, such analyses have been completed for many domains including fighter pilots (Endsley, 1993), bomber pilots (Endsley, 1989), TRACON (Terminal Radar Approach Control) ATC (Endsley and Jones, 1995), infantry platoon leaders (Strater, Endsley, Pleban, and Matthews, 2000), army brigade-level officers (Bolstad, Riley, Jones, and Endsley, 2002), and two positions in a shipboard command information center (CIC; Strater, Endsley, and Plott, 2004; Strater and Endsley, 2005).

Frequently, the problem of determining which aspects of the situation are important for a particular operator's SA has been approached using a form of cognitive task analysis called Goal-Directed Task Analysis (GDTA). In such an analysis, the major goals of a particular position are identified, along with the subgoals that are necessary for meeting each goal. For each subgoal, the major decisions to be made or questions to be answered are identified. The SA needs for making these decisions and carrying out each subgoal are subsequently determined (Endsley, Bolte, and Jones, 2003). By focusing on goals rather than tasks, this methodology seeks to identify the information needs directly without considering how the operator will acquire the information, as the method may change from one operator to another or as new technologies may be fielded. In addition, goals form the basis for decision making in many complex environments. Finally, the GDTA seeks to determine the ideal information needs of the operator, or everything the operator would want to know, rather than just the information that can be gained from existing technologies and information sources.

For example, for our GDTA of infantry platoon leaders, the overall goal hierarchy listed "Attack, Secure, and Hold Terrain" as the overarching objective. This was then broken down into seven primary goals, with secondary goals and subgoals under each that may be employed to meet the mission objectives. For each subgoal, some of the questions the platoon leader would consider were listed, followed by the SA elements necessary to answer these questions. Figure 7.2 illustrates the SA requirements for goal 1.1—Avoid enemy detection (Matthews, Strater, and Endsley, 2004). Beneath this secondary goal are three subgoals: 1.1.1—Project enemy behavior, 1.1.2—Avoid danger areas, and 1.1.3—Utilize available cover and concealment. A complete explanation of the goal hierarchy can be found in Strater et al. (2000).

STEP 2: IDENTIFY AND DEVELOP SA MEASURES

Before developing training programs, it is critical to identify appropriate measures to assess the effectiveness of the training. Because SA is a multivariate construct, training programs could conceivably improve SA along one parameter, such as knowledge for enemy locations, while producing poorer SA for other parameters. Thus, sensitive, valid, and reliable measures are needed to determine the full impact of the training program on trainee SA.

SA measures can be broadly classified into five basic types (for more detailed information on SA measures, see Endsley and Garland, 2000). *Process indices* examine how individuals process their environment, such as using eye-tracking devices or investigating communications patterns. In contrast, *performance measures* attempt to "infer" SA from the end result—for instance, based on the assumption that if more kills are scored, SA must have been higher. Similarly, *behavioral measures* also try to "infer" SA from the actions that individuals choose to take, based on the assumption that good actions will follow from good SA and vice versa. More directly, *subjective measures* assess SA by asking individuals to rate their SA on a scale; these subjective estimations may be made by the individuals themselves or by experienced observers. *Objective measures* also directly assess SA, but in this case, an individual's perceptions of the environment are compared to some "ground truth" reality.

In general, we prefer to use direct measures of SA for establishing baseline performance, identifying differences in SA of novices and experts, evaluating competing design concepts, and assessing the impact of training programs. Aside from the fact that inferred measures of SA are fairly circular in logic and therefore, more problematic to employ in developing an understanding of SA

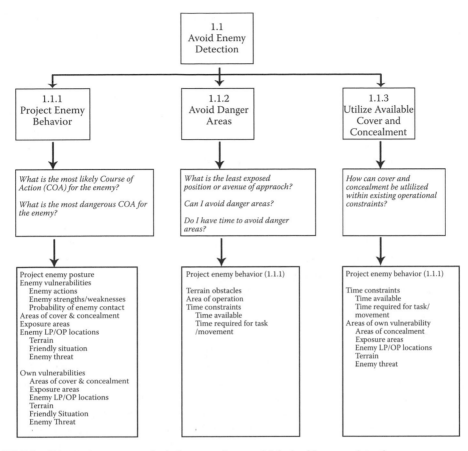

FIGURE 7.2   SA requirements analysis for secondary goal 1.1. Avoid enemy detection.

within a domain, direct measures provide far more detail about the SA construct itself, which is useful in these endeavors.

Although subjective measures of SA are attractive in that they are easy to administer, several limitations should be noted regarding this approach to assessing SA. Individuals making subjective assessments of their own SA are often unaware of some information (e.g., there is an enemy just over the next hill). Subjective measures also tend to be global in nature and, as such, do not fully exploit the multivariate nature of SA to provide the detailed diagnostics available with objective measures. For our infantry studies, we adopted a subjective self-rated measure of SA, the Mission Awareness Rating Scale (MARS), developed specifically for use in infantry field studies (Matthews, Beal, and Pleban, 2002). MARS provides a subjective self-evaluation of the perception, comprehension, and projection elements of SA and knowledge of how to achieve mission goals, as well as the mental effort required for each.

For our infantry studies, we developed a Situation Awareness Behaviorally Anchored Rating Scale (SABARS) based on the SA requirements analysis, comprising 27 items of key observable behaviors related to developing SA in a Military Operations on Urban Terrain (MOUT) environment, such as communicating clearly with higher echelons, subordinates, and adjacent units. A final query regarding the platoon leader's overall SA was added, for a total of 28 items. Each item was rated on a five-point scale, ranging from *very poor* to *very good,* by a trained observer/controller experienced in the domain (Strater et al., 2000).

Objective measures collect data from the individual on his or her perceptions of the situation and compare them to what is actually happening to score the accuracy of SA at a given moment in time. This type of assessment provides a direct measure of SA and does not require participants or observers to make judgments about situational knowledge based on incomplete information. Objective measures can be gathered in one of three ways: real time (during simulations), during interruptions in the simulation, or after the test (following task performance).

One common approach to objectively measuring SA is the Situation Awareness Global Assessment Technique (SAGAT; Endsley, 1988b, 1995b). Using SAGAT, a simulated exercise is frozen at randomly selected times, information sources (e.g., communication channels, virtual displays) are blanked, and the exercise is suspended while participants quickly answer questions about their current perceptions of the situation. These responses are compared to "ground truth" to provide an objective, unbiased assessment of SA. Because of the necessity of freezing the action and blanking information displays, SAGAT is particularly well suited for simulation-based studies.

For our infantry studies, a SAGAT version was developed that utilizes a customizable PC-based computer program that presents 21 standard queries targeting assessment of all three levels of SA (perception, comprehension, and projection) at discrete points in time. Queries addressed major SA issues such as locations of strongest and weakest enemies and friendly forces, number of casualties suffered by the officer's platoon, and expected enemy and civilian actions over the next five minutes. An example of a SAGAT query screen is shown in Figure 7.3 (Strater et al., 2000). The questions identified in the SA requirements analysis described earlier in the chapter formed the question pool for development of the measures used in our infantry studies.

STEP 3: IDENTIFY SA DEFICITS WITHIN THE DOMAIN

After identifying the SA requirements and developing appropriate measures, the next step is to determine where training can best be applied to improve SA. Here, we employed the following three-part strategy for meeting this objective: (1) analysis of existing research and training literature to identify factors associated with high and low SA, (2) a survey of experienced trainers in the domain to define key SA problem areas and skill deficiencies, and (3) further analysis of existing data to determine linkages between SA and decision making. By identifying areas of low SA within

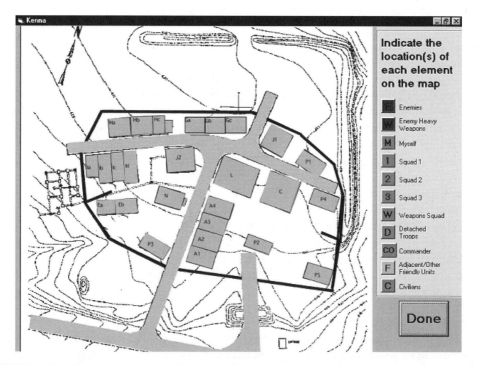

FIGURE 7.3   Infantry platoon leader SAGAT: sample query.

the domain, we can selectively target our training on those abilities where improvement is most critically needed. Each component of this strategy will be described, showing how we utilized this approach to identify SA deficits within the infantry domain.

Analysis of Existing Research and Training Literature

First, SA training should incorporate the results of existing research on SA. Much of the available research on SA has been conducted in the aviation arena. Although the SA requirements of a pilot who relies heavily on cockpit instrumentation for information vary greatly from the SA requirements of an infantry platoon leader, it is plausible that many of the general findings will have validity in both situations. A literature review identified six general principles believed to be highly relevant in many domains (Strater, Jones, and Endsley, 2001).

Principle 1: Emphasis on planning and preparation—Pre-mission planning provides a critical framework for SA, creating expectations to which future events and environmental features are matched. Prince and Salas (1998) found that experienced pilots completed more thorough preflight preparation than less experienced pilots. Similarly, Serfaty, Macmillan, Entin, and Entin (1997) found that expert battlefield planners did not develop their plans more quickly than novices, but rather investigated the situation carefully, seeking more information prior to developing their plans. Improvements in the planning process could then be expected to produce not only enhanced SA, but also better decision making.

Principle 2: Focus on higher levels of SA—Some studies have shown that experts and novices may focus most of their attention on different levels of SA. For example, experts attend more to context (Level 2), whereas novices concentrate on surface cues (Level 1; Federico, 1995). In a study of decision making in armored units, Brezovic, Klein, Calderwood, and Thordsen (1987) found that students in an armored officer basic course noticed the same cues as the instructors training the course but were unable to draw accurate inferences from those cues. The ability to interpret and understand cues is a vital skill in developing higher-level SA and in guiding decision making and action.

Principle 3: Thorough information gathering—Orasanu and Fischer (1997) found that better-performing flightcrews spent more time gathering information to aid in decision making, whereas poorer-performing crews quickly moved to option comparisons. Cohen, Thompson, Adelman, Bresnick, and Riedel (1999) found that experts spend more time verifying their findings than novices, who are more likely to make decisions based on initial information. These findings suggest that the ability to monitor assumptions and identify errors is a key skill in maintaining high levels of SA.

Principle 4: Task management and prioritization—Interruptions, task-related and other distractions, and overall workload pose a high threat to SA. Good task management strategies appear to be critical to dealing with these problems. For example, Schutte and Trujillo (1996) found that the best-performing teams in nonnormal situations were those that employed a task management prioritization strategy based on perceived task criticality. Both an event-driven, or interrupt-driven, strategy (dealing with each interruption as it came up) and a procedural-based strategy produced poorer performance. The ability to accurately assess the importance and severity of events and tasks allows individuals to actively manage their work flow to avoid situations in which they are overloaded and potentially miss critical information.

Principle 5: Contingency planning—Contingency planning has been noted to be a critical skill that can lead to high levels of SA (Endsley, 1988a, 1995a). Amalberti and Deblon (1992) found that a significant portion of experienced pilots' time was spent in anticipating possible future occurrences. Experienced pilots also appear to spend significant time in active contingency planning in flight (Serfaty et al., 1997), which serves to reduce workload during critical events. Using projection skills (Level 3 SA), these pilots are able to actively seek important information in advance of a known immediate need for it and thus plan for various contingencies.

Principle 6: Pattern comparison and contrast—Although experts are able to perform pattern matching to situations previously encountered, they rarely rely on simple pattern matching, but use it as a tool to guide their understanding of the situation. Experts look at a situation to determine how it differs from a mental model or a pattern previously encountered. Calderwood, Crandall, and Baynes (1988) found that once experts have generated a course of action (COA), they look for information that contraindicates their COA; in contrast, novices seek information that confirms their COA as the best choice. Although pattern matching provides the opportunity to more quickly understand a situation, matching information to the wrong pattern can be difficult to correct. In one study, after researchers intentionally induced application of an erroneous model, conflicting information was presented (Jones, 1997). Only 35% of these conflicting cues resulted in detection of the false model. SA training, therefore, should not only include opportunities to develop exposure to patterns of action and behavior but should also intentionally vary the patterns to aid operators in identifying critical cues in each situation.

Survey of Key SA Skills

In addition to analyzing existing research, it is essential to solicit input from experienced operators or trainers in the targeted domain. To support the development of our infantry SA training program, a survey was developed and distributed to both commissioned and noncommissioned officers who train platoon leaders (Strater, Jones, and Endsley, 2001). Survey respondents were asked to identify, for each activity, whether it (1) was not a major SA problem, (2) caused moderate SA problems, or (3) caused frequent SA problems for new platoon leaders.

Survey results indicated the following as causing frequent SA problems: (1) failure to communicate key information to other platoons, (2) failure to determine the location of the opposing forces' direct or indirect fire support, (3) failure to determine the location of the opposing forces' heavy weapons, and (4) poor time management. Results also indicated two major Level 1 SA problem areas for new platoon leaders: communications and information gathering on the combat readiness of the opposing force. At the higher levels of SA, new platoon leaders failed to understand the implications of information about the enemy (Level 2 SA) and had difficulty projecting a possible enemy COA, as well as their disposition around heavy weapons (Level 3 SA).

In addition to these areas, several other specific items were identified as being major problem areas where targeted training could produce improvements in SA. Of all the items on the survey, time management was found to be the most problematic, closely followed by task prioritization. Attentional narrowing was another frequent problem; others included not assembling bits of information together into a coherent picture, not specifying an alternate COA, and poor contingency planning. These results coincide with the findings from other domains and indicate several areas where training intervention could be useful for enhancing platoon leader SA.

Investigation of Existing Research Data for Linkages between SA and Decision Making

Where research has already been conducted within the domain, results of this research needs to be leveraged for inclusion in the training effort. Often, supplemental data analysis can be conducted that may provide insights into how SA develops and how experienced leaders employ the information available. An initial study of platoon leader SA found that more experienced leaders were significantly better than less experienced ones at identifying locations of both the enemy and units of their own platoon on a map (Strater et al., 2000). Specifically, their Level 1 SA was better for both the enemy and their own platoon elements. Their Level 2 and 3 SA were better only for enemy units, particularly in identifying the highest threat and the strongest enemy location. In contrast, less experienced officers were better at identifying the strongest friendly location (Level 2 SA). As higher levels of SA require cognitive effort and focused attention, this result indicates that more experienced officers focused greater processing effort on the enemy, whereas less experienced officers focused greater processing effort on their own troops, which corresponds with information from the training survey that indicates this is a problem area for new platoon leaders.

The SAGAT and SABARS data were analyzed in detail to determine which SA elements might be most important for good infantry decision making and performance. These data were subjected to a detailed comparison with decision data collected during the same study (Pleban, Eakin, Salter, and Matthews, 2001). Decision data were grouped into seven categories: Communicates to Commander, Allocates Personnel Appropriately, Requires Communication from Platoon, Coordinates with other Platoons, Conducts Unforecasted Action, Provides Orders to Platoon, and Follows Commander's Orders.

Several intriguing results were found in this analysis. First, leaders who merely possessed good Level 1 SA were more likely to follow procedures and communicate to the commander as expected, whereas leaders with good Level 2 and 3 SA were less likely to communicate with the commander, perhaps indicating either a higher confidence in their own judgments or a false sense of security. Leaders were less likely to require communication from the platoon if they knew the location of exposed units within the platoon (Level 2 SA). Once again, this indicates a higher confidence in their knowledge. Leaders were more likely to take an action not anticipated by scenario developers if they accurately knew the number of casualties (Level 1 SA), could predict the next civilian action (Level 3 SA), and knew who had the advantage in the situation (Level 2 SA), which may indicate that leaders with better SA across levels are more innovative and able to think beyond traditional ideas and strategies.

Finally, failure to provide orders to the platoon as expected was predicted by accurate knowledge of who had the advantage in the situation and which friendly positions were exposed to enemy fire (Level 2 SA), as well as inaccurate knowledge of those not in communication (Level 1 SA). In other words, it appears that leaders with better Level 2 SA (comprehension) but poorer Level 1 SA (perception) were worse at providing complete and accurate orders to their own platoon. Again, this finding indicates that leaders with better SA at the comprehension and projection levels (Level 2 and 3 SA) were less likely to conduct the expected actions in the prescribed manner. Whether this outcome reflects an overconfidence in their abilities and those of their team, or whether these individuals have additional skills in monitoring the situation which extend beyond the bounds of the expected observable behaviors is unknown. Nonetheless, these findings implicate key areas where training may improve communications and information flow in infantry operations.

STEP 4: DEVELOP TRAINING PROGRAM TO TARGET SELECTED SKILLS

Once SA deficits and opportunities have been identified, one can begin to design a training program to teach the targeted skills. Fundamental to the acquisition of SA is an array of individual factors. In training, it is the individual factors that are modified, the means by which the various other inputs to the system are shaped by the individual's abilities, experience, and expectations. SA training strives to modify these initial individual factors and, thus, enhance the information processing capabilities of the trainee by providing experiences and opportunities for the development of a richer understanding of the operational environment. Therefore, training SA should be directed at increasing the rate at which an individual's abilities, experience, and expectations develop. Key mechanisms identified to increase SA include pattern matching to schema and mental models for higher levels of SA, development of automaticity in physical skills, and effective use of goal-directed processing, as well as higher-level metacognitive skills involving the development of accurate expectations (through premission planning), contingency planning, and self-checking. These coping mechanisms ease the individual's cognitive demands, reducing information overload through processes such as automaticity and pattern matching.

In addition, research on the implementation of training programs must inform the development process also. For example, Ross, Pierce, and Baehr (1999) investigated fire-support training and found that just introducing new technologies into existing curricula was not sufficient to improve training. Learning is facilitated through realistic experiences in which trainees are required to solve inherently intriguing problems. The trainee must be cognitively immersed in the challenge of the scenario for true learning to occur. Again, this supports the notion of simulations as an excellent venue for training delivery.

For the infantry platoon leader trainee, the specific skills we targeted for improvement included time management, task prioritization, communications, contingency planning, and schema development to enhance pattern-matching skills. As will be described next, two scenario-based computer simulation training modules (SA Planner and SA Trainer) were developed for this Infantry Situation Awareness Training (ISAT) program.

SA Planner

The first area targeted for improving SA in infantry operations was assessing time requirements and prioritization for tasks. The SA Planner employs interactive scenarios within the context of an Operation Order (OPORD) with associated graphics. The platoon leader identifies necessary mission tasks, places sequential tasks in order, determines time and personnel requirements, and identifies tasks critical to mission success. At the end of each screen, feedback is given and the platoon leader corrects mistakes. Time is a critical element in many infantry missions. ISAT provides the opportunity to hone skills in time estimation and prioritization, which allows the platoon leader to determine how much time to allot to each task.

SA Trainer

The SA Trainer is an interactive, scenario-based simulation that allows the soldier to deploy troops inside his or her area of operations (AO). When an event is triggered, the platoon leader selects actions from a menu (see Figure 7.4). Critical cues are provided by means of soldier

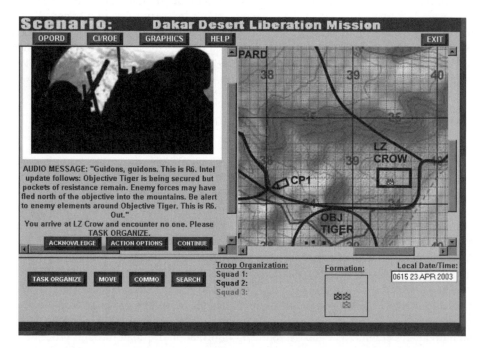

FIGURE 7.4   SA Trainer: sample program screen.

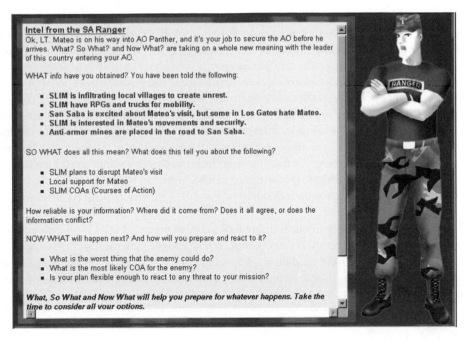

Intel from the SA Ranger
Ok, LT. Mateo is on his way into AO Panther, and it's your job to secure the AO before he arrives. What? So What? and Now What? are taking on a whole new meaning with the leader of this country entering your AO.

WHAT info have you obtained? You have been told the following:

- SLIM is infiltrating local villages to create unrest.
- SLIM have RPGs and trucks for mobility.
- San Saba is excited about Mateo's visit, but some in Los Gatos hate Mateo.
- SLIM is interested in Mateo's movements and security.
- Anti-armor mines are placed in the road to San Saba.

SO WHAT does all this mean? What does this tell you about the following?

- SLIM plans to disrupt Mateo's visit
- Local support for Mateo
- SLIM COAs (Courses of Action)

How reliable is your information? Where did it come from? Does it all agree, or does the information conflict?

NOW WHAT will happen next? And how will you prepare and react to it?

- What is the worst thing that the enemy could do?
- What is the most likely COA for the enemy?
- Is your plan flexible enough to react to any threat to your mission?

What, So What and Now What will help you prepare for whatever happens. Take the time to consider all your options.

FIGURE 7.5 SA Trainer: sample post-SAGAT SA ranger feedback.

reports, civilian queries, and graphical pop-ups of photo or video cues (e.g., cigarette butts and trampled grass).

Three scenarios were developed for the SA Trainer, and all are sufficiently complex that they can be repeated for additional training benefit. By repeating scenarios, the trainee can learn from prior mistakes, identify the important cues, and understand what they mean. The SA Trainer instructs the platoon leader to think of the three levels of SA in terms of

- *What?*—What did I see, hear, etc.? (Level 1 SA)
- *So what?*—What does it mean for my mission? (Level 2 SA)
- *Now what?*—What does it indicate might happen next? (Level 3 SA)

Thus, the program provides feedback and encourages a mindset to question and critically evaluate information.

In addition to this experiential learning, at periodic intervals the scenario is halted and SAGAT is administered. At the end of each SAGAT halt, feedback is provided on what is happening and what the soldier should consider. Inside this feedback screen are bulleted points with data that the soldier has acquired. The program emphasizes that these are not facts but information to evaluate. A sample screen of this feedback is shown in Figure 7.5.

The SA Trainer provides exposure to a variety of scenarios to allow the platoon leader to gain experience in detecting significant cues and identifying prototypical situations. While allowing the platoon leader to focus on these goals, training on contingency planning and communication skills are introduced gradually, with little emphasis in Scenario 1, more emphasis in Scenario 2, and heavy emphasis in Scenario 3.

STEP 5: VALIDATE TRAINING PROGRAMS

Training program validation is an important step in the process. Techniques developed for training SA must be carefully tested and evaluated to determine their effectiveness. In particular, control groups should be employed to determine whether the training programs and concepts employed have the desired effect. Furthermore, because SA is a complex, multivariate construct, validation testing should employ measures that investigate SA across a range of requirements and that are sensitive to changes in any parameter. For instance, a training program could be developed that would help novice platoon leaders focus more attentional effort on what the enemy might be doing. If the platoon leader's SA for future enemy actions improved after training but declined for friendly actions, the overall effect might not be desirable. Because attention is a limited resource, care must be taken to determine the full impact of any attentional reallocation resulting from the training. This is an important issue that can often be overlooked. The degree to which trained skills in developing SA translate into improved performance must also be assessed in conjunction with other measures. Performance can be impacted by far more than just SA; thus, good performance is not necessarily indicative of good SA, neither is poor performance always proof of poor SA.

We applied this critical step in our training development process to the ISAT program by conducting validation testing of the SA Trainer during combat fatigue field exercises in Norway (Strater et al., 2004). The purpose of this validation study was to determine the effectiveness of transfer of simulation-based training to task performance in a real-world field exercise. Details of this study are presented next.

Participants

Eighty cadets from the Royal Norwegian Naval Academy were divided into four platoons that were subdivided into ten assigned squads. Two platoons comprised two squads and the other two, three squads. Half the squads were randomly selected to receive the SA Trainer CDs. Each day, one platoon participated in the test scenario, conducting an assault as two squads. So, when a platoon with three squads participated, the three squads were reorganized, at the cadets' discretion, into two squads. Unlike in the U.S. system, cadets in Norwegian military academies are generally experienced personnel with prior military service; however, as naval personnel, were not generally experienced in infantry operations. In the training exercise selected for testing, the cadets functioned as infantry war fighters.

Materials and Procedure

Two weeks prior to the field exercises, training CDs were distributed to all cadets in the selected squads. Cadets were asked to complete each scenario at least once and encouraged to repeat scenarios. A two-hour group training session was conducted immediately before the exercises to insure that all trained cadets received a minimum level of training. Mean reported training time was 2.7 hours, with a low of 20 minutes from a cadet who missed the group training session to a high of 8 hours.

During the exercises, cadets embarked upon a series of combat missions within the context of a multinational effort to eliminate guerilla forces from an allied country. In the test scenario, squads conducted a coordinated assault to eliminate two suspected Special Forces camps, which were actually civilian refugee camps with tents, clothes hung on trees, and cooking fires. When the cadets arrived at the camp, the "refugees" were cooking, talking, laughing, and listening to music on the radio. In short, they did not behave like Special Forces. Cadets either attacked as ordered, or refused to attack and entered the camp.

A paper-and-pencil SAGAT-like questionnaire was administered twice during the mission, first on landing in the area, then again on mission completion, prior to an After Action Review (AAR). Unlike a traditional SAGAT, the requested information was not removed, but cadets were asked to answer the questions from memory only, without referring to notes, maps, etc. With the final SAGAT, the MARS (Matthews et al., 2002) was also administered.

TABLE 7.1

ANOVA and Means for Selected SAGAT Queries

SAGAT Query	F	p	Mean Percent Correct	
			Trained	Untrained
What is your current grid location?	8.700	0.005	0.000	0.187
How many enemies are within 500 m of your location?	4.110	0.048	0.108	0.299
What is your mission?	2.931	0.093	0.785	0.711
What will the enemy do next?	2.719	0.105	0.406	0.224

Note: $N = 50$

Results

SAGAT data was collected from only 50 of the 80 cadets, including 28 cadets in the SA training condition. Differences between the trained and untrained group were found on four of seven scored queries. Significant or near-significant differences are shown in Table 7.1. Untrained cadets performed better at identifying their location and the number of enemy soldiers within 500 m (both Level 1 SA). In contrast, trained cadets were better at identifying the mission type (Level 2 SA) and predicting what the enemy would do next (Level 3 SA).

With regard to the subjective assessment of SA, MARS data showed no significant differences between trained and untrained cadets' ratings of the quality of their SA but revealed differences between their ratings of the effort required. Specifically, trained cadets reported a mean effort to predict what would happen next of 3.25 (where 4 is very difficult and 1 is very easy), whereas the mean effort for untrained cadets was 2.33 (see Table 7.2). Trained cadets also reported expending more effort to achieve mission goals.

In terms of task performance, of eight assaulting squads, only two correctly refused to assault the refugee camp. One successful squad was entirely composed of SA-trained cadets, whereas the other successful squad was a mixed squad with both trained and untrained cadets. Squad leaders, however, for both successful squads were trained. Although encouraging, this difference was not statistically significant ($p = .23$).

Discussion

The acquisition of superior SA is a complicated process for infantry war fighters. Initial intelligence, as well as intelligence updates from a number of sources, must be integrated with directly observed information. Overall, there were indications of training effects. Trained cadets led both squads that successfully refused to assault the refugee camps. However, tremendous pressure was placed on them to assault the camps even when they reported that these were not Special Forces camps. This suggests that refusal to attack may indicate confidence in SA, rather than SA itself. The mixed SAGAT results, where some questions were more accurately answered by untrained cadets,

TABLE 7.2

ANOVA and Means for Selected MARS Items

MARS Item	F	p	Mean Values	
			Trained	Untrained
Difficulty (mental effort) predicting what will occur next	9.047	0.004	3.250	2.333
Difficulty (mental effort) deciding how best to achieve mission goals	5.622	0.021	2.750	2.500

Note: $N = 70$

whereas trained cadets more accurately answered others, could merely be a product of the limited sample size. It may be relevant that untrained cadets had better SA for two Level 1 SA queries, whereas trained cadets had better SA for two higher-level SA queries. The MARS data provides the clearest support for a training effect. Trained cadets reported that it was somewhat more difficult to predict what would occur. They also employed more mental effort to determine how to best achieve their goals.

These findings are consistent with the purpose behind the SA Trainer, namely, to teach platoon leaders to think about SA and focus on the necessary steps to developing SA in the field. Training cadets to actively engage the environment to seek out needed information increases the cognitive demands on them to analyze the situation; however, this is a necessary process for the development of superior SA. With increased experience, these processes can become more automatic. Interestingly, although trained cadets reported having to work harder to gain Level 3 SA and determine how to best achieve their goals, they did not report a corresponding increase in the quality of their SA, indicating that the training had not resulted in overconfidence. It should also be noted that a training time of 2.7 hours may be insufficient for the development of schemata and mental models that produce automaticity. Nevertheless, if limited training can produce greater efforts on the part of the trainees to consider the implications of information they have received, it demonstrates that simulation-based training programs can be used to aid development of the skills necessary to gain and maintain the higher levels of SA.

STEP 6: IDENTIFY TRAINING MODIFICATIONS NEEDED

Developing a training program to improve SA is an iterative process. Results of testing give program developers valuable information on what parts of the program are successful, as well as those portions that are less effective. This information is then used to improve the training program to better target the desired skills.

For example, in the development cycle of our ISAT program, early testing of the SA Trainer by both cadets and instructors at the U.S. Military Academy at West Point yielded much useful feedback. Participants indicated that too many steps were necessary to acknowledge a message. This complaint was addressed by placing the Acknowledge Message button at the bottom of the screen, so it is immediately available when a message appears. Also, as participants wanted to be able to select several actions at once, the program was altered to allow selection of several communication items (i.e., relay message to platoon sergeant, squad leaders, and adjacent platoons, as well as send situation report [SITREP]). However, the sequential nature of other actions dictates that they must be selected individually. For instance, if you see a civilian and select "Kill," and then select "Question," the dead civilian will be unable to respond. Changes made to the SA Trainer after the usability testing resulted in a final program that was easier for trainees to use.

GENERAL DISCUSSION AND IMPLICATIONS FOR FUTURE RESEARCH

Determining which areas or components should be included in SA training programs involves gaining a better understanding of the domain of interest and how SA plays a role in such an environment. This chapter presented a six-step process for developing programs to target the skills and knowledge bases necessary for the development of superior SA and are summarized as follows:

- *Step 1: Identify domain-specific SA requirements*—A variety of methods can be used for this analysis, including expert elicitation, direct observation of domain tasks, analysis of manuals and checklists, and cognitive task analysis methodologies such as GDTA.
- *Step 2: Identify and develop SA measures*—These include process indices, indirect behavioral and performance measures, and direct subjective and objective measures. Metric

selection decisions should balance ease of implementation against the level of detail, accuracy, and specificity needed to establish training effectiveness.

- *Step 3: Identify SA deficits within the domain*—A variety of techniques can be effectively employed to determine SA deficits, including instigating a research investigation to identify differences between those with good and poor SA, analyzing existing research and training data, surveys, and analysis of SA errors within the domain.
- *Step 4: Develop training programs to target selected skills*—SA training attempts to influence the individual's knowledge bases, skills, and cognitive coping mechanisms to enable them to more effectively develop SA. Key skills targeted generally include communication and team processes, and key mechanisms include pattern matching and improved schemata and mental models.
- *Step 5: Validate training programs*—Validation is critical to insure that training programs impart the desired skills and produce the anticipated results. Because it is a multivariate construct, care must be taken to employ measures that are sensitive to changes in the diverse parameters that comprise SA.
- *Step 6: Identify training modifications needed*—The development of training programs that target complex skills such as SA is an iterative process. Results of early testing should be incorporated into the training program to produce a final product capable of more effectively improving SA.

We have successfully demonstrated the generalizability of our structured SA-oriented training development process to other domains. For example, guided by this process, we developed and tested an SA training program for general aviation pilots (see Bolstad, Endsley, Howell, and Coste, 2002). The program comprised six different training modules designed to teach skills that underlie the development of good SA: checklist completion, ATC comprehension, psychomotor skills, time-sharing, contingency planning, and preflight planning. Each module was evaluated in terms of its ability to improve knowledge of the training material, situation awareness, and performance in general aviation flying. Overall, the modules were shown to be somewhat successful in improving these fundamental skills, leading to greater knowledge of checklists, improved reaction time in responding to ATC clearances, and improved performance on a psychomotor tracking task. The time-sharing training module improved participants' ability to perform four tasks concurrently. The preflight and contingency planning training modules led to some improvement in planning performance. Results also provided limited support to the effect of the training modules in improving SA.

The aforementioned research described a training program for improving an individual's SA. Equally important is developing training programs to enhance SA at the team level. However, training team SA is not as simple as having every team member train with the individual SA program. Team SA is more complex and requires training such skills as coordination and information sharing. A team SA program needs to train both individual- and team-level processes (Endsley, 1995a). To date, very few programs have been developed for training team SA. One notable example is a course developed for training team SA in the aviation maintenance environment. Based on a detailed analysis of the SA requirements of maintenance technicians and the interactions between the various teams involved in aircraft maintenance, the course featured modules in crew resource management (CRM) review, shared mental models, verbalization of decisions, shift meetings and teamwork, feedback, and factors that have an impact on SA. Implemented at a major airline, early results from the program showed that 89% of the recipients viewed it as either useful or very useful, and 83% reported a moderate or large change in their behavior on the job (Endsley and Robertson, 2000b).

Although this study demonstrated that some aspects of team SA can be trained, programs for training team SA are much more complex than training targeted at individual SA. As with individual SA, team SA is not static but results from the recurrent system of seeking, sharing, and processing information that takes place within a team (Salas, Prince, Baker, and Shrestha, 1995). Because of this, to enhance team SA, training needs to focus on complex communication behaviors and team planning. This can be accomplished by systematically exposing the team to a variety of scenarios in which they must work dynamically together to assign workload and tasks (Salas et al., 1995). Simulations, therefore, also provide a useful vehicle for training team as well as individual SA by providing the needed realism to train these critical team processes.

CONCLUSION

Given its dynamic, multivariate nature, there is no one clear method for training SA that is applicable to all domains. One approach may focus on first evaluating ways in which SA errors occur and then developing training programs designed to prevent these errors. Other techniques may involve identifying the cognitive components underlying the development and maintenance of SA and then creating programs to train these essential core skills. Still more comprehensive methods may seek to identify and evaluate individuals classified as having higher levels of SA and develop programs that leverage on these expert skills. Finally, the requirements for training team SA will be different from training SA at the individual level. Notwithstanding which approach is adopted, simulations can be used to support these efforts by offering training programs the capability to focus on targeted learning objectives, provide trainees with tailored feedback, incorporate task realism into the training, evaluate training effectiveness, maintain cost effectiveness, and increase trainee motivation. Furthermore, regardless of which training method or technique is employed, key to the success of any program aimed at enhancing SA will be to select skill areas that are most receptive to training and that provide the most benefits to the end user, as well as employing a multifaceted approach to evaluating training effectiveness. The SA-oriented training development process described in this chapter is well suited to guide training designers in achieving this objective.

ACKNOWLEDGMENTS

Work on this chapter was partially supported through participation in the Advanced Decision Architectures Collaborative Technology Alliance (ADA CTA) sponsored by the U.S. Army Research Laboratory (ARL) under Cooperative Agreement DAAD19-01-2-0009. The views and conclusions contained herein, however, are those of the authors and should not be interpreted as representing the official policies, either expressed or implied, of the ARL, U.S. Army, U.S. Government, or the organizations with which the authors are affiliated.

The authors would also like to gratefully acknowledge the support of Haydee M. Cuevas, Ph.D., for her assistance in organizing and editing this chapter.

REFERENCES

Amalberti, R. and Deblon, F. 1992. Cognitive modeling of fighter aircraft process control: a step towards an intelligent on-board assistance system, *International Journal of Man-Machine Systems*, 36: 639–671.
Artman, H. 1999. Situation awareness and co-operation within and between hierarchical units in dynamic decision making, *Ergonomics*, 42(11): 1404–1417.
Bolstad, C. A., Endsley, M. R., Howell, C. D., and Costello, A. M. 2002. General aviation pilot training for situation awareness: an evaluation, paper presented at the Human Factors and Ergonomics Society 46th Annual Meeting, Baltimore, MD, October 2002.
Bolstad, C. A., Riley, J. M., Jones, D. G., and Endsley, M. R. 2002. Using goal directed task analysis with Army brigade officer teams, paper presented at the Human Factors and Ergonomics Society 46th Annual Meeting, Baltimore, MD, October 2002.
Brezovic, C. P., Klein, G. A., Calderwood, R., and Thordsen, M. 1987. Decision Making in Armored Platoon Command (Prepared under contract MDA903-85-C-0327 for U.S. Army Research Institute, Alexandria, VA (KATR-858(B)-87-05F), Yellow Springs, OH: Klein Associates Inc.

Calderwood, R., Crandall, B. W., and Baynes, T. H. 1988. Protocol Analysis of Expert/Novice Command Decision Making During Simulated Fire Ground Incidents, in Klein and Calderwood, 1996, ARI Research Note 96-43, Yellow Springs, OH: Klein Associates Inc.

Cohen, M. S., Thompson, B. B., Adelman, L., Bresnick, T. A., and Riedel, S. L. 1999. Training Battlefield Critical Thinking and Initiative (Prepared under contract DASW01-97-C-0038 ARI Research Note 2000-01), Arlington, VA: U.S. Army Research Institute for the Behavioral and Social Sciences.

Collier, S. G. and Folleso, K. 1995. SACRI: A measure of situation awareness for nuclear power plant control rooms, in D.J. Garland and M. R. Endsley (Eds.), *Experimental Analysis and Measurement of Situation Awareness*, Daytona Beach, FL: Embry-Riddle University Press.

Endsley, M. R. 1988a. Design and evaluation for situation awareness enhancement, *Human Factors Society 32nd Annual Meeting,* Vol. 1: 97–101, Santa Monica, CA: Human Factors Society.

Endsley, M. R. 1988b. Situation Awareness Global Assessment Technique (SAGAT), paper presented at the National Aerospace and Electronics Conference (NAECON), New York.

Endsley, M. R. 1989. *Final report: Situation Awareness in an Advanced Strategic Mission* (NOR DOC 89-32), Hawthorne, CA: Northrop Corporation.

Endsley, M. R. 1993. A survey of situation awareness requirements in air-to-air combat fighters, *International Journal of Aviation Psychology*, 3(2): 157–168.

Endsley, M. R. 1995a. Toward a theory of situation awareness in dynamic systems, *Human Factors*, 37(1): 32–64.

Endsley, M. R. 1995b. Measurement of situation awareness in dynamic systems, *Human Factors*, 37(1): 65–84.

Endsley, M. R. 1995c. A taxonomy of situation awareness errors, in R. Fuller, N. Johnston, and N. McDonald (Eds.), *Human Factors in Aviation Operations*, Aldershot, England: Avebury Aviation, Ashgate Publishing, Ltd.

Endsley, M. R. and Bolstad, C. A. 1994. Individual differences in pilot situation awareness, *International Journal of Aviation Psychology*, 4(3): 241–264.

Endsley, M. R., Bolte, B., and Jones, D. G. 2003 *Designing for Situation Awareness: An Approach to User-Centered Design*, New York: Taylor & Francis.

Endsley, M. R. and Garland, D. J. (Eds.), 2000. *Situation Awareness Analysis and Measurement,* Mahwah, NJ: Lawrence Erlbaum Associates.

Endsley, M. R., Holder, L. D., Leibrecht, B. C., Garland, D. C., Wampler, R. L., and Matthews, M. D. 2000. Modeling and Measuring Situation Awareness in the Infantry Operational Environment (No. 1753), Alexandria, VA: Army Research Institute.

Endsley, M. R. and Jones, D. G. 1995. Situation Awareness Requirements Analysis for TRACON Air Traffic Control (TTU-IE-95-01), Lubbock, TX: Texas Tech University (Submitted to the FAA).

Endsley, M. R. and Robertson, M. M. 2000a. Situation awareness in aircraft maintenance teams, *International Journal of Industrial Ergonomics*, 26: 301–325.

Endsley, M. R. and Robertson, M. M. 2000b. Training for situation awareness in individuals and teams, in M.R. Endsley and D.J. Garland (Eds.), *Situation Awareness Analysis and Measurement*, Mahwah, NJ: Lawrence Erlbaum Associates.

Federico, P. A. 1995. Expert and novice recognition of similar situations, *Human Factors,* 37(1): 105–122.

Gaba, D. M., Howard, S. K., and Small, S. D. 1995. Situation awareness in anesthesiology, *Human Factors*, 37(1): 20–31.

Jones, D. G. 1997. Reducing situation awareness errors in air traffic control, *Human Factors and Ergonomics Society 41st Annual Meeting*, Vol. 1: 230–233, Santa Monica, CA: Human Factors Society.

Jones, D. G. and Endsley, M. R. 1996. Sources of situation awareness errors in aviation, *Aviation, Space and Environmental Medicine*, 67(6): 507–512.

Kass, S. J., Herschler, D. A., and Companion, M. A. 1991. Training situational awareness through pattern recognition in a battlefield environment, *Military Psychology*, 3: 105–112.

Matthews, M. D., Beal, S. A., and Pleban, R. J. 2002. Situation Awareness in a Virtual Environment: Description of a Subjective Awareness Scale (Research Report 1786), Alexandria, VA: U.S. Army Research Institute for the Behavioral and Social Sciences (ADA399408).

Matthews, M. D., Strater, L. D., and Endsley, M. R. 2004. Situation awareness requirements for infantry platoon leaders, *Military Psychology*, 16: 149–161.

Orasanu, J. and Fischer, U. 1997. Finding decisions in natural environments: the view from the cockpit, in C. E. Zsambok and G. Klein (Eds.), *Naturalistic Decision Making*, Mahwah, NJ: Lawrence Erlbaum Associates.

Pleban, R. J., Eakin, D. E., Salter, M. S., and Matthews, M. D. 2001. Training and Assessment of Decision-Making Skills in Virtual Environments (Research Report No. 1767), Alexandria, VA: U.S. Army Research Institute for the Behavioral and Social Sciences (ADA389677).

Prince, C. and Salas, E. 1998. Situation assessment for routine flight and decision making, *International Journal of Cognitive Ergonomics*, 1(4): 315–324.

Ross, K., Pierce, L. G., and Baehr, M. C. 1999. *Revitalizing Battle Staff Training* (ARL-TR-2079), Aberdeen Proving Ground, MD: U.S. Army Research Lab.

Salas, E., Prince, C., Baker, D. P., and Shrestha, L. 1995. Situation awareness in team performance: implications for measurement and training, *Human Factors*, 37(1): 123–136.

Schutte, P. C. and Trujillo, A. C. 1996. Flightcrew task management in non-normal situations, *Proceedings of the 40th Annual Meeting of the Human Factors and Ergonomics Society*, 244–248, Santa Monica, CA: HFES.

Serfaty, D., Macmillan, J., Entin, E. E., and Entin, E. B. 1997. The decision making expertise of battle commanders, in C. E. Zsambok and G. A. Klein (Eds.), *Naturalistic Decision Making,* Mahwah, NJ: Lawrence Erlbaum Associates.

Sollenberger, R. L., and Stein, E. S. (1995). A simulation study of air traffic controller situational awareness. In D. J. Garland and M. R. Endsley (Eds.), *Experimental analysis and measurement of situation awareness* (pp. 211–217). Daytana Beach, FL: Embry-Riddle Aeronautical University Press.

Stark, J. M., Comstock, J. R., Prinzel, L. J., Burdette, D. W., and Scerbo, M. W. 2001. A preliminary examination of situation awareness and pilot performance in a synthetic vision environment, paper presented at the Human Factors and Ergonomics Society 45th Annual Meeting, Minneapolis/St. Paul, MN, October 2001.

Strater, L. D. and Endsley, M. R. 2005. Designing to enhance situation awareness in the CIC, paper presented at the Human Systems Integration Symposium, Arlington, VA.

Strater, L. D., Endsley, M. R., Pleban, R. J., and Matthews, M. D. 2000. Measures of Platoon Leader Situation Awareness in Virtual Decision-Making Exercises (ARI research Report 1770), Alexandria, VA: U.S. Army Research Institute for the Behavioral and Social Sciences (ADA390238).

Strater, L. D., Endsley, M. R., and Plott, C. 2004. Development of an Automated Measurement Battery to Assess Innovative Concepts and Technologies for Shipboard Applications: Phase I Final Report, Dahlgren, VA: Naval Surface Warfare Center, Dahlgren Division.

Strater, L. D., Jones, D. G., and Endsley, M. R. 2001. Analysis of Infantry Situation Awareness Training Requirements (ARI Technical Report 1123), Alexandria, VA: U.S. Army Research Institute for the Behavioral and Social Sciences (ADA399391).

Strater, L. D., Reynolds, J. P., Faulkner, L. A., Birch, D. K., Hyatt, J., and Swetnam, S. 2004. PC-based Training to Improve Infantry Situation Awareness (No. Technical Report 1146), Arlington, VA: U.S. Army Research Institute for the Behavioral and Social Sciences.

Tlauka, M., Stanton, D., and McKenna, F. P. 2000. Dual displays, *Ergonomics*, 43(6): 764–770.

Trollip, S. R. and Jensen, R. S. 1991. *Human Factors for General Aviation,* Englewood, CO: Jeppesen Sanderson.

U.S. Bureau of Transportation. 1997. Transportation Statistics Annual Report (No. BTS97-S-01), Washington D.C.

Wright, M. C., Taekman, J. M., and Endsley, M. R. 2004. Objective measures of situation awareness in a simulated medical environment, *Quality and Safety in Health Care,* 16: 65–71.

8 Performance Assessment in Simulation

Steven Hall and Michael T. Brannick

CONTENTS

Performance assessment is a key element in simulation. In a training context, performance assessment will lay the foundation for feedback to the pilot or flightcrew, and in a research context, it is typically the key to assessing the impact of various factors of interest, such as training or equipment design. There is no single way to measure performance, and practical issues typically limit the type and amount of performance data that can be collected during a simulation session.

For convenience we classify measures along two dimensions. First, we describe measures as being either subjective or objective. Subjective measures are provided directly by human judges. For example, an instructor might rate a crew *satisfactory* on a paper-and-pencil scale of mission analysis. Objective measures are provided by simulators as the result of recordings or calculations. For example, performance might be defined in terms of deviation from a desired flight path or flight parameter (i.e., airspeed, heading, etc.) or in terms of external pilot behavior, such as pushing a button. For the second dimension, we describe measures as being either qualitative or quantitative. By qualitative, we mean measures that are categorical in nature. For example, one might either simply pass or fail a maneuver. For another example, a pilot's behavior might be allocated by an instructor to a category such as *assertiveness* or *decision making*. Quantitative measures, on the other hand, indicate magnitude. For example, altitude and vertical speed are both quantitative. We also consider numerical ratings given by judges to be quantitative if the ratings indicate degree, so a pilot given a rating of four is indicated by an instructor as being more proficient than another pilot given a rating of three under similar circumstances.

The choice of the performance assessment technique should be based on the purpose of the simulation and practical limitations. Training scenarios may require feedback for specific flight-crew behavior. Such feedback may include both subjective appraisals of quality of behavior and objective information about the frequency or timeliness of behaviors. Research endeavors typically seek to examine the impact of specific factors on some outcome, such as flight technical error (FTE) or perceived workload. The former can be efficiently quantified with objective data, whereas the latter is typically assessed with subjective workload survey instruments.

The purpose of this chapter is to present both subjective and objective measures of performance that are commonly used in simulation. A thorough discussion of measurement reliability accompanies the subjective measurement discussion, whereas the objective section emphasizes logistical and practical issues associated with automated methods of performance assessment.

SUBJECTIVE METHODS OF PERFORMANCE MEASUREMENT

In general, humans are excellent at sensing and perceiving information. We can also become very adept at knowing what to perceive, that is, we learn what is (and is not) worthy of attention in a given situation. In many cases, if we want to evaluate human performance, there is no other choice but to use expert judgment. For example, if we want to evaluate the quality of coordination of two pilots working together in a cockpit, we will most likely be forced to rely on the judgment of an instructor pilot. For these reasons and others, humans are often used as performance measurement devices. Not surprisingly, the most commonly used measures of work performance are based on human judgment (Landy and Farr, 1983).

PURPOSE OF PERFORMANCE MEASURES

Simulators are typically used to train and evaluate skilled performance. For example, a flight simulator can be used to teach navigation skills. Performance measures, therefore, should support the training and evaluation functions of simulators. Numerical (quantitative) evaluations of proficiency are typically of primary interest in simulators. Such measures are useful in evaluating and documenting individual skill levels for certification or for adequacy of preparation in dealing with the real (not simulated) task. Although numerical evaluations are not very useful in providing developmental feedback in training, they are useful in evaluating the quality of a training program. That is, evaluations of proficiency can be used in program evaluation research.

SPECIAL PROPERTIES OF PERFORMANCE MEASURES IN SIMULATORS

Often the individual using the simulator (the target of evaluation) is aware of the evaluation, and the evaluation has consequences for the target (e.g., certification). In such circumstances, the performance measure should be considered to be one of maximal performance rather than typical performance. Because of the consequence of the measurement and also because the performance measure is related to skills that the target considers important, such evaluations can be threatening or anxiety provoking to the target. In some cases, the apprehension that results from being evaluated can interfere with performance of the task, thus resulting in a poorer evaluation.

Not only does the simulator encourage maximal performance but it does so for a limited time. Typically, the simulator is used to teach or evaluate specific skills. The instructor and student will use the simulator for a time brief enough to allow them to maintain their attention on that specific task. This means that ratings evaluating simulator performance are less taxing for memory than are typical performance appraisal ratings, which often cover job performance for a year. Further, for a given session, the experience in the simulator is designed to target one or more skills, such as navigation or coordination. Such training and evaluation design considerations help both the judge and target focus on a limited range of behaviors compared to typical job performance ratings.

There are both advantages and disadvantages to the use of humans as judges of performance in simulators. From the standpoint of measurement, one of the main drawbacks to using human judges is that such judges may disagree with one another (see Guion, 1998). Kenny (1991) developed a general model of consensus and accuracy of ratings of interpersonal perception. The factors in the model included (a) the amount of information given to the judges, (b) the degree to which the judges attend to the same behaviors, (c) the degree to which the judges make similar inferences or interpretations of the same behaviors, (d) reliability or consistency of the target (ratee) behavior, (e) degree to which the judges base their ratings on irrelevant behavior, and (f) degree of communication of impressions of the target prior to rating.

Of Kenny's factors, items (b), (c), and (d) appear the most important for performance ratings in simulators. We discuss factors (b) and (c) here, and factor (d) later in the chapter. The amount of information given to different judges (factor a) tends to be similar for a given scenario using a given simulator. For example, two judges might watch the same videotape of pilots flying a simulator. Even though two judges watch the same participants in the same simulator at the same time, they may disagree in their evaluation of what they saw for several reasons. The judges may attend to different behaviors, so one sees something that the other does not (factor b). For example, only one of two instructors may notice that the copilot has become lost. The judges may interpret the same behavior to mean different things (factor c). Again, one judge may find a behavior overly confrontational, but another judge may find the same behavior to be appropriately assertive. When judges record behaviors, make ratings, or otherwise produce evaluations, they may do so in idiosyncratic ways. One judge might assign an assertive behavior to an interpersonal dimension, but another might classify the same behavior as belonging to decision making, flexibility, or some other dimension (for general discussions of performance ratings, see Landy and Farr, 1980, 1983).

DEFINING AND ASSESSING RELIABILITY

There is a very substantial literature on the reliability of measurement (e.g., Crocker and Algina, 1986; Nunnally and Bernstein, 1994; Wigdor and Green, 1991). There is a somewhat more manageable literature on the reliability of judges (e.g., Shrout and Fleiss, 1979). Because judges commonly disagree, anyone who uses judges to evaluate performance in simulators should conduct a study to compute one or more indices that quantify how well the judges agree with one another. In this section, we illustrate the more commonly used indices of how well judges agree with one another. We provide recommendations for choosing suitable estimators for the most commonly occurring situations in practice. The choice of disagreement index depends primarily on two issues: (a) whether the judgments are qualitative or quantitative, and (b) whether the differences in means across judges are important or meaningful.

Data Requirements

To study how well judges agree with one another, we have to collect data. Ideally, we should have a large, representative sample of judges and a large, representative sample of targets (pilots, teams, technicians, or whomever gets judged). Judges and targets should be crossed so that each judge sees each and every target and provides the judgment of interest for each (e.g., whether a pilot passes a specific test, or an evaluation of the degree to which a team showed good coordination). The benefit of such a study is that you will actually learn what you want to know, that is, your evaluation of how well judges agree will be accurate. Unfortunately, such data collection can be rather expensive. Practical constraints may force a less informative design.

At a minimum, we have to have at least two judges and some number of targets; the minimum possible number of targets is two, but some larger number is really needed for the calculations to be meaningful, say ten targets for the sake of argument (see Flack, Afifi, Lachenbruch, and Schouten, 1988, for choosing the number of targets). Table 8.1 shows hypothetical data for three judges (represented as columns) on ten targets (represented as rows). The judges have recorded their judgments in the form of numbers ranging from 1 to 5. These judgments can be thought of either as categorical (polite, assertive, etc.) or quantitative (e.g., 1 = poor to 5 = excellent) for purposes of illustration.

Qualitative versus Quantitative

Qualitative ratings are categorical. An example of a categorical rating is one in which the judge merely indicates whether a pilot passes or fails a simulated task. Sorting teams of pilots on the basis of their working styles into groups with labels such as *cooperative, confrontational, rational,* and *polite* would be another example. Qualitative ratings are labels applied to performance that either indicate group membership or falling above or below some threshold to indicate passing or failing in a task.

Quantitative ratings indicate magnitude or degree of something. Ratings made on a scale from "poor" to "excellent" indicate increasing proficiency and can be assigned numbers (e.g., 1 to 5) that correspond to degrees of proficiency. Some argue that judges' ratings are not measures in the same

TABLE 8.1
Ratings from Three Judges on Ten Targets

	Judge		
Target	1	2	3
1	5	5	5
2	4	3	3
3	3	3	3
4	5	4	5
5	2	1	3
6	4	3	3
7	2	2	2
8	1	1	2
9	5	4	5
10	4	4	5
M	3.5	3.0	3.6
SD	1.43	1.33	1.26

sense as measures provided by thermometers or airspeed indicators (for more detail on the issues, see Annett, 2002). Regardless of one's position on the issue, we feel that it is useful to act as if ratings are quantitative measures because the results of doing so are helpful in practice.

A QUALITATIVE INDEX

If the judgments are categorical (qualitative), then disagreements can be quantified using percentage agreement and other indices of association. Although percentage agreement is easy to compute and (on the face of it) easy to interpret, it can be misleading. Suppose one judge assigns "pass" to 100% of the targets, and an other judge assigns "pass" to 80% of the targets. Then percentage agreement will be 80%, which looks good on the face of it. However, because there is no variance in the first judge's ratings, there is no statistical association between the two sets of judges' ratings. The statistic we recommend for the analysis of categorical judgments is called *Cohen's kappa*, or just *kappa* for short (Cohen, 1960). Kappa adjusts percentage agreement for chance agreement, so the agreement is reduced if a large amount of it would be expected by chance.

Suppose the data in Table 8.1 were categorical. To compute kappa, we would first compute a contingency table that shows the agreement in assignment to categories (see Table 8.2). Note that for the first target, all three judges agreed that the target was a "5"; so "3" is recorded in the fifth column. For the second target, two of the judges called it a "3" and one called it a "4," so a "2" is written in the third column and a "1" is written in the fourth column. The rest of the rows proceed in a similar manner.

The formula for kappa is

$$K = \frac{P(A) - P(E)}{1 - P(E)},$$

where *P(A)* is the proportion of times that judges agree, and *P(E)* is the proportion of times that we would expect the judges to agree by chance (Siegel and Castellan, 1988, p. 285). Note that, in general, we have k judges, N targets, and m categories. In our example, we have $k = 3$ judges and

TABLE 8.2
Contingency Table

Target	1	2	3	4	5	S_i
			Category			
1	—	—	—	—	3	1
2	—	—	2	1	—	.33
3	—	—	3	—	—	1
4	—	—	—	1	2	.33
5	1	1	1	—	—	0
6	—	—	2	1	—	.33
7	—	3	—	—	—	1
8	2	1	—	—	—	.33
9	—	—	—	1	2	.33
10	—	—	—	2	1	.33
C_j	3	5	8	6	8	
p_j	0.1	0.167	0.267	0.2	0.267	

$N = 10$ targets for a total of kN or 30 judgments. To compute chance agreement, we hypothesize that row frequencies will be proportional to column totals. We find column totals by adding across the rows for each column. The totals are shown in the second-to-last row of Table 8.2, labeled C_j. To find the proportion of judgments in each category, we divide the column totals by the total number of judgments, that is, C_j/kN. The result is shown in the last row of Table 8.2, labeled p_j. The proportion of agreement expected by chance is

$$P(E) = \sum_{1}^{j} p_j^2$$

$$= .1^2 + .167^2 + .267^2 + .2^2 + .267^2$$

$$= .22$$

Now, we need to compute the proportion of agreement, $P(A)$. One way to do so is to first compute agreement for each target, S_i. We can do so with the following equation:

$$S_1 = \frac{1}{k(k-1)} \sum_{1}^{m} n_{ij}(n_{ij}-1)$$

$$= 1/(3)(2)[0 + 0 + 0 + 0 + (3)(2)]$$

$$= 6/6 = 1.$$

The observed proportion of agreement among the judges is the average agreement over targets:

$$P(A) = \frac{1}{N} \sum_{1}^{N} S_i$$

$$P(A) = \frac{1+.33+1+...+.33+.33}{10} = .50.$$

Finally, our value of kappa is

$$K = \frac{.5-.22}{1-.22} = .36$$

which is a rather modest level of agreement.

QUANTITATIVE INDICES

Is the Difference in Means Meaningful?

There are several indices of interjudge reliability that we can use when the ratings are quantitative. If the difference in means among judges is not meaningful or not important, we can use the correlation coefficient or a certain type of intraclass coefficient (the fixed case). On the other hand, when the difference in means among judges is meaningful, we can use another intraclass coefficient (the random case). We will define the indices and explain the reasons for the choices among indices as we go along.

Correlation Coefficient

Suppose that the data in Table 8.1 are quantitative and indicate instructor ratings of the level of proficiency of targets in completing a task in a simulator. One index of the degree to which judges agree about the relative standing of targets is the correlation coefficient, sometimes called Pearson's r (see Guion, 1998, p. 311):

$$r = \frac{\sum z_X z_Y}{N},$$

where

$$z_X = \frac{X - M_X}{SD_X},$$

and N is the number of pairs (targets), X is the raw score given by a judge, M is the mean rating for a judge, and SD is the standard deviation (sample, not population estimate) of the judge's ratings. The correlation coefficient is computed once for each pair of judges and indicates the degree to which the judges' scores rise and fall together across targets.

The correlations among the three judges' scores are shown in Table 8.3. All three correlations are quite large, indicating substantial agreement among the judges. Notice, however, that, as shown in Table 8.1, Judges 1 and 3 tended to give higher scores than did Judge 2. The correlation can be quite high even though the judges have very different mean ratings. The ratings from a very lenient judge and a very severe judge will be highly correlated so long as they both tend to rate the same targets relatively high and relatively low, even though they do not agree on the specific numbers that are assigned to a target. Note that the correlations appear to indicate higher agreement among the judges than did kappa. This is because, if the judgments are categorical, any disagreement is as substantial as any other disagreement. (If it misses, an inch is as good as a mile.) The correlation, however, essentially gives credit for being close.

For research purposes, the correlation coefficient is often used to show the degree of association between two variables. In such a context, a difference in means is often of no importance. However, in applied contexts, we typically collect data to make decisions about people. In such a circumstance, differences in means across judges become very important. For example, one judge may pass or certify a performance that another judge would fail. Clearly, disagreements of this nature would be important.

Intraclass Correlations

Intraclass correlations (ICCs) can estimate how well judges agree with one another while taking mean differences into account. There are several different ICCs that can be computed. All of them are related to the analysis of variance (ANOVA). We will illustrate the use of two of these. To compute the ICCs, we first need results from an ANOVA in which the ratings are the dependent variable, and the judge and target are the independent variables. Table 8.4 shows the way in which the data would be input to a computer, and Table 8.5 shows the ANOVA results. Notice that we have labeled one sum of squares BMS for *between targets mean square,* another is labeled JMS for *between judges sum of squares,*

TABLE 8.3
Correlation Matrix

Judge	1	2	3
1	1	—	—
2	.93	1	—
3	.86	.86	1

TABLE 8.4

Data Layout for ANOVA and ICC Computation

Rating	Judge	Target
5.00	1	1
4.00	1	2
3.00	1	3
5.00	1	4
2.00	1	5
4.00	1	6
2.00	1	7
1.00	1	8
5.00	1	9
4.00	1	10
5.00	2	1
3.00	2	2
3.00	2	3
4.00	2	4
1.00	2	5
3.00	2	6
2.00	2	7
1.00	2	8
4.00	2	9
4.00	2	10
5.00	3	1
3.00	3	2
3.00	3	3
5.00	3	4
3.00	3	5
3.00	3	6
2.00	3	7
2.00	3	8
5.00	3	9
5.00	3	10

TABLE 8.5

ANOVA Summary Table

Source	Sum of Squares	Degrees of Freedom	Mean Square	Label
Judge	2.07	2	1.03	JMS
Target	44.97	9	5.00	BMS
Judge*target	3.93	18	0.22	EMS

TABLE 8.6

Computation of Intraclass Correlations

Formulas	Numbers

One Random Judge

$$\frac{BMS-EMS}{BMS+(k-1)EMS+k(JMS-EMS)/n} \qquad \frac{5-.22}{5+2(.22)+(3(1.03-.22)/10)}=.84$$

One Fixed Judge

$$\frac{BMS-EMS}{BMS+(k-1)EMS} \qquad \frac{5-.22}{5+(2).22}=.88$$

All k (Three) Random Judges

$$\frac{BMS-EMS}{BMS+(JMS-EMS)/n} \qquad \frac{5-.22}{5+(1.03-.22)/10}=.94$$

All k (Three) Fixed Judges

$$\frac{BMS-EMS}{BMS} \qquad \frac{5-.22}{5}=.96$$

and the last is labeled EMS for *error mean square*. In this design, there is only one observation per cell, so the interaction and error terms are not separately estimable (Shrout and Fleiss, 1979).

Shrout and Fleiss (1979) described the computation of two general classes of ICCs, namely, random and fixed. The typical ANOVA interpretation of random and fixed effects would be that random ICCs consider judges to be sampled from some larger population, whereas the fixed ICCs consider the judges in the study to be sampled from only the judges of interest. However, the main difference in the two formulas is the way in which mean differences in judges are handled. The random ICCs reduce the index of agreement for differences in means across judges, but the fixed ICCs do not. Therefore, the choice of ICCs is better informed by the way in which data will be collected and used in practice. If, in the actual use of the ratings (that is, when the simulator is used for actual training, performance evaluation, etc., and the judges' evaluations actually count), the same judge or judges evaluate all targets, then a fixed ICC should be used. On the other hand, if different judges evaluate different targets, then a random ICC should be used. In most practical applications, there are multiple judges, and each target is rated by only one judge. Therefore, the random ICC will usually apply in practice.

In our current study, we have three judges (the jargon is that $k = 3$). We can estimate the reliability of a single judge, or we can estimate the reliability of the average of all three judges. We can do this for both the random- and fixed-effects cases. The computations are illustrated in Table 8.6 for all four possibilities (random versus fixed case, and one versus three judges). Notice that reliability estimates are larger for the fixed-effects case than for the random-effects case. This is because the JMS term appears in the denominator of the random-effects estimates but not for the estimates in the fixed-effects estimates. The JMS term is the estimate of variance due to differences in means among the judges. The difference in results between the fixed and random cases will depend on the size of the differences in mean ratings from the different judges.

Number of Judges

Note also in Table 8.6 that increasing the number of judges from one to three increases the reliability estimate. As we noted previously, the typical case in practice is for a single judge to rate each target. That single judge is usually not the same for all targets. In such an instance, the reliability estimate that would apply is the estimate for one random judge. In our study, the value for that estimate was .84, which is respectable for some purposes. However, we might want a better reliability if the rating has serious consequences for the target (e.g., if the rating causes the target to lose time on the job). We can use a variant of the Spearman–Brown formula to estimate the number of judges we would need to obtain any given level of reliability. The formula we need is (Shrout and Fleiss, 1979)

$$m = \frac{\rho^*(1-\rho_L)}{\rho_L(1-\rho^*)},$$

where ρ_L is our estimate of one (random, in our case) judge, ρ^* is our aspiration level, and m is the resulting number of judges. We have to round off m to the next highest integer, as judges cannot be expressed in fractions. Suppose we wanted to achieve a reliability of .90; we would find that

$$m = \frac{.9(1-.84)}{.84(1-.9)} = 1.71 \cong 2.$$

Therefore, we would need two (random) judges to assure a reliability of at least .90.

To recapitulate the distinction between fixed and random judges in practical applications, suppose we have a pool of five instructors, of whom two will be available to rate each crew on each simulation, but the same two instructors will not always be paired; the random judges formula would then apply because differences in the judges' means would influence the ratings. On the other hand, suppose we have only two instructors available, and these two must evaluate each and every crew. In that case, the fixed judges formula would apply because differences in means among the judges would not influence the ratings.

There is also a third possibility, that is, there is some absolute standard that is based on the ratings (e.g., there is a numerical scale from one to five, with a passing point of three). In such a case, the calibration of the judges becomes of interest. However, we are unaware of well-developed psychometric approaches to evaluating such a calibration. In such instances, calibration would hinge upon having a gold standard of performance, and these are rarely available in practice. If such instances were widely available, then human judgment would probably be unnecessary.

Other Designs for Assessing Agreement among Judges

For studying interjudge reliability, we advocate that each judge evaluate each and every target. Such designs present logistical challenges for researchers, particularly in terms of getting multiple judges together. It is often possible to make recordings (e.g., videotape) of targets' responses to simulations to ease the burden of gathering multiple judges at once. Once recorded, the target can be evaluated more or less at the judges' leisure. More complex designs in which some nesting of targets within judges can also be used (see Crocker and Algina, 1986; Cronbach, Gleser, Nanda, and Rajaratnam, 1972; DeShon, 2002; Shavelson and Webb, 1991). However, you will probably have to hire a statistician to analyze the data and compute the reliability estimate.

There are also methods that can be used when each judge sees only a single target. Such methods include ICC(1) (Shrout and Fleiss, 1979) and r_{wg} (James, Demaree, and Wolf, 1984). However, we recommend against using such methods because they have serious flaws as indices of agreement between judges. ICC(1) can be used in situations where judges can be grouped in some way and differences can be compared across groups; essentially, this amounts to using ANOVA between subjects to estimate reliability. The problem with this design is that we do not know if the differences come from the targets or the judges (or both) because different judges see different targets. The r_{wg} method compares a distribution of judges' ratings having variance against a distribution where scores are distributed uniformly. However, this is not a method that provides reliable estimates (Kozlowski and Hattrup, 1992).

ENHANCING RELIABILITY

Reliability of measurement is essential for the measures to be useful in training or performance evaluation (see Baker and Salas, 1992, 1997). The main approaches to improving the reliability of subjective performance measures are (1) increasing the number of judges, (2) changing the task, and (3) training the judges. We have already described how to estimate the number of judges needed to obtain any desired level of reliability. Unfortunately, increasing the number of judges is often prohibitively expensive. A single judge may be all that is available.

Changing the Task

An excellent discussion of rating scales and formats can be found in Guion (1998, pp. 542–562). As Guion noted, the consensus of researchers in this area is that format effects due to appearance are small. That is, it makes little difference whether the scales are shown horizontally or vertically, whether the scales have five or seven response categories, or whether numbers or words are used to label the response options. This is not to say that careful scale development is not important. It is important because it specifies the task (the content of the items) ultimately given to the judge. Reliability among judges can be improved by making the judges' tasks easier.

One way to do this is to make the ratings more easily observable, quantitative, and behavioral. That is, relatively concrete, observable behaviors are easier to evaluate or record than relatively abstract concepts that must be inferred from subtle patterns of behavior. It is easier to count incidents of team members shouting at one another than it is to infer the degree of hostility being felt in the same team. Although reliability is increased by making the judges' tasks simpler, there is often a price to be paid for this simplicity. Often, simpler ratings are deficient, meaning that they do not fully capture the construct that was intended. Hostility can be expressed in many different ways, of which shouting at team members is only one. If the judges consider only shouting, then their reliability (agreement) should be good. However, the resulting measure will be an index specifically of shouting and will be a deficient measure of hostility.

Rater Training

Rater training is often a good method to use to improve agreement between judges. There are many kinds of rater training available. Probably the current favorite is the frame of reference training (Bernardin and Beatty, 1984). Good training programs involve training in attention (teaching the set of observed behaviors relevant to the construct of interest) and standards for evaluation (Bernardin and Buckley, 1981). For example, suppose we are interested in crew decision making. During a simulated mission, the crew encounters an equipment problem (say, a boost pump failure). How does the crew handle this problem? Training might include attending to how long it takes the crew to break out the checklist, whether they skip steps in the checklist, whether there is concurrence among crew members on a specific step, and so forth. Training on the evaluative part might include what behaviors indicate satisfactory, above-average, and below-average performance on the problem. We recommend training that is specific to the simulation and evaluation form being used. Generic training, or training aimed at reducing common rating errors, is not likely to improve the reliability of judges' ratings.

Table 8.7 shows some possible formats for items dealing with decision making. Some of the items are very simple checklist items such that the judge merely records whether the behavior was observed. Another item asks the judge how the crew did on the event (boost pump failure) as a whole. The final item asks about decision making in general. Notice how the judge's cognitive work increases as the generality of the item increases. For the specific checklist items, the judge just has to attend to a specific behavior and record what happens. For the boost pump item, the behaviors are circumscribed by the boost pump event, but the judge must evaluate the proficiency of the crew,

TABLE 8.7
Example Rating Scales

Checklist Items (Check the Appropriate Box for Each Item)			Yes		No
1. Checklist out within 30 seconds of boost pump failure			[ ]		[ ]
2. Checklist complete within 2 minutes of start of checklist			[ ]		[ ]
3. Problem fuse correctly identified			[ ]		[ ]

Global Evaluations (Circle the Number That Indicates Your Opinion)	1 = Poor	2 = Below Average	3 = Average	4 = Above Average	5 = Excellent
1. Overall handling of boost pump failure	1	2	3	4	5
2. Decision making	1	2	3	4	5

which involves comparing the behaviors of the crew to some standards of quality of performance. The final item asks the judge to recall and integrate behaviors from multiple events into an overall evaluation of decision making. In addition to the boost pump failure, there may be other events built into the scenario. The judge has to remember how the crew handled the other events and somehow aggregate multiple behaviors before rendering an overall judgment. As we mentioned previously, as scales become more specific, reliability increases, but so does deficiency.

SPECIAL PROBLEMS WITH SIMULATORS

The Gouge

Many kinds of training and evaluation involving simulators require one or more scenarios that are developed to evaluate or teach specific things. Once developed, the scenarios are typically used for a period of months or even a year or more. As people experience the scenarios, they may tell others what they encountered. After a period of time, those encountering the simulation are not at all surprised by what happens during the simulation. When some people can prepare in advance but others cannot, the measures obtained will most likely mean different things for the two groups because they are being measured under different conditions. This can be a problem, particularly after the scenario becomes well known.

One potential solution to such a problem is to develop rapidly reconfigurable event sets. The idea is for the instructor or simulator operator to quickly change the scenario in such a way that the participants will not know what to expect. The benefit is that the participants cannot avoid a proper evaluation by preparing for a specific event. There are disadvantages to such an approach as well. Time and effort are required to develop multiple scenarios intended to tap similar skills and behaviors. Perhaps more seriously, there is some doubt about whether different events can provide comparable information. For example, in the assessment center literature, exercises that appear to tap similar skills produce scores that are not highly correlated with one another. It is difficult to guess how participants will respond to an event built into a scenario. There is no empirical basis to guide the choice of events, so a successful outcome for rapidly reconfigurable event sets is uncertain.

Instructor Attitudes

Psychologists typically have an inductive approach to decision making. They like to collect the relevant behaviors, evaluate them, and come to a decision about a person. So, for example, if psychologists have to certify a person as competent to complete a task, they will first analyze the task to determine what behaviors need to be completed. Then they will determine conditions for successful performance, that is, define performance standards. They will create the simulation to allow for the proper conditions and behaviors, and then watch the participant in the simulation. They will record and evaluate the participant's behaviors. If the behaviors meet the predetermined standard, they will certify the person. The recorded data are the basis of the decision.

Instructors, like managers, often do not share the psychologists' mindset. To many, the rating forms do not serve as a source of evidence from which a decision can be made. Rather, the forms serve as documentation of a decision that has already been rendered. Some instructor pilots, for example, feel that the important thing is their word or decision about whether a pilot is competent to fly. To them, the forms are a waste of time; all that is necessary is a "yes" or "no" from the instructor pilot. Such instructors will complete the forms if they are forced to, but one should not expect highly reliable data from such an individual.

We recommend that subjective performance assessment forms be developed as much as possible in cooperation with the judges who will be using them. If the judges find them overly burdensome, difficult to understand, or irrelevant to the purpose of the simulation, they will not be motivated to use them properly. Without the cooperation of the judge, reliability of the ratings will be poor.

OBJECTIVE METHODS OF PERFORMANCE MEASUREMENT

Some may see objective measures* of performance as a relatively simple way to assess "true" pilot ability. Objective measures may seem simpler to use and easier to validate, but such is not always the case. There are real limits to the utility of objective data in assessing pilot performance, and the costs associated with getting objective data are sometimes prohibitive. On the other hand, objective measures can provide valuable information about pilot performance for certain flight maneuvers; furthermore, the quantitative performance measurement process can be perfectly replicated across pilots, sessions, researchers, simulation platforms, and even in real aircraft. There are situations where subjective measures of performance are not feasible or precise enough for the research at hand. Certain aspects of flight performance, such as "stick and rudder" skill, are arguably best measured with data provided directly by the simulator. Certain tasks, such as instrument approaches, lend themselves to assessment with objective data. This is not to say that subjective performance assessments are of no value in such situations; on the contrary, both measurement approaches should be used when possible, as the two approaches will each provide unique information about different aspects of flight performance.

Ironically, using objective measures of flight performance is sometimes more difficult than using subjective measures. Even though there are benefits to using objective data (e.g., reliability, precision, and standardization), there are potentially high costs involved in obtaining and analyzing objective data. The difficulty involved in using objective measures of performance will vary depending on the flight tasks being assessed—whether or not additional parameters such as team functioning are being assessed—and the simulation platform and software being used. End users of objective performance measures may disagree on the actual meaning of the outcome data or how to most effectively use such measures. In applied situations, pilots, instructors, and managers may be reluctant to use or even record objective measures of performance. The bottom line is that using objective measures in flight performance research is not easy, not simple, and not necessarily superior to the use of subjective methods, but they can certainly add value in many situations. The focus of this section is on the objective measurement of FTE during specific flight maneuvers. Other aspects of pilot behavior and performance, such as workload or situational awareness, are not considered.

---

* The phrase *objective measures* in this chapter refers specifically to measurements based on flight data provided by the simulator.

Automated Data Collection Systems

Many simulation platforms have the capacity for automated data collection. Most simulation packages, either directly or through a third-party add-on, have the ability to output flight parameter information at some sampling rate. Output formats vary from text files to graphs of the aircraft's position through time. Text file output is usually done so that each line of data represents a given set of flight parameters at a given point in time. Data collection rates are usually flexible and are sometimes set as high as 60 samples per second. Some systems allow the user to specify the parameters to be saved, whereas others dump a predefined set of parameters. In some cases, instantaneous rate-of-change data can be collected, allowing the researcher to examine flight performance in terms of "smoothness."

Systems vary in terms of what data can be collected, but usually both flight parameter data (e.g., position, airspeed, course deviation indicator [CDI] needle deflection, etc.) and pilot input data (e.g., control surface input, button presses, etc.) can be collected. Also, the data are usually time stamped, thus allowing the researcher to coordinate specific events and activities across data collection platforms. These time stamps facilitate synchronizing flight data with other sources of data such as cockpit video and audio recordings and eye-tracking information. A word of caution to the researcher: not all data collection programs will use the same reference clock for time stamping purposes!

Data collection software is readily available for the Elite and Microsoft Flight Simulator (MSFS) software packages. Elite sells a data collection module separate from the simulation software, whereas FlightRecorder 8.1 is freely available from the Internet for use with MSFS. Similarly, Frasca's latest simulators are configured from the factory to collect flight parameter data. Surprisingly, some of the more advanced simulation systems that we have worked with do not readily make such data available, but usually these data can be accessed with some minor programming. In some situations, physically getting the data from the simulator is easier than getting permission from the manufacturer to access the data in the first place.

Most data collection programs are designed to record raw data, which often results in a rather lengthy data file. To date, we have not seen a commercially available product that will scientifically analyze flight performance, but we have seen custom-made packages that analyze FTE in real time given specific flight criteria. Unfortunately, these packages are not readily available, leaving most researchers with lengthy data files saved by the commonly available data collection packages.

Flight Technical Error

Objective data can be used to generate various measures of FTE. FTE quantifies the degree to which the position or orientation of the aircraft deviates from some ideal state. In other words, FTE metrics focus on the pilot's ability to make the aircraft attain some predetermined goal specified by an external agency; hence, FTE is probably best used as a measure of "stick and rudder" skill.

FTE and pilot performance are certainly not synonymous. There is much more to safely operating an aircraft than FTE can quantify. On the other hand, a pilot's ability to maintain precise control of the aircraft is a prerequisite for successful operations.

Data feeds from simulators are ideal for FTE computations, but deriving meaningful FTE-based performance metrics requires a great deal of planning. The following subsections detail various forms of FTE measures and their potential uses.

Deviation-Based Metrics

Deviation metrics are the backbone of most FTE measures. As the name implies, a deviation metric compares a given flight parameter to a specific value for that parameter. For example, the pilot may be instructed to maintain an altitude of 5000 feet, and actual altitude data collected at some sampling rate are compared to this target value. The difference between the two values is the raw outcome of interest. A similar metric can be computed using positional data. The pilot is instructed to maintain a flight path, specified via Global Positioning System (GPS) or perhaps a VOR (very high frequency omnirange) radial, and the actual position of the aircraft is compared to the target flight path.

Root Mean Square Error

Deviation data must be aggregated in some way to create a single outcome metric of interest. One of the most common methods of aggregation is to compute the RMSE. It works by first squaring each deviation, averaging these squared deviations, and taking the square root of the average to return to the original units. By doing so, the polarity of the deviations is eliminated, and gross deviations are exaggerated. If an observed flight path has no deviations from the desired flight path, RMSE will equal zero. Given this lower bound of zero, the distribution of RMSE will not be normal and will violate a basic assumption for most parametric statistic procedures. To address this issue, RMSE data can be transformed using the natural logarithm function, and this will usually result in a distribution of RMSE data that appears normal (see the data in Figure 8.1).

The data in the figure were collected during a flight simulation study where pilot performance was assessed as a function of keeping the aircraft centered on the glide slope during a simulated instrument approach. Deviation from the glide slope was measured using the deviation (in dots) of the glide slope needle on the CDI, where a value of zero dots indicates perfect alignment with the glide slope. The raw data are presented in the left panel of the figure and clearly show the skewed nature of RMSE (this skewed shape can be reproduced with virtually any RMSE data). On the right, the data were transformed using the natural log function, producing a more normal distribution. This allows the use of ANOVA and other general linear models to be applied to the performance data. A problem with such transformations is that they obscure the meaning of the data so that the transformed outcome measures are no longer directly interpretable. This is especially problematic for deviation-based metrics expressing FTE in terms of average deviation and so forth; but non-transformed RMSE values have limited real-world interpretability and are not negatively impacted through transformations.

RMSE cannot be interpreted as a simple average deviation because the square transformation gives more weight to gross deviations. Similarly, RMSE values cannot be simply compared to pre-scribed performance standards, such as the Federal Aviation Administration (FAA) practical test standards (PTS) to determine whether or not some criterion level of performance was met. On the other hand, RMSE is a very sensitive measure of flight performance and is more likely than other indices of performance to show differences across different instrumentation systems, training pro-grams, or other manipulated scenarios.

Changes in performance can be assessed using RMSE data, but observed differences in RMSE values across groups or treatments are not directly interpretable. This issue can be addressed by reporting effect sizes as opposed to just reporting means and F tests (Cohen, 1994). Researchers should consider using either Cohen's d, which expresses group mean differences in terms of pooled standard deviation units, or omega squared, which is an estimate of variance accounted for in the outcome metric by some manipulated variable.

Number of Deviations and Time-Outside Standard

Rantanen and Talleur (2001) have discussed several other deviation-based performance metrics. The number of deviations (ND) outside a tolerance indicates the pilot's ability to control the veloc-ity of the aircraft during a tracking task. It is similar to counting the number of times a car runs off a racetrack. Low ND values are desired, but may be misleading because the aircraft could stray

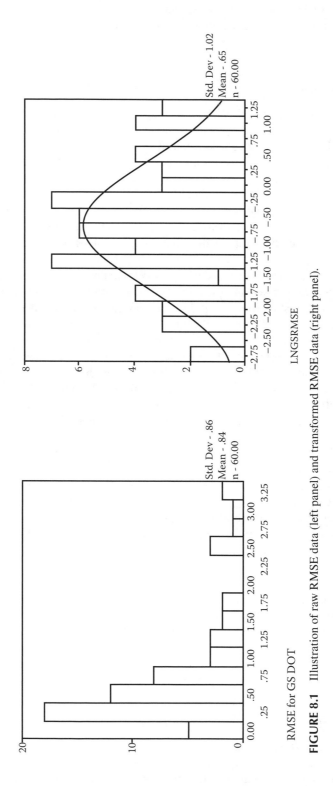

FIGURE 8.1   Illustration of raw RMSE data (left panel) and transformed RMSE data (right panel).

outside tolerance only once but stay outside the desired flight path for the duration of the flight. As such, ND value must be interpreted in light of the amount of time spent outside the tolerance, that is, time in deviation (TD). TD values add information beyond RMSE and ND, and low TD values reflect higher levels of performance.

Time within FAA Practical Test Standard

The notion of objective criterion performance measurement can be taken a step further by comparing the amount of deviation to some preset standard of performance. For example, a researcher could use FAA practical test standards to define acceptable and unacceptable levels of deviation. The time within standard (TWS) metric is conceptually similar to the TD metric discussed earlier, the main difference being that TWS focuses on the amount of time spent within a standard, and TD focuses on the amount of time spent outside the standard. The goal of the TWS metric is to quantify performance relative to known and accepted standards in such a way that the metric is conceptually friendly and directly interpretable.

The FAA has dictated standards of performance for the various pilot ratings and endorsements for various phases of flight. For example, the ATP (airline transport pilot) standard for an instrument approach is 1/4-scale deflection on the localizer and glide slope, and ±5 knots on airspeed. In contrast, the standard for an instrument approach under the instrument rating test standards is 3/4-scale deflection on the localizer and glide slope, and ±10 knots on airspeed. These criteria were designed to be applied by instructor pilots, but can easily be applied to objectively measured flight data. The end results are measurements of the proportion of time spent within either the ATP or instrument rating standards, whether or not a specific landing approach met the ATP or instrument rating standard, and, at the group level, the proportion of pilots in a sample that performed at the ATP or instrument rating level.

TWS data can be used in many ways. For example, the TWS for a single maneuver being performed by a single pilot can be established and used to provide easily understood feedback to the pilot (e.g., 75% of the last approach was within ATP standards). Such data could be compared across trials in order to establish the learning curve for a particular pilot (see Mengelkoch, Adams, and Gainer, 1971). To enhance the quality of the feedback, TWS data can be compartmentalized across various flight parameters, such as glide slope tracking, localizer tracking, airspeed, etc.

TWS data can also be used to estimate the proportion of a specific pilot population that can fly to a specified FAA standard by quantifying maneuver performance in a binary fashion. A pilot who completes a maneuver with a TWS score less than 1 would be failed on that maneuver. Once a group of pilots have been tested and scored on that maneuver, it is easy to compute the proportion of the sample that was able to successfully complete the maneuver. These data can be generalized to some broader population on the whole, assuming that random sampling procedures are followed. Such estimates can be compared across treatment groups in order to determine the real-world impact of a system on average pilot performance. This kind of treatment effect is directly interpretable and will likely be preferred by program sponsors and the aviation sector in general. In either use, the advantage of TWS over RMSE is that the participant and end users (including program sponsors) can examine the TWS numbers to determine whether the impact of a treatment or intervention is practically meaningful.

Although the TWS metric has the benefit of being easily and directly interpreted, it does have the drawback of being prone to ceiling effects. This is especially likely when the standard being applied is an easy standard or if the pilots under evaluation are high performers. In such cases, a more sensitive measure, such as RMSE, will be required to differentiate the performances. On the other hand, if performance in some area by some population of pilots is already at a high level, various interventions designed to improve pilot performance cannot have a practical positive impact. Another drawback to the TWS metric is that it is not a sensitive measure of performance, meaning that small improvements in performance or heterogeneous improvements in performance are not likely to be detected when using this metric even if the improvement in performance is real.

The researcher may choose to examine specific phases of flight (i.e., takeoff, cruise, approach, landing, etc.) or performance during specific maneuvers (i.e., turns about a point, stalls, level flight, etc.). Objective measurement techniques based on real-time data dumping allow the researcher to examine specific phases of flight or even segment-specific maneuvers to decompose performance across the various components of a maneuver or phase of flight. It is important to remember that different phases of flight require different KSAOs (knowledge, skills, abilities other characteristics) to complete successfully, and knowing that a pilot is able to fly an instrument approach well does not necessarily mean that he or she will perform well in other phases of flight. Similarly, changes in training or aircraft instrumentation may impact performance differently across different maneuvers or phases of flight. Systems designed to enhance performance under IFR (instrument flight rules) conditions may not enhance performance under VFR (visual flight rules) conditions.

NON-FTE MEASURES

Not all aspects of pilot performance can be directly measured via positional or orientation data. There are a number of pilot tasks that can be measured via automated data collection mechanisms that can provide additional information about pilot performance.

Rates of Change

Most simulators can provide rate of change data associated with roll, pitch, and altitude. Some aircraft operators may wish to establish criteria with regard to how fast the pilot changes the orientation of the aircraft to enhance passenger comfort, or more aptly, reduce the likelihood that passengers become airsick. The maximum rate of change can be extracted for a given maneuver and compared to some maximum allowed rate. If the pilot exceeds the maximum allowed rate, the pilot would fail that maneuver. If performance is being scored on a point system, points might be deducted for exceeding the maximum rate.

Operators may also wish to evaluate vertical velocity at touchdown in the interest of equipment longevity and passenger comfort. Harsh landings (i.e., touchdowns with a high vertical speed component) are not only uncomfortable for passengers but can also cause structural damage to the aircraft. Some operators use onboard flight recorders to evaluate real-time flight data following incidents in flight (such as passenger injury or aircraft damage). These same protocols can be used in simulation-based pilot performance evaluations.

Control Input

Some flight scenarios require quick and decisive action by the pilot, such as specific button or switch activation, throttle adjustment, or yoke input. Other research projects might wish to investigate the frequency or magnitude of surface controls or the sequence of control activations. Again, most simulators can provide such data. Switch and button activation is usually recorded in terms of button or switch position for a given time frame, and whereas control surface and power plant settings are typically given as numbers on some scale.

The key to using such data is to construct scenarios that require specific inputs relative to specific events. The analyst must know when the event was initiated and the response made by the pilot. Control input data can also be used to flag segments in a flight scenario. For example, the researcher may be interested in FTE on approach once flaps are dropped to 10°.

Switch activation data are especially useful when used to evaluate human interface design for communication and navigation equipment. Such evaluations can be performed using the "virtual" devices included as part of the software, where the pilot uses a keyboard or mouse to control the virtual device. More sophisticated simulators will use physical switches to control the function of virtual equipment. Similarly, physical mock-ups of radio stacks are commercially available, allowing the pilot to interface with a set of physical communications equipment. If funding is not a problem, the researcher can procure a specific avionics package and interface the package into the flight simulation software. This usually requires the construction of both hardware and software interfaces to allow the equipment to communicate with the software.

SUMMARY

There are a variety of ways to define and measure pilot performance. The desired usage of the data should drive the choice of measurement. Aircraft operators and pilot training centers tend to prefer subjective measures provided by SME (subject matter expert) evaluations of performance, whereas researchers tend to prefer objective measures. Each has its strengths and weaknesses, and the optimal choice is not always clear.

Regardless of the method chosen, steps should be taken to ensure that the measure is psychometrically sound. Whenever human judges provide ratings, disagreements among them are very likely, and efforts must be made to understand the magnitude of such disagreements, that is, we must estimate reliability. If the magnitude of such disagreements is large, then action must be taken to improve reliability. Although reliability is seldom a problem with objective measures (at least when it comes to the calibration of the machine; the pilot's consistency of performance may be another matter), the researcher should be careful to properly interpret observed differences. It is easy to overstate the practical significance of observed differences in FTE measures; we suggest that the researcher translate any observed differences in performance to real-world consequences (e.g., reduced risk, enhanced passenger comfort, etc.).

REFERENCES

Annett, J. 2002. Subjective rating scales: Science or art? *Ergonomics, 45,* 966–987.

Baker, D. P., & Salas, E. 1992. Principles for measuring teamwork skills. *Human Factors, 34,* 469–475.

Baker, D. P., & Salas, E. 1997. Principles for measuring teamwork: A summary and look toward the future. In M. T. Brannick, E. Salas, & C. Prince (Eds.), *Team performance assessment and measurement: Theory, methods, and applications.* Mahwah, NJ: Erlbaum.

Bernardin, H. J., & Beatty, R. W. 1984. *Performance appraisals: Assessing human behavior at work.* Boston: Kent Publishing.

Bernardin, H. J., & Buckley, M. R. 1981. Strategies in rater training. *Academy of Management Review, 6,* 205–212.

Cohen, J. 1960. A coefficient of agreement for nominal scales. *Educational and Psychological Measurement, 20,* 37–46.

Cohen, J. (1994). The Earth is round (p < .05). *American Psychologist, 49,* 997–1003.

Crocker, L., & Algina, J. 1986. Introduction to classical and modern test theory. New York: Holt, Rinehart, and Winston.

Cronbach, L. J., Gleser, G. C., Nanda, H., & Rajaratnam, N. 1972. *The dependability of behavioral measurements.* New York: Wiley.

DeShon, R. P. 2002. Generalizability theory. In Drasgow, F., & Schmitt, N. (Eds.), *Measuring and analyzing behavior in organizations: Advances in measurement and data analysis.* San Francisco: Jossey-Bass.

Flack, V. F., Afifi, A. A., Lachenbruch, P. A., & Schouten, H. J. 1988. Sample size determinations for the two rater kappa statistic. *Psychometrika, 53,* 321–325.

Guion, R. M. 1998. *Assessment, measurement, and prediction for personnel decisions.* Mahwah, NJ: Erlbaum.

James, L. R., Demaree, R. G., & Wolf, G. 1984. Estimating within-group interrater reliability with and without response bias. *Journal of Applied Psychology, 69,* 85–98.

Kenny, D. A. 1991. A general model of consensus and accuracy in interpersonal perception. *Psychological Review, 98,* 155–163.

Kozlowski, S. W. J., & Hattrup, K. 1992. A disagreement about within-group agreement: Disentangling issues of consistency versus consensus. *Journal of Applied Psychology, 77,* 161–167.

Landy, F. J., & Farr, J. L. 1980. Performance rating. *Psychological Bulletin, 87,* 72–107.

Landy, F. J., & Farr, J. L. 1983. *The measurement of work performance: Methods theory and applications.* New York: Academic Press.

Mengelkoch, R. F., Adams, J. A. & Gainer, C. A. (1971). The forgetting of instrument flight skills as a function of the initial level of proficiency, (Report No. NAVTRA DEVCEN 71-16-18), U.S. Naval Training Center: Port Washington, NY.

Nunnally, J. C., & Bernstein, I. H. 1994. *Psychometric theory.* New York: McGraw-Hill.

Rantangen, E. M. & Talleur, D. A. (2001). Measurement of pilot performance during instrument flight using flight data recorders. *International Journal of Aviation Research and Development,* 1(2), 89–102.

Shavelson, R. J., & Webb, N. M. 1991. Generalizability theory: A primer. Newbury Park, CA: Sage.

Shrout, P. E., & Fliess, J. L. 1979. Intraclass correlations: Uses in assessing rater reliability. *Psychological Bulletin, 86,* 420–428.

Siegel, S., & Castellan, Jr., N. J. 1988. *Nonparametric statistics for the behavioral sciences.* New York: McGraw-Hill.

Wigdor, A. K., & Green B. F. (Eds.). 1991. *Performance assessment for the workplace* (Vol. I). Washington D.C.: National Academy Press.

9 The Future of Simulation

Peter A. Hancock

CONTENTS

Simulacrum: An image or representation of something—an unreal or vague resemblance.

PROEM

I argue that, in the coming decades, the conception of simulation will undergo a metamorphosis as the fundamental assumptions about what constitutes simulation evolve under the driving force of progressive technological innovation. The primary stimulus for development will come from the need to explore all processes through which humans interact with technology. Such future interaction will find operators working on representations of task spaces, presented via diverse forms of sensory display (see Mouloa, Gilson, and Hancock, 2003). As the linkage between these display representations and actual system configurations will be contingent solely upon the software connections—and given that the metaphor for representation will be judged by its operational effectiveness, not the degree to which it replicates the appearance of the actual system—the difference between what is simulation and what is actual operation will disappear. The definition of simulation in such circumstances will depend solely on whether the operator actually effects change in the real-world system or is alternatively using, evaluating, or training at the time on exactly the same display connected to an electronic surrogate. In multiple-operator, multiple-system configurations, even this criterion will eventually fail to hold any permanent distinction because momentary control of the action affecting the system will be passed between individuals at different times. At this juncture, simulation will have passed the Turing Test for reality.

In systems where the only criterion difference between real and surrogate worlds is visual fidelity (conceived for enclosed control-room activities such as emergency response centers), it is feasible that visual projection capabilities will soon meet or exceed that which the eye encounters in the real world. It is to be anticipated that further progress in the visual realm will take us toward *super-simulation* in which what can been seen in a computer-generated reality exceeds that which can be seen outside such a facility. Given our knowledge of the human visual system and the technical focus on improving graphical representations, we are now passing quickly into this evolutionary stage. Super-simulation in vision will stimulate the desire for super-simulation in all other sensory modalities, and in the foreseeable future, we shall pass the comparable Turing Tests for all of the major sensory systems. At that juncture, we shall be incapable of distinguishing between a computer-generated and a physically generated world. Human factors will have a critical voice in contributing to and evaluating these developments because many of the barriers along this avenue of progress are composed of questions about human–system interaction. To create such supersimulated worlds, we shall want to know much more about cognitive and emotional capacities and individual variations in human abilities and attributes.

Early improvements may well be seen in relation to work with handicapped individuals who will benefit most immediately from the blurring of reality and simulation. Some of these notions have been expressed in both science fiction and film media, and their aspirations tend to anticipate scientific progress. The fundamental problems that follow will then concern the very nature of experiential reality itself. This is a philosophical issue and is addressed at the end of this chapter, where I seek to show what constraints bind us to our present reality, and what forces may emerge to divorce us from what we have previously been pleased to call the "real world."

> The intentions of a tool are what it does. A hammer intends to strike, a vise intends to hold fast, a lever intends to lift. They are what it is made for. But sometimes a tool may have other uses that you don't know. Sometimes in doing what you intend, you also do what the (tool) intends without knowing. (Pullman, 2000)

THE FUNDAMENTAL AND PRACTICAL REASONS FOR SIMULATION

Similar to robotics and artificial intelligence (AI), the bedrock impetus behind simulation is its capacity to support the efforts of human beings to artificially recreate themselves, and to control the world around them. Unlike robotics and AI, simulation is neither necessarily anthropocentric nor fundamentally anthropomorphic. Nevertheless, simulation has, throughout its history, been focused largely on the creation and recreation of "real" environments, often under the mandate of either entertainment or more serious practical necessities like military training. The most obvious stimulus, and therefore the source of support for simulation, will continue to be the interest in gaming and in the training of individuals and teams for subsequent performance in real and often dangerous situations. Consequently, in the immediate future, simulation is likely to continue on its present course and follow these established trends.

One growing concern for simulation, however, will emanate from the need for researchers to explore complex dynamic processes in disciplines ranging from chemistry and physics to geology, mathematics, and medicine. In fact, virtually all areas where humans pursue understanding can and will benefit from the dynamic and malleable representations that simulation renders. This will be a burgeoning aspect of the world of applied simulation. Even in light of this growing range of applications, the fundamental motivation behind future simulation will remain essentially involved with our never-ending quest to attain mastery over that which we can presently perceive, but over which we cannot at present exert control (Hancock, 1997a). Given these traditional and emerging drives, such as the desire for control and a pragmatic need for exploration in surrogate or transferred environments, it is an exercise in both logic and imagination to distill the future of simulation.

SIMULATIONS IN THE PAST

Those who want to see far into the future must first look well into the past. So, before we address what might be coming, a glimpse into the past can help us set our quest in motion. The first thing we need to recognize is that simulation is not a modern invention. Indeed, models and representations for practical employment have been around for many centuries. For example, the architectural model for San Petronio in Bologna, Italy, built in 1390, was 59 ft long and allowed people to walk inside to visualize what the finished building would be like. There is even evidence that Greek architects employed models in a similar manner some five centuries before the birth of Christ (see King, 2001). Clearly then, modeling and simulation are nothing new. Dependent upon the degree to which we let our definitional boundaries of the word "simulation" dissolve, we can even include artifacts such as religious icons as representations or simulations. One particularly interesting example can be seen in some of the great European Gothic cathedrals where, on the floor of the nave, was inlaid a maze, the one remaining at Chartres in northern France being an outstanding example (Figure 9.1). The primary purpose of these constructions was to act as surrogates for pilgrimages to Jerusalem. For those too old, too sick, too poor, or too pressed for time to accomplish the actual journey, the maze allowed completion of the journey symbolically. Eventually, of course, we shall recover this symbolic aspect for our more technically replete simulations.

The true origin of modern technical simulation may be attributed to Brunelleschi's demonstration of perspective. A Florentine architect, Filippo Brunelleschi (1377–1446) is best known for his construction of the dome of Santa Maria del Fiore, which remains the visual icon representative of Florence to the present day. Prior to Brunelleschi's interest and demonstration in perspective, medieval painting was predominantly nonrepresentational and, to us, a strange mixture of two-dimensional and fractal depictions (see the discussion of the use of the camera obscura technique by Hockney, 2001). Brunelleschi's concern was not expressed in terms of the word "simulation," but this was exactly what he achieved. With respect to the object of simulation, he chose one of the city's most famous sites, one which would be immediately recognizable to his fellow Florentines—the Baptistry of San Giovanni. Standing just inside the door of the Cathedral of Santa Maria del Fiore (with which his name would forever be linked), Brunelleschi painted a small

FIGURE 9.1   The maze at Chartres Cathedral is one of the few remaining. It was used as a surrogate representation for symbolic pilgrimages to the Holy Land. An early "simulation," its validity depended upon the credence ascribed by the user. Our future simulations will also eventually embrace this functional symbolism.

FIGURE 9.2 Illustration of Brunelleschi's mixed reality simulation. This illustration of the middle 1400s shows the situation as it would appear to the observer. At the center top of the door, one can see the eye-point and the hole through which the observer views the scene. In the mirror that the right hand is holding, one can see the painted panel secured by the fingers of the left hand. The mirror, in this case, shown as a circular one, can be temporarily removed and the observer then sees the real scene, shown in the figure at the edges of the mirror, for example, where the chin appears. The painted panel can be repositioned over the real scene to provide the artist's surrogate. The panel surface above the painted building is a reflective one so as to allow the sky to change dynamically and further complete the illusion. Arguably the origin of formal simulation, this was a magical wonder when first created. (Illustration by Lauriann Jones.)

panel of the baptistry outside in the correct perspective, with the cathedral doorway as a frame. Using the vanishing point as his reference location, he created a small hole in the panel. Thus, Brunelleschi could replicate exactly what individuals would see when they looked out of the door, by replacing the real scene with a static painted representation. This element of the simulation worked excellently. However, Brunelleschi faced the problem of simulation dynamics. It was acceptable that people did not appear in his painted scene; after all, the locale was not always populated with pedestrians. But what of the sky? Although there might be no moving terrestrial objects, were not the clouds always moving? Brunelleschi came up with an ingenious solution, which was characteristic of his highly inventive capacities. He solved the problem by making the display a hybrid one. The top part of the display panel was covered with a mirror like surface which reflected the actual sky above—surely one of the first examples of mixed reality (see Figure 9.2). The illusion was so convincing that it changed how people (and particularly how artists) represented their world (see also Hockney, 2001). Today, we should applaud this inventor as perhaps the spiritual godfather of simulation.

With the impact of Brunelleschi's demonstration, it was little wonder that subsequent competitions awarding commissions to construct specific parts of the Cathedral of Santa Maria del Fiore required the proposer to produce a model so that the city fathers could judge between different conceptions. One has the feeling that Filippo Brunelleschi would have been very happy at today's computer-aided design (CAD) station, visualizing the innovations he is now recognized for. But his unique simulation was for just this one fixed scene, and if any of the circumstances changed, such as the observer turning around, the illusion was immediately lost. The freedom to explore completely simulated worlds had to wait hundreds of years, until the present era. It is across these centuries that we now traverse to prognosticate upon our own future.

ON PREDICTING THE FUTURE

Predicting the future has many advantages. First, many of the developments that we are bound to see are direct, linear extrapolations of currently existing trends. For example, display resolution will improve, and networked computational systems will increase in capability and will be used to enhance multimodel experience. The design and facility of head-mounted units will undergo significant improvements. Indeed, for those who have ever seen the "Dayton Grasshopper," or any of the early forms of head-mounted systems This latter line of progress will already be evident. With respect to computational capacity, although we have not reached the clear physical barriers to computer speed, it is important to understand that we shall soon have to be concerned with the impending approach of these inherent limits. Despite the continuing progress in recent decades (see Moravec, 1988), it is evident that we cannot continue to double computational capacity at the rate we have been doing. However, the point in time when fundamental physical computational constraints will start to curtail simulation enacted on a network of parallel machines is perhaps a little too far in the future to affect the expected life span of the present chapter. Other linear forms of progression will include much greater research efforts on the integration of visual input with input from other sensory systems to enhance the overall experience of "presence." Audition, tactile stimulation, and olfaction will each play greater roles in improving the fidelity of all simulation. As a consequence, we shall have to make significant methodological progress in understanding and measuring the sense of presence in order to gauge the evolving state of the art.

Thus, the trick in prognostication is to attach some spurious numeracy to these predictions of linear or geometric progression and then feign surprise and publicize to the greatest possible extent the moments when such states of development are reached. Recognition then as a futurist depends upon a fallacy in reader's memories in which the author emphasizes all the successful predictions and relies on the frailty of human memory in failing to recall all the predictions made by the futurist that failed to reach fruition. I shall not engage in such legerdemain; but I am warning the interested reader that touts of all sorts, be they astrologers, financial advisors, or tabloid seers, all rely upon this fallibility of human memory (see Gardner, 2000; Schacter, 2001). However, if I am right in my predictions, be prepared to hear about it on multiple occasions; if I am wrong, I shall hope the publisher prices this book at the usual exorbitant rate!

Linear extrapolations are not the problem in predicting the future; it is the nonlinear leaps of progress, often fueled by a concatenation of unusual and often unforeseeable developments, which represents the great challenge. In the realm of simulation, this challenge is significant indeed as simulation lies at the confluence of so many volatile sciences. Obviously, any major stride in computer science directly affects simulation and its progress. This is equally true for both hardware and software innovations. However, computation alone is not the be all and end all of simulation. Psychology and the cognitive and neuro sciences have an enormous influence on what will develop in simulation because the laws of simulated worlds are largely psychological rather than physical. Indeed, it could be argued that the central point of simulation is to eventually free individuals from these physical and psychological constraints, a brief discussion of which I present later. But this is not the end of the confluence of forces. Many of the future developments in simulation will depend upon artists and those in the entertainment field whose conceptions and ideas are far removed from the groove of scientific thought. The minds of such individuals entering into the mix provides many quirks and bijouteries, and this is perhaps the major reason for their inclusion. However, all contributions need to be tempered to a scientific understanding. We can add much more to the factors influencing simulation's development. Among these, we have not yet included customers and their diverse desires, issues, and challenges, which will fuel the financial segment and so help shape the agenda of progress. The forces involved in the cauldron of simulation development are so varied and so tangential to each other that it is almost inevitable that they will produce nonlinearities that will have mainstream influence on all simulation technologies.

One of the possible nonlinearities of progress in simulation already being pursued is the way in which we get information into the brain itself. It may well be that, in the near future, we find that the eye is a relatively limited channel through which to get information to the visual cortex. The complexities, inversions, and selectivity of the retina might well prove to be the bottleneck in moving information across the cortical barrier. Where, then, is the sense of spending millions of dollars improving visual graphics systems for marginal overall gains when direct neural stimulation provides some orders of magnitude better return? To illustrate the possibilities involved in all forms of short-circuiting of the simulation process, it is critical to have an underlying theoretical framework of goal-directed behavior. One such framework is illustrated in Figure 9.3, which deviates from the normal linear stimulus–response information-processing perspective to emphasize the recursive nature of the perception–action/action–perception process (see Flach, Hancock, Caird, and Vicente, 1995; Hancock, Flach, Caird, and Vicente, 1995). In dealing with a recursive (in this case, actually a spiraling) process, one can essentially start and finish anywhere in the circular representation, but for the sake of convenience and clarity let us use the environment as the initial point of departure. In contemporary, electronic simulation, we replace the proximal (immediately perceived) world with its computational surrogate. Previous forms of simulation (such as those used in movie production) used physically erected sets that looked solid, but had, in actuality, little substance. The purpose of each of these forms, similar to the purpose of stage magic, is to "fool" the sensory systems. Often this is done by taking advantage of foibles and illusions well-known to perceptual psychologists.

Obviously, the next developmental stage of simulation is a hybrid one. Similar to the part-real, part-electronic combinations discussed later (see Figures 9.4 and 9.5), the synthesis of part-electronic and part-direct cortical stimulation will be the next breakthrough stage in evolution. The logical step to full simulation via cortical stimulation will be an obvious, feasible, and embraced challenge. However, notice that the goal of all these efforts is to communicate the perceived world to the user. The next important conceptual step is to understand that simulation needs to make a transition from perception to action. For this progression, we will need to know much more about

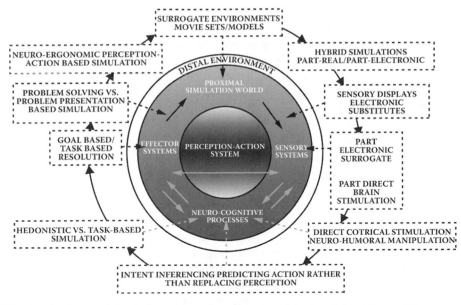

FIGURE 9.3 The future of simulation expressed as a function of the site of simulation and its representation. This sequence shows the fundamental purpose of simulation as breaking the barrier between the perceiver and the perceived, and between the same actor and the act.

the tasks, the goals, and, more generally, the intent of the user. At such a point in time, our concern becomes much more directed as to why simulation is necessary. If we are controlling, or practicing to control, complex systems in dangerous situations, the need to perform overrides the imperative to represent. If we can project simulations directly to the cortex, can we not similarly extract response directly from it? This being so, the surrogate and the experiential reality can be simply set together in a closed-loop relation (see Bush, 1945). There are movements toward creating such technologies as companions to input simulation, in which the neurological state initiates action in the real world via machine activation. This area, given the name *neuroergonomics*, is, at present, in its infancy (see Hancock and Szalma, 2003; Parasuraman, 2003). In the future, it promises to complement the advances in the perceptual augmentations of simulation by creating a way for the brain to directly affect the world. As we more fully understand human response in the context of expanding technological capacities, we shall see how simulation is a crucial component in dissolving the barrier between virtually expressed intention and subsequentially realized reality. At such a juncture one has, collectively, to be extremely wary of what one wishes for, as intent will almost immediately be translated into action. Simulation will be critical in showing us the outcome of our intentions prior to their physical expression. However, this is for the far-off future. Let us return to a little more near-term scenario.

THE PRACTICALITIES OF SIMULATION

Up to the present, I have largely engaged in speculation about the possible futures of simulation and the fundamental driving forces behind said progress. However, to those involved in the practicalities of simulation, such discourse may well seem almost completely superfluous. After all, those who are beset by pragmatic needs are concerned with the advantages simulation can render tomorrow and not in the far-off horizon of the decades to come. Therefore, it is incumbent upon me to consider these near-term issues because simulation science has, for most of its existence, been a very practical concern.

Those looking to employ simulation in the near term have to ask very pointed questions about whether it can save them time, money, and/or even lives in return for their investment of resources when compared to alternative approaches to their respective problems. Simulation is almost always appreciably cheaper than operations on the real system. Almost any technology we can think of, such as process control, aviation, commercial vehicle operations, and others, are much more expensive to train on the system itself than on a valid simulation. Of course, the problem of effective skill transfer always remains, but for technologies such as the space shuttle, one simply cannot train on the system itself as there are just too few of them in existence. For technologies such as nuclear reactors that are in constant operation, training on the actual system is neither feasible nor advisable. It is here that the cost-effectivity of simulation steps to the fore and makes its case.

Being able to achieve one's goal of operator training in the cheapest possible manner actually drives most practical decisions in our cost-conscious world today. Indeed, it was this focus on training that served historically to separate simulation from mainstream in human factors. As Chapanis, Garner, Morgan, and Sanford (1947) noted, training and thus simulation were largely the domain of the personnel psychologist who evolved into the industrial/organizational specialist of mainstream psychology. In contrast, human factors and human engineering scientists come from the roots of experimental psychology. This irrational division between human factors and simulation science is still evident to some degree in, for example, the comparable evolution of the Human Factors and Ergonomics Society and the American Psychological Association's Division 21 on Applied Experimental Society, although the latter organization has by itself a complex history. Fortunately, this rift has been healed by a much closer association that should now serve to bring human factors and simulation applications much closer together, hopefully to the strong benefit of each (Kennedy, 2004).

Although the simple fact of cost often dictates decisions, such deliberations are also often constrained by time. Building actual systems, or even full-scale mock-ups and models, can take an extensive amount of time, and in business worlds where time and money are considered interchangeable, the argument again comes down to the fundamental cost to achieve the goal. Simulations can be run so as to allow the consideration of an almost endless number of "what-if" scenarios. For actual systems or even models in which catastrophic consequences put an end to the physical entities, the cost of running a failure scenario can be prohibitive (as those who used model boards for early flight simulation know only too well). In the software world, the cost is essentially zero.

Allied to this argument is the question of risk exposure. Whereas actual models and even systems themselves can be rebuilt, human beings cannot. It is often the case that the practicalities of simulation are specifically for training in high-risk circumstances where failure is not an option. In simulation, we can engage in multiple attempts. In comparable real-world systems, these become one-shot trials in which one or more lives are clearly on the line. Again, this is a protection of resources and, in business terms, falls back to cost. However, when, for example, an instructor pilot and a student are killed in a crash, more than money is lost. Thus, for simulation to continue to function healthily in the future and even to burgeon, it needs to make very explicit its advantages in terms of time, money, and safety to the customers. Quantifying these advantages through mutually inspectable and reliable assessment methods remains an important goal of the simulation scientist.

SIMULATION AND TRAINING

Simulation has always supported training. Giving individuals' surrogate experiences in advance of events has always been considered an important advantage of simulation. However, for future simulations, much harder questions will be asked about the cost and effectiveness of such training. This implies that the behavioral scientist and the simulation technologist will have to work in even closer association to perpetuate simulation's advantage. In the near future, it will not be sufficient to merely present scenarios that approximate expected conditions and then expose individuals to these general circumstances. There will have to be a much more targeted approach as to what specific skills need to be trained and what component elements of such skill development can best be served by exposure to simulations. Thus, we could construct situations to familiarize the individual with general contextual information as to the global environment of operations. Alternatively, we could provide support for the assimilation of specific strategic skills such as decision making. For example, we could provide simulation support specifically for purpose-directed psychomotor skills of extremely high value, such as surgical expertise. It is evident that the nature of the cues that compose such simulations vary according to the skill set that is required for transfer. As has been previously pointed out (Kantowitz, 1992), this means that future simulations need to focus on the psychological variables necessary for skills support and cease to be driven solely by appearance and technological innovations. It may well be that the best simulation for supporting specific continuous psychomotor skill transfer (e.g., driver training) is simply a dynamic line display, and all other elements of the sensory display (such as texture) actually distract from such transfer. Thus, future researchers will have to ask very hard questions about the goal of simulation use and tailor the simulation created to those specific goals. In this line of evolution, we may well get some surprising paradoxes such as the one described earlier, where reducing the apparent fidelity of simulation improves its specific utility. Such developments await a much more systematic understanding of what facilitates simulation-based skill assimilation for subsequent real-world transfer (see also Morris, Hancock, and Shirkey, 2004).

Practical simulation is not only used for training (see Aldrich, 2004). Indeed, one can argue that the role of simulation in the process of design and systems acquisition might, in the future, be even greater than training (cf., Agard, 1980; Lane, Kennedy and Jones, 1994). It has been noted that the degree to which training is needed in human–machine systems reflects the degree of flaw in the original design. As an absolute statement, this is certainly subject to debate. However, it is true that some design improvements obviate the need for more extensive training, and so, in the search for ever-more cost-efficient systems, the wise procurer will think carefully about up-front investment in design. Here, of course, simulation again steps to the fore. The physical and cognitive operational characteristics of any system can be presented first in simulation and quickly changed to search for optimal, or at least improved, design options. However, this is a somewhat static view of the design process. I have argued previously (Hancock, 1997b) that, in the future, design will be a much more fluid and interactive process. Because systems themselves will be much more dynamic, generative, and evolutionary, the linkage between simulation and design will also be a much more flexible and interactive one. Indeed, as noted earlier, operators of the future need not necessarily know whether they are working on the actual system or practicing on a perfect surrogate; this same blurring will happen with the process of design, also. In other words, fluidity will be of much higher value, and the idea of the fixity of final products or finished simulations will begin to fade. The days of nomothetic, or generalized, simulations are numbered. The future will require much greater flexibility and a much greater focus on the individual as designer, operator, user, trainee, or customer. The future watchword of simulation will be customization or, perhaps more realistically, individuation (see Hancock, 2003a).

DISCOURSE BETWEEN TWO WORLDS

Whatever the trajectory of future simulation, I think it is safe to assert that there will be two fundamental considerations. Both concern the nature of the simulated worlds. I predict, without much temerity, that we will see a continued focus on improving real-world replication. In contrast, there will be a steadily growing interest in representing artificial environments. Since the very earliest forays into simulation, one of the main concerns has been with the practical issue of presenting simulacra of the real world. Obviously, the roots of simulation lie in training, in which it has been assumed that the most effective course is to expose individuals to a complete representation of an environment before they have to face the real situation. The less forgiving the real-world situation, the greater the utility of simulation. Little wonder then that the military has always been at the forefront of simulation technology as it is the quintessential institution engaged in exposing individuals to real-world threats. One of the mantras of this line of development has been "the better the simulation, the more effective the transfer of developed skills to the real world." The issue here, as noted previously, lies in the nature of the necessary skills. Simulation developers have been computer scientists and engineers, not psychologists. Engineers use a face validity, "existence-proof" measure of simulation quality. In seeking to control issues such as frame rate, polygon frequency, texture mapping, stair stepping, and the like (each of which are largely issues in computational speed), they focus on the appearance of the world, rather than on its psychological characteristics. Their traditional yardstick for improvement is to enter the simulation, and if it looks better and more like the real world, that is progress. The problem focus is on the technical barriers and glitches that prevent this metric of appearance from reaching better levels. Unfortunately, simulations are built for people and built for a purpose, and often such purpose and subject interaction are subtly at odds with the appearance metric. Let me give one illustration, although the reader will find many other examples in this text. In constructing wraparound ground-vehicle simulations, it is often the case that attempts are made to provide a high-fidelity visual appearance of the whole field, which can extend to a 360° field of view. Problematically, the human visual system does not register such levels of detail throughout its range, and indeed devotes detailed processing only to a very narrow 2°, the foveal visual field. Providing highly realistic, detailed information in the person's visual periphery is therefore not only computationally wasteful, it can induce simulation sickness and therefore negate the very reason for the simulation in the first place (see Stanney, 2002; and see Stanney, Kennedy, Chapter 6, this book). Few people can acquire important skills to be transferred to real-world operations while they are nauseous. Fortunately, as simulation research has begun to foster much greater interdisciplinary contributions and is now often encountered as a team effort, such issues as nominal realism versus psychological composition are receiving significant and deserved attention. It is a simple prediction that such interactive teams will make significant strides not merely in the improvement of simulation effectiveness but also in distilling composite measures of progress that include both computational and psychological parameters.

HYBRID SIMULATION WORLDS

Before passing on to the issues of assessment, it is important here to comment directly on the most interesting initiative that concerns simulations of mixed or hybrid forms. It is easy to see that simulation has made great strides in replicating certain forms of sensory stimulation, with vision being the outstanding one. It is equally easy to see that simulation has made relatively little progress in some comparable areas such as tactile stimulation. Here, I do not go into the reasons as to why this is so, but it does reflect, in part, the state of knowledge and research progress, as well as the result of practical resource allocation, in the immediate past. Be that as it may, we are left with a conundrum that simulation is close to fooling some sensory systems, whereas, others are hardly touched at all. The interim solution to this problem is the use of mixed or hybrid worlds in which the visual and auditory cues are computer generated, whereas the tactile cues remain firmly rooted in our present reality. Such a compromise results in the use of many overlay technologies such as blue screens, which have been pioneered and long-used in the entertainment industry. There is great near-term promise for these technologies, which are now beginning to have numerous practical uses. The illustrations shown in Figures 9.4 and 9.5 are from the University of Central Florida's Media Convergence Laboratory, and are taken from its mixed reality innovation test bed. As noted earlier, not only are these important steps in simulation evolution, they mark the way to other hybrid forms once further technical developments have been accomplished. Consequently, the way they integrate information sources is a most instructive development.

FIGURE 9.4 Illustration of a virtual forest, showing individuals experiencing a hybrid reality composed of a physical substrate with virtual overlays. (Copyright 2003 Media Convergence Laboratory, University of Central Florida, reproduced with permission.)

ASSESSING THE PROGRESS OF SIMULATION TECHNOLOGIES

To comprehend the problem of measuring the progress of simulation technologies, let us begin in a very roundabout manner; namely, by considering why (I think) ventriloquists are so awful. As a child and later as an adult, I have had to squirm in embarrassment when watching a "nominal" (amateur or, unbelievably, even professional) ventriloquist go through the shtick of "throwing" their voice to an unconvincing dummy. First, the voice is rarely thrown very far. In fact, in most cases, there is only four or five inches between the perfomer and the clacking mouth of a wooden puppet, or even more horrendously, a decorated sock! Fortunately, this pursuit seems to have disappeared from our major media, but still persists in what I prefer to call distributed pockets of psychological disturbance. The failure of the ventriloquists' illusion is evident in the decreasing age of their audience. Nowadays, unless restrained, even five-year-olds hoot such performances off the stage. Perhaps it can now quietly and reverently return from whence it came, which was: the adult-to-baby game of peek-a-boo.

The problem is quite evident. The so-called artists seek to suspend reality by relocating causation from themselves to alternate entities. But the illusion simply does not work. Ventriloquists can never throw their voice sufficiently far so that an facing audience can "see" the voice as if it were coming from the different location (i.e, the dummy). Hence, the dummy is always designed to be visually attractive, with a large moving mouth. The putative entertainers augment this nominal suspension of belief by adopting the stereotypical funny voice and by the minimal movement of their own mouths. Similar to that of a bad magician whose rabbits and pigeons are leaping and flying from the dress-coat, we see through and deride the failing illusion of the sad performer. In a general sense, ventriloquists are trying, albeit however slightly, to pervert the laws of physics and produce the appearance of sentience and causation in an obviously inanimate object. Note that the conversational and comedic aspects of ventriloquism are exactly parallel to the two-man stand-up comedy act, but in the latter, we do not experience any dissonance as the two individuals are both clearly seen as sources of causation. In essence, the sad ventriloquist is the equivalent of the failed simulation software and hardware engineer. They have tried to produce an illusion and manifestly failed. However, how and why the illusion fails are crucial questions for the future of simulation.

FIGURE 9.5 The top image is the physical appearance of the environment, and the bottom image is the complete environment with the virtual elements that provide the totality of the experience. (Copyright 2003 Media Convergence Laboratory, University of Central Florida, reproduced with permission.)

THE TURING TEST OF SIMULATION

To a degree, all simulations fail. Perhaps this failure is what we actually mean by simulation, that is, a degraded version of reality. However, soon this degree of failure or degradation will become so disappearingly small that those exposed to simulation will be hard put to tell the difference. All human sensory systems have a limit to their resolution capacities, and simulation capabilities will sequentially approach these individual limits for each specific sensory system. Paradoxically, because vision is a distal sense, in that it decodes information that is largely remote from the actual retinal site of activation, the visual capacities of simulation are rapidly approaching the level of reality. I have labeled this as the "Turing Test" of simulation because, analogous to the way that Alan Turing constructed a test for machine intelligence, the inability to tell the real from the simulated world constitutes a watershed threshold (Turing, 1950). For audition, this threshold is a little further removed. Not only are auditory displays serial representations, they are omnidirectional and very sensitive to change in locality. Also, quite bluntly, we know much more about vision, having dispensed many Nobel Prizes for vision research. Compared with the funding for vision, audition research is the poor cousin. Unfortunately, the most proximal sense, that of touch, receives virtually no funding in comparison. The few brave souls who labor in the field of tactile kinesthesis are made aware of this lack on a daily basis but—and again paradoxically—it is the barriers to the simulation of touch that are likely to be the last to fall in the search for the final passage of simulation's Turing Test. Subjectively, we attempt to assess this overall experience through a "subjective" sense of "presence." This latter construct represents the degree to which we are willing to suspend our disbelief of the simulation shortfall. As presence improves, so we approach closer to passing the Turing Test.

One method of achieving this passage early is by finessing the problem of touch. Instead of artificial actuators attempting some form of direct stimulation, one can merely substitute the actual real world for this part as in the hybrid simulations discussed in the previous section (see Figures 9.4 and 9.5). Transportation simulation is already well along the way to crossing the reality threshold. Using the strong advances of visual and auditory projection, the problem of touch is circumvented by having the individual sit in a cab of some sort, often taken from an actual vehicle. Providing stationary tactile cues is now taken care of, and the issue devolves to a question of providing appropriate dynamic motion cues to match events represented in the visual and auditory displays. In current high-end, single-seat aircraft simulators, this experience gets close enough to reality to make pilots sweat in hazardous situations. Of course, one can finesse the problem of vision and audition also by simulating naturally degraded worlds such as those occupied by fog in which both visual and auditory displays are, naturally, reduced. However, depending upon what it is we are intending to simulate, the feasibility of passing the Turing Test increases daily.

SUPER-SIMULATION

Human sensory systems have finite resolution capabilities. They address only a restricted portion of the electromagnetic range and have intrinsic limitations in both spatial and temporal acuity. Thus, what we experience as reality is a highly restricted "window" on a much richer world. Simulation is not bound in the same way. Indeed, it has been noted that whereas the laws of physics bound real worlds, it is the laws of psychology that bound virtual ones. So, if we pass the simulation Turing Test, what then? Due to the fact that many physical constraints can be fractured in simulation, it is both feasible and practicable to generate representations beyond real-world fidelity; these capacities, which I have labeled "'super-simulation," are the next evolutionary step. Of course, we already have several forms of super-simulation. We can already present the individual with displays of information taken from infrared and ultraviolet ranges, and scale them to be displayed via intrinsic visual capacities. We could also render the same isomorphisms in both auditory and tactile-kinesthetic worlds in which stimulation beyond the normal range can be mapped into the spectrum of normal capacities. This would, for example, allow us to hear what dogs experience, and via teleoperation we could "touch" worlds where no human has yet been. Variations in temporal presentation are also very familiar to us through entertainment media in which slow-motion or time-lapse photography either slows down or speeds up real-time events, respectively. The variation in visuospatial resolution is rather akin to the use of dynamic binoculars that provide a radically increased magnification resolution in some specified part of the visual field (where, of course, auditory and tactile-kinesthetic analogs are also feasible). In some sense, the latter manipulation then replicates visual structure and function of the fovea and periphery in the retina where an area of especially high sensitivity is bound by a surrounding region of lower resolution. In super-simulation, the boundaries of space, time, and electromagnetic range of innervations are no longer immalleable, and I fully expect to see the exploitation of these dimensions continue in the future to an even greater degree. Finally, as with earlier observations, the actual content of such incarnations is bound only by imagination as we have already seen in many entertainment "worlds."

THE MORAL DIMENSION OF SIMULATION

As well as the technical future of simulation, there is also a growing concern for its moral dimension, which it is important to consider here. In recent decades, we have seen the growth of the World Wide Web and the massive impact it has exerted in a number of fields. However, even the most cursory survey of the Web shows that one of the dominant themes is pornography, or more properly, explicit sexual content, since pornography is very much in the eye of the beholder (Lawrence, 1929). In public, many individuals deplore this tendency, and yet such images and activities must find a widespread and ready market; otherwise they would not be so plentiful. Our attitude toward this issue often reflects our own individual moral grounding, and questions of usage and censorship vary according to the different regions of the world and the cultural diversity in which such use is embedded. Many individuals agree that limitations on some aspects—for example, on child pornography—are needed, and this consensus allows a groups to designate certain activities as illegal. However, is public condemnation to be extended to purely private circumstances, and what role does enforcement play in such situations? Such questions represent the horns of moral dilemmas with which future simulation scientists must inevitably wrestle (see Hancock, 1998, 2003b). What is clear is that sex is a fundamental human drive and, like other forms of physical activity, sexual activity, too, can be represented in simulation situations. Given the fundamental nature of this drive, it can be anticipated that much effort will go into producing surrogates. However, what does this say for reality? If simulation were to reach a level of sufficient viability in reproducing tactile cues as well as visual and auditory stimulation, would this represent a breakdown in real-world sexual activity, which would pale by comparison with its unlimited and unconstrained electronic substitute? By extension, would this mean the curtailment of other social relationships? Teenagers already spend enormous amounts of time playing in their own rooms in electronic game worlds. Simply imagine the alternatives that could be rendered by advanced simulation possibilities. Indeed, how many of us would return to a mundane real-world existence given the choice of ultimate fantasy worlds?

It is not solely this "virtual isolation" which is of concern. What do we do about those individuals who wish to conduct illegal, illicit, or threatening activities and seek to use the facility of simulation to advance these goals? Indeed, the terrorists of September 11, 2001, took extensive advantage of simulation to achieve their ends (Hancock and Hart, 2002). Do we take the scientists' traditional dissociation excuse and indicate that the fruits of science are morally neutral until they are put to specific ends though social and political implementation (see Hancock, 2003b; Parasuraman, Hancock, Radwin, and Marras, 2003)? It was this very dilemma that had to be faced by Oppenheimer in the creation of the atomic bomb, which was certainly never a neutral technology. Thus, the future of simulation is not merely a technical challenge but promises to be one of radical social import. The creators of technology can no longer legitimately claim moral neutrality and perhaps simulation science is an area that can address this thorny but vital issue. Can we, indeed should we, find and impose limits?

A PHILOSOPHICAL VALEDICTION

I cannot leave a discourse on the future of simulation without explicit speculation as to these wider personal and social implications. Such projections are, of necessity, eventually to be founded in philosophical discussions. I know that such deliberations can be anathema to a segment of readers who are pragmatic and practice oriented, who are hereby excused, without prejudice, to proceed directly to the final, summary section. However, the pillars of philosophy are the foundations of society, and as the future of simulation promises to shake these very pillars, this brief excursion is more than justified.

Perhaps the most relevant place to begin is with considerations of the nature of reality. The British empiricists Locke (1690), Berkeley (1710), and Hume (1739) were among the vanguard of modern philosophers to question the fundamental nature of experience itself. It is evident that our moment-to-moment experience is derived overwhelmingly through our immediate sensory stimulation, and the basic question is whether all experience is contingent upon this ongoing stream, as other potential contributions are themselves contingent upon remembered experiences extracted from the same source. Locke's original comments on newborn children, as tabulae rasae upon which nature writes as if on empty page, is one radical position in the ongoing nature–nurture contention. Contemporary biogenetics tells us that the situation is much less absolutist than this, and that newborns are equipped with many innate capacities to help them deal with the challenges of the environment. In essence, Locke considered individual memory as an important player in the totality of experience, but did not, at that time, comprehend the notion of inherited genetic capacities (essentially a genetic memory) that would help frame the very earliest forms of experience. Our contemporary knowledge helps us understand that, indeed, reality is more than the stimulation of the moment.

Following Descartes, the question of reality as illusion became an important philosophical issue. Could it be, independent of the nature of all previous experience, that what was perceived as reality was actually illusion? Descartes could imagine an all-powerful entity (which he expressed as a devil, but in simulation terms might merely be an exceptionally capable computer) that could present to his senses a sufficiency of stimulation so that he was fooled. His only comfort was the fact that such a computer could not deal with the pure intuition that made it possible for him to doubt that illusory reality. His famous aphorism, *"cogito ergo sum,"* assumes that the very essence of self is thought, not perception—although in this he was also mistaken to some degree. Berkeley identified that all-powerful being as God and asked the most sensible of questions as to whether matter actually existed. His argument is most instructive, especially for future simulation scientists. Berkeley, himself a bishop of the Church, was a believer in the omnipotence and infallibility of God—omnipotence, meaning God could do anything; infallible meaning God was perfect. Since God was perfect, God would not make mistakes. Thus, God would not engage in any action that itself was not the most economic and efficient method of achieving a specific aim. From this, Berkeley argued that God could put directly into the mind of each individual the experience of reality, omnipotence allowing this difficult but conceivable action to take place. This being so, creating matter, that is, creating an intermediary mechanism for the perception of reality is not really needed. We do not need to go through the step of "perceiving" external objects because God can project such an image directly to the brain. Therefore, God being both infallible and omnipotent, matter is unnecessary—*quod erat demonstrandum* (Q.E.D.). This wonderful solipsist conundrum has never been resolved and, indeed, there are good grounds to believe that empirical resolution may be impossible. Today, we do not believe in this solipsist assertion, not because of any proof to the contrary but rather because of much greater doubts about the presence, actions, and capacities of any particular deity. Berkeley's argument however remains unassailed.

The question for the future of simulation in this context is—can we play the role of God? In actuality, this is logically equivalent to the passage of the Turing Test for simulation reality. At present, when we are in a simulation, we remain very much aware that we are in that simulation, not least in part because we remember entering that environment and agreeing, at least to some extent, to suspend our disbelief. The sense of reality would be much enhanced if, for example, we woke up to such a simulation, where the power of the continuous stream of memory played a diminished role. Similar to other concerns about the basic nature of individual existence, developing simulations that slowly and surreptitiously introduce artificially mediated parts of the environment into naturally occurring situations may help fully suspend our disbelief.

Contemporary psychologists and neuroscientists are very aware that the content of consciousness is a dynamic interplay between the stream of incoming information interacting with the centralized, largely memory-mediated processes. In this manner, to fabricate a true reality, simulation will have to embrace much more than simple surrogate sensory displays. It will have to dig deeply into the nature of memory and the facets of individual differences that connote personal identity and idiographic experience. Thus, the creation of "constrained" realities, that is, those in which the individual personally, voluntarily, and knowingly "buys" into the premises and constraints of the surrogate world, is not far off, and for many gaming situations, is already here. A convincing replacement world for non-cooperative, non-voluntary participants is further away, and designs will continue to rely on support from real-world surroundings for some time to come. Although the barriers are daunting, such problems are not insurmountable, and as we understand more about problematic issues such as tactile-kinesthetic stimulus replacement and the integrated experience of consciousness, we will eventually achieve other realities; but what then?

Simply creating persuasive other worlds is only the first step. Since our present concern is with the philosophical issues, let us cast aside, albeit temporarily, the pragmatic drivers that will power the future of simulation and ask the greater social questions. Let us suppose we can now create infinite alternative universes (and by this I mean that the users will be able to dynamically construct and control any object or agent in their "worlds" and that some method has been found to port the material essentials, for example, food, oxygen, water, etc., into these worlds). In such worlds, the user will be able to instantly satisfy any physical or cognitive desire. Who would wish to occupy such a world? Having occupied it, who would wish to return to this one? Coming back to "reality" would mean encountering individuals who are odd, unpleasant, incompliant, uncaring, polemic, sadistic, and even murderous. Who would take these characters over a collective of purpose-built electronic substitutes having infinite empathy, pity, love, and caring? In essence, what would happen to the fabric of human society when the necessity of social cohesion is fractured? The philosopher Rousseau (1762) asked much the same questions some centuries ago, arguing that any social bond is one in which one trades a degree of security for a restriction in autonomy. Further, he had a recommendation for those who wished to exercise untrammeled autonomy because they could not accept the restrictions of civilized society—he recommended they go to America! There, he argued, they would find a "new" world where the pressure of population on land was sufficiently small that people could "do their own thing." This transmigration of the discontent was not, of course, the preferred immigration policy of the Native Americans of the time. In today's world, Rousseau's contract is no longer voluntary and, therefore, no longer a viable contract. An individual born today cannot effectively decide to opt out, find unclaimed but productive land, work on that land, and remain socially isolated. There are individuals and small groups who try to sustain such isolation, and some (such as the Amish) have a degree of success. Other individuals and groups are, for differing reasons, not successful, especially when they directly encounter the unsympathetic power of society at large. In this sense, the cases of the Unabomber and the Branch Davidian group are particularly instructive and recent examples (Reavis, 1998). Given the prior claim on all lands of the world, today's social contract is imposed on individuals by force variously disguised in order to maintain a relatively stable collective. In this inherent tension, is there an opportunity for simulation science? I suggest there is.

Given the current population, it is evident that we will not reach any planetary system sufficient to support human sustenance and expansion in the time we have available (although growth is actually slowing in some regions). Neither, despite all the optimistic prognostications, are we liable to find a voluntary balance in global population. Given that there is little actual (effective) real estate for pioneers to explore and that the pressures on land continually increase, can the simulation sciences represent the "new" world? In the film *The Matrix* (Silver, 1999), we are shown warehoused individuals stockpiled for their power generation capabilities (a very doubtful premise). However, it may be that such warehousing is much more aligned with excessive population. Indeed, we already warehouse those elements of society who are termed criminal. Two hundred years ago, we ported such individuals to "new" worlds, such as the forced migration of "criminals" to Australia (see Hughes, 1987; Rees, 2002) by the English. Today, we essentially have no such remote lands to be exploited. Could we port such individuals to simulated worlds? Immediately, the question of cruelty and purposelessness come to the fore, but like the colonies of old, simulation worlds need not be inherently unproductive, and much of value may be brought back from these electronic potentialities to the one that will remain "mother reality."

Sufficiently advanced, future simulations can therefore act to change society once more in order to present choice to individuals. The problem with this is that, as human beings are inherently structured to accept options involving the least effort, who would be left to tend the machinery, advance the technology, and frame mother reality? My answer would be that it will, as it has always been, those who embrace challenge, see opportunity, and turn adversity into progress. As America once was, as the West once represented, as the Apollo program once exemplified, future simulation can represent the new frontier.

SUMMARY AND CONCLUSION

The future of simulation is bright. There continue to be many circumstances in which we wish to train individuals, and yet, not expose them immediately to dangerous situations. The traditional custom of military forces will continue, and the ever-burgeoning demand for entertainment will also drive simulation technology to improve. However, as well as progressing along these traditional lines, simulation will begin to expand and, in some ways, dissolve. I expect to see dissolution in the actual process itself. Since advanced system operators already act on representations of systems, and not directly on systems themselves, they already (to a degree) act on simulations. That this simulation changes between the actual system and a computer surrogate (and back again) could be easily achieved, and the substituted remain opaque to the operator. However, the flexibility and change in simulation will not stop there.

Simulation has often been used in the design process. The future will see a much more interactive role for simulation here, and in the same way we will find it difficult to parse simulation for training from simulation for operations; we will find it similarly difficult to parse simulation for design from simulation in operation. If the future continues to emphasize speed and flexibility, these dissolutions of definition will also be accelerated. Further, we will see much greater customization. In general, human factors has gone from its earliest forms in which individuals built and customized their own tools, through eras of mass production to adaptive systems, and are now finally returning to individualization (see Hancock, 2003a). In the near future, everyone will expect their respective simulation(s) to adapt to themselves and their own personal settings. Simulation will have to follow this trend and also show ever-increasing cost-effectiveness through a much greater focus on what the goal of the simulation is and how to achieve that goal at the least cost. The future looks bright—but don't worry! It is coming whatever you do!

ACKNOWLEDGMENTS

I would very much like to thank Robert Tyler, Brian Goldiez, John Wise, and Robert Kennedy for their comments on an earlier version of this chapter. Preparation of this chapter was facilitated by grants from the U.S. Army. The first was the Multiple University Research Initiative-Operator Performance under Stress (MURI-OPUS) Grant (#DAAD19-01-0621). The second was from the Advanced Decision Architecture Consortium (# DAAD 19-01-0009). The views expressed in this article are those of the author and do not necessarily reflect the official policy or position of the Department of the Army, the Department of Defense, or the U.S. government. The author would like to thank Elmar Schmeisser, Sherry Tove, and Mike Drillings for providing administration and technical direction for the first grant, and to Mike Strub for the second grant.

REFERENCES

AGARD. 1980. *Fidelity of simulation for flight training.* AGARD Advisory Report No. 159, Harford House, London.

Aldrich, C. 2004. *Simulations and the future of learning.* Wiley: San Francisco.

Berkeley, G. 1710. *Treatise concerning the principles of human knowledge.* Tonson: London.

Bush, V. 1945. As we may think. *The Atlantic Monthly,* July. Boston Atlantic Publishing.

Chapanis, A., Garner, W. R., Morgan, C. T., & Sanford, F. H. 1947. *Lectures on men and machines: An introduction to human engineering.* Systems Research Laboratory: Baltimore, MD.

Flach, J., Hancock, P. A., Caird, J. K., & Vicente, K. (Eds.), 1995. *Global perspectives on the ecology of human-machine systems.* Lawrence Erlbaum: Mahwah, NJ.

Flexman, R. E., & Stark, E. A. 1987. Training simulators. In: G. Salvendy, *Handbook of human factors.* John Wiley and Sons: New York. pp. 1012–1038.

Gardner, M. 2000. *Did Adam and Eve have navels?* W. W. Norton: New York.

Hancock, P. A. 1997a. *Essays on the future of human-machine systems.* Banta: Eden Prairie, MN.

Hancock, P. A. 1997b. On the future of work. *Ergonomics in Design,* 5(4), 25–29.

Hancock, P. A. 1998. Should human factors prevent or impede access. *Ergonomics in Design,* 6(1), 4.

Hancock, P. A. 2003a. *Individuation: Not merely human-centered but person-specific design.* Paper presented at the 47th Annual Meeting of the Human Factors and Ergonomics Society. Denver, CO.

Hancock, P. A. 2003b. The ergonomics of torture: The moral dimension of evolving human-machine technology. *Proceedings of the Human Factors and Ergonomics Society,* 47, 1009–1011.

Hancock, P. A., Flach, J., Caird, J. K., & Vicente, K. (Eds.), 1995. *Local applications in the ecology of human-machine systems.* Lawrence Erlbaum: Mahwah, NJ.

Hancock, P. A., & Hart, S. G. 2002. Defeating terrorism: What can human factors/ergonomics offer? *Ergonomics in Design,* 10(1), 6–16.

Hancock, P. A., & Szalma, J. L. 2003. The future of neuroergonomics. *Theoretical Issues in Ergonomic Science,* 4(1-2), 238–249.

Hockney, D. 2001. *Secret knowledge.* Viking Studio, Penguin: New York.

Hughes, R. 1987. *The fatal shore.* Knopf: New York.

Hume, D. 1739. *A treatise of human nature.* Noon: Cheapside, London.

Kantowitz, B. H. 1992. Selecting measures for human factors research. *Human Factors,* 34(4), 387–398.

Kennedy, R. S. 2004. Personal communication.

King, R. 2001. *Brunelleschi's dome.* Penguin Books: New York.

Lane, N. E., Kennedy, R. S., & Jones, M. B. 1994. Determination of design criteria for flight simulators and other virtual reality systems. *Proceedings of the IMAGE Conference,* Tucson, AZ, 12–17 June.

Lawrence, D. H. 1929. *Pornography and obscenity.* Faber and Faber: London.

Locke, J. 1690. *An essay concerning human understanding.* Basset: London.

Moravec, H. 1988. *Mind's children: The future of robot and human intelligence.* Harvard University Press: Boston.

Morris, C. S., Hancock, P. A., & Shirkey, E. C. Motivational effects of adding context relevant stress in PC-based games training. *Military Psychology,* in press.

Mouloua, M., Gilson, R., & Hancock, P. A. 2003. Designing controls for future unmanned aerial vehicles. *Ergonomics in Design,* 11(4), 6–11.

Parasuraman, R. 2003. Neuroergonomics: Research and practice. *Theoretical Issues in Ergonomic Science,* 4(1–2), 5–20.

Parasuraman, R., Hancock, P. A., Radwin, R. A., & Marras, W. 2003. Defending the independence of human factors/ergonomics science. *Human Factors and Ergonomics Society Bulletin,* 46(11), 1, 5.

Pullman, P. 2000. *The amber spyglass.* Random House: New York.

Reavis, R. J. 1998. *The ashes of Waco: An investigation.* New York.

Rees, S. 2002. *The floating brothel.* Hyperion: New York.

Rousseau, J. J. 1762. The social contract: On principles of political right. (Translation G.D.H. Cole.) www.consitution.org/jjr/socon.htm

Schacter, D. L. 2001. *The seven sins of memory.* Houghton-Mifflin: Boston.

Silver, J. (1999). *The Matrix.* Hollywood: Warner Brothers. Filmstrip.

Stanney, K. M. (Ed.) 2002. *Handbook of virtual environments: Design, implementation and applications.* Lawrence Erlbaum: Mahwah, NJ.

Turing, A. M. 1950. Computing machinery and intelligence. *Mind,* 59, 433–460.

Section II

Application

10 Human Factors and Discrete-Event Simulation

Linda Trocine and Dahai Liu

CONTENTS

ABSTRACT

In this chapter we introduce the subject of discrete-event simulation. It is a tool for modeling processes with events that occur at discrete points in time. Discrete-event simulation modeling has been a successful tool in aiding improved performance of manufacturing systems and operational service systems such as banking operations and hospital emergency rooms. We provide an overview of the steps involved in discrete-event simulation studies and how it can be used as an aid in decision making.

The rest of the chapter is dedicated to demonstrating how discrete-event simulation has been used and could be used as an aid in planning and decision making of systems with consideration for the humans involved in those systems. This is accomplished with a review of relevant literature of the use of discrete-event simulation in human factors, a list of potential application concepts, a simple example, and a list of resources. Discrete-event simulation is a proven tool for optimizing the use of resources such as machines and operators, but discrete-event simulationists have an opportunity to model the human elements with greater detail.

DISCRETE-EVENT SIMULATION

This book is about human factors and simulation. In general, most of the literature conjoining these two subjects focuses on virtual-world simulations wherein a human is operating in a simulated world. Computer simulation is also helpful in making better use of resources. Systems engineers model complex operational systems with *discrete-event simulation* to ultimately reduce costs, reduce time in system, increase production, or to better allocate expensive resources. Discrete events are those events that happen at discrete points in time. Examples of events that occur at discrete points in time are arrivals of customers at a bank and completion of assembly tasks on a production line. Discrete-event simulation has been used in a wide range of application areas for several reasons. For one, the system may not yet exist, in which case making decisions about the system's flow and resources may be simulated beforehand to aid decision making. For another, it may be far too expensive to reallocate resources in an existing system to see whether there is overall system improvement and, for a third, it may not be safe to experiment on a physical system to reduce system costs, whereas it is safe to experiment on a simulated system. In this chapter, it is our goal to introduce the human-factors community of researchers to discrete-event simulation as a tool for optimizing process-oriented systems.

In a banking service simulation model, customers arrive at the service location, wait in a queue, get serviced, and then depart. However, the time between arrivals of customers varies, the type of service the customer needs varies, and the time it takes to be serviced varies. Hence, the departure time of the customer is a random variable. One way to measure the average total time it takes for a customer to be serviced from arrival to departure is through simulation. Then, the only way to experiment on the system—such as by changing the proportion of service types the customer requests, changing the number of operators servicing customers, or changing the mix of operators by skill to service the customers, without impacting the existing customers—is through discrete-event simulation.

Modeling Complex Systems

The best textbook on the subject of discrete-event simulation is by Law and Kelton (2000). We refer the reader to this text for an excellent introduction to the subject: why simulation is necessary for these types of system problems, how to do all the modeling properly, how to validate the model, how to interpret the model output, and finally, how to systematically experiment with the model and optimize measures of performance. We give a brief overview of many of these steps in the following subsections. The key focus in carrying out simulation modeling and analysis is on improving some measure of performance. We describe a banking service operation to illustrate the steps in simulation modeling. The key measure of performance in such a system is to provide service in such a way that the average time a customer is in the branch office is minimized.

INPUT MODELING

In the banking service example given in the last section, we said that the time between arrivals of customers varies. That is, the interarrival time is a random variable. Person A arrives at 9:00 a.m., B at 9:01 a.m., and C at 9:05 a.m. The interarrival time between A and B is 1 minute, and between B and C is 4 minutes. The interarrival time is not constant but varying in the number of minutes. Simulationists observe the existing system to fit a theoretical distribution of the interarrival time. The steps are to collect data, hypothesize distributions, estimate parameters, and then conduct goodness-of-fit statistical tests. Usually the interarrival times are fitted with an exponential distribution (Law and Kelton, 2000). Alternatively, the modeler may use the empirical distribution (directly from observed interarrival times), or, if no data from an existing system are available to collect, the simulationist will rely on expert opinions and will fit a simple distribution such as the triangle or uniform distributions. The simulationist then goes through the same steps for the next random input variable in the system. In our banking service example, he or she would estimate the probabilities that the customer will select different services, such as deposits, withdrawals, or new account requests. Finally, in this example, the simulationist would then collect data and fit a distribution for the service time it takes to complete each type of transaction.

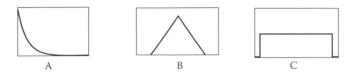

FIGURE 10.1   Three theoretical distributions: (A) is exponential, (B) is triangular, and (C) is uniform.

RANDOM VARIATES

Once the modeler completes the data collection and the fitting of the distributions for the input processes, the next step is to implement the model in a discrete-event simulation software package. We provide a list of popular software packages in Table 10.5. The software will generate random numbers that will be transformed into the appropriate distributions (e.g., exponential, normal, triangular, etc; Figure 10.1) that the simulationist fit during input modeling.

THE SIMULATION MODEL

Once the input distributions are derived, the simulationist implements the model into a simulation software package such as one from Table 10.5. The simulationist goes through a process of verifying the model during and after implementation. The verified model is run over a course of some period of simulation time (e.g., a full day at the bank for the banking service model). The simulation software manages the recording of events, the processing of events, and the collection of statistics. These statistics are the output of the simulation model and must be validated and interpreted. We discuss this next.

OUTPUT ANALYSIS

The statistics that the simulation software collects include the total time for a customer to receive service (from arrival to departure time) in our system. The available statistics are rich and include the minimum time for any customer, the maximum time, the average time, and the standard deviations of times. Each run of a simulation model will produce different results because the simulation output is a random variable. So, simulationists will replicate the running of the simulation and have the simulation software produce confidence intervals of the parameters of interest.

In the banking example, once the model is finished and we produce statistics on the key measures of performance (e.g., the average time customers are in the branch for service), we must validate the model. This means we should collect data from the existing system that shows how long it really takes for customers to depart the branch after arriving for service and compare this to the simulation model output. There are several approaches to validating the model, but the key point is that the output of the model should resemble the output of the real system. Once the model is validated, then the simulationist can experiment with it to see what changes the bank's manager may choose to implement to improve service to customers.

DECISION MAKING WITH DISCRETE-EVENT SIMULATION

With a validated simulation model, the decision maker will want to use the investment in the simulation model to make informed decisions. In the banking example, such decisions may have to do with when to let tellers go on break, how many tellers to staff, or whether to arrange tellers into two groups, each with its own queue: one for short transactions and one for longer-duration transactions.

A small model may require little computer time for the simulationist to run and analyze. However, most simulation modeling problems are much larger or complex than our banking example, so an efficient and systematic approach to experimentation is necessary. We encourage modelers to use proven experimental designs to measure not only the effect on the output measure of performance of a change in a single input variable (called a *main effect*) but also the joint effects of changing two input variables simultaneously (called an *interaction effect*). Individual effects between the two input variables and their joint interaction effect can be separated during statistical analyses. A suitable class of designs for such experiments is the full factorial designs, which measure all main effects and all interaction effects among the independent variables. The suitable class of designs for more than a few input variables (e.g., 5 to about 15) are the fractional factorial designs. Besides the excellent overview in Law and Kelton (2000), we refer the readers to Myers and Montgomery (1996) for a complete introduction to the design of such experiments and the analyses of resulting observations.

Once an experimental plan has been followed and analyses conducted, ranking and selection methods that distinguish negligible differences in system configurations from significant differences may be utilized to choose the best system configuration—best in terms of the measure of performance. In the banking example we might compare four system configurations; such ranking and selection methods will allow us to choose the configuration that will most dramatically reduce the average customer's time in our bank branch.

This brief introduction to discrete-event simulation was intended to introduce terms and concepts. Historically, discrete-event simulation has been applied to problems emphasizing material costs, (expensive) machine time utilization, and efficient operations. We now show how discrete-event simulation may be applied to make policy decisions about humans within those systems. After all, the systems exist to serve human needs.

HUMAN FACTORS AND DISCRETE-EVENT SIMULATION

In this section we provide some background literature that demonstrates how others have applied discrete-event simulation to questions of improving system design with respect to the human. This is followed by a discussion of the inputs and outputs that are relevant in this context. Then we illustrate a labor-intensive manufacturing system that benefits from the application of discrete-event simulation to the staffing of tasks. The last subsection lists discrete-event simulation software packages and other resources for applying the tool.

A Sampling of Literature

Early examples of the application of discrete-event simulation to questions of human factors are presented in Siegel and Wolf (1969). Their book provides four simple examples and one larger model. In the first example, the task is to land an aircraft on an aircraft carrier. The task analysis identified 37 subtasks for final approach. The simulation model was validated by comparing the four possible outcomes: wave off, mediocre landing, good approach, and excellent landing, with 162 actual carrier landings. The models measured idle time and overloading of the pilots. The second example was the launching of an air-to-air missile. The model included over 20 subtasks, the choice of which depended on equally probable alternatives of locating the target. The output measure of performance of the model was whether the pilot successfully completed the task within a time limit. The third example was the process of in-flight refueling of an aircraft. Four expert pilots listed the subtasks and the typical time required to complete each subtask. This model had over 20 subtasks and was validated with 16 test flights. The model measured the wait time for each pilot (strike pilot and tanker pilot), the overloading of pilots, and the number of nonessential tasks ignored by pilots when time was of the essence. The fourth example involved a radar operator and pilot intercepting an intruding aircraft. This model included over 50 subtasks and measured the stress level of both the radar operator and pilot, and the number of successful intercepts.

Siegel and Wolf (1969) also implemented group simulations where naval officers and crew were selected to complete several group tasks necessary to complete a mission lasting several weeks. Three alternative assignment strategies were modeled: selecting workers by specialty, by opportunities for training, or by selecting the best personnel for tasks. Input factors in this problem included worker's proficiency, overtime load, morale, and worker's work orientation (self-, crew-, or mission-oriented). Other factors modeled in the problem were environmental factors and communications complexity within the group. Outputs of the simulation model were overall system efficiency, crew morale, and overtime loadings. Decisions could ultimately be made about assigning crew to tasks to avoid overloading the crew and to increase crew morale while getting the important tasks in a mission done correctly.

We found little literature on the use of discrete-event simulation for human factors following the work in 1969 by Siegel and Wolf until recently. Moroney and Cameron (1994) described using discrete-event simulation of an air traffic control system to teach students about human factors in system development. According to Moroney (personal communication, March 7, 2003), the Defence Research and Development Canada (DRDC-Toronto, formerly DCIEM) developed the simulation model in MicroSaint in 1994. The model was constructed with task times from the literature. It was then validated with six ATC volunteers across 25 scenarios ranging over varying numbers of aircraft and update intervals. The DCIEM validated the model against observed data and found it was particularly good at predicting the level at which air traffic control operators make significant numbers of errors, referred to as the saturation level (DCIEM, 1994). Moroney still uses the model in his "Human Factors in Systems" course at the University of Dayton, Ohio.

Two relevant papers were presented at the 41st Annual Meeting of the Human Factors and Ergonomics Society. Both papers described the use of the discrete-event simulation tool Micro Saint™ in human factors problems. The first looked at human performance in a medical application (Archer and Archer, 1997). The purpose of the model was to investigate the feasibility of using discrete-event simulation for assessing effects of errors and changes in procedures to ultimately reduce errors in medical processes. The model utilized a comprehensive task analysis of a type of cancer treatment. At each step in the process the introduction of a human error was simulated and varied to estimate the overall effect of human errors on the total system. However, subject matter experts subjectively chose the human error rates. The authors admit the validity was limited with the model, and determining error rate probabilities was difficult (Archer and Archer, 1997).

The second example from the Human Factors and Ergonomics Society meeting measured the necessary crew size of a Coast Guard vessel, accounting for the need for humans to sleep and for the regular tasks that the crew performed (Lee, 1997). The key question answered is: How many crew are needed to safely and effectively operate a complex system such as a Coast Guard ship? The model allows for manipulation of crew size, work schedule, maintenance policies, and voyage profiles (i.e., timing and duration of port calls). Lee describes a multipronged approach to validating the model and confirmed its validity with high correlation between model output and observed data from the ships' logbooks. Wetteland, Bowen, and French (2002) also used discrete-event simulation to estimate workload and fatigue among crew serving on U.S. Navy and Coast Guard vessels to ultimately predict the appropriate crew size.

A final example is Baines and Kay (2002). These authors set out to model human performance in designing manufacturing systems. Part of their intent was to feed inputs into discrete-event simulations that are widely used and valued in manufacturing system design. They recognized that a manufacturing system's performance would likely be affected by worker morale, alertness, personality, and social conditions, as well as the work environment. They collected data and applied their methods to a Ford Motor Company assembly plant in the U.K. However, rather than modeling the system in discrete-event simulation, they chose to model just the human characteristics with an artificial neural network. The output of the neural network was worker performance, which was intended to feed the discrete-event simulation. Because of limited testing, validation was never completed and the model was not used beyond this point (P. Siebers, personal communication, February 11, 2003).

Cox and Popken (2003) utilized discrete-event simulation to identify effective risk-management strategies and to eliminate ineffective ones with respect to human exposure to, and human health impacts from, food-borne pathogens. Islo (2001) used discrete-event simulation to model complex organizational systems with human actor entities. The organization was a model of models of the main functions of the organization. Each of these had several layers of nested models down to models of each individual human in the organization. Each human was modeled in two parts, one of their observable work, and the other with their internal cognitive processes about their work. The model was implemented in SIMULA. It was recommended by Islo for strategic planning purposes by organizations to improve organizational performance.

Finally, Schweickert, Fisher, and Proctor (2003) described methods for collecting relevant data necessary for simulating cognitive processes. In particular the authors showed that existing task analysis methods might be reused for the simulation. The authors then showed that many means and standard deviations of common activity durations have been captured and published in the literature. Where activity durations are not available, they propose using a multidimensional scaling technique with linear regression to estimate the mean duration times for the several tasks of unknown duration. This involves having experts rank-order the average durations of all pairs of the several tasks, entering values into a multidimensional scaling program, and using the output and some absolute durations to regress the durations of all the tasks. These may then be input into the simulation model. This concludes our summary of relevant applications of discrete-event simulation for human factors. Next, we propose other application concepts potentially worth pursuing.

APPLICATIONS

In any system that involves humans to produce the work or operate parts of a system, there is opportunity to consider the human elements within a simulation of that system. We have identified some of the system inputs that consider the human in Figure 10.2.

These include policies for workers' rest breaks and the characteristics of a crew relevant to the system of interest. Such characteristics might be anthropometric, or to do with age, or visual acuity, personality, and so forth. Related to this is the proficiency of the individuals with respect to the tasks they perform within that system. Such proficiency might be characterized by subjective levels such as expert, moderate, and beginner, and may include prior training. In turn this may select a distribution of the time it takes to perform tasks with the system. The person's work orientation is also an input to a system. Orientation is defined here as in Siegel and Wolf (1969), referring to whether a worker is focused on his- or herself, on the entire crew, or on the mission. Environmental inputs may

FIGURE 10.2 Modeling human factors in a system: inputs, outputs, and within-system aspects.

be a factor in systems with respect to how fast the workers are fatigued. The social environment and social conditions within a system may influence the safety of the humans and the number of errors that occur. Finally, the number of tasks, the range of tasks, and the sequence of tasks are part of the modeling process and are required to model the human's role within the system.

Once the system receives its inputs, intermediate effects on the human may be measured or tracked, including fatigue, stress, accidents, alertness, morale, and the time to complete tasks. The workload of an individual at any point in time may also be measured.

The measures of performance of the total system are the typical ones such as throughput, errors, queue length, wait time, and efficiency. Additionally, the overloading of the humans operating within that system is an important output measure. Furthermore, mission success may take on more than one of the other outputs. Any of the output measures of performance may be influenced by the human factor's input variables and the effects of the system activities on the humans operating in that system. We next provide an illustrative example of how one might apply discrete-event simulation to modeling throughput, including that of the humans operating within that system.

EXAMPLE

We demonstrate a simple application of discrete-event simulation to a tablecloth factory. The factory has six workers that work together on one 8-hour shift each work day. There are three types of work involved: fine work, moderate work, and heavy work. Fine work includes threading needles, sewing the pieces of fabric together, sewing trim on the tablecloths, and finishing the edges. The heavy work involves loading the fabric bolts into the cutting machine, removing the cut pieces, transporting the cut pieces to the sewing stations, and loading the finished tablecloths on a cart to distribution. The moderate work involves folding the finished tablecloths and packing them into their individual, transparent folders for display in the retail location.

The company decision makers want to decide the appropriate staffing model—that is, how to assign these six workers into the three types of work to:

1. Balance the workload among the three different types of work
2. Maximize the daily production throughput of tablecloths

Table 10.1 shows the task time in minutes for each of the three types of work—fine, moderate, or heavy—according to triangular distributions. A triangular distribution is used when data do not exist to fit a theoretical distribution. It is elicited from subject matter experts by asking three questions: What is the minimum time it takes to complete the task? What is the typical time to complete the task? What is the maximum time to complete the task? This distribution has a range from maximum to minimum and a mode that is equal to the typical task time. Table 10.2 lists the interval between rest breaks for each type of task to recover from fatigue. Again, we used triangular distributions for the break interval. By policy each break will last 15 minutes.

TABLE 10.1

Time in Minutes to Perform the Different Task Types in Making a Tablecloth

Task Type	Time in Minutes		
	Minimum	Typical	Maximun
Fine	20	25	30
Moderate	12	15	20
Heavy	2	5	10

TABLE 10.2
Interval Time in Minutes between Breaks for Different Types of Work

	Interval between Breaks in Minutes		
Task Type	Minimum	Typical	Maximun
Fine	20	30	40
Moderate	30	60	90
Heavy	30	60	90

The model was implemented in the academic version of Arena v5.0. The model is shown in Figure 10.3.

Each node in the model has meaning in Arena. The first node is called *material arrival.* At the beginning of an 8-hour shift, all the fabric is made available for the entire day in this node. The second node, *assign attributes,* is where the process and distributions are recorded. In the third node, *assign break time,* the rate of breaks is entered. The next five nodes represent the process of moving bolts of fabric material, cutting the fabric, moving the pieces to the sewing stations, doing the fine work of sewing, and finally packing the finished tablecloths. The last two nodes of the model collect statistics about the process.

The nodes in Arena allow for modeling the workers' rest breaks. We used this to represent the human operator, who needs rest breaks before resuming work. Figure 10.4 shows the Arena setup of the triangular distributions in this example for fine, moderate, and heavy work, based on the distributions in Table 10.1.

The workload of the human operators is indirectly measured by their average utilization and thus average busy time in Arena. The simulation model was run using different combinations of numbers of workers assigned to the three types of work to yield the following result. The eight most meaningful of the ten possible assignments of six workers to three types of work are shown in Table 10.3. Each of these eight assignments, referred to as models here, was executed, and the utilization percentage of the operators in the three types of work was recorded (see Table 10.4). Also recorded is the number of tablecloths produced based on the worker assignments. The P utilization column shows the proportion of time the physical-work workers were busy during an 8-hour shift. Model 1 shows that the one person doing this work was busy 78% of the day. The one moderate-work worker was busy 79% of the time, whereas the four fine-work workers were busy 37% of the time. This arrangement of workers yielded 24 units of tablecloths in an 8-hour shift. Recall that our objective is to produce the maximum number of tablecloths possible while not overworking the operators. Both models 2 and 6 will result in the maximum number of tablecloths produced (30 each) while keeping the overall utilization of workers no higher than 78% of the time on their shift, which is below the OSHA recommendations of 80%. This simple model demonstrates that discrete-event simulation can be used to aid decision making to consider the human operators' needs in the staffing of tasks and setting rest break policies to maximize throughput of a system.

SOFTWARE AND TRAINING RESOURCES

Some of the most popular discrete-event simulation software packages are listed in Table 10.5. Though only a couple of the companies' websites refer to modeling the human factors aspects of simulated systems, we contend that any of these packages will fit the paradigm. The premier conference on discrete-event simulation is the Winter Simulation Conference, which occurs in the second week of each December, is an excellent venue to get started in discrete-event simulation. This conference offers breakout sessions on simulation software packages, on the basics of simulation modeling, and on a variety of applications.

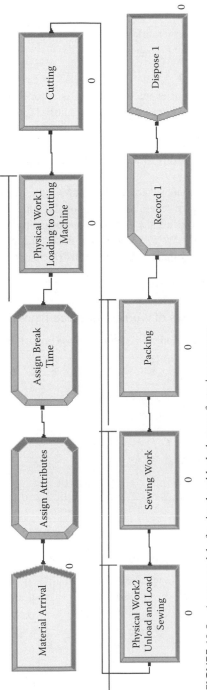

FIGURE 10.3 Arena model of a simple tablecloth manufacturing process.

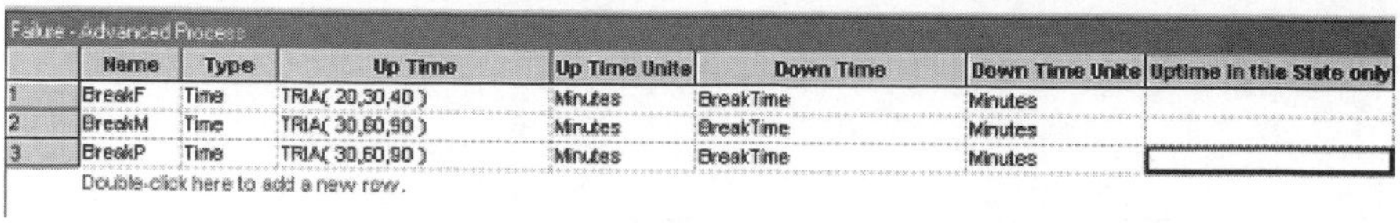
Failure - Advanced Process

	Name	Type	Up Time	Up Time Units	Down Time	Down Time Units	Uptime in this State only
1	BreakF	Time	TRIA(20,30,40)	Minutes	BreakTime	Minutes	
2	BreakM	Time	TRIA(30,60,90)	Minutes	BreakTime	Minutes	
3	BreakP	Time	TRIA(30,60,90)	Minutes	BreakTime	Minutes	

Double-click here to add a new row.

FIGURE 10.4 Arena setup of break times for different tasks.

CONCLUSION

In this chapter we introduced discrete-event simulation as a tool to aid in decision making of discrete time-oriented processes for optimizing some measure of performance such as throughput. We provided an overview of the steps involved and provided references for more detailed instructions on how to do discrete-event simulation modeling. We showed how it is of value in manufacturing and service operations to answer questions that are otherwise impossible to solve.

We followed the introduction with a discussion of human factors in the context of discrete-event simulation. We provided an overview of several references of the application of discrete-event simulation in processes where human factors are the primary measures of performance or influence other measures of performance significantly. We followed this with some application concepts of discrete-event simulation for human factors, a simple example to illustrate the process, and some resources.

TABLE 10.3
Alternative Assignments of Workers to Three Types of Work

	Physical Workers	Moderate Workers	Fine Workers
Model 1	1	1	4
Model 2	1	2	3
Model 3	1	3	2
Model 4	1	4	1
Model 5	2	1	3
Model 6	2	2	2
Model 7	3	1	2
Model 8	3	2	1

TABLE 10.4
Results of Eight Alternative Staffing Models and Number of Tablecloths Produced

Models	P Utilization	M Utilization	F Utilization	Production
Model 1	0.78	0.79	D.37	24
Model 2	0.73	0.52	0.5Q	30
Model 3	0.78	0.32	0.77	29
Model 4	0.78	0.10	0.67	13
Model 5	0.50	0.81	0.71	26
Model 6	0.57	0.49	0.76	30
Model 7	0.34	0.78	0.76	25
Model 8	0.35	0.21	0.69	13

TABLE 10.5
Discrete-Event Simulation Software Packages

Software Package (Alphabetically)	
Arena	Promodel
Awesim	Simprocess
Extend V6	Simulate
Micro Saint	Witness

Human factors and discrete-event simulation are both rapidly growing disciplines. Our goal was to introduce the human factors audience to discrete-event simulation as another tool in the toolbox for solving difficult systems problems.

REFERENCES

Archer, Rick and Susan Archer. 1997. Discrete event simulation of remote afterloading Brachytherapy cancer treatment. *Proceedings of the Human Factors and Ergonomics Society 41st Annual Meeting.* 1061–65.

Baines, T. S. and J. M. Kay. 2002. Human performance modelling as an aid in the process of manufacturing system design: A pilot study. *International Journal of Production Research.* 40(10): 2321–34.

Cox Jr., Louis Anthony and Douglas Popken. 2003. A simulation model of human health risks from chicken-borne Camphylobacter jejuni. *Journal of the Franklin Institute.* 9(1–2): 55–84.

Defence and Civil Institute of Environmental Medicine. 1994. The Development of a Task Network Model of Operator Performance in a Simulated Air Traffic Control Task. Report DCIEM-94-05. Toronto: DCIEM.

Islo, Henry E. 2001. Simulation models of organizational systems. *International Journal of Technology Management.* 21(3–4): 393–419.

Law, Averill M. and W. David Kelton. 2000. *Simulation Modeling and Analysis,* 3rd ed., Boston: McGraw-Hill.

Lee, John D. 1997. Validation of a simulation model to evaluate crew size. *Proceedings of the Human Factors and Ergonomics Society 41st Annual Meeting.* 978–82.

Moroney, W. F. and J. A. Cameron. 1994. Using discrete event and air traffic control simulations in teaching human factors in systems development: Part I—Syllabus. *Proceedings of the Human Factors and Ergonomics Society 38th Annual Meeting.* 989.

Myers, Raymond H. and Douglas C. Montgomery. 1996. *Response Surface Methodology in Product and Process Optimization,* 2nd ed., New York: John Wiley.

Schweickert, Richard, Donald L. Fisher, and Robert W. Proctor. 2003. Steps toward building mathematical and computer models from cognitive task analyses. *Human Factors.* 45(1): 77–103.

Siegel, Arthur I. and J. Jay Wolf. 1969. *Man-Machine Simulation Models.* New York: John Wiley.

Wetteland, Clyde R., Shane Bowen, and Jonathan French. 2002. Task network modeling: Resolving manning issues in complex environments. *IEEE Conference on Human Factors and Power Plants.* 41–45.

11 Virtual Reality in the Training Environment

*Dylan Schmorrow, Denise Nicholson, Stephanie J. Lackey,
Robert C. Allen, Kristie Norman, and Joseph Cohn*

CONTENTS

CHAPTER OVERVIEW

This chapter explores the role of virtual reality (VR) systems in the military training environment. It begins with a discussion of some of the current and future training challenges that VR can solve. These include enabling the warfighter to continue training despite the ever-increasing operational tempo and enabling the military to provide low-cost deployable training systems. In order to provide a framework for understanding these challenges, and some of the ongoing efforts that address them, a real-world VR application is described. Once this framework is established, the chapter then moves to an exploration of the enabling technologies that can be brought to bear on these challenges. This includes both instructional technologies as well as hardware/software technologies. Each technology is matched with a discussion regarding how these technologies can be integrated into a single VR training system within the detailed real-world example application. This chapter ends with a brief discussion of future directions for VR-based training technologies.

TRAINING CHALLENGES

VR technology has the potential to revolutionize the manner in which simulation-based training is implemented. Nowhere is this need for enhanced training more evident than in the military training domain. Continual increases in operational tempo and mission complexity force instructors to seek innovative solutions to meet these ever-increasing training demands. Research has shown that higher order cognitive skills and team process behaviors are extremely perishable (Cannon-Bowers, Burns, Salas, and Pruitt, 1998); therefore, frequent refresher training on advanced team and decision-making skills is required. However, the military—in particular, the navy and marines— are typically deployed at sea for long periods of time. Traditional training methodologies that are primarily instructor and classroom-based are not accessible to deployed forces. Moreover, cost and time considerations deny them the opportunity to practice on their operational systems during their deployment. The subsequent reduction in combat readiness for these forward-deployed units has created the requirement for providing training solutions in deployed environments. At the same time, the requirement to train deployed forces while at sea generates its own unique set of issues. Not only must these training systems be deployable, they must also be designed in such a way as to maximize training under often extreme conditions.

Ensuring adequate training within these unique parameters is by no means simple. Instructors will not be present to provide real-time and after-action review (AAR). Realistic training scenarios may be difficult to devise while deployed. Ensuring that these training systems will be easily usable is also a major concern. One unique solution to these challenges is offered by VR training systems. However, despite all of the recent interest in applying this technology, system developers are frequently left without any proven method for ensuring success. The Virtual Technologies and Environments (VIRTE) team, an Office of Naval Research (ONR)-driven research and development consortium, aims to integrate fleet-driven training requirements with cutting-edge technology solutions to provide training systems that support these requirements.

REALIZING THE TECHNOLOGICAL POTENTIAL OF VIRTUAL REALITY: A NAVAL EXAMPLE AND APPLICATION

VR research to date has focused primarily on technological developments rather than on the systematic selection and integration of these technologies into fielded systems that maximize training effectiveness. Realizing this need, the VIRTE team is developing, testing, and evaluating the effectiveness of prototype VR-based solutions for the training challenges faced within a single operational domain, Expeditionary Warfare (Lyons, Schmorrow, Cohn, and Lackey, 2002).

This domain involves both individual and teamwork behaviors and, as such, is an ideal setting for demonstrating the power of VR training solutions. The initial research focus for VIRTE was to create and to empirically validate an effective process for combining sound training strategies with VR technologies and to determine a set of human-centered metrics for ensuring design success. VIRTE leverages numerous years of research in this field conducted by the Naval Air Warfare Center Training Systems Division (NAWCTSD). These R&D efforts include: Virtual Environment Training Technologies (VETT) (Martin, Sheldon, Kass, Mead, Jones, and Breaux, 1999), Conning Officer Virtual Environment (COVE) (Roberts, 2001), and Virtual Environment for Submarines (VESUB) (Hays, Vincenzi, Seamon, and Bradley, 1998; Seamon, Bradley, Hays, and Vincenzi, 1999).

VIRTE trainees will be immersed in prototype simulators of key Expeditionary Warfare craft and interact with other entities generated by military simulations such as Joint Semi-Automated Forces (JSAF). The simulators are high level architecture (HLA)-compliant, PC-based, and deployable. VIRTE prototypes interface to a realistic and robust synthetic natural environment, including wind, sea state, waves, rain, tide, fog, buildings, and terrain. Additionally, VIRTE is developing Computer-Generated Forces (CGF) that have the capability to simulate teammates and adversaries during scenario execution so that meaningful team practice can be accomplished even when an entire team is not available (Cohn, Lackey, Soles, Lyons, Allen, Schmorrow, Stanney, and Graeber, 2003). This is an important capability that will enable fleet operators to practice in the deployed environment whenever they have time available. VIRTE aims to carefully integrate virtual

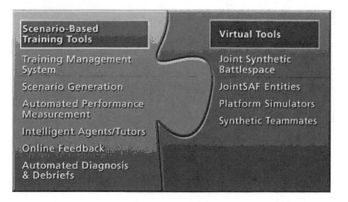

FIGURE 11.1 VIRTE joining SBT and VR tools. (Adapted from Lyons, D. M., Schmorrow, D., Cohn, J. C., and Lackey, S. J., 2002. *Proceedings of the Image 2002 Conference*.)

technologies, simulation environments, and automated tools tailored to the specific training needs of the Expeditionary Warfare community (Figure 11.1).

The VIRTE program consists of three phases or demonstrations. The first, Demo I, focuses on the Expeditionary Warfare Triad. The second, Demo II, addresses Military Operations in Urban Terrain (MOUT). A combination the first two demonstrations will constitute Full Spectrum Combat in Demo III (Figure 11.2).

Demo I. While VR systems have demonstrable efficacy within specific domains such as training flight skills (Reid and Cyrus, 1974; Bell and Waag, 1998), their ability to support multidomain and multiteam training has not been fully explored. The VIRTE program is intended to demonstrate the effectiveness of applying VR technology in order to train multiple, distinct teams to perform a range of tasks in synchrony. The selected domain, Expeditionary Warfare, was chosen in part because of its inherent cross-platform nature. This community consists of landing craft air-cushioned (LCAC) vehicles, advanced amphibious assault vehicles (AAAV) and tilt-rotor aircraft (MV-22 Osprey) (Figure 11.3). Although each of these craft fulfills different mission requirements, together they form the cornerstone of the Navy's Expeditionary Maneuver Warfare Plan (United States Marine Corps, 2001).

The LCAC is a hovercraft whose primary mission is to deliver troops, supplies, and vehicles from a ship to an already secured (beach) landing site. As such, the LCAC has effectively no offensive capabilities and scant defensive ones. The primary crew consists of a craftmaster, who flies the LCAC; a navigator, who develops the mission (flight) plan and provides on-the-spot guidance for modifying this plan as necessary; and an engineer, who ensures that all the LCAC systems are functioning properly throughout the mission. The AAAV is a vehicle currently under development

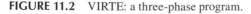

FIGURE 11.2 VIRTE: a three-phase program.

FIGURE 11.3 VIRTE focuses on providing deployed training solutions for the expeditionary warfare community. This community includes air, land, and sea elements. Left: landing craft air-cushioned (LCAC); center: advanced amphibious assault vehicle (AAAV); right: the MV-22 (Osprey) is a tilt-rotor craft currently under development. (Adapted from Lyons, D. M., Schmorrow, D., Cohn, J. C., and Lackey, S. J., 2002. *Proceedings of the Image 2002 Conference.*)

that is envisioned as providing Marine infantry with the capability for high-speed water and land maneuvers while carrying over a dozen infantry members. Unlike the LCAC, the AAAV is meant to operate under hostile conditions, in both offensive and defensive positions. Thus, the AAAV crew consists of a driver, who maneuvers the vehicle, a gunner, who operates the weapons system, and a commander, who performs command and control functions. Finally, the MV-22 is a vertical short takeoff and landing (VSTOL) aircraft, currently under development, that takes off and lands like a helicopter but flies like an airplane. Its primary mission is to provide air dominance over a battlefield. It will be employed by the Marines, the Navy, and the Air Force and, as such, will have different crew configurations for each service.

As should be evident, each of these craft requires crews of varying sizes in order to perform its mission. These crewmembers must maintain constant communication with each other in order to ensure success. Moreover, during any given mission, each vehicle must interact with other vehicles to achieve the overall goal of performing an all-out assault on beaches. Thus, there is a distinct need for training at both the intracrew level as well as the intercrew level.

Demo II. Whereas Demonstration I focuses primarily on developing vehicle-based platforms that would be controlled by individual users, Demonstration II focuses on harnessing the benefits of computer-based simulation to directly train the users—essentially, individual Marines—in the art of military operations in urban terrain (MOUT). MOUT is essentially combat in an urban environment, in which small-sized teams (typically four members) are required to move from building to building within one or more sections of a city, systematically clearing out enemy forces from each structure before progressing to the next one. MOUT is a highly dynamic and almost entirely unpredictable proposition, with each building presenting its own unique set of navigation and strategic challenges. Exact solutions to these challenges cannot be taught in advance. This, in turn, means that each team must determine, in real-time, how best to deploy its small assets to secure key positions within a building, without sacrificing flexibility, maneuverability, and team cohesion.

The essence of MOUT is captured in a set of techniques known as Initiative-Based Tactics (IBT), in which team members are able to generalize their skill sets to essentially any combat situation. Yet, for a variety of reasons, MOUT is a combat skill that is difficult to train. For example, developing an adequate understanding of IBT requires large amounts of time, and requires team members to independently move and interact more realistically with objects, as well as each other, within a diverse range of training environments and scenarios. As well, any MOUT training must condition these teams to operate under stress and to deal with unpredictable force-on-force engagements. Current training solutions do not adequately support this. Such solutions include developing small generic mockups of villages (known as combat towns) as well as providing individual Marines with time in legacy-type training systems. Combat towns, while allowing Marines the opportunity to apply in practice what they have learned in theory during classroom exposure, are expensive to maintain and have high pass-through demands. The large number of students and the fairly small number of such training towns means that individual classes move through this portion of training quickly and students typically have little chance to consolidate their classroom training through this real-world exposure. Legacy-type training systems are essentially marksmanship and Shoot/Don't Shoot training systems, which focus on enhancing individual skills rather than on developing more abstract warfighting strategies.

Consequently, these training tools fail to support many critical aspects of training that lead individuals to higher levels of MOUT competency. The Demo II system endeavors to change this state of affairs. By providing a distributed, networked virtual environment within which to train, trainees will be able to develop, and practice in, a broad range of training scenarios. As well, with its emphasis on integrated cutting-edge Human Behavior Representations (HBR) (Cohn et al., 2003), the Demo II system will allow a higher degree of training realism through force-on-force engagements with computer driven adversaries of various skill levels. Equally important, by relying on VR technology, which promises an ever-shrinking physical footprint, the Demo II system will make training more accessible. In turn, this will allow deployed Marines to maintain a more consistent training sustainment level and should reduce ramp-up time and skills decay at both the individual and the unit level.

Demo III. The final phase of the VIRTE program is planned to focus on integrating the advanced technologies for natural human interaction within synthetic environments developed during Demos I and II to address Full Spectrum Combat, also know as Combined Arms (see Figure 11.4). The Marine Corps' principle organization for conducting missions across the spectrum of military organizations is the Marine Air-Ground Task Force (MAGTF) (U.S. Marine Corps, 2003). The MAGTF is composed of four elements: Command Element, Ground Combat Element, Aviation Combat Element, and Combat Service Support Element. VR is a perfect environment to explore advanced training concepts for this MAGTF domain. The VIRTE goal is to realize the full

FIGURE 11.4 VIRTE Demo III will integrate the advanced VR methods and technology for full spectrum combat.

benefits of simulation-based training to provide MAGTF training, mission rehearsal, and AAR for all combat forces. The capability will allow training to occur at multiple levels from individual operators to battle group commanders, in operations that are too costly, dangerous, or impossible to do with live forces. The approach is to apply VIRTE's advanced concepts to the next generation of training simulations that the Navy and Marine Corps procure, including infantry, combat vehicles, fire support, ground support aircraft, command, and control. Potential new technologies will include interfaces to live command and control for experimentation, advanced concepts of augmented cognition to maximize human performance (Schmorrow and Kruse, 2002), rapid database construction, and advanced AAR and visualization tools.

ENABLING TECHNOLOGIES AND APPLICATIONS

Ongoing research and recent technological developments have rendered both instructional training and VR technologies to the military training community. The instructional training technologies include Scenario-Based Training (SBT), Afloat Training Exercise and Management System (ATEAMS), and Intelligent Tutoring Systems (ITS). Each of these techniques supports different aspects of an overall simulation training system package. For instance, SBT generates curricula through a validated process of planning, execution, and assessment. ATEAMS provides training management tools for instructors. ITSs create an automated environment in which to train procedural skills in order to master one set of predefined set of tasks.

Improvements in computer technologies extend the capability and range of VR technologies. Some VR technologies include displays, haptics, synthetic natural environments (SNE), CGFs, and locomotion. Displays and haptics increase the immersion level of a VR participant (trainee). An SNE substitutes the natural environment in the same way that CGFs are capable of replacing roleplayers and instructors. Locomotion provides the opportunity for the VR participant to perform movements in the virtual environment that replicate physical movement the natural environment. The instructional strategies complement technological developments in VR capabilities.

In order to better understand the individual instructional and virtual technologies and how they support one another, it is useful to discuss each in more detail. Each of the following sections matches an instructional or virtual technology with an existing or potential real-world example from the VIRTE program.

INSTRUCTIONAL STRATEGIES

Scenario-Based Training (SBT). As summarized by Lyons, Schmorrow, Cohn, and Lackey (2002), the SBT approach provides guidelines for training individuals and teams in environments that require complex interaction between humans and technology. It should be noted outright that SBT reflects a fundamentally distinct approach to supporting training as compared to traditional methods. In most classroom environments, training is delivered through a series of lessons, which together constitutes curricula (Cannon-Bowers et al., 1998). However, in SBT, training is embedded within an overarching scenario, which, in essence, becomes a dynamic curriculum (Oser, Cannon-Bowers, Salas, and Dwyer, 1999). To arrive at this scenario, the SBT process depends on a full-field analysis of all aspects of training from identifying training requirements, to developing the scenario to support these requirements, and to analyzing and assessing trainee performance.

There are four basic tenets of learner-oriented design upon which the theory underlying SBT is based. First, learning is a cognitive and behavioral process. Second, a systematic approach to learning will facilitate skill acquisition and retention. Next, performance must be systematically measured to ensure that the intended effect of training is achieved. Finally, training for complex environments requires a scenario-based approach (Oser et al., 1999). These core assumptions lead

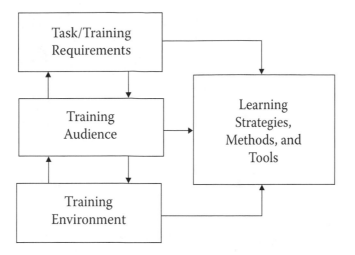

FIGURE 11.5 A conceptual model of learning. (Adapted from Oser, R. L., Cannon-Bowers, J. A., Salas, E., and Dwyer, D. J., 1999. Enhancing human performance in technology-rich environments: guidelines for scenario-based training. In E. Salas (Ed.), *Human/technology interaction in complex systems*: Vol. 9. Stamford: JAI Press, pp. 175–202.)

to the conceptual model of the learning environment, which drives the mechanics of the SBT components and guidelines (Figure 11.5).

This model focuses on the training audience, but systematically incorporates task requirements and training environment characteristics in order to generate learning strategies, methods, and tools. To accommodate the training audience, the model supports tasks of varying complexity levels as well as teams of varying size. Team training factors provide a foundation upon which to design training requirements. For example, training situations involving teams require careful consideration including (1) the team members' shared understanding and expectations (Cannon-Bowers, Salas, and Converse, 1995), (2) the organization of the team (Urban, Bowers, Monday, and Morgan, 1995), and (3) the physical location and proximity of team members involved in a training exercise (Dwyer, Fowlkes, Oser, Salas, and Lane, 1997). Task characteristics, including temporal and information requirements (Oser et al., 1999), direct the identification of task requirements as a whole. Characteristics of the training environment also play a key role in developing an effective learning environment. They include: (1) training event frequency, (2) training cycle length, (3) level of realism incorporated into the environment, and (4) number of training locations (Oser et al., 1999). Following the identification of the training audience, task requirements, and training environment, learning strategies, methods, and tools may be defined, developed, implemented, and evaluated.

SBT Guidelines and Phases. SBT operationalizes the tenets of learner-oriented design using a three-part cycle consisting of systematic planning, execution, and assessment (Figure 11.6).

The planning process begins with the identification of the trainee's required tasks, linked to individualized learning or training objectives, which correlate to competencies needed for his/her job. The events simulated during the execution of a scenario are chosen to create opportunities for the trainee to practice, or fine-tune their skills identified in the planning process. Each training objective and scenario event is associated with an expected level of performance for the trainee. The assessment phase of the SBT cycle calls for observers or automated systems to make performance diagnoses and provide feedback. Finally, maintaining a performance archive and skill inventory, which can be polled to prioritize training objectives for future training exercises, completes the cycle (Cannon-Bowers et al., 1998; Schmorrow, Lyons, Stanney, Lackey, Schaffer, and Cavitt, 2002). The following SBT guidelines create the foundation for the three phases of the SBT cycle (Oser et al., 1999).

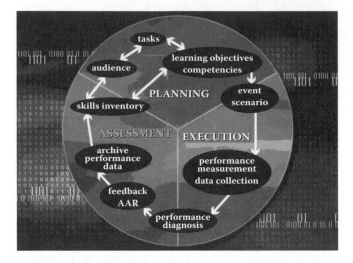

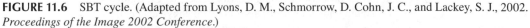

FIGURE 11.6   SBT cycle. (Adapted from Lyons, D. M., Schmorrow, D. Cohn, J. C., and Lackey, S. J., 2002. *Proceedings of the Image 2002 Conference.*)

SBT GUIDELINES

Planning

1. Define and document the overall focus of the scenario from the current skill inventory and the historical performance of the training audience.
2. Determine and document the tasks to be trained, based on the skill inventory and historical performance data.
3. Develop and document clear instructional objectives for the scenario.

Execution

1. Develop scenario events and scenario scripts that are based on realistic circumstances and are representative of real-world conditions and workload.
2. Develop performance measurement tools and standards around the scenario events that provide a clear link between instructional objectives and participant performance.
3. Develop a strategy and tools for diagnosing performance trends based upon previously defined performance measures and standards relating to the scenario events and instructional objectives.

Assessment

1. Conduct post-scenario debriefs (feedback) based on the instructional objectives of the scenario.

SBT Applied to VIRTE. VIRTE capitalizes upon SBT strategies, methods, and tools. Numerous training and engineering payoffs result from implementing the SBT guidelines into the architecture of VIRTE. Because the scenario is the curriculum, SBT is uniquely designed to aid in the development of virtual training environments where the trainee is immersed into a simulated environment. SBT is well suited to the technical complexity of VIRTE due to the emphasis SBT places on technical requirements and the factors that influence those requirements. The nature of the training systems planned for VIRTE focus specifically on team performance. SBT answers that need by designing methods and tools to quantifiably enhance team performance. From an engineering perspective, the linkage of scenario components in SBT facilitates an architectural systems. Advancements in cognitive science, particularly in the development and refinement of CTA methods and CGF/Human Behavior Representation (HBR) techniques based on executable cognitive architectures (Pew and Mavor, 1998), have enabled development of embeddable cognitive model-based agents used to assist humans in a variety of contexts. By combining the state-of-the-art simulation capabilities with cognitive model-based agents, advanced training systems can be developed to enable humans to train and practice individual and team skills in simulated environments that more closely resemble a user's real-world environment. This merging of technologies can also mitigate some of the resource and time costs typically associated with team training involving human team members and instructors using real versus simulated systems.

In VIRTE, the products of the CTA support the development of CGFs known as synthetic agents or "synthers." A comprehensive discussion of the synther development can be found in a later section titled "Computer Generated Forces."

Human–Computer Interaction (HCI). The discipline of human–computer interaction (HCI) is concerned with the design, execution, and assessment of interactive systems that relate to the human's work and tasks (Dix, Finlay, Abowd, and Beale, 1998). The three main elements of HCI are (1) the human, or user, which include both individuals and groups of individuals, (2) computer systems, which range in size and capabilities from personal digital assistants (PDAs) to standard laptops to large-scale systems, and (3) the interaction between (1) and (2). The interaction can be direct (i.e., the user interacts directly with the computer system, inputting commands and receiving feedback, e.g., as occurs when using word processing applications). It can also be indirect, in which case the user has little interaction with the computer system. An example of indirect interaction would be starting a batch processing task, and then leaving the computer system until the processing is completed (Dix et al., 1998).

The HCI evaluation can be applied to a computer system (referred hereto simply as the system) that the user is currently working with, a system under development, or a system being considered for purchase. The HCI evaluation focuses on the user's tasks and work and attempts to find a system that will better support the user in completing those tasks/work (Nickerson and Landauer, 1997).

When helping to design and/or assess computer systems the HCI professional attempts to uncover information relating to each of the components described above. First, the professional must know who the user of the system is. The professional needs to understand the profile of the typical user, the needs of the user, and the work/tasks of the user that the system is intended to support. The professional must also understand the goals that the system is intended to meet, both from the user's perspective as well as from the user's organization, if any. The system is usually intended to help increase productivity, improve performance, provide capabilities not currently available, and/or reduce manning requirements. From the user's perspective, the professional needs to find out what makes a system easy or difficult to use or learn. The professional must also determine the type of interaction, direct or indirect, that will occur between the user and the system (Nickerson and Landauer, 1997).

There are many tools and methods that the HCI professional may employ while evaluating a system. Examples include task analyses, user interviews, observational analysis, user testing, performance analysis, and applying knowledge gained in related fields such as human factors and cognitive psychology. The goals of the HCI professional are as varied as the methods employed. For example, the initial step in a task analysis would be to define the goals of the users and/or organization to determine how computers (or other tools) can help achieve those goals. The professional would then establish what the user's tasks are and how they currently accomplish them. This knowledge can be gained through observation, structured interviews, questionnaires, and documentation. Based on this data, the professional can construct storyboards of potential systems, or redesigns of a current system, and evaluate the design(s) using the targeted user group as participants in the evaluation process. In general, the goal of the HCI professional is to determine the tasks or activities that can best be augmented by the system and/or to increase the usefulness of the system at the workplace, home, recreational areas, etc. (Nickerson and Landauer, 1997). It should be emphasized

design that gains input for one component from the output of other components (Lyons et al., 2002). This, in turn, reduces the resources required to collect and analyze data. By facilitating resource reductions, SBT will aid VIRTE in addressing those issues associated with reduced manning situations (Oser et al., 1999).

VIRTE instantiates the SBT stages in a specific fashion. During the Planning phase, a mission needs evaluation is conducted. For the Execution phase, an overarching scenario supporting interactions among all craft platforms, as well as SBT scenarios supporting individual craft types are developed. For the Assessment phase, automated systems deliver instructor-like or roleplayer feedback and collect data to support AARs. These efforts to support team performance evaluation are elaborated upon below.

Planning: Mission Needs Evaluation. Lyons et al. (2002) indicate that perhaps the most crucial portion of the SBT process is identifying the instructional objectives, determining what elements support these objectives, and deciding how to incorporate these elements into a training scenario. This aspect of SBT provides the framework upon which the other efforts will ultimately be built and evaluated. The implementation of this guidance is oftentimes extremely difficult, despite the obvious benefits. Consider the overarching goal of VIRTE: to provide a virtual integrated expeditionary warfare triad simulation. This goal assumes, a priori, that two types of training will be provided (see McIntyre and Salas, 1995, for discussion on levels of training): task-level training (training for the individual, such as a LCAC Craftmaster or a member of a Marine Expeditionary Unit) and team-level training (the LCAC crew members must coordinate with each other). The specific identification of an adequate training scenario that supports these objectives is left in the hands of the experienced instructional developer, working intimately with the users for whom the VR simulation is being designed. The basic steps for the Mission Needs Evaluation process are described in Figure 11.7.

Taking the Virtual Environment LCAC (VELCAC) system as an example, the key requirements for VELCAC, as identified by discussions with multiple Subject Matter Experts (SMEs), are to provide a deployable platform that affords users the opportunity to define the environmental characteristics of the region in which they will be operating as well as the dynamic properties of the craft they will be operating. As a secondary set of requirements, VELCAC should support team interactions both within a single boat as well as between multiple boats. Finally, the ability to train the craftmaster position when the navigator is unavailable (Worcester and Worcester, 2001). These requirements result in the definition of a general scenario, within which users could define specific parameters. Embedded within these requirements is a set of performance metrics that can then be

Step 1: Identify Instructional Objectives
    Functionality: What needs to be simulated to
    support Objectives?
    Fidelity: How to display it?

Step 2: Analyze and validate
    Interviews
    Questionnaires
    <Repeat Steps 1 and 2 as needed>

Step 3: Develop supporting scenario
    Review with Subject Matter Experts

Step 4: Transition requirements and scenario to
System Engineers

FIGURE 11.7 Mission Needs Evaluation steps. (Adapted from Lyons, D. M., Schmorrow, D., Cohn, J. C., and Lackey, S. J., 2002. *Proceedings* of *the Image 2002 Conference.*)

used during the assessment stage to provide a measure of success. Upon completion of these efforts, this entire package is then handed to the systems engineers.

During the Mission Needs Evaluation, the planning phase of the SBT cycle is implemented. The audience addressed in this case are two LCAC crew members: craftmaster and navigator. A key element to LCAC mission success, and therefore mission rehearsal, is contact avoidance while en route to the beach. A specific set of communication exchanges must clearly and correctly occur in order to avoid colliding with another vehicle or object. Communication during a specific type of event serves as an example of a task. Instructional objectives and competencies can be based upon the task analysis of the set communication exchanges. The instructional objective(s) derived can then be instantiated as one or more events within a scenario event(s). The system designed addresses a specific audience by identifying a specific task, which is converted into an instructional objective directly related to mission success, and incorporating that task as an event into the scenario designed. VIRTE implements SBT by designing the scenario based upon specific instructional or training objectives that evolve from tasks identified as crucial to mission success for the LCAC community.

Execution: Developing the Scenario. The execution phase of the SBT cycle includes completion of a carefully designed scenario of events, collection of performance data, and measurement of performance criteria. Once the specific events are defined and developed into a mission rehearsal or training scenario, the execution of the scenario naturally takes place during an actual mission rehearsal or training exercise. Data collection also takes place at this time so that previously defined performance measures, which are correlated to the training objectives and competencies, may be evaluated.

Extending the LCAC example of contact avoidance, crew members will complete a mission rehearsal scenario by participating in a simulated exercise. During the scenario, another simulated craft will enter the pathway of the VELCAC. In order to properly manage the collision avoidance event, the craftmaster and navigator will be expected to complete previously defined communication exchanges. Human or automated observers will collect data regarding this specific scenario event and the data will then be used to evaluate the performance of the craftmaster and navigator.

Assessment: Evaluating Trainee/Team Performance. SBT's execution phase serves as the foundation for the assessment phase. Data collected during scenario execution can be compiled and support performance diagnosis, immediate feedback, and AAR materials. The performance data can also be archived so that a skills inventory or database may be maintained. The archive can then be used to generate an updated skills inventory, thus starting the next iteration of the SBT cycle.

Continuing the contact avoidance example for the VELCAC, human and/or automated observers collect data regarding a collision avoidance event and the performance of the craftmaster trainee. The data can then be assessed accordingly to evaluate the live craftmaster's performance (Lyons et al., 2002). Automated systems provide immediate feedback and the data that can support AAR. This system omits the use of a performance archive and skill inventory because it is intended as a deployed, expert-level mission rehearsal system, rather than a training system designed to meet the needs of trainees at varying expertise levels.

VIRTE integrates SBT's validated process and VR tools in order to improve training within the Expeditionary Warfare domain. The advantages of the SBT approach include a curriculum in the form of a scenario, emphasis on technical requirements, reduction in resources, and methods and tools to quantifiably enhance team performance.

Task Analysis (TA). One of the overriding issues that any VE (virtual environment) developer faces, prior to designing a new VE simulation is determining how to design a system that will support the user's training needs. Typically, designers adopt a "Brute Force" method, taking as their guidance the belief that by designing a simulation that perfectly matches every aspect of the real world they will ensure adequate training (Cohn, Breaux, Nguyen, and Schmorrow, 2001a). However, as Bowers, Salas, Prince, and Brannick (1992) and Locke (1986) point out, it is becoming increasingly clear that such high levels of fidelity may not afford parallel increases in performance. In fact, low-fidelity systems have been shown to provide effective training transfer (Ortiz, 1994). A more structured approach is to determine what information (world-based knowledge, perceptual

cues/stimuli) enables task performance (*task elements*) to then develop a model for task performance based on these elements and, finally, to design a simulation to support these task elements (Cohn et al., 2001). The typical approach for identifying these elements is to perform a task analysis (TA).

There are many types of TAs, such as job task analyses and work task analyses, from which to choose. The selection will depend, to a large extent, on the overarching goals for which the knowledge thus generated will be used. Each technique, in its own way, provides an understanding of tasks and work flow patterns, as well as identifying primary objects or artifacts that support tasks, information needs (both inputs and outputs), workarounds that have been adopted, and exceptions to normal work activities. Regardless of the approach used, the result of the task analysis is one or more task flow diagrams, with a supporting narrative depicting user-centered task activities, including task goals, information needed to achieve these goals, information generated from achieving these goals, and task organization (i.e., subtasks and interdependencies) (Stanney et al., 2000). The TA technique upon which we choose to focus is the Cognitive Task Analysis (CTA) (Card, Moran and Newell, 1983; Corbett, Koedinger, and Anderson, 1997). CTA, as the name suggests, emphasizes the cognitive nature of the task, rather than the behavioral nature of the task. Thus, CTA is well suited for eliciting knowledge in support of VIRTE's CGF role players because it is concerned not with training novices to perform specific perceptual-motor tasks, but, rather, with providing experts with training on abstract concepts. Of course, had VIRTE been concerned with other aspects of the task, another type of task analysis appropriate to those levels would be chosen.

As Chipman, Schraagen, and Smith (2001) indicate, there is no single CTA method that can be applied to every task. In fact, one of the key drawbacks of CTA is its lack of standardization. Nevertheless, a common theme running through all CTA formats is the notion that performance of complex tasks depends on an individual's ability to access knowledge and to make (often novel) decisions (Hackos and Redish 1998; Kirwan and Ainsworth, 1992). An additional challenge for those simulations that bring together multiple users is the emphasis on teamwork, and the identification of those elements that support training a particular skill. The CTA for teams (Team Task Analysis) is a relatively new field, with even less history attached to it than more traditional CTA (Blickensderfer, Cannon-Bowers, Salas and Baker, 2000). Despite this, there are general principles that one should follow when performing a CTA, as depicted in Figure 11.8.

As indicated in Figures 11.7 and 11.8, a clear link between the mission needs analysis and the TA(s) and, thus, CTA(s) exists. The overlap is inherent to the process of defining, conceptualizing, and documenting the domain at hand.

TA Applied to VIRTE. VIRTE researchers performed TAs for each platform within the program; a CTA conducted as part of the VELCAC effort serves as an example.

One way in which the knowledge elicited through a CTA can be applied is to represent it in a formal cognitive architecture. Advancements in computer hardware, processing power, and memory have enabled simulation developers to produce more realistic and more easily deployable simulation

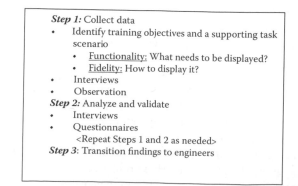

FIGURE 11.8   Cognitive task analysis procedure.

that the HCI professional should not assume that a computer system is necessarily the best system to meet the user's needs. It is quite possible that other tools or systems would better serve the user. Thus, the HCI professional should not be biased toward computer systems in general or toward one type of computer system over another (Dix et al., 1998).

HCI Applied to VIRTE. In order to improve the efficiency of the developmental cycle of the demonstration products (VELCAC, VEHELO, VEAAAV), VIRTE is employing various method-ologies, including usability analysis, task analysis, and HCI analysis before products are purchased or developed. One major goal of the HCI analysis was to determine which visual and haptic display devices, or combination of devices might best be suited for a deployable VELCAC system. The HCI analysis employed several of the methods mentioned earlier, including results of a task analysis, user profiles (derived from questionnaire data), user interviews, observational analysis, organiza-tional requirements, documentation, and application of scientific findings from human factors and other related fields. The results of this analysis will be discussed in the "Displays in VIRTE" and "Haptics in VIRTE" sections.

Afloat Training Exercise and Management System (ATEAMS). The Afloat Training Exercise and Management System (ATEAMS) is designed to meet fleet standards for Mission-Essential Objective-Based Training (OBT). The OBT process is a methodical training approach that defines the duties a ship, team, or crew member must discharge, the manner in which these duties must be discharged, and the standard to which they must be performed. In the past, OBT data has been collected manually through paper forms. That is, training objectives for each ship were written and bound in paper binders. Terminal objectives (objectives that the ship, team, or crew member train to), enabling objectives (objectives that, when performed correctly, allow the crew to meet the terminal objectives), and performance measures could be found in these binders. Each organization within a ship, e.g., combat systems or navigation, had its own set of terminal and enabling objec-tives, as well as performance measures (Hession, Burns, and Boulrice, 2001).

The use of paper as a data collection and analysis tool has several disadvantages onboard ship. These include inefficient scoring (the instructor may have to flip through several manuals to find the correct scoring sheet), misplacing one or more sheets, inaccuracy during data collection, as well as complexity of posttraining analysis. A requirement for a streamlined data collection tool was initi-ated, ATEAMS (Hession et al., 2001), as previously mentioned.

ATEAMS is a software application that is designed to manage the basic training of teams and individual naval crew members in both live and simulation-based training exercises. It has the capability to create training materials for individual crew members as well as teams. Through ATEAMS, naval commands can select training objectives via several methods. They can select objects through the Universal Naval Task List (UNTL) or Fleet Exercise Publications (FXPs). In addition, the command can select objectives through mission selection, a given training team, watchstations or watchteams (Stretton, 2001). ATEAMS allows commands to plan training events, generate OBT scenarios and data collection requirements, support both briefs and debriefs, support data collection and storage, provide a means by which trend analysis of performance can be conducted, and provide training data to the various Naval Training Commands. For example, instructors can select which training objectives they wish to present on a given day through ATEAMS. They can use the ATEAMS scenario generation module to create a scenario or modify preexisting training scenarios for that crew. The instructor can specify the types of craft that will participate in the exercise, the environmental factors, the location of the training exercise, and which team members or teams will participate. One goal of the ATEAMS project is to integrate it with the Battle Force Tactical Training (BFTT) simulation system. That is, once a scenario is created, its characteristics will be fed into BFTT, which will then run the scenario created through ATEAMS. ATEAMS also generates performance measurements for each participant, which can be either printed out or placed on a handheld computer or PDA. After the training exercise data has been collected, the instructor can take the handheld computer or PDA and upload it back into ATEAMS. The data can be rapidly organized and used for debriefing purposes. In addition, the data can be archived by the instructor through ATEAMS. ATEAMS also allows the instructor the option of inserting suggestions for the focus of future training exercises (Hession et al., 2001; Stretton, 2001).

ATEAMS Applied to VIRTE. As mentioned previously, VIRTE implements an SBT approach to develop, and ultimately validate, effective prototype VR-based solutions to the training challenges faced within the Expeditionary Warfare domain. Previous research has indicated the advantages of implementing the SBT cycle as well as the need for automated data collection tools. ATEAMS is a tool that can easily be adapted to the Expeditionary Warfare environment, because it uses commercial off-the-shelf (COTS) software for database development. Thus, Marine-specific Mission Essential Task Lists (METLs) can be added to the ATEAMS database and used for the developing, planning, briefing, executing, debriefing, and storing phases of the SBT cycle. The advantage of ATEAMS is that it is an automated tool that simplifies the SBT process.

Additionally, it may be possible to incorporate intelligent agents or CGFs into the ATEAMS/ BFTT system. Such agents can be used to filter and collect data that is more difficult for the human to filter/collect, e.g., factors that lead to a violation in battlespace geometry, the result of which could be fratricide. The agents could be used to flag such violations to the instructor, freeing his time for other training needs.

Intelligent Tutoring Systems (ITSs). Conventional ITSs are used to teach procedural skills with an end goal of mastering a predefined set of tasks. Traditional ITSs consist of four components: expert model, student model, pedagogical model, and communication module (Beck, Stern, and Haugsjaa, 1996). The expert model contains the domain knowledge to be presented and is a model of how someone skilled in a particular domain represents knowledge. The student model consists of specific information related to the individual trainee concerning their level of mastery in a particular domain. The pedagogical model is comprised of teaching strategies and how the presentation of instructional material should be handled. Lastly, the communication module controls the interactions between the instructional system and the trainee as well as the instructional system and external simulation components such as an SNE and vehicle platform simulator (Soles and Lackey, 2002).

Mechanisms that diagnose student performance and modify curricula/lessons typically characterize standard ITSs. Student diagnosis implies that the ITS must make inferences concerning the behavior exhibited by the trainee and then update the student model with the newly acquired information about the trainee's knowledge state and skill level. The curriculum/lesson modification mechanism applies the updated information contained within the student model to determine how to proceed with instruction (Lajoie, Azevedo, and Fleiszer, 1998). To perform these functions, the tutor must be able to (1) solve problems in the task domain at an expert level, (2) explain the reasoning processes used to obtain these solutions, (3) understand trainee misconceptions, and (4) sequence elements of instructions automatically so that one builds on another. Ideally, a diagnostic tutoring system employs various teaching strategies such as direct instruction and questions, hints, explanation, diagnosis and assessment techniques, and instructional management skills. Some of these teaching strategies are difficult to model because the process involves using student diagnosis to adjust teaching strategies in a highly interactive simulation environment (Soles and Lackey, 2002).

ITS Applied to VIRTE. The vision for the VEAAAV automated instructional components is two-fold: (1) aid live instructor in the schoolhouse setting, and (2) provide training without the benefit of a live instructor for deployed or Embedded Training (ET). In a schoolhouse setting, an instructor typically prepares the training simulator, provides a briefing for the trainee(s), observes the exercise, and aggregates data collected from various sources during the exercise in order to perform an AAR (Cohn et al., 2003). The AAAV mission needs analysis indicates a need for automated instruction and data collection, but not necessarily intelligent tutoring for the schoolhouse setting.

However, the nature of ET—specifically, the lack of live instructors in deployed settings— requires a more autonomous system. VIRTE researchers recommend ITS technology as described earlier to

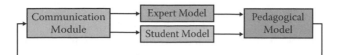

FIGURE 11.9 Traditional ITS components. (Adapted from Cohn, J. V., Lackey, S., Soles, R., Lyons, D., Allen, R., Schmorrow, D., Stanney, K. and Graeber, D., 2003. Conference on Behavior Representation in Modeling and Simulation, Scottsdale, AZ.)

fulfill the role of a live instructor. Inherent to the recommended design are the four models/modules shown in Figure 11.9, as well as a diagnostic system capable of generating inferences about the knowledge state and skill level underlying a trainee's behavior. Thus, the recommended VEAAAV ITS could adjust instruction based on systematic updates to the student model. With this information, a trainee's actions could be compared with that of an expert. Trainees could then be advised when and how their behavior differs from an expert's performance of the same task given the same circumstances. Differences between an expert's and the trainee's behavior could be addressed through immediate feedback and/or an AAR system (for more on this topic, see Cohn et al., 2003). By providing these capabilities, and tracking trainee performance over multiple exercises the ITS would not only simulate mission critical events, but also simulate live instruction with an experienced instructor.

VIRTUAL REALITY TECHNOLOGIES

Displays. A virtual reality is a computer-generated space through which individuals or groups of individuals interact. Virtual reality, like any other computer system, has both input and output devices. One purpose of VR output devices is to isolate the user from the real world. This isolation will, ideally, lead to a sense of immersion (Pimentel and Teixeria, 1992). Immersion in the virtual world is the degree to which the user feels he is part of the virtual world, which is also referred to as the sense of presence that the user has. Factors that govern immersion include, but are not limited to, the level of interactivity a person has with the virtual world, the update rate of the display, and the field of view (FOV) of the display equipment. Many of these factors are visual, thus stressing the importance of the visual system in the virtual world. However, it is important to note that none of these factors, either individually or in combination, lead to the greatest sense of presence, because these factors are individual-specific. Thus, a factor that may lead to a greater sense of presence for one person may have no effect on another.

Wright (2000) states that when choosing a display, six factors should be considered: the visual nature of the task, the collaborative nature of the task, facility constraints, underlying application software, budget, and availability of in-house expertise. Displays that can be used for virtual reality fall into three major categories. These are (1) head-mounted displays (HMDs), which include mixed reality displays, (2) projection displays, which include flat screen and curved screen displays, and (3) monitors.

HMDs. Generally, the screens of an HMD are liquid crystal displays (LCDs), cathode ray tubes (CRTs), or fiber optics. However, new display technologies, such as electro luminescent (EL) and retinal scanning displays (RSD), are being fielded and may replace the aforementioned display components.

There is a trade-off between resolution of an HMD and its FOV, with cost being the governing factor. Generally, high resolution HMDs have small FOVs. Most low-end HMDs use LCDs for their display element. The price of these units can vary between $500 and $80,000, with an average price being approximately $4,000. In comparison, the price of CRT and fiber-optic units ranges between $7,000 and $165,000, with an average price of approximately $45,000. In general, the higher priced units either have large FOVs, higher resolution, or both (Bevan, 1995; Able and Cojocari, 1996).

Generally HMDs are self-contained units, i.e., the wearer cannot view the outside world. However, mixed reality displays combine real and virtual information through the use of some visual display system. Mixed reality is a concept that encompasses both augmented reality and augmented virtuality. The first process is the augmentation of the real environment with virtual information, whereas the second process is the augmentation of the virtual world with real-world information (Ando, Matsumoto, Takahashi, and Shimizu, 1999). Different display device configurations can be used in mixed-reality situations. These include both video-based and optical-based systems. The former uses one or two video cameras mounted on an HMD and fuses the real-world image with computer-generated images. The latter uses beam splitters that reflect computer-generated images onto semitransparent mirrors through which the wearer sees the real world (Hua, Girardot, Goa, and Rolland, 2000; Rolland and Fuchs, 2000). Both optical-based and video-based mixed-reality systems are generally referred to as *see-through displays*, although in the latter case the user does not "see-through" an object (e.g., a semitransparent mirror) to view the real world. An exotic form of a see-through display is the relatively new retinal scanning display (RSD) technology. This technology uses a laser to paint pixels directly on a user's retina. An example of a retinal-scanning device, provided by Microvision, Inc., is called Spectrum™. This device is a see-through HMD that employs a retinal scanning display. According to Microvision, RSD delivers resolution quality superior to that delivered by any comparable display technology (2001). Based on information found at Microvision's website, this technology still does not produce full color but only monochrome (red or green). According to Siuru (2001), the FOV of the RSD is approximately 60°. If so, this means that much of the peripheral FOV will still be visible to the user, reducing the user's sense of immersion/ presence within a VE.

Projection Displays. Another method that can be used to create an immersive virtual environment is through the use of projection displays. These displays provide a large FOV and therefore may be more immersive than other display devices such as monitors. According to Wright (2000), general considerations when choosing this type of display include application, budget, and ease of use.

Wright (2000) states that the most important display metrics of projection displays include FOV, resolution, brightness, contrast, and color uniformity. However, the author states that resolution may not be as important as other factors, such as engaging the peripheral FOV, and the ability to scan (e.g., by turning one's head). Note that the FOV for large displays is dependent upon the distance that the user stands from it. For example, a 24-inch monitor has a 45° FOV when viewed from 2 feet and a 30° FOV when viewed from 3 feet. In contrast, a 24-foot-wide flat screen has a 100° FOV when viewed from 10 feet.

According to Wright (2000), another way to classify projection displays is grouping them into five categories: benches, flat-screen walls, spatially immersive rooms, curved-screen theaters, and concave-screen domes. Flat-screen displays use at least one projector. Compared to multiprojector units, a one-projector wall does not require a large amount of space and is inexpensive (Wright, 2000). Wall displays typically employ a flat, ridged vertical surface that is usually mounted on a wall. One disadvantage of one-projector wall displays is a limited FOV, which may adversely affect performance, particularly when detection of targets coming in from the periphery is important. A diminished sense of presence in the VE can also be attributed to limited FOV (Evans and Narayanan, 2000). In addition, interaction with such displays tends to be passive (just viewing things) and done indirectly (e.g., using a wand to move through the environment) (Wright, 2000).

Multiple projector displays are available and help solve some of the aforementioned problems. Wright (2000) refers to these rooms as spatially immersive rooms. For example, the electronic visualization lab developed the CAVE™ (Cave Automatic Virtual Environment) at the University of Illinois at Chicago. The working area of a CAVE environment is approximately 9 m^2 (Green and White, 2000), with the top and one side of the cube empty. The other three sides of the walls are 6-m rear projection screens, with a fourth projector aimed at the floor (Defanti, Sandin, and Cruz-Neira, 1993). The user enters the cave wearing liquid crystal glasses manufactured by Crystal Eyes. The lenses in these glasses cycle between clear and opaque 60 times a second. Meanwhile, every 60th of a second, a pair of stereoscopically different images is projected onto each projection screen. Each image on the projection screens is displayed for 1/120 of a second. The crystal shutters are synchronized in such a way that as one closes, the other clears. The cycle is 120 times a second. Thus, each eye sees a slightly different image the result of which is an illusion of three dimensions (Defanti et al., 1993). However, this system is currently very expensive, costing over half a million dollars (Defanti et al., 1993). In addition, due to an incorrect perspective parallax, only the user that has the device that controls movement can determine the viewpoint of the environment. Thus, although spatially immersive rooms can accommodate many people, only one person is tracked, and therefore only one person is afforded the correct visual perspective and will have a completely undistorted view of the display surfaces (Evans et al., 2000). Keystoning or warping of the viewed image can also occur in a CAVE system (Hua et al., 2000). Another disadvantage of this system is its complexity (Wright, 2000). A final caveat is that the space utilized for the CAVE needs to be relatively dark and large, approximately 30 feet (9.3 m) across by 20 feet (6.2 m) deep.

Curved-screen theaters are similar to flat-screens except that they wrap "around" the user(s) thereby providing more of an immersive experience for the user by engaging more of the user's peripheral FOV. Evans and Narayanan (2000) note that curved-screen displays or Visionariums share similar limitations to the CAVE system. Visionariums use multiple projectors and large screens—usually curved—and a large graphics engine. Because of this, they are usually quite expensive, take up a great deal of space (they are designed for presentations and the like), and require a darkened environment. According to Evans and Narayanan (2000), the projectors of these systems need to be adjusted monthly.

Concave-screen domes are hemispheric display screens upon which images are projected. For example, the VisionDome™, created by Alternate Realities Corporation, is a single-projection, 3-D display. The image is projected onto a hemispheric screen that provides a 180° FOV with a maximum resolution of 1600 by 1200 pixels (1.92 million pixels). The user does not need to wear any equipment to view the display. In addition, the equipment is relatively inexpensive and comes with a focus-free lens. The single lens also helps to promote image uniformity, in terms of brightness and pixel distribution. The VisionDome comes in three dome sizes: 4m, 5m, and 7m in diameter, the largest being able to accommodate 45 people (Evans et al., 2000). Despite this, Wright (2000) notes that the images of curved-screen tend to be less accurate than the flat screen images. To mitigate this shortcoming, Evans and Narayanan (2000) recommend that images displayed onto the VisionDome first be predistorted through spherical geometry to be properly displayed on the dome. However, the VisionDome has a "sweet-spot," i.e., an area on the display—approximately one-fourth the diameter of the screen—that provides undistorted views of the display. Outside this area, distortion occurs due to the curvature of the screen. Evans and Narayanan (2000) state that this sweet spot is larger than those found in other curved displays and that, unlike tiled displays, the VisionDome is a seamless screen that produces no hard edges.

Monitors. Monitors consist of one or more standard computer or television monitors that, depending on the make and model of a given unit, can vary in specifications for FOV, resolution, contrast ratio, etc. Many monitors are capable of high resolution (1600 by 1200 pixels) and support photopic-viewing conditions (up to 100 cd.m^{-2}) (May and Badcock, 2002). If a stereoscopic display is required, the user would need to wear a pair of glasses—for example liquid crystal™ glasses—while the display presented a pair of stereoscopically different images projected onto the screen. Depending on the FOV of the monitor, as well as the number of monitors used, a user's sense of presence may be severely reduced by this system. However, as noted earlier, a limited FOV may not be a problem, depending on the task being performed (Defanti et al., 1993). Other methods of presenting stereoscopic displays include anaglyphic glasses and autostereoscopic systems. The former does not yield true color, whereas the latter tends to be small displays (May and Badcock, 2002). In addition, monitors have the advantage of being readily available commercially and are also inexpensive relative to the other display options listed above. If a large FOV is required using one monitor only, then size becomes an issue. That is, the length of the cathode ray tube (CRT) increases as the screen's height and width increase, resulting in a bulkier and heavier CRT. Newer technology, such as electro luminescent or plasma displays, should mitigate this problem (May and Badcock, 2002).

Displays in VIRTE. As mentioned earlier, an HCI analysis was conducted for the VELCAC system. One goal of this analysis was to determine which display device would be best suited for this system. In terms of the human component of the HCI process, the HCI analysis revealed, through user interviews, that the LCAC crew would not use the VELCAC if was too complex (because they don't have the time). The user profile revealed that most of the LCAC community had limited experience with computers. These two points indicated that the VELCAC system had to be extremely user-friendly. The user profile also revealed that the LCAC community was composed entirely of males and that a percentage of them wore glasses. These facts had implications for the display system if it were determined that a head-mounted display (HMD) was the device of choice. That is, the lenses of the HMD would need to accommodate people that wore glasses. If the HMD allowed for an inter-pupillary distance (IPD) adjustment, then that adjustment would need to account for the IPD range of the male population. In a similar manner, the headband of the HMD should accommodate the head diameter of most males.

Observations within the LCAC revealed that a wide FOV was needed, especially for the craftmaster who at times would need to look behind the vehicle to maintain his situational awareness. This analysis also revealed that the instrument panels employed some digital readouts and had relatively small labels. These facts indicated that the VELCAC display device must have adequate resolution so the crew members could read their instruments in the VE. The requirement of adequate resolution is a concern in relation to HMDs, which tend to have lower resolution than most display devices (see Able and Cojocariu, 1996; Fitzsimons, 2001).

The HCI analysis then examined the computer component of the VELCAC system. Based on organizational requirements, it was determined that the VELCAC system had to be PC-based, portable, and deployable. The latter two facts meant that the system had to have a small footprint and needed to be able to handle the operational environment, including the shipboard environment. Such environments are subject to various sea states (calm to rough), vibrations, temperature and humidity fluctuations, and salt water contamination, as well as other contaminants, such as grease. Therefore, the display component of the system had to be ruggedized.

The above analyses eliminated all display devices except HMDs and monitors. The advantages and primary limiting factors of the eliminated devices can be found in Table 11.1.

A review of studies examining performance effects and other issues relating to HMDs and monitors was then conducted. The primary goal was to examine performance issues relating to each display device in VEs. A secondary goal was to evaluate each device using the organizational requirements mentioned above. The two systems being compared were an HMD system with tracking technology (most likely an optical tracking system) and a multiple monitor configuration with touch screens. The former system would use wireless haptic gloves for the engineer and navigator.

TABLE 11.1
VELCAC Display Devices Considered and Eliminated

Display Device	Advantages	Primary Limiting Factor(s)
Retinal scanning	High resolution	Monochromatic/cost
Augmented virtuality (chroma-keying)	Interaction fidelity	Complexity
Projection displays (single/multiple)	Large FOV	Cost/deployability/complex/interaction fidelity
Domes	Large FOV	Cost/deployability/complex/interaction fidelity
OEL displays	Lightweight/flexible	Maturity

TABLE 11.2

Advantages of HMD and Multiple-Monitor Systems

√ = Has Advantage	HMD System	Multiple Monitors
Functional FOV	√	
Color reproduction		√
Ease of use		√
User comfort		√
Weight (of system)	√	
Deployable environment (field hardened)		√
Portable	System-dependent	System-dependent
Cost	System-dependent	System-dependent
Maintenance		√
Support personnel needed		√
Deleterious effects of ambient light		√
Resolution		√
Jitter in visual scene		√
COTS (availability)		√
Simulator sickness		√

Each system would provide physical control surfaces to the craftmaster. Table 11.2 summarizes the results of these analyses.

As can be seen in Table 11.2, the multiple-monitor configuration generally had the advantage over an HMD system. Neither system had an advantage in deployability, primarily because the HMD system would require a tracking system that can take up a lot of space and that is susceptible to motion, causing jitter in the visual scene and/or miscalibration effects during training. The monitor system could potentially be bulky, although flat panel displays would help mitigate this problem. In terms of cost, neither system was given an advantage because that is related to the type of devices that would be purchased.

The main consideration with an HMD system are its ease of use and susceptibility to jitter, the latter factor being a contributor to simulator sickness. As mentioned previously, the LCAC community stated that it would not use the device if it were difficult to use. Although not known for certain, it is unlikely that there would be shipboard personnel dedicated to the operation and maintenance of the VELCAC. If that is the case, then the LCAC crew would have to operate the system. In this regard, one drawback to the HMD system is that the tracking system can easily become out of phase in a dynamic environment, such as that found on a moving vessel. If this were to occur, the LCAC crew would be unable to use the system. The primary advantage of the HMD system is its functional FOV. This would provide the craftmaster with the capability to quickly acquire information from any point in the visual field in a natural manner, i.e., by simply turning his head. It should be noted that the functional FOV is one reason that a multiple-monitor configuration was recommended versus a single monitor per position. The primary disadvantages of a multiple-monitor configuration are size and functional FOV. As mentioned, the former could be mitigated by the use of flat panel displays. The latter could be mitigated if the monitors had a large enough FOV to cover the visual field that the craftmaster needs to see in order to operate his vessel in a normal manner without having to use a mouse or other devices to move the visual scene.

Based on the above analysis, the multiple-monitor configuration was recommended as the system of choice with touch screens as the input device, followed by the HMD system with wireless haptic gloves as the input device. It was also recommended that an evaluative empirical study, comparing LCAC crew performance when using the two systems, be conducted onboard ship, because that is the most severe environment in which this system is to be used. Other analyses, including usability analysis, could be conducted in conjunction with this study.

Haptics. Haptics, through the sense of touch, allow users to learn about and interact with objects and their surroundings in real as well as virtual environments. Some examples of everyday haptic interfaces include keyboards, mice, and trackballs. Although these interfaces provide some tactual feedback to the user, the feedback that they do provide is indirect. However, an active haptic interface, such as an exoskeletal glove or a forceball, can provide the user with controlled feedback (Biggs and Srinivasan, 2002) that lets the user "feel" the unique attributes of an object (Youngblut, Johnson, Nash, Wienclaw, and Will, 1996). Using an active haptic interface in simulations not only allows for more immersion on the part of the user, it has also been attributed to improved subject performance. Not only are users quicker to respond (approximately a 20% increase), they also tend to learn in half the time, and make 50% fewer mistakes. Several attributes are thought to contribute to the improvement in performance. First, active haptic interfaces provide natural constraints that allow the user to ascertain information about the virtual environment, such as when a wall has been reached so the user does not proceed through it. In addition, these interfaces are designed to decrease "information clutter." An example of this is a beeper set to vibrate mode. It gives "the right message ('You have a page'), to the right person (the owner), at the right time" (Biggs and Srinivasan, 2002, p. 95).

To create a successful haptic interface, according to Biggs and Srinivasan (2002), one must bear in mind not only the appropriate hardware for sensing and display, but also certain aspects of the human haptic system. One consideration is that an interface used by the fingers gives greater speed and precision than one used by other body parts, such as a shoulder. Another factor to consider when designing a system is that the user can bear some software lags and still remain immersed in the program. Finally, research suggests that interfaces that permit two-handed interaction offer significant advantages over one-handed, because participants can perform spatial input in about half as much time when they use their preferred hand as compared to their nonpreferred hand.

Types of Feedback. Haptic interfaces produce two types of feedback: force and tactile. Force feedback refers to the forces that act upon the muscles, joints, and tendons. Although force feedback is appropriate for coarse object interaction, investigators have also recognized the need for more detailed displays within the regions of contact or tactile feedback, which are the forces that act on the skin. Tactile feedback is much more difficult to replicate than force feedback. For example, imagine trying to provide feedback in such a way that a person can distinguish between a cotton cloth-covered surface and a felt-covered surface. The replication problem is not just mechanical; it also involves trying to understand and simulating the correct forces (Pimentel and Teixeria, 1992). However, to provide realistic sensations, both tactile and force feedback should occur simultaneously (Youngblut et al., 1996).

Types of Haptic Interfaces. There are several types of haptic devices, including wired clothing, exoskeletons, wands, six degrees of freedom (df) devices, biological input sensors, and pen-based devices (Pimentel and Teixeria, 1992).

Wired Clothing. Wired clothing, usually a glove, is clothing that is wired to measure the amount of bend in body joints. These devices fit over and move with the limbs or fingers of the user. Due to the fact that wired clothing is "kinematically similar to the arms and hands that they monitor and stimulate, they have the advantage of the widest range of unrestricted user motion " (Biggs and Srinivasan, 2002, p. 105). They also appear to be the most intuitive, interaction device-type currently available. Because the wired clothing mimics the body's movements, positioning, task time, and accuracy are minimized, compared to the same parameters produced with other haptic devices. Increased positioning accuracy may also be attributed to the users' physically moving their bodies to face the target, enhancing "the perception of spatial layout of the depth dimension by creating multiple viewpoints and increasing motion parallax" (Werkhoven and Groen, 1998, p. 441). As position-measuring systems, body-based devices (gloves, suits, etc.) are relatively inexpensive and comfortable to use (Pimentel and Teixeria, 1992). One problem associated with gloves is that hand size varies. Thus, the loops over each finger joint may not be in the optimal position for all persons. A second problem associated with these devices is their fragility; they are fairly fragile and can break relatively easily. In addition, the clothing is generally wired to a computer; thus, problems of entanglement with the wires may occur. Moreover, gloves typically do not measure the bend in the last joint of each finger (Pimentel and Teixeria, 1992). Lastly, the body parts that are displayed in the virtual environment may not be in line with the user's body parts and, therefore, may degrade performance in the virtual environment (Werkhoven and Groen, 1998).

Exoskeletons. These gloves use hinged metal joints that are placed, individually, above all finger joints of the hand. Thus, the problem of differences of individual hand size is eliminated (Pimentel and Teixeria, 1992). Unfortunately, some of these devices are more costly than their wired counterparts. In addition, external wires, such as those which would be attached to peripheral devices like a wand, are more likely to become tangled in the hardware of this type of glove (Pimentel and Teixeria, 1992).

Wands. Wands are small diameter, tube-like devices that can be employed in a variety of ways. Wands typically have several activation switches mounted on them. In the virtual world, a wand can be made to look like any type of hand-held device, including guns, paintbrushes, a hand, etc. One way that a wand can be employed is as a selection device. For example, the user can be given a finger icon that moves according to the position of the wand. Once the user positions the finger over a virtual button, the user can press a switch on the wand to activate the virtual device (Pimentel and Teixeria, 1992). The wand can also function as a navigational device. For example, the user can point the wand in the preferred direction and push a button, which subsequently moves the user toward the said direction (Pimentel and Teixeria, 1992). A disadvantage of wands is face validity, meaning the wand may not have the appearance or feel of the device it represents.

Six df Devices. Six df devices include both joysticks and forceballs, and are used for movement within the virtual world. Joysticks are the oldest and most well known of these devices. Although they were initially manufactured for the control of aircraft, the newly manufactured joysticks are force-reflecting (Biggs and Srinivasan, 2002). Like wands, joysticks may not have face-validity. Forceballs are composed of a stationary ball, which is about the size of a baseball, an armrest to which the ball is mounted, and several buttons installed at the base of the armrest. The forceball itself does not move; rather, the force applied to the ball is measured and sent to the computer. For example, if a user wanted to rise straight up in the virtual world, he would pull up on the force ball (Pimentel and Teixeria, 1992).

Biological Input Sensors. These devices process physical activities that are less direct than the activities discussed above, e.g., electrical activity generated by muscles or voice recognition, and convert this activity into computer control commands. For example, if electrodes that measure skin tension are placed near the eyes the user can, by squinting or blinking, enter various commands via computer to the virtual world. These devices are especially useful for the handicapped population (Pimentel and Teixeria, 1992). However, like wands and joysticks, these devices lack face validity.

Pen-Based Devices. According to Biggs and Srinivasan (2002), pen-based devices are force-reflecting interfaces for use in VEs. The Phantom, from SensAble Technologies, is a leading interface that is available in a multitude of models, with three or six df. One problem associated with these devices is their lack of mobility, because they are generally mounted on a table.

Miscellaneous Devices. Freedom 6S by MPB Technologies Inc. (2002), is a six df desktop device that allows an interaction between a user and a telemanipulator or with objects in a VE. Through translation and rotation, the operator feels forces, which simulate reality. Another device is the Thunderseat by Thunderseat USA (2002), which is a recliner/chair with a joystick in the arm and a subwoofer in the bottom. Vibrations are emitted through the chair via the subwoofer, enhancing the haptic experience for the user.

Haptics in VIRTE. Since the VELCAC was meant to be portable, configurations that used hard equipment mockups of the LCAC knobs, dials, buttons, and control surfaces were not considered.

This meant that the interface between the user and computer would have to be virtual. In addition, the HCI analysis of the visual display system influenced the type of interaction device that would be chosen for the VELCAC. As the display device would either be an HMD or a multiple-monitor configuration, the interface device would either be a haptic device or a touch screen. The interface device is related to the interaction component of the HCI process. This portion of the HCI analysis was based primarily on observational analyses, user interviews, and the results of the task analysis. The results of these processes revealed that the craftmaster needs the physical feedback provided by his control surfaces. Since virtual controls could not provide this type of feedback, it was determined that the craftmaster must be provided with physical controls that match his vessel's controls in conjunction with tactile feedback provided by vibratory motors or other devices. The same analyses revealed that the navigator and engineer do not need high-fidelity physical feedback. Therefore, a haptic glove or a touch screen would provide adequate feedback for these users. Finally, it was determined that the LCAC crew occasionally used gestures in the operational environment. Therefore, if an immersive VE was used for the VELCAC, an avatar representation of each crew member would be needed.

Most of the haptic display systems and input devices examined in this chapter would not be suitable for a deployed VELCAC. Like visual displays, each device has advantages and disadvantages. Some of the disadvantages of the haptic devices include cost (exoskeletons), complexity (exoskeletons), fragility (wired clothing, exoskeletons), lack of face validity (joysticks, spaceballs, wands), limited range to user's body size (wired clothing, gloves), and cable/wire entanglement problems (wired clothing, exoskeletons, wands, biological input sensors, gloves).

Although wired clothing and/or gloves would seem to be the ideal device, they are limited by the body size of the user and also have the problem of cable entanglement, something not likely to increase user acceptance of the system. A wand would seem to be a good choice. However, if the user is wearing an HMD, then the problem of dropping and trying to relocate the wand occurs. In addition, the wand lacks face validity, meaning the LCAC community would need to take time to learn how to use it—something they are not likely to have. Table 11.3 details the trade-offs with respect to the LCAC for each device described.

For a monitor system, the most suitable input device depends, in part, on what needs to be manipulated within the simulation. If only the knobs and dials of the LCAC need to be manipulated, then a touch screen would seem to be the best input device. This is based on increased face validity of actions taken with a touch screen. That is, touching a button with the finger is more like the real-world action than is touching the button with the cursor of a mouse. However, this again needs to be determined empirically as well as tested for usability issues.

TABLE 11.3
Side-by-Side Comparison of Haptic Display Characteristics in Relation to the VELCAC Environment

Haptic Device	Face Validity	Range of Motion	Possibility of Entanglement	Body Fit	Complexity
Wired clothing	High	High	High	Person-dependent	Medium
Exoskeletons	High	Low	High	Good	High
Wands	Low	High	Medium	N/A	Low
Spaceballs	Low	Low	Low	N/A	Medium
Joysticks	Low	Medium	Low	N/A	Low–medium
Biological input sensors	Low–high	Low–high	Low–high	Low–high	Low–high
Vibratory gloves	High	High	High	Person-dependent	Medium
Air bladder gloves	High	High	High	Person-dependent	Medium

SYNTHETIC NATURAL ENVIRONMENT (SNE)

A simulation environment "consists of the operational environment surrounding the simulation entities including terrain, atmospheric, bathyspheric, and cultural information," (Defense Modeling Simulation Office, 2002). The factors that influence as well as affect each of these components are also integrated. Synthetic environments (SE) present an opportunity to achieve these goals. SEs are described as internetted simulations functioning at a high level of realism that may be composed of a single computer or distributed network of computers possessing convincing special effects and behavior models (Defense Modeling Simulation Office, 2002). The term *synthetic natural environment* (SNE) is used here to indicate the synthetic environment used to represent the natural, or operational, environment.

To create the virtual world within which the individual platform or vehicle simulators operate, multiple databases play a part in the generation of an SNE. A number of specific data elements must be provided. Some of the common data elements required are described in Table 11.4 (Source for Environmental Representation and Interchange Service [SEDRIS] a, 2002a).

Multiple applications draw upon the elements provided by databases to support the production and maintenance of an SNE. An overview of some of the applications identified by SEDRIS (2002a/b) can be found in Table 11.5.

TABLE 11.4
Data Elements Commonly Integrated into Synthetic Natural Environments

Data Element	Description
Terrain surface	Digital elevation model that provides the foundation for terrain surface and geometry
Terrain features	Man-made or natural features including vegetation, hydrology, roads, obstacles, etc.
3-D models and icons	Characteristics of structures, buildings, and other 3-D models within the area of interest
Textures, images, and colors	Color and texture are critical for systems used to visualize the surface of the terrain
Object and feature attributes	Attributes or data required by the user or a computational task of the simulation system, such as infrared signatures
Environmental models	Elements of the environment, including smoke, rain, and haze
Other data	Predetermined events that do not require full simulation, such as explosion effects, water flow in a river, or state transition of specific objects

---

TABLE 11.5
Application Categories Commonly Used to Create Synthetic Natural Environments

Application Category	Description
Semiautomated forces (SAF)	Provide additional friendly or opposing elements to augment manned simulators and can produce tactical behaviors for vehicles
Sensor simulation	Radar, infrared, and night vision simulation devices
Computer image generators (CIG) and visual systems	Create 3-D images of the environment and display them to crew members at frame rates that create the illusion of animation and continuous motion
Constructive simulation	Representation of an aggregation of forces instead of individual vehicles, usually part of a higher echelon of war-gaming applications
Electronic and paper maps	Orient operators of manned, semiautomated, or constructive forces and assist with environmental interaction

SNE's aim is to create environments that embody conditions, circumstances, and characteristics of the specified operational environment. Accomplishing these goals requires the skillful integration of databases, software applications, and computer hardware.

SNE WITHIN VIRTE

Providing a consistent representation of the environment within which a distributed simulation occurs is a core requirement to distributed simulation (SEDRIS, 2002b) and is, therefore, a core requirement for VIRTE. The modeling and simulation community has begun to supply virtual tools that address these needs to support and provide meaningful distributed training. VIRTE capitalizes upon advances in these technologies to create a realistic SNE.

The majority of the SNEs in VIRTE are provided by JSAF. The Joint Forces Command Experimentation Directorate, J9, sponsors the development of JSAF. Due to JSAF's close ties to the U.S. Navy and Marine Corps and its technological capabilities, JSAF is a natural choice for a program such as VIRTE. As of publication, JSAF is the most widely used SNE in the U.S. Navy, including programs such as the BFTT for shipboard training and the Navy Aviation Simulation Master Plan (NASMP). Additionally, the U.S. Marine Corps employs JSAF within the Deployable Virtual Training Environment (DVTE) program (E. Harvey, personal communication, May 10, 2003).

The JSAF simulation system generates models to represent infantrymen, vehicles, ships, aircraft, munitions, and buildings. JSAF furnishes terrain databases, object feature attributes, environmental, behavior, sea-state models, mapping capabilities, and other data (Marine Air-Ground Task Force Staff Training Program, 2001). Individual platform simulators within VIRTE generate sensor simulation data in concert with JSAF. The visual systems employed are supported by multiple applications, are platform specific, and include Vega and Vega Prime, ModStealth, and NetImmerse CIGs to create 3-D models, textures, colors, and images. The skillful integration of JSAF and other virtual tools makes it possible to represent the real world with a SNE in VIRTE.

COMPUTER-GENERATED FORCES (CGF)

Although vehicles, environmental factors, and some infantry entities are represented by the SNE, CGFs provide human behavior models within a simulation system (Defense Modeling and Simulation Organization, 2002). CGFs can be used to replace human operators, teammates, and adversaries, and therefore, create an atmosphere where an entire training crew need not be present in order for one or more crew members to participate in meaningful training. A panel assembled by the National Research Council asserts modeling human behavior within military training simulation is "essential to successful applications in ... distributed interactive simulation" (Pew and Mavor, 1998). Although development of this field is in its infancy (Pew and Mavor, 1998), research is ongoing.

Many human behavior modeling architectures exist. Pew and Mavor (1998) summarize several behavior modeling architectures including:

- Adaptive Control of Thought (ACT-R)
- COGnition as a Network of Tasks (COGNET)
- Executive-Process Interactive Control (EPIC)
- Micro Saint
- Neural Networks
- Soar

The architectures vary widely in theoretical foundation and implementation. Some of the architectures mentioned are grounded in theories of human cognition and performance, such as ACT-R, COGNET, EPIC, and Soar. Others predict human behavior based on discrete-event simulation principles, Micro Saint, or computational approaches, and Neural Networks. VIRTE applies three of these architectures as described in the next section.

CGFs IN VIRTE

Demo I incorporates a CGF in the VELCAC simulation platform. The VELCAC mission rehearsal system requires a simulated role player to fulfill the duties of the navigator position. A simulated, or synthetic, Navigator is implemented by a COGNET model, and performs tasks such as making internal and external reports, and monitoring ownship course and speed. This allows a live craft-master participant to interact with a synthetic navigator in the absence of a live role player and to participate in mission rehearsal in the same manner as he would with a live navigator (Soles and Lackey, 2002).

In Demo II, both ACT-R and Soar CGFs, provide computer-generated adversaries for an urban combat environment. These CGFs are designed to be autonomous synthetic adversaries capable of making decisions, interacting with live trainees, and taking tactical action. For example, if a CGF adversary is confronted by a live trainee, the CGF is capable of deciding whether to stay and fight, flee, or surrender. Another goal is to achieve human-like intelligence capabilities in support of command and control functions. In this case, the CGFs may perform communication functions to organize and inform one another of their position and mission progress.

VIRTE's CGF technology applies cutting edge human behavior modeling techniques to provide simulated teammates and adversaries. This strategy takes another step closer to virtual training environments, where even one live participant can gain meaningful training in the absence of other live role players.

Locomotion. Depending on the tasks being performed within a VE and the goals of the VE system, locomotion can be one of the easiest or one of the most difficult modalities to implement. There are two primary factors that determine the difficulty level of implementing locomotion within a VE. One factor relates to the level of immersion required in the VE. That is, will the VE be fully immersive, partially immersive, or nonimmersive. Fully immersive VEs occur when the real environment is obscured from the user's view, as is the case with HMDs. Partially immersive VEs would occur when the user can see both the VE and the real environment, as occurs in mixed-reality displays. Finally, nonimmersive VEs would be 3-D environments that are represented on computer monitors or single-projection display units. Milgram, Takemura, Utsumi, and Kishino (1994) provide a hierarchy of reality, ranging from the real environment to a VE. Augmented reality occurs when the real world is primary in the visual scene, but is augmented by computer images. Augmented virtuality occurs when computer images dominate the visual scene but are augmented by information from the real environment (see Figure 11.10).

The second factor relating to level of difficulty of implementing locomotion within a VE relates to the tasks and goals that the VE system is intended to support. If the task(s)/goals(s) are simple, then implementing locomotion within a VE is generally a straightforward process. For example, if the

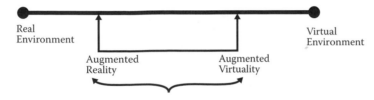

FIGURE 11.10 Levels of reality. (Adapted from Milgram, P., Takemura, H., Utsumi, A., & Kishino, F., *Telemanipulator and Telepresence Technologies.* [SPIE Vol. 2351–34].)

user's movement task was to move through the VE in order to examine the interior of a building for the purpose of architectural design/redesign, then the locomotion method would be relatively uncomplicated, whether the user was immersed or not. In the former case, the user could use a joystick or glove to input commands to the VE system. In the latter case, the user could employ a mouse, keyboard, or joystick to move through the environment. However, if the user's task(s) and goal(s) require him be immersed in, and move through, the VE with a high degree of fidelity, e.g., walk, run, and crouch as executed in the real environment, the difficulty of implementation of locomotion increases greatly. In this case, it is necessary for the user's body to be connected to the computer image generation engine in some manner. Currently, the user is either outfitted with magnetic, optical, or inertial trackers that register the position of a user's body, which is sent to the computer which then translates the positional information and renders (draws) the body representation (avatar) in the VE.

The number of devices that can be used to move a person though an immersive VE seems to be limited only by the human imagination. Devices include foot pedals, switches mounted on weapons, treadmills (traditional and omni-directional), walking in place routines, concave dishes, gloves (gesture methods), pressure mats, voice commands, etc. Of course, technological limitations are also a restrictive factor when implementing motion in the VE. There are currently no devices that would allow a person to move through the VE in a completely natural manner. Consider, for example, the types of movements that a Marine would execute in battle. He can walk and run. He can sprint, then stop in a split second. He can execute sharp angle turns, crouch, walk while crouching, and go from a standing to a prone position or vice versa. He can roll on the ground, crawl on the ground, and jump through windows. He can move in tight formations with fellow Marines, enter and exit vehicles and buildings, etc. Additionally, the Marine could be handling/using any number of weapon systems during any of these movements. All these movements would generally be executed with speed and strength. Now consider a Marine tethered to a VE system, attempting to execute these same maneuvers. The likely result is that (1) the equipment could not accommodate all movements and (2) the equipment would be destroyed.

Locomotion in VIRTE. Demo II of VIRTE will likely involve a Marine fire team engaging enemy forces in a MOUT environment. The scenario is expected to consist of a team entering and clearing a building of enemy forces. This scenario presents a great challenge to the VIRTE team because a Marine moves with speed, force, and in a variety of ways. Because of technological limitations, the goal of VIRTE Demo II is to provide "the ability for team members to independently move and interact *more realistically* within simulated environments, to practice initiative based tactics and rehearse missions" (emphasis added, Templeman, 2001 p. 3). VIRTE is attempting to provide natural control of locomotion within a VE. It is also attempting to facilitate weapons handling such as aiming and reloading (Templeman, 2001). Figure 11.11 conceptually illustrates a Marine fire team suited up in VE devices.

Completely natural movement within a VE cannot be achieved with today's technology. Thus, VIRTE is examining how Marine training can best be supported *more realistically* given the current and near-future state of the art of movement capture technology.

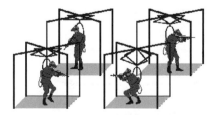

FIGURE 11.11 Four-man team in VE gear. (Adapted from Templeman, J., 2001. *CQB for MOUT (Close Quarters Battle for Military Operations in Urban Terrain).* Paper presented at the VIRTE Demo 2 Program Planning Meeting, March 2001.)

One way that VIRTE is attempting to improve movement through the VE is through the use of hybrid tracking systems, i.e., optical and inertial trackers. A hybrid system is being considered because optical trackers provide a high degree of accuracy but introduce latency into the system. Additionally, they can be plagued by line-of-sight problems. Inertial trackers have a low degree of latency but tend to drift over time. It is hoped that these two systems can compliment each other and cancel out each other's deficiencies (Templeman, 2001).

In terms of motion devices, members of the VIRTE team have developed a system dubbed Gaiter. Gaiter consists of a centering harness and associated scaffolding that always keeps the user centered at or near the center of the scaffolding while allowing the user to walk, run, and turn in any direction. VIRTE team members are attempting to improve on the work already conducted with Gaiter, including using the way that users tend to lean and push on the harness as an additional source of information (Templeman, 2001).

IDENTIFYING INSERTION POINTS

The capabilities available from today's VR modeling and simulation technologies provide far greater options for the development of training systems than were available only a few years ago. Current technology solutions range from revolutionary new designs for full mission training systems that are typically used in schoolhouse training, to modules in curriculum of Computer-Based Training (CBT) for conventional schoolhouse and Distance Learning (DL) sessions.

By designing the VR architecture to be modular, with interoperable components, the components can be interchangeable to fit a variety of customer requirements driven by the intended use of the trainer. For instance, the VIRTE system can be configured to interface with high-fidelity crew station mock-ups for a stand-alone skill trainer such as one of the VEAAAV configurations intended for New Equipment Team Training at a schoolhouse. Another example is being developed for the LCAC community for training operators in a schoolhouse atmosphere on a new cockpit configuration under a Service Life Extension Program. This customer faces the difficult task of re-training operators to not only be able to accomplish tasks that they are already proficient in with a totally new interface, but to also educate them on the concept of operations for new functionality.

The same underlying simulation environment from the schoolhouse versions can also be loaded onto a suite of networked laptops with lower-fidelity interfaces. These systems provide a basic functional interface, with perhaps a gaming joystick verses the high-fidelity gunner control, to deliver a lower-cost option for mission rehearsal and refresher training. The target training audience includes operators that are already familiar with the specific controls but wish to train team coordination or prepare for a particular mission. This option provides the ability to distribute the trainers to many more operators and could be a deployable squadron asset, thus increasing the opportunities for training.

Another option is to reuse VR software modules such as the synthetic environment as the basis of a future embedded training system to be delivered with the actual vehicle. This could be accomplished by loading the training capability onto the actual mission computers to stimulate the on-board sensors or, depending on the hardware available, could require additional hardware such as a hardened laptop or augmented display, which would be considered an appended system (Lockheed Martin Advanced Technology Laboratories, 1998; Zachary, Cannon-Bowers, Burns, Bilizarian, and Krecker, 1998).

Ultimately, the result of such an approach enables the above-mentioned systems, each developed for a separate intended use, to be interoperable. This provides the capability for multiple simulation systems to operate together for collective training in a distributed fashion. This leads the VIRTE team toward the goals of current naval programs such as the Navy and Marine Corps Aviation Simulation Master Plans and the Marine Corps DVTE program (Howard, 2002; Coalescent Technologies, 2003).

ONR's VIRTE program has the objective to transition prototype modules into a variety of systems for schoolhouse, embedded/appended, mission rehearsal, and distributed training systems. This objective is driven by requirements documented in formal technology transition agreements with acquisition program customers.

CONCLUSIONS AND FUTURE DIRECTIONS

Virtual tools like the displays, Synthetic Natural Environments, Computer-Generated Forces, haptics, and locomotion devices provide the means by which to train within virtual environments. However, in order to extend the capability of automated training and mission rehearsal further than ever before, the inclusion of instructional technologies such as Scenario-Based Training, Cognitive Task Analyses, Human–Computer Interaction Strategies, Training Management Systems, and Intelligent Tutoring Systems is vital.

VIRTE integrates these instructional technologies and VR tools in order to improve training within the Expeditionary Warfare domain. VIRTE addresses critical training challenges ranging from increased operational tempo and mission complexity to enhanced requirements for deployed forces, without excluding cost as a constraint. The advantages to this approach include a curriculum in the form of a scenario, emphasis on technical requirements, reduction in resources, and methods and tools to quantifiably enhance team performance. All of which support or are supported by VR tools.

Perhaps the most valuable benefit provided by merging instructional technologies and VR tools is the quantifiable enhancement to team training in a deployable, virtual environment. All platforms in VIRTE involve advanced team skills. The process employed to design, implement, and test the team training effectiveness is driven by the SBT architecture, facilitated by CTAs, HCI strategies, ATEAMS, and ITS methodology, and then instantiated through VR tools.

The integration of instructional technologies into VR mission rehearsal and training systems appears to be part of the natural progression toward improving automated instruction. VIRTE has a unique opportunity to substantially advance the state of the art in the field of automated training. The strength of the VIRTE program resides not only within the technological advances produced, but the increased training effectiveness rendered through appropriate and skillful insertion of instructional and VR technologies into the training continuum.

REFERENCES

Able, K., & Cojocariu, C., 1996, May. *Head mounted displays.* (Available from the Institute for Simulation and Training: Visual Systems Laboratory, 32800 Progress Drive, Orlando, FL 32826–0544.)

Ando, T., Matsumoto, T., Takahashi, H., & Shimizu, E. 1999., Head mounted displays for mixed reality using holographic optical elements. *Memoirs of the Faculty of Engineering, 40,* 1–6.

Beck, J. Stern, M., & Haugsjaa, E., 1996, Fall. Application of AI in Education. *ACM Crossroads Student Magazine 3.1.* Available:http://www.acm.org/crossroads/xrds3-1/aied.html.

Bell, H. H., & Waag, W. L., 1998. Evaluating the effectiveness of flight simulators for training combat skills: a review. *The International Journal of Aviation Psychology, 8*(3), 223–242.

Beringer, D. 1983., The pilot-computer direct-access interface: Touch panels revisited. In Jensen, R. (Ed.), *Proceedings of the 2nd Symposium on Aviation Psychology.* Columbus: Ohio State University, Aviation Psychology Lab.

Bevan, M. 1995. Headmounted displays. *VR NEWS, 4*(4), 20–29.

Biggs, S. J., & Srinivasan, M. A., 2002. Haptic interfaces. In Stanney, K. (Ed.), *Handbook of Virtual Environments.* Mahwah, NJ: Lawrence Erlbaum Associates.

Bowers, C., Salas, E., Prince, C., & Brannick, M., 1992. Games teams play: A method for investigating team coordination and performance. *Behavior Research Methods, Instruments and Computers, 24*(4), 503–506.

Cannon-Bowers, J. A., Burns, J. J., Salas, E, & Pruitt, J. S., 1998. Advanced technology in scenario-based training. In Cannon-Bowers, J. A., & Salas, E. (Eds.), *Making Decisions Under Stress* (pp. 365–374). Washington D.C.: American Psychological Association.

Cannon-Bowers, J. A., Salas, E., & Converse, S. A., 1995. Shared mental models in expert decision making teams. In Castellan, N. J., Jr. (Ed.), *Current Issues in Individual and Group Decision Making,* (pp. 221–246). Hillsdale, NJ: Erlbaum.

Coalescent Technologies. 2003. *Coalescent Technologies: Distributed Virtual Training Environment.* Available: http://www.ctcorp.com/performance15.html.

Cohn, J. V., Lackey, S., Soles, R., Lyons, D., Allen, R., Schmorrow, D., Stanney, K., & Graeber, D., 2003. *Theory-Driven Development of Instructional Agents: An Example from an Operational Training system*. Presented at the 2003 Conference on Behavior Representation in Modeling and Simulation, Scottsdale, AZ.

Defanti, T. A., Sandin, D. J., & Cruz-Neira, C. C., 1993. A room with a view., *IEEE Spectrum*, 30–33.

Defense Modeling Simulation Office. 2002. Online M and S Glossary. Available: https://www.dmso.mil/public/resources/glossary.

Dix, A. J., Finlay, J. E., Abowd, G. D., & Beale, R., 1998. *Human-Computer Interaction*. Great Britian: Prentice-Hall Europe.

Dwyer, D. J., Fowlkes, J. E., Oser, R. L., Salas, E., & Lane, N. E., 1997. Team performance measurement in distributed environments: The TARGET's methodology. In Brannick, M. T., Salas, E., & Prince, C. (Eds.), *Team Performance Assessment and Measurement: Theory, Methods, and Applications*, (pp. 137–153). Mahwah, NJ: Erlbaum.

Evans, F., & Narayanan, A., 2000. Immersive data visualization with the VisionDome. *Proceedings of SPIE*, *3960*, 238–245.

Fitzsimons, B., 2001. Helmet mounted displays. *Military Training and Simulation News, 3*(5), 32–36.

Green, M., & White, L., 2000. The cave-let: A low cost projective immersive display. *Journal of Telemedicine and Telecare, 6* (Suppl. 2), 24–26.

Hays, R. T., Vincenzi, D. A., Seamon, A. G., & Bradley, S. K., 1998. *Training effectiveness evaluation of the VESUB technology demonstration system* (TR-1999-002). Orlando, FL: Naval Air Warfare Center Training Systems Division.

Hession, P. J., Burns, J. J., & Boulrice, G., 2001. *AFLOAT training, exercise, and management system (ATEAMS) hand-held device (HHD)*. Paper presented at the 23rd Interservice/Industry Training, Simulation and Education Conference, Orlando, Florida.

Howard, L., 2002. *NAVAIRSYSCOM (PMA 205), Navy aviation simulation master plan*. Available: http://www.avtechtra.navy.mil/nattc_esc/nattc_esc_pcola_13MAR02/CAPT%20HOWARD.ppt.

Hua, H., Girardot, A., Gao, C., & Rolland, J. P., 2000. Engineering of head-mounted projective displays. *Applied Optics, 39*(22), 3814–3824.

Lajoie, S. P., Azevedo, R., & Fleiszer, D., 1998. Cognitive tools for medical informatics. In Lajoie, S. P. (Ed.), *Computers as Cognitive Tools II: No More Walls: Theory Change, Paradigm Shifts and Their Influence on the Use of Computers for Instructional Purposes*, (pp. 1–45). Amityville, NY: Baywood Publishing.

Lockheed Martin Advanced Technology Laboratories. 1998. *Advance embedded training*. Brochure. Koontz, R: Author.

Lyons, D. M., Schmorrow, D., Cohn, J. C., & Lackey, S. J., 2002. Scenario based training with virtual technologies and environments. *Proceedings of the Image 2002 Conference*.

Martin, M. K, Sheldon, E., Kass, S., Mead, A., Jones, S., & Breaux, R. 1999. *Using a virtual environment to elicit shiphandling knowledge*. Paper presented at the 21st Interservice/Industry Training, Simulation and Education Conference, Orlando, Florida.

May, J. G., & Badcock, D. R., 2002. Vision and virtual environments. In Stanney, K, (Ed.), *Handbook of Virtual Environments: Design, Implementation, and Applications*. Mahwah, NJ: Lawrence Erlbaum Associates.

McIntyre, R. M., & Salas, E., 1995. Measuring and managing for team performance: Emerging principles from complex environments. In Guzzo, R., & Salas, E. (Eds.), *Team Effectiveness and Decision Making in Organizations* (pp. 149–203). San Francisco, CA: Jossey-Bass.

Milgram, P., Takemura, H., Utsumi, A., & Kishino, F., 1994. Augmented reality: A class of displays on the reality-virtuality continuum. *Telemanipulator and Telepresence Technologies*. (SPIE Vol. 2351–34).

MPB Technologies, 2002. *MPB Technologies, products and services*. Available: http://www.mpb-technologies.ca/mpb/products/space/freedom.html.

Nickerson, R. S., & Landauer, T. K., 1997. Human-computer interaction: Background and issues. In Helander, M. G., Landauer, T. K., & Prabhu P. V. (Eds.), *Handbook of Human-Computer Interaction*. The Netherlands: Elsevier Science.

Oser, R. L., Cannon-Bowers, J. A., Salas, E., & Dwyer, D. J., 1999. Enhancing human performance in technology-rich environments: guidelines for scenario-based training. In Salas, E. (Ed.), *Human/Technology Interaction in Complex Systems* (Vol. 9, pp. 175–202). Stamford: JAI Press.

Pew, R. W., & Mavor, A. S. (Eds.). 1998. *Modeling Human and Organizational Behavior: Application to Military Simulations*. Washington D.C.: National Academy Press.

Pimentel, K., & Teixeria, K., 1992. *Virtual Reality: Through the New Looking Glass*. New York: McGraw-Hill.

Reid, G. B., & Cyrus, M. L., 1974, December. *Transfer of training with formation flight trainer* (AFHRL-TR-74-102). Brooks Air Force Base, TX: Air Force Human Resource Laboratory. (No. AD A009638).

Roberts, B., 2001. *COVE—A shiphandling trainer with an attitude.* Paper presented at the 23rd Annual Interservice/Industry Training, Simulation and Education Conference, Orlando, Florida.

Rolland, J. P., & Fuchs, H., 2000. Optical versus video see-through head-mounted displays in medical visualization. *Presence, 9*(3), 287–309.

Schmorrow, D. D., & Kruse, A. A., 2002. Improving human performance through advanced cognitive system technology. *Proceedings Interservice/Industry Training Simulation Education Conference 2002,* Orlando, FL, 2002.

Schmorrow, D. D., Lyons D. M., Stanney K. M., Lackey S. J., Schaffer, R., & Cavitt, D., 2002. Virtual Technologies and Environments. *Proceedings from the IEEE Virtual Reality 2002 Conference, Orlando, FL.*

Seamon, A. G., Bradley, S. K., Hays, R. T., & Vincenzi, D. A., 1999, April. *VESUB Technology Demonstration: Project Summary* (TR-1999-002). Orlando, FL: Naval Air Warfare Center Training Systems Division.

Soles, R. W., & Lackey, S. J., 2002. Implementation of synthetic and instructional agents in virtual technologies and environments. *Proceedings of the 2002 Interservice/Industry Training, Simulation, and Education Conference.*

Source for Environmental Representation and Interchange Service. 2002a. *Creating environmental databases for use in real-time networked interactive simulation.* Available: http://www.sedris.org/abt_trpl.htm.

Source for Environmental Representation and Interchange Service. 2002b. *History and development pholosphy in SEDRIS.* Available: http://www.sedris.org/ab_2trpl.htm.

Stretton, M. L., 2001. *Afloat training, exercise, and management system (ATEAMS): Enabling objective-based training.* Paper presented at the 23rd Interservice/Industry Training, Simulation and Education Conference, Orlando, Florida.

Templeman, J., 2001. *CQB for MOUT (Close Quarters Battle for Military Operations in Urban Terrain).* Paper presented at the VIRTE Demo 2 Program Planning Meeting, March 2001.

United States Marine Corps. 2001. *Concepts and Issues 2001: Forging the Future Marine Corps.* Washington D.C.: Programs and Resource Department.

United States Marine Corps. 2003. *Concepts and Programs 2003.* Available: http://www.globalsecurity.org/military/agency/usmc/magtf.htm.

Urban, J. M., Bowers, C. A., Monday, S. D., & Morgan, B. B., 1995. Workload, team structure, and communication in team performance. *Military Psychology, 7,* 123–139.

Werkhoven, P. J., & Groen, J., 1998. Manipulation Performance in Interactive Virtual Environments. *Human Factors, 40*(3), 432–442.

Worcester, L. L., & Worcester, P. J., 2001. *VIRTE Virtual Technologies and Environments: Program Report,* (Vol. I). Washington: Potomac Institute.

Wright, D., 2000. A survey of projection-based immersive displays. *Proceedings of SPIE 3957,* 482–492.

Youngblut, C., Johnson, R. E., Nash, S. H., Wienclaw, R. A., & Will, C. A., 1996. *Review of virtual environment interface technology* (IDA Paper P-3186). Alexandria, VA: Institute for Defense Analysis.

Zachary, W., Cannon-Bowers, J., Burns, J., Bilizarian, P., & Krecker, D., 1998. *An advanced embedded training system (AETS) for tactical team training.* Fourth International Conference on Intelligent Tutoring Systems, San Antonio, TX.

12 The Transformation of Shiphandling and Navigation Training

Alton G. Seamon

CONTENTS

FROM SEXTANTS TO SATELLITES

Shiphandling training can be traced back thousands of years when sailing by latitudes was commonplace. First tools included sextants, celestial, knots, wet-bulbs, wooden protractors, handdrawn charts, and similar tools of the period. Many references exist that develop concepts of the who, what, where, and how of navigation. The reality is that early shiphandling and navigation had no substitution for training the basic components of navigation besides on-the-job learning. Egress to and from ports in the intercoastal waterway systems of the world were accomplished by sight only. Many shipwrecks occurred due to a lack of information regarding hazards that could be encountered while transiting the channels. Groundings occurred due to a lack of accurate navigational information. Collisions occurred due to poor seamanship and shiphandling capabilities. Areas of navigation have significantly improved over the centuries and ships have become more reliant on the navigation tools developed to ensure safe navigation. The International Code of Signals is the primary means of understanding the rules developed for navigation in the world's waterways and on the high seas. Ships have increased in size to the point where many ships must adhere to severely restricted requirements and procedures to safely navigate in waterways. Development of tools and training systems as well as training prospective ship handlers on the job has become paramount to minimize the potential for accidents occurring while transiting restricted channels of navigation. The military has taken the lead on development of these tools of the trade. Development of navigation training systems has continued to excel with the progression of technology into the 21st century.

Many systems used for training navigation teams, sea captains, navigators, ship handlers, and in the military, officers of the deck (OOD), have been replaced with more technically sound, accurate, and precise navigation tools and information. The sky is not the limit. We now delve into the heavens of outer space utilizing satellites to broadcast electronic signals to ships to accurately identify the ships' location anywhere on Earth. The international committees in support of navigation work diligently to insure that navigational markings, known hazards, and rules of navigation are maintained and distributed in the quest to reduce the occurrence of navigational accidents such as groundings and collisions. Prevention of these types of incidents, in fact, impacts the environment in which we live. We should not forget about the *Exxon Valdez*—the huge oil tanker that went aground, causing major impacts on wildlife and the environment; and the USS *San Francisco* grounding in the Pacific on January 8, 2005, or the USS *Jacksonville* collision with a Saudi Arabian tanker, causing thousands of dollars in damage to both vessels; or the USS *Memphis'* grounding near Fort Lauderdale, Florida. These accidents—failures in navigation and shiphandling as well as violations of the "rules of the road"—were avoidable incidents and collisions that impacted communities, the environment, and people's lives. These are just a few examples of why emphasis must be placed on developing new and more precise navigating tools, navigational principles, and training systems so that these types of events might be avoided in the future. Training cannot eliminate human error, but we can strive to minimize it by the development of systems to assist in training ship handlers in accident prevention.

An example of the progression of training technology over the past 50 years is that of the evolution of navigational training tools used in training the U.S. Navy submarine force. In the mid-1960s, the military determined that specialized training was required to ensure the safe navigation of nuclear-powered submarines. These ships navigated waterways uniquely, in that strict adherence to operating within marked channels was paramount due to their deep draft nature and lack of maneuverability, as well as operating restrictions. The eyes of the submarine are their periscopes, radars, and fathometers, assisted from the bridge by the ship's captain, an officer of the deck, and a lookout who diligently stand watch for navigational hazards and obstructions that might inhibit safe passage. Due to the ever-increasing size and decreasing maneuverability of these vessels, more sophisticated and accurate means to assist in this treacherous passage needed to be developed and exercised. The U.S. Navy determined that detailed training of these newly developed tools was required to ensure that personnel were trained to the maximum possible. A training system consists of the planned interaction of people, materials, and techniques, with the goal of improved human performance as measured by established criteria on the job (Hays, 1992). The complex nature of navigating narrow channels and waterways has always challenged even the most experienced of ship handlers. The advent of technology increased much of the accuracy in navigation, but often left personnel trusting and complacent. As technology replaces conventional, it is easy to get comfortable and reliant on the expectations it can provide, often unwittingly reducing the burden of responsibility and attentiveness of personnel. A lack of attention to details and overconfidence in the technology can result in less familiarity with the skills required to perform conventional navigation when necessary. Accidents happen, but they are unacceptable. Increased training is needed to operate the systems that are designed to prevent them. The limited time submarines spend on the surface is not sufficient to exercise navigation teams to the maximum extent necessary to maintain proficiency.

The navy has long been teaching the concepts of shiphandling. Development of submarine piloting and navigation trainers began in the late 1960s, and has progressed with technology to the development of virtual reality (VR) training systems. Shiphandlers require unique skills and keen senses to achieve superior capabilities. A nautical term often used to describe this set of skills is seakeeping or "seaman's eye" (Hays, Castillo, Bradley, and Seamon, 1997), defined as "the total situation awareness of the shiphandling environment and the ability to safely maneuver the vessel in all conditions." Seaman's eye has always been a component (although not clearly expressed in the task requirements of training), an element, or sense necessary to effectively train navigational concepts in shiphandling.

EARLY NAVIGATION AND SHIPHANDLING TRAINERS

The development of navigation and shiphandling training systems started with actual shipboard equipment. Developers then tailored the training system by incorporating simulation aspects. Submarine training utilized periscopes and ancillary equipment coupled with man-made visual models of the intended scenario and induced the perceptual and cognitive components by manipulating the optical presentation and the environment to achieve the targeted training tasks. Board models were built on plywood that depicted the surrounding area of interest and populated it with the necessary components to present a realistic scene. Plastic models of ships were used as contacts. Navigational aids were constructed and placed in appropriate geographical locations. The surface was painted to represent the surrounding body of water. And finally, the images were manipulated to project the correct perspective when looking through the periscope at the modeled image. Although functional and capable of training shiphandlers and navigation teams, these early training systems showed that developers lacked a full understanding of the importance of designing in cognitive components of the tasks. The continued development and understanding of training requirements progressed as technology improved to support new concepts to deliver training.

SUBMARINE PILOTING AND NAVIGATION (SPAN) TEAM TRAINING

SPAN incorporated many lessons learned from early systems that were exercised in real training environments. Computer-generated visual representations of the navigation environment, coupled with electronics and improved tools, sparked an increased interest in training tasks never before capable without being onboard ship. SPAN pioneered the concept of training in a simulated and stimulated environment for the military. Periscope visual presentation was significantly enhanced over early designs to provide realistic perceptions of the task, coupled with stimulated radar presentations on actual tactical equipment to provide hands-on training capabilities. Many elements of improved training and performance measurement were a direct result of these developments. However, recent technology advancements in visual systems and radar simulation have made replacement of the existing SPAN a significantly more cost-effective means of providing the training capability for upgrading the existing trainers.

Changes in technology aboard submarines require major changes in how training is conducted to meet the requirements for training all elements of submarine operations. Many of the existing training systems are expected to experience increasing reliability and maintainability problems, with training-unique and commercial components reaching their end of life. The latest and most advanced National Geospatial-Intelligence Agency (NGA) chart and geodetic survey data combined with technology will be used in developing the visual and radar databases that will permit rapid updates of the training environment, thus allowing for specific waterway training for any location throughout the world. The instructor/operator will be able to develop scenarios and initiate, control, and monitor exercises. In addition, the instructor will have the capability to participate as a shiphandling team member. These factors will foster detailed team training evaluations and after-action reviews to access performance of the trainee.

MINI-SUBMARINE PILOTING AND NAVIGATION

A low-cost alternative training system (Mini-SPAN) has been developed to replace the SPAN in the interim to support minimal training tasks. The Mini-SPAN has been developed by Naval Air Warfare Center Training Systems Division (NAWCTSD) from the Submarine Skills Training Network (SubSkillsNet) family of navigation products and is packaged (COTS-based delivery system) in such a manner to allow for continuous navigation training. This system permits training of multiple students simultaneously and supports the key elements of navigation and thus allows for realistic interactions between all team players of the shiphandling and navigation task. SPAN

2000 is the primary navigation training system at all submarine training sites and is supplemented by Mini-SPAN, which will remain a significant asset in training specific piloting tasks focusing on principles and procedures of navigation and the use of the tools required to perform those tasks. Many of the supporting requirements are simulated, thus reducing manpower required to exercise the training system and team members to achieve successful training. The critical components of navigation equipment and the realistic presentation are now accomplished with the advent of the SPAN 2000 and the subsequent phases of revisions.

The SPAN 2000 trainer provides dynamic real-time practical team training in restricted waterway piloting and navigation procedures, and techniques for training operational submarine navigation, shiphandling, and piloting teams. It is vissioned that provisions will be made to permit the state-of-the-art Virtual Environment Submarine Shiphandling Trainer (VESUB) to be integrated to allow OOD shiphandling training with the state-of-the-art periscope visual scene presentations and radar landmass presentations of the new SPAN 2000. All the normal periscope, radar, piloting, shiphandling, navigation, depth monitoring, and communication components required on board the submarine to transverse restricted waterways will be integrated into the training environment.

SUBMARINE PILOTING AND NAVIGATION 2000

The SPAN 2000 provides instructors with the ability to train submarine teams in the procedures and techniques required for open ocean and restricted water piloting and navigation. SPAN 2000 provides realistic simulation of submarine and traffic ship's performance characteristics in a simulated environment. The environment will be modeled at a high level of fidelity to provide relevant cues from wind, currents, visual landmass, cultural features and navigation aids, and the generation of radar returns from other vessels, buoys, rain squalls, and landmass. The SPAN 2000 includes the following supporting components: tactical/commercial radar, periscope visuals enhanced with environmental conditions, ships fire control and sonar functions, depth finders/fathometer information, global positioning system (GPS) data, advanced digital plotting systems, tactical computer simulation and stimulation, and incorporation of the newest in electronic voyage management systems.

Integrating the SPAN 2000 with the VESUB 2000 trainer described below will utilize the virtual head-mounted display (HMD)/head tracking system to create a bridge view that the OOD would normally experience when ship-handling the submarine through restricted waterways. These two training systems integrated together will allow for total training of the piloting and navigation teams. The SPAN 2000 is designed to be completely COTS-based with software architecture flexible enough to easily accommodate changes and upgrades to allow for piloting and navigation training well into the 21st century.

VIRTUAL ENVIRONMENT–SUBMARINE SHIPHANDLING 2000 (VESUB)

The VESUB 2000 is a virtual reality-based computer system used to provide submarine OOD individual instruction in the knowledge and skills necessary to successfully and safely pilot a surfaced submarine through restricted waterways, avoiding collisions and grounding. Waterways and harbor piloting and shiphandling has become extremely demanding due to environmental conditions and increased ship traffic. The trainer allows the student to be immersed in a virtual waterway scene under varying geographic, environmental, and emerging conditions. The student is also able to communicate with other virtual team members of the submarine crew while piloting the submarine. The VESUB system achieves three of the primary elements of VR by incorporating high-fidelity visuals (sight), realistic sounds (auditory), and voice recognition and synthesis (speech) into the virtual environment (VE).

The objective of the VESUB research project was threefold:

1. To develop, demonstrate, and evaluate the training potential of a stand-alone VR-based system for submarine shiphandling training
2. To determine if this system could be integrated with existing SPAN training simulators
3. To determine the viability of VR technology as a training tool

VESUB proceeded as a multiphased program, consisting of:

1. Requirements determination
2. Formative evaluations
3. Training effectiveness evaluation (TEE)
4. Transition of R&D results to support the acquisition of operational systems (VESUB 2000)

The submarine OOD mans the bridge with the assistance of a lookout and, many times, a junior officer of the deck (JOOD). His responsibilities include all aspects of ship's evolutions, including the safe navigation and piloting of the ship. In his shiphandling tasks, he must demonstrate an understanding of the environment, limitations of channels and harbors, available navigational aids, contact management, and rules of the nautical road.

The placement of the OOD, literally on the top of the submarine, with a 360-degree view of his surroundings, provided an excellent setting for a VE. In addition to this visual plane, the submarine OOD manages a complex task in the execution of his responsibilities. Though isolated on the ship's bridge, he monitors and observes the environment, and directs the actions necessary to CONN (maneuver) the submarine through harbor and channel. He communicates his desires through voice commands over electronic circuits and receives both voice and visual confirmations of his orders. Because of the important visual component of the task and the Navy's need for a simulation capability, the surfaced submarine shiphandling task was determined to be a prime candidate for examination of the effectiveness of VR systems for training applications.

PERCEPTUAL AND COGNITIVE TASK ANALYSIS

A perceptual and cognitive task analysis was conducted using "seaman's eye", the collective skills required by the OOD during surface evolutions, as a means to focus the effort. Through interactions with expert consultants, like submarine commanding officers, navigators, assistant navigators, and harbor pilots, the research and development team derived the following definition of "seaman's eye" to guide the perceptual and cognitive analysis:

> The total situation awareness of the shiphandling environment and the ability to safely maneuver the vessel in all conditions.

Iterative probing of subject matter experts (SMEs), using focused group discussions at navy training facilities and in the NAWCTSD laboratory, detailed 8 perceptual and 12 cognitive components that make up this complex concept (see Table 12.1). These components were used to make hardware, software, and instructional decisions during the formative evaluation and later phases of the project (Hays, Vincenzi, Seamon, and Bradley, 1998).

FORMATIVE EVALUATIONS

The formative evaluation phase was conducted in the laboratory at NAWCTSD. Whenever the contractor delivered an improved iteration of the VESUB software, it was evaluated against the functional requirements by the VESUB research team. Data for the formative evaluations were

TABLE 12.1

Perceptual and Cognitive Components of "Seaman's Eye"

Perceptual Components

1. Locating and identifying navigation aids

2. Judging distance

3. Identifying the start and completion of turns

4. Locating, identifying, and avoiding obstacles

5. Sense of ship's responsiveness

6. Recognizing environmental conditions

7. Recognizing equipment failures

8. Detecting and filtering communications

Cognitive Components

1. Understanding the relationship of visual cues to their representations on charts

2. Understanding relative size and height/range relationships, and angle on the bow (AOB)

3. Understanding advance and transfer

4. Understanding the effects of tides, currents, wind, and seas

5. Understanding rules of the road

6. Understanding relative motion (direction and speed)

7. Understanding methods to differentiate and prioritize traffic contacts

8. Understanding ship's operation under harbor directives

9. Understanding methods to deal with uncooperative traffic

10. Understanding correct operation of ship's systems

11. Understanding when and how to take corrective actions

12. Understanding effective communication procedures

also collected from 11 fleet and school SMEs and 9 Navy reservists with shiphandling experience following extensive exposure to VESUB. As soon as the formative data were collected, the results were provided to AME to guide system improvements. The formative evaluations focused on both the functionality of the trainee interface (e.g., the fidelity of objects in the visual scene, the functionality of the voice recognition system, and the hydrodynamics of the ship models) and the usability of the instructor/operator station (IOS).

Training Effectiveness Evaluation (TEE)

TEE Approach. The TEE for the VESUB technology demonstration system was conducted at the Submarine Learning Facility in Norfolk, Virginia, and the Naval Submarine School in Groton, Connecticut, during the winter and spring of 1998. The TEE used Navy trainees with various levels of shiphandling experience (novice to expert) to determine the effectiveness of the VESUB system and to help determine how the technology can be integrated into Navy training. At each site, the VESUB system was set up in a room where the TEE could be conducted without interfering with ongoing training.

Forty-one participants experienced three VESUB scenarios. The first was an orientation scenario to allow them to experience and practice system functionality. The second was a training scenario that targeted several specific shiphandling tasks (derived from the perceptual and cognitive task analysis), and the third was a comparable scenario to test the trainees' improvement on these shiphandling skills. Prior to the first scenario, demographic data were collected and a comfort questionnaire was administered to assess the participants' physical condition. After completion of each scenario, the comfort questionnaire was again administered to assess any physical changes experienced by the participants. Finally, each participant provided comments on the VESUB system and recommendations for its use and improvement.

TEE Results. Data were collected on 15 shiphandling variables grouped into 7 skill categories. A mixed factorial analysis of variance (ANOVA) design, with experience as the between-subjects variable and scenario session (training and testing) as the within-subjects variable, found significant learning (skill improvements) for all experience levels (0 to 14 years) on 11 of the 15 variables. For example, trainees improved:

- 39% in checking range markers
- 33% in visually checking the rudder
- 13% in issuing correct turning commands
- 57% in contact management skills
- 44% in reaction time during a man overboard (MOB) event
- 29% in using correct commands during the MOB event
- 40% in using correct commands during a yellow sounding event

No major simulator side effects problems were found. Less than 5% of the trainees experienced side effects that were detrimental to training, even though trainees averaged almost 2 hours in the HMD. Details on these and other TEE data are presented in Hays et al. (1998).

SIMULATION AND TRAINING ISSUES

Over the course of the VESUB research project, team members learned a variety of lessons about the problems of developing a complex state-of-the-art VE training system. Though resources often limited project response to these lessons, their importance to VESUB and its follow-on training system, as well as other training systems that employ similar processes, could prove to be significant.

These lessons included a wide range of issues, from hardware and software configuration management and legacy system interfacing, to speech and visual system integration. Other key areas included task-specific detailing for accuracy and training effectiveness, as well as project management and control issues that are not often considered during project planning. Discussing these lessons as they relate to the VESUB functionality requirements established by the team should provide a better level of understanding of the nature and difficulty faced by developers in the VE arena.

The VESUB device was developed utilizing COTS hardware and software. The primary components include an IOS; an extremely high-fidelity visual system; submarine mockup to support the area of regard for the training task of the submarine bridge; voice recognition and synthesis system, and audio system with a microphone to support the myriad of communications necessary that allow the trainee to give all commands and receive appropriate repeat backs of the standardized interior communications of submarines; screen displays and projectors for instructors and additional trainees to monitor the training events being performed as well as to support scenario replays; high-resolution HMD, which trainees wear to immerse them into a full 360-degree view of the training environment; head tracking system to coordinate trainee motion with the simulation; and a color printer to allow printing of specified data in support of scenario after-action review and playback.

Trainer instructional capabilities allow the instructor to develop unique training scenarios for any harbor database utilized. These capabilities include complete control of ship traffic patterns and placement of all ships in the environment, control of environmental conditions (e.g., visibility, cloud cover, time of day, weather, currents, sea state, and wind). The instructor can use a variety of methods to enhance critical environmental cues, perform scenario playback (after-action review), and insert ownship malfunctions to enhance the real-time training experience. The instructor has various methods (including automated) for measuring performance and providing feedback to the trainee. Scenarios with increasing levels of difficulty can be provided by the instructor to enhance systematic improvement ownship handling skills. The instructor station includes an instructional control computer with display and keyboard, a trainee view monitor, printer, voice recognition/ synthesis system and communication system. The VESUB system allows the OOD to view the selected harbor or restricted waterway (database) to acquire piloting skills to ensure safe maneuvering of the submarine, especially actions to avoid grounding and collision. Currently 30 harbor databases have been modeled with the ability to add and modify additional harbors throughout the world. Currently six VESUB systems have been fielded to the fleet and have received astounding results. The success of the VESUB 2000 system can be directly related to the in-depth analyses accomplished by Dr. Robert T. Hays and his team during the entire development process at NAWCTSD in Orlando, Florida.

REFERENCES

Hays, R. T., 1992. Systems concepts for training systems development: *IEEE Transactions on Systems, Man, and Cybernetics,* 22(2), 258–266.

Hays, R. T., Castillo, E., Bradley, S. K., & Seamon, A. G., 1997. A virtual environment for submarine shiphandling: Perceptual and hardware trade-offs. In Chinni, M. J. (Ed.), *Proceedings of the 1997 Simulation Multi Conference: Military, Government, and Aerospace Simulation (April 6-10, 1997).* Simulation Series 29(4), 217–222. San Diego, CA: The Society for Computer Simulation International.

Hays, R. T., Seamon, A. G., & Bradley, S. K., 1997, November. *User-oriented design analysis of the VESUB technology demonstration system* (NAWCTSD TR 97-013). Orlando, FL: Naval Air Warfare Center Training Systems Division. (Defense Technical Information Center No. ADA 332 570.)

Hays, R. T., Vincenzi, D. A., Seamon, A. G., & Bradley, S. K., 1998, June. *Training effectiveness evaluation of the VESUB technology demonstration system* (NAWCTSD TR 98-003). Orlando, FL: Naval Air Warfare Center Training Systems Division. (Defense Technical Information Center No. ADA 349 219.)

Seamon, A. G., Bradley, S. K., Hays, R. T., & Vincenzi, D. A., 1999, April. VESUB Technology Demonstration: Project Summary (NAWCTSD TR 99-002). Orlando, FL: Naval Air Warfare Center Training Systems Division.

Tenney, Y. L., Briscoe, H., Pew, R. W., Bradley, S. K., Seamon, A. G., & Hays, R. T., 1996. *Virtual environment submarine officer of the deck simulation and training: Preliminary requirements recommendation* (NAWCTSD SR 96-002). Orlando, FL: Naval Air Warfare Center Training Systems Division.

13 Space Adaptation Syndrome and Perceptual Training

Mustapha Mouloua, Janan A. Smither, and Robert S. Kennedy

CONTENTS

INTRODUCTION

BACKGROUND

A vexing problem within the medical life sciences is the "space adaptation syndrome" reported to afflict about one-half of all shuttle astronauts and mission specialists (Homick, Reschke, and Vanderploeg, 1984; Ishii, 1993; Nguyen, 1996; Reschke et al., 1998; Thornton, Pool, Moore, and Vanderploeg, 1987). The symptoms resemble those found with other forms of motion sickness (Money, Watt, and Oman, 1984), particularly those that are reported in visual rearrangement studies (Kottenhoff, 1957; Welch, 1978, 2000a), and in ground-based flight simulators (Kennedy, Lilienthal, Dutton, Ricard, and Frank, 1984). Cue conflict or neural mismatch (Reason, 1970) theory suggests that the constellation of symptoms is triggered by decorrelation between sensory stimuli (Kennedy, Berbaum, and Frank, 1984; Oman, 1991; Parker, Reschke, Arrott, Homick, and Lichtenberg, 1985). In other words, the disparity between and within vision, vestibular, and somatic messages is the cause (Benson, 1978; Guedry, 1965). Thus, as one initially moves about in the weightless environment, the sensory channels provide incompatible information about spatial orientation and bodily movement, and this sensory conflict leads to nausea and motion sickness (Ishii, 1993). Preadapting astronauts to the visual/vestibular conflicts before embarkation to immunize them against space adaptation syndrome is the subject of this proposal. An old theory (von Holst, 1968) called *reafference* may have relevance for new findings (Welch, 2000a, 2000b).

Under terrestrial conditions, tilting the head to one side causes the otolith to roll (shear) sideways, a stimulus which is interpreted as "head tilt." Rolling of the otolith to the front or back occurs only under linear acceleration and is so interpreted. Under orbital conditions, in microgravity, however, head tilt does not produce a sideways rolling of the otolith; this leads to sensory conflict and subsequent nausea. This otolith tilt-translation hypothesis is one possible explanation for the current finding that an estimated 50% of shuttle astronauts experience space motion sickness during the initial 24–72 hours of orbital flight. On returning to earth, the astronauts must readapt to terrestrial conditions. Parker et al. (1985) were able to document this readaptation and to link it with altered eye movements; others have made this point, also (e.g., Watt 1996). These results, both in space and after return to Earth, involve learned responses to altered inertial environments, and it appears that nausea may function as a negative reinforcer in bringing them about.

Continued exposure in motion sickness-producing environments usually results in a lessening of the symptoms. It has been suggested that the process of overcoming motion sickness has much in common with adaptation to optically induced distortions of the visual field (Cohen, 1977; Jones, and Gonshor, 1972; Welch, 1978). For example, when observers wear goggles containing wedge prisms or mirrors that displace the visual field to one side or reverse it, and interact actively in their environment, visual–motor errors decline and behavior soon becomes normal. The basis for this adaptation is a resolution of the imposed conflict between vision and proprioception-kinesthesis, so that touch conforms to vision. Likewise, virtually all space travelers adapt to the conditions that produce motion sickness during the flight, although this adaptation may not be completed for several days (Ishii, 1993; Reschke et al., 1998; Welch, 2000a). Reports of astronauts and mission specialists with more than one flight suggest that adaptation also occurs across flights, whereby symptoms experienced in subsequent missions appear to be less severe than on the first flight (Parker et al., 1985). Procedures for speeding up the rate of adaptation would be useful. Preadapting space travelers to sensory conflicts before embarkation to immunize them against space adaptation syndrome would be even better.

Vanderploeg, Stewart, and Davis (1985) have shown that of the 22 space travelers who have had an opportunity for more than one flight, 11 were sick in various degrees on their first flight, and 11 were not. Of the 11 who were not sick, all were symptom-free on their second exposure. Of the 11 who were sick on their first flight, 9 experienced symptoms on their second flight (although to a lesser extent) and 2 did not. Even though the time between space flights was protracted, the adaptation obtained on the first flight appeared to carry over to the second. The data from these 22 repeated-measures subjects implies high reliability for space adaptation syndrome. The calculated reliability for this outcome is greater than $r = 0.82$. Considering this level of criterion reliability, the inability to predict who will become sick and who will not (Money et al., 1984) suggests that all of the relevant factors are not included in the prediction. The provocative vestibular tests employed by various scientists (Lackner and Graybiel, 1984; Lentz, 1984; Lentz and Guedry, 1978; Oman, Lichtenberg, and Money, 1984; Reschke, Homick, Ryan, and Mosely, 1984) generally entail the assessment of motion sickness symptomatology, including vomiting, following a strong, abrupt (usually less than 30 minutes), and relatively unpracticed stimulus. Yet " ... in their current form these tests do not assess after-reactions, adaptive capacity, or adaptive retention" (Lentz and Guedry, 1978). However, we know that adaptation occurs, and if there are individual differences in adaptability, perhaps the combination of both provocative and adaptation testing would improve our ability to predict who will develop symptoms aloft.

In recent years, the possibility that space motion sickness might interfere with performance has been a concern. As the word "interfere" suggests, the concern has been that space motion sickness might interrupt ongoing activities. There is no doubt, for example, that frank emesis does so. The viewpoint presented here suggests another possible relation between space adaptation syndrome and performance, namely, that nausea as a negative reinforcer might lead to responses that could, in principle, be performed long after the motion sickness proper had subsided. Based on work performed by Parker et al. (1985), the responses most likely to be affected are head and eye movements. The subject, it should be noted, would have no direct awareness of learned eye movements. There is no necessity, of course, for learned nausea-avoidance responses to affect performance adversely. On the other hand, this possibility cannot be excluded a priori. With better understanding of space adaptation syndrome, especially the adaptation that accompanies various head and eye movements in reducing or preventing nausea, both the dimensions of any such problems and possible solutions to them should become clear.

The plasticity of the central nervous system permits humans to adapt to temporary ecological changes. These short-term accommodations may be considered under the general rubric of "adaptation to the environment." Welch (2000b) concludes that "Human beings (and perhaps mammals in general) are able to adjust their behavior, and to a much lesser extent their visual perception, to any sensory rearrangement to which they are actively exposed, given that this rearrangement remains essentially constant over time." Several texts (Dolezal, 1982; Welch, 1978) and reviews (Harris, 1965; Held, 1965; Kennedy, 1970; Lackner and Dizio, 1998; Welch, 2000a, 2000b) make important points, but are silent concerning the implications for space adaptation syndrome. A workshop (McCauley, 1984) and other literature (Kennedy and Frank, 1986; Kennedy, Frank, and McCauley, 1984) have found this line of investigation useful in understanding simulator sickness, and the same point has been made for the virtual environment technology (Stanney, Mourant, and Kennedy, 1998; Welch, 2000a). For the space adaptation syndrome, it is important to know whether any studies have shown transfer of adaptation from one environment to another—not merely adapting to one environment. The literature studying the transfer of adaptation between two conditions is scant (Welch, 2000a, 2000b), but some studies are available (Dobie and May, 1990; Dobie, May, Fischer, and Elder, 1987; Dobie, May, Gutierrez, and Heller, 1990; Fineberg, 1977; Fregly and Kennedy, 1965; Fried, 1962; Goodenough and Tinker, 1931; Graybiel and Lackner, 1983; Harm and Parker, 1993; 1994; Taub and Goldberg, 1973; Welch, Bridgeman, Williams, and Semmler, 1998). We would argue that since humans are adaptable, the effects of almost any environmental stressor on performance physiology will change over time, and adaptation will ensue and follow certain rules. If these rules were known, predictions could be made.

INDIVIDUAL DIFFERENCES IN ADAPTATION

It is probable that different individuals adapt at different rates (Welch, 2000a). Evidence for this view is clear-cut in the motor learning literature (Jones, 1970; Kennedy, Jones, and Harbeson, 1980), but it is less obvious in the perceptual learning literature. What we do not know are the rules of how adaptation transfers over environments and whether some individuals possess more of this ability than others do. The work of Graybiel and Lackner (1983) comes closest to what we mean about transfer of adaptation. They showed changes in performance of two types: (a) that individuals adapt similarly to three different provocative measures of motion sickness (Lackner and Graybiel, 1984) and (b) individuals' rates of acquiring and losing adaptation are consistent in different situations (Graybiel and Lackner, 1983).

Human beings vary in both the speed and magnitude of their adaptation to a given perceptually distorted environment (Welch, 1978, 2000a, 2000b). Furthermore, although there are very few studies relevant to this issue, it appears that these individual differences are reliable over time. Test–retest correlations average about .75 for adaptation to prismatic displacement (Redding, 1973a; Welch, Choe, and Heinrich, 1974) and optical tilt (Mack, 1967; Redding, 1973b), whereas a split-half reliability coefficient of .83 has been obtained for adaptation to head movement-induced illusory motion of the visual field while wearing right-left reversing goggles (Kottenhoff, 1957).

Crawshaw and Craske (1976) correlated prism adaptation in different experimental situations. Their study may be flawed in that they used the terminal level of performance as an index of adaptation. Their correlation values between the two conditions were .17 and −.19. One might argue that a better approach would be to obtain the acceleration of the acquisition curve (slope) in the two conditions. Conceivably, rapid adapters would adapt more quickly in both, regardless of where their terminal level performances were. Terminal level is only, to some extent, an index of adaptation. The second issue that one might argue is that, conceivably, the reliability of the measure of adaptation is also imperfect. To some extent, this would reduce the overall correlations also. It is recognized that several other perceptual events and situations result in adaptation (for example, delayed auditory feedback [Katz and Lackner, 1977]) and that similar principles would apply from a perceptual integration standpoint. Thus, there appear to be "quick adapters" and "slow adapters" (and those in

between), at least in Welch's (1978) data. A question of interest is what, if any, personal characteristics correlate with (and therefore are predictive of) these different "adaptive styles." In brief, the
answer is that very few of the more obvious characteristics have been found to predict adaptability.

Although provocative tests of motion sickness reveal generally positive correlation with zero
"g" induced sickness (Reschke et al., 1984), there is a substantial amount of unexplained variance.
Kennedy (1970) has suggested and Reason and Graybiel (1972) have found experimentally that
adaptability is a strong predictor of susceptibility to motion sickness. Specifically, rather than looking for overriding personality characteristics as potential correlates of individual differences in
motion sickness, emphasis could be placed on a careful assessment of people's "perceptual adaptation traits," performances, and idiosyncratic behavioral tendencies. For example, the number and/or
extent of incidental head movements that a person makes during a baseline (nonmotion) period
might correlate with the amount of motion sickness experienced in a subsequent motion environment. Another potential correlate of motion sickness response might be the observer's characteristic
absolute and difference thresholds for visual and vestibular motion, each measured separately in
a nonmotion environment. Perhaps people who are especially sensitive to unconflicted visual and/
or vestibular motion will respond more dramatically or quickly and/or adapt more gradually to a
motion environment in which these two senses are placed into conflict than will individuals with
higher thresholds.

Gender and age do not seem to be related to adaptation rate (Welch, 1978). Neither do many of
the well-known "paper-and-pencil" test measures of personality. For example, Welch (1978) reported
a study in which level of adaptation (as measured in several different ways) to prism-displaced
vision failed to correlate with scores on the California Psychological Inventory, the Trait Anxiety
Scale, the Achievement Anxiety Test, the Tennessee Self-Concept Scale, the Internal–External
Locus of Reinforcement Test, and the Extroversion Scale. On the other hand, Kottenhoff (1957)
did obtain a correlation of .72 between degree of introversion/extroversion and level of adaptation
to loss of visual position constancy while wearing right–left reversing goggles. Introverted subjects
experienced an increase in illusory motion, whereas the more extroverted subjects showed either
no change or a decrease (i.e., adaptation). It is of more than passing interest that extroversion as
measured by forms of the Maudsley Personality Inventory has a test–retest reliability of only r = .60
(Kennedy, 1972) so that if one were to correct Kottenhoff's correlation for attenuation (Guilford,
1954), he would have >95% of the variance accounted for in his predictor.

With the exception of Kottenhoff's (1957) experiment, adaptability to distorted environments has not been predictable based on general personality characteristics. A more fruitful
strategy for detecting such correlates may be to perform a microanalysis of the specific perceptual and perceptual–motor behaviors required by a particular distorted environment. Thus, for
example, the common laboratory situation of reaching for targets while wearing light-displacing
prism goggles involves, among other things, the ability to accurately fixate the visual target (i.e.,
where it appears to be through the goggles), to accurately guide the hand to the target, to accurately gauge the initial prism-induced reaching error, and to correct the error. It has been shown
(Warren and Platt, 1974; Welch, unpublished data) that people differ reliably in their ability to do
each of these subtasks and, more importantly, that these differences are correlated with subsequent adaptation. For example, Warren and Platt (1974) found that people who have good control
of their eyes (i.e., are able to very accurately fixate the visual target) but relatively poor control
over their reaching responses, reveal little visual adaptation to prismatic displacement and com-
mensurately greater *proprioceptive* adaptation. Just the reverse proportions of these two types of
adaptation were obtained for subjects with poor eye control, but good hand control. Both Welch
(unpublished data) and Warren and Platt (1974) have reported that the instruction to point at a
prism-displaced target is not interpreted in the same way by all subjects. Specifically, some subjects take this to mean that, after the initial prism-induced error, they should quite deliberately
point to where they know the target to be physically located. Frequently, these "object pointers"
aim for a location that actually appears to them to be off to one side of the displaced image and,

by so doing, very quickly succeed in pointing accurately, sometimes as soon as the second trial. Other subjects continue to point to where the target appears to be located, only gradually correcting their errors. It is perhaps significant that these "image pointers" also fail to show as large a postexposure negative aftereffect as the "object pointers," indicating that they have achieved less substantial adaptation.

THE LONG-TERM RETENTION, CONDITIONING, AND TRANSFER OF ADAPTATION

A number of studies have demonstrated a close relationship between adaptation to perceptual rearrangement and traditional situational learning (Welch, 1978). Of present interest is the evidence concerning the degree to which adaptation (a) exhibits transfer to new situations (stimulus and/or response generalization), (b) is retained for relatively long periods of time, (c) reveals "savings" on subsequent "relearning" sessions, (d) is subject to discriminative conditioning, and (e) can be maintained for two (or more) different distorted environments at the same time. Although we are aware that the adaptive responses measured in these studies may not be identical to those occurring in space adaptation syndrome, it is felt that the research discussed in this section will suggest the issues, kinds of tasks, training regimes, and measures that will prove useful in providing astronauts and other space travelers with some degree of generalized "inoculation" against the perceptual and perceptual–motor disruptions caused by the environment of micro- and macrogravity to which they are exposed.

In principle, adaptation, like learning, can be measured immediately or some time after. Second, it can be measured by means of the same tasks and stimulus conditions in which it was acquired or by other situations to which it may (or may not) generalize. The two present concerns are (a) evidence for the existence of *long-term* adaptation effects and (b) an assessment of the degree to which adaptation *generalizes* to other tasks and types of perceptual rearrangement

LONG-LASTING ADAPTATION EFFECTS

The traditional assumption in experiments on adaptation to visual rearrangement has been that because such adaptation involves the contradiction of a lifetime of normal visual and visuomotor experience, it must necessarily be fragile, short-lived, and easily abolished by the reinstitution of nondistorted vision. This assumption has led most investigators to test for adaptation as quickly as possible after the exposure to visual rearrangement has occurred. There are, however, a number of observations that belie the notion that adaptation is a short-lived phenomenon.

First, it has been casually observed in a number of experiments involving two or more adaptation sessions spread over a period of time that, on sessions subsequent to the first one, subjects will manifest some initial (albeit partial) adaptation as soon as the distorting goggles are in place. This observation has been reported for adaptation to prismatic displacement in terms of (a) visuomotor aftereffects and reduction of effects (Hein, 1972; Klapp et al., 1974; Lackner and Lobovits, 1977; Welch et al., 1974; Wooster, 1923), (b) shifts in visual direction (Welch et al., 1974), and (c) modifications of felt eye position (McLaughlin and Webster, 1967). It has also been reported for visual adaptation to optical curvature (Festinger et al., 1967; Slotnick, 1969). In every instance, the effect was unexpected and only mentioned as a secondary finding of the experiment.

Similar to the preceding phenomenon is the fact that in several experiments adaptation has been found to increase in strength over a series of adaptation sessions, each of which is separated by an extended period of normal vision (Kinney, Luria, Weitzman, and Markowitz, 1970; McGonigle and Flook, 1978; Peterson and Peterson, 1938; Snyder and Snyder, 1957).

Observations of a more controlled nature concerning the ease with which some people are able to shift from one perceptual environment to another come from studies of underwater perception. Luria and Kinney (1970) and Luria et al. (1967) have shown that professional divers experience much less initial face mask-induced visual distortion when entering the water and less visual after-effect when leaving the water than is true for inexperienced divers.

The most extensive study of long-term adaptation has been carried out by Jones and Holding (1975). They used pattern contingent color aftereffects and showed that adaptation magnitude declines only with testing. By using a series of postadaptation time delays, they were able to show that significant adaptation effects could be observed for months after a single 15-minute adaptation period. Harris (1980) has suggested that other types of adaptation may also last for extended peri-ods. Savreau (1979) has demonstrated that motion contingent color effects last at least a week, and Wolfe (1985) has demonstrated that over 4 minutes of adaptation leads to a long-lasting tilt afteref-fect. Boynton and Das (1966) report a related event.

The presence of partial adaptation many months after the original exposure to the visual rear-rangement and the ability to maintain adaptation to two different perceptual situations simultane-ously may be interpreted in several ways. Some investigators (e.g., Held, 1968; Klapp et al., 1974) have assumed that these effects represent the persistence of adaptation (i.e., incomplete decay). This seems unlikely, however, since there is typically fully sufficient interpolated normal visual and visuomotor experience to completely abolish the adaptive shift. One likely alternative is that adaptation (partial or complete) can be conditioned to the situational cues associated with it and is elicited whenever the observer is once again in the presence of these cues. A second, although not mutually exclusive, possibility is that after extensive experience subjects develop a perceptual or perceptual–motor flexibility by which they can easily shift from an unadapted to adapted state, and vice versa, or between two different states of adaptation as soon as they identify the particular envi-ronment in which they have been placed. In short, they have learned to adapt, an ability that might be referred to as an "adaptation set," analogous to the more familiar but almost forgotten "learning sets" (e.g., Harlow, 1959).

GENERALIZABILITY

Traditional studies of adaptation to perceptual rearrangement have used tasks that are rather simi-lar, if not identical, to those practiced during the adaptation period (Welch, 1978). Consequently, little is known about the degree to which adaptation might transfer to tasks that are very different from those encountered during adaptation. Likewise, there is scant information concerning whether one's adaptation to one form of perceptual rearrangement will either transfer to, or predict, one's adaptability to another form of rearrangement.

Melamed et al. (1979) discuss the fact that "the total prism shift in target pointing is equal to the algebraic sum of the shifts in the other two measures" (e.g., visual shift and proprioceptive shift—the equation being TP = VS + PS). Although a two-component linear additive model of prism adaptation is attractive, one wonders whether the effect of spacing the subject's responses during the exposure period may not be a factor. Regarding the first of these two aspects of general-ization, Kinney et al. (1970), using prismatic displacement, combined three exposure activities with the same three tasks used as pre- and posttests of adaptation. The tasks were (a) placing a small chess piece marker on a square within a checkerboard grid, (b) reaching under a transparent table for a target, and (c) rapidly spearing a bull's-eye with a wooden dowel. Every subject was measured on all three tasks during the pre- and postexposure periods, but engaged in only one of them during 5 minutes of prismatic exposure. The greatest amount of adaptation (about 65% of the total possible compensation) occurred for the trained task. The nontrained tasks for a given exposure condition revealed generalized adaptation, but with some decrement.

Redding (1973a, 1973b, 1975a, 1975b) has examined the second issue of generalization: whether adaptation to one form of distortion will influence adaptation to another form. He found that when subjects were confronted (in a single session) with a visual field that was, simultaneously, prismati-cally displaced *and* tilted, adaptation to each of these distortions occurred at the same rate as when subjects were adapted to each separately. Furthermore, the magnitude of subjects' adaptation to one distortion was not correlated with the magnitude of their adaptation to the other. Thus, it would appear that displacement and tilt adaptation are independent processes that do not transfer to one another. Because the perception of visual location and orientation may be based on qualitatively different processes, the preceding failure of transfer may not be too surprising. Alternatively, perhaps for transfer to occur from one type of adaptation to another it is necessary to implement a much more extensive training regime on each, perhaps alternating between the two types of distortion.

Jell, Ireland, and LaFortune (1985) reported a reduction in human optokinetic after nystagmus in one direction or another, depending on the exposure history of the subject. It is well known that optokinetic after nystagmus can be reduced due to damage or destruction of the labyrinth and by lesions in parts of the parahypoglossal nuclei or pretectum. The 1985 Jell et al. study also revealed changes, but the authors do not comment on whether this change is due to lowered arousal or mere drop-off in the values of cumulative eye displacement, duration, or slow phase nystagmus. The authors conclude that this is simple habituation and used cumulative displacement as their most sensitive parameter. The authors suggest that "psychological habituation" (Collins, 1974) may have been a factor.

In a 1987 study (Kennedy et al.), subjects were adapted to Purkinje stimulation (Benson and Bodin, 1966) involving approximately 0.5 minutes of bodily rotation, followed by a head turn about an axis orthogonal to that of the preceding rotation. This situation produces dizziness, illusory visual motion, and difficulty walking. The experience is similar to the effects of Coriolis stimulation, except that with the latter the head movements take place during rotation rather than afterward. It was first hypothesized that repeated exposure would cause a decline in the experience of the effects from the Purkinje stimulation. The question was then to see whether this adaptation would transfer to a situation of so-called pseudo-Coriolis (Dichgans and Brandt, 1973) stimulation in which, instead of the subject being rotated, the surrounding visual field is turned and the subject moves his head.

The Kennedy et al. (1987) study was designed to evaluate whether adaptation acquired in one stimulus condition involving unusual vestibular stimulation would transfer to another condition where similar, but not identical, conflicting inputs were presented. The amount of transfer was significant, and somewhat unexpected, because in previous studies the hallmark has been the specificity of adaptation (Guedry, 1965). The training condition entailed bizarre stimulation of the cupula endolymph system from the postrotatory effects (the Purkinje stimulus). The adaptation to this bizarre stimulation transferred to a condition in which the stimuli to the canals and otoliths are the same as would occur with no physical rotation present. This fact implies that the transferred adaptation was not merely some form of suppression or fatigue at the sensory level, but a higher-order modification within the central nervous system. Possibly this is the source of its generalizability.

Dobie et al. (1990) successfully replicated the Kennedy study where they found that subjects exposed to bodily rotation exhibited increased tolerance to visually induced self-vection (VISV). However, exposure to VISV did not result in greater tolerance to bodily rotation. Harm and Parker (1994) examined the relationship between perceptual reports obtained during a space mission and in preflight adaptation trainer (PAT) devices. Perceptual reports from the astronauts indicated that the PAT device had features similar to those encountered in microgravity. The reports also suggested that these similarities reduced some of the symptoms of space motion sickness during space flight. More recently Welch et al. (1998) examined the possibility that the human vestibulo-ocular reflex (VOR) is subject to dual adaptation (the ability to adapt more completely after repeated exposure to sensory rearrangement) and adaptive generalization (the ability to adapt more easily to new sensory rearrangement because of prior dual adaptation training). These researchers showed both adaptation and dual adaptation of the VOR, but no adaptive generalization when tested with a target/head gain of 1.0.

Clearly, there is little research concerning the generalizability of adaptation to perceptual rearrangement as it applies to space motion sickness. More studies are needed on this issue, particularly (given the present concern) with long-term generalization.

REDUCING SYMPTOMATOLOGY THROUGH PERCEPTUAL TRAINING

Space adaptation syndrome develops in conditions in which nauseogenic stimuli are present for a long period. The perceptual situation of an astronaut or pilot exposed to unusual gravitational-inertial forces (including zero and subzero gravity) for some period has been compared in many ways to that found in experiments involving perceptual rearrangement, such as optically induced displacement, curvature, tilt, or right–left reversal (Welch, 1978, 2000a). In both instances, the observer is confronted with a variety of inter- and intrasensory conflicts that initially disrupt perception and behavior, and may cause nausea (Dolezal, 1982). Likewise, in both situations people reveal an ability to adapt to these imposed conflicts, as manifested in a reduction or elimination of the initial disruptive responses. Thus, overcoming motion sickness, correcting performatory behavior, and regaining normal perception when one is subjected to unusual gravitational forces may involve many of the same processes as adaptation to perceptual rearrangement in general. The similarity between the processes of overcoming space adaptation syndrome and experimentally imposed perceptual rearrangement provides the motivation for the present proposal.

Based on recent studies where we have developed software to rapidly reconfigure virtual reality (VR) devices conducted in our laboratory (Kennedy et al., 2001), we have obtained evidence that changing specific aspects of the VR device—gain, polarity, head tracking, phase relation, and transport delay—produces systematic and replicable changes in the incidence and severity of motion sickness symptomatology. In other words, with software modification we have developed VR research to study the perceptual rearrangement problem where we have been able to develop quantifiable dose–response relationships that have been successful in eliciting graded motion sickness responses among our participants. The present study used this software to rapidly reconfigure a VR device in order to develop a paradigm for reducing the symptoms of space motion sickness through perceptual training.

Either graded motion sickness was induced through the systematic distortion of the relevant characteristics of the VR device or repeated exposure to self-propelled rotation trials was used until adaptation was attained. The generalization of this adaptation was then tested with the use of an optokinectic nystagmus (OKN) drum. More specifically, we created a pseudo-Coriolis condition through the VR device by reversing head-tracking polarity. This was done with an adaptation protocol where symptoms were kept at a manageable level. Subsequently, we attempted to transfer this adaptation to a pseudo-Coriolis condition induced by a vection drum rotating at 120° per second. Through this process, we set out to demonstrate the feasibility of this Phase I research which was to transfer perceptual adaptation acquired in one environment and relief of symptoms in environments not yet experienced.

EFFECT OF PREADAPTATION TRAINING ON VIRTUAL REALITY EXPOSURE

Twenty adults (10 males and 10 females) ranging between the ages of 18 and 34 were tested on the effect of preadaptation training on virtual reality and vection drum exposure. The training consisted of a simulated rotary stimulation (SRS) procedure in which participants were asked to raise their right hands above their heads and grasp their right earlobe with their left hand, bend at the waste and spin in a clockwise direction under self-propelled condition. The participants spun 10 times in 30 seconds (10 rpm), and this constituted a trial. One or more moderators were always available to support unsteady performers. After standing, they were asked to rate their dizziness and walk a 7-foot line on the floor. The steps taken were counted until the participant stepped away from the line.

The SSQ is a self-report checklist consisting of 27 symptoms that are rated by the participant in terms of degree of severity on a 4-point Likert-type scale (Kennedy et al., 1993). Participants were asked to complete a simulator sickness questionnaire (SSQ) before the exposure to the virtual reality device. Participants who evidenced high preexposure scores were excused from the experiment and were compensated for a minimum of 1 hour of participation. The SSQ was also administered following VE exposure and following OKN drum exposure. Thousands of subjects have been tested using this questionnaire and normative data are available for different represented devices and conditions.

For the experimental group, the study was conducted in five sessions over 5 days. On the first 4 days, participants in the experimental group experienced five trials of the SRS that lasted for about 2 hours. In the fifth session on the final day (the only day in the control case), control and experimental subjects were exposed to the VE and to pseudo-Coriolis in the OKN rotating drum (control subjects experienced one SRS to establish their baseline). Following each task in the study (SRS, VR, and OKN drum) the participants were given an hour of posttesting (SSQ, past-pointing, and posture tasks) at 0-, 30-, and 60-minute intervals.

When participants first arrived for the experimental session, they read and signed an informed consent form. Participants were informed that all records of their participation and their performance will be held in strict confidentiality, that the data files and analyses will be anonymous (data will have a number assigned to it and will not be linked to their name), and that no individual data will be reported. Specifically, all data were coded using participant identification (ID) numbers only, and only the investigative team was able to identify participants by their ID numbers during the data collection part of the experiments. Participants were informed that the data would not be used for any purpose other than the scientific goals of the experiment. Additionally, participants were informed that participation in the study was voluntary; refusal to participate would not result in any penalty or loss of benefits to which they were otherwise entitled, and that they could withdraw from the study at any time if they choose to do so, without penalty.

Following completion of the informed consent, each participant was given three questionnaires to evaluate his or her eligibility to participate in the research: (1) Research Participant Information Questionnaire, (2) Simulator Sickness Questionnaire, and (3) Motion History Questionnaire. Once participants were deemed eligible to participate, they performed the preexposure tests: postural stability, past pointing, and vestibulo-ocular reflex test (OR). (The apparatus-based tests [posture, past pointing, and VOR] and the paper-and-pencil questionnaires are not taxing to the participant, nor conducive to discomfort, and reports of their usage abound in the scientific literature. Norms are available for these tests from >1600 cases.)

After participants exited the virtual environment, they were asked to complete the postsimulator sickness questionnaire (SSQ), which served as our main dependent variable, followed by the more objective (posture and past pointing) tests. Participants were required to remain at the test site for at least 60 minutes following the virtual reality exposure to ensure that any effects experienced because of the exposure have dissipated. During this time, the SSQ was administered at 15-minute intervals, and the posture and past-pointing tasks were administered at 30 minutes and 60 minutes following VE exposure. If necessary, additional tasks (games involving eye–hand coordination available in any toy store) were given to the participant as a "de-spin" procedure to help the participant readapt to the natural environment (F. E. Guedry, Jr., 1989, personal communication). The postural stability and past-pointing performances were compared to scores before VE exposure to verify that they were not noticeably different. Additionally, subjects were asked about their physical condition. If they requested that they remain, they were allowed to stay at the experimental site until adverse feelings subsided. If the researcher determined that they might need further time to recuperate, participants were advised to remain at the experimental site until the symptoms subsided or they had a means of transportation away from the experimental site other than themselves. However, before being permitted to leave the experimental site, participants could not be experiencing any characteristic symptoms of motion sickness (reported on the post-SSQ) or postural disequilibrium. Participants remained in the laboratory until all symptoms had subsided.

In session two, participants from both groups were asked to enter the OKN drum and to be seated facing forward. They were then instructed on how and when to use the response key in the drum. Participants were then asked to close their eyes until the experiment began. The participants were then told to open their eyes and gaze directly at the rotating inner surface of the drum until a perception of circular self-motion (CV) was experienced. Once CV was experienced, participants signaled its presence by pressing the handheld button. Next, while the drum continued to turn, participants were asked to tilt their head 45° toward the left shoulder and to rate their dizziness. This pseudo-Coriolis stimulation has been shown to induce motion sickness (Dichgans and Brandt, 1973). Each participant then turned his/her head upright and made another rating. This procedure was repeated for the right shoulder and again upright before the drum was stopped (total time about 2 minutes). The drum rotated at a velocity of 120°, a rate we knew would produce substantial pseudo-Coriolis experience at a 1-second head-tilt to 45° and then 45° return to upright in 1 second. This procedure allowed us to repeat, in a 30-minute session, this sequence enough times so that adaptation ensued without losing a substantial number of subjects due to emesis.

After participants exited the OKN drum, they were asked to complete the postsimulator sickness questionnaire (SSQ), which served as our main dependent variable, followed by the more objective (posture, past pointing, and VOR) tests. Participants were required to remain at the test site for at least 60 minutes following the OKN drum exposure to ensure that any effects experienced because of the exposure have dissipated. During this time, the SSQ was administered at 15-minute intervals, and the posture, past pointing, and VOR tests were administered at 30 minutes and 60 minutes following the OKN drum exposure. If necessary, additional tasks (games involving eye–hand coordination) were given to the participant to aid the participant in readapting to the natural environment. The postural stability and past-pointing performances were compared to scores before (pre-SSQ) VE exposure in order to verify that they were not noticeably different. Subjects were tested prior to being released to go home.

The analysis of dizziness ratings showed a significant main effect of adaptation training on VR exposure. This significance indicates that the experimental group who had the training with simulated rotary stimulation reported lower rates of dizziness (mean = 1.41) than the control group who did not experience simulated rotary stimulation (mean = 3.79). As Figure 13.1 shows, the difference in the dizziness rates was higher among the control group than the experimental group showing transfer of adaptation into the VR condition as a function of prior simulated self-propelled rotary stimulation exposure.

Similarly, the analysis also showed the same effect of adaptation training on VR as reported in the SSQ following VR exposure. As Figure 13.2 shows, higher simulation sickness ratings were reported by the control (mean = 44.25) than the experimental (mean = 9.72) group and these values

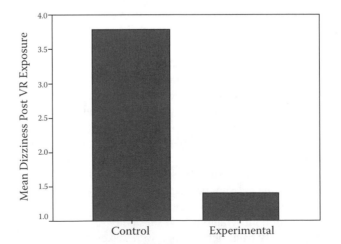

FIGURE 13.1   Mean dizziness post-VR exposure.

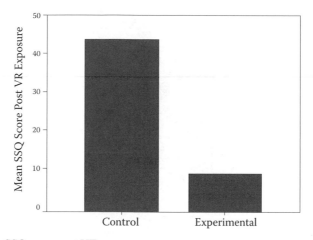

FIGURE 13.2 Mean SSQ score post-VE exposure.

compare favorably to scores from subjects exposed to space and sea sickness where similar high values are obtained. The experimental group in this study exhibited scores that resemble or are lower than the scores of experimental pilots when exposed to flight simulation and control subjects exhibited higher score than that group.

EFFECT OF PREADAPTATION TRAINING ON VECTION DRUM EXPOSURE

The multivariate analysis of variance (MANOVA) showed a significant effect of adaptation training on vection drum exposure, indicating that the experimental group who had prior training with simulated rotary stimulation and VE exposure reported lower rates of dizziness (mean = 1.63) than the control group who did not experience simulated rotary stimulation and VE exposure (mean = 3.92). As Figure 13.3 shows, the difference in the dizziness rates was higher among the control group than the experimental group showing adaptation in the vection drum (OKN) condition as a function of simulated rotary stimulation and VE exposure. Similarly, a MANOVA yielded a significant effect of adaptation training on simulation sickness (SSQ) following the vection (OKN) drum exposure. As

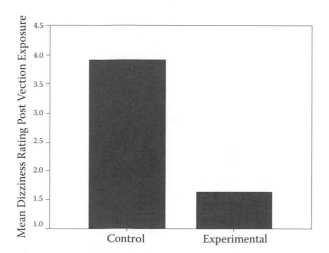

FIGURE 13.3 Mean dizziness rating postvection exposure.

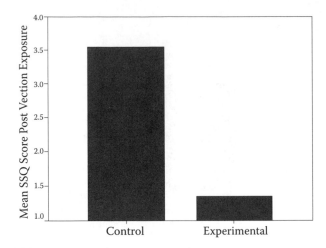

FIGURE 13.4 Mean SSQ score postvection exposure.

Figure 13.4 shows, higher simulation sickness ratings were reported by the control (mean = 61.71) than the experimental (mean = 17.20) group.

CONCLUSION

The present findings indicate that adaptation to sensory rearrangement, in the form of training with simulated rotary stimulation, can be obtained through training in both the virtual and vection drum environments. These findings are consistent with previous findings by Kennedy et al. (1987) who similarly reported that prior adaptation to rotary simulated or Purkinje stimulation transferred to pseudo-Coriolis as was demonstrated by the large difference in reported dizziness between the control and experimental conditions. In this study, Kennedy and his associates used only a self-propelled turning test and transferred to a vection drum condition. These findings suggest that training in the form of simulated self-propelled rotary stimulation and virtual environment exposure help reduce the level of sensory rearrangement found or experienced in certain simulation sickness-related tasks and are consistent with the predictions made by Watt (1996).

Unlike previous findings by Guedry (1965), the present study reconfirmed our previous findings that the adaptation transfer is not task specific and could be extended to tasks that are not identical. Moreover, the present findings are also consistent with previous results by Dobie et al. (1990) who reported increased tolerance to visually induced self-vection (VISV) as a function of bodily rotation exposure. Although it is clear from the present findings that exposure to bodily rotation is beneficial for reducing motion-related dizziness symptoms, it is not well understood whether this adaptation phenomenon can manifest itself in both directions. Previous studies have not extensively studied the double-direction effect of perceptual learning and adaptation in distorted environments. One reason may be that there is more "reafference" (von Holst, 1968), in the self-propelled condition and less in the more passive VR and vection conditions. This difference should be examined in future research. Understanding these issues will help alleviate space adaptation syndrome.

Similarly, the present study partially supports the results by Harm and Parker (1994) and Welch et al. (1998) who previously reported both adaptation and dual adaptation of the VOR, but failed to obtain adaptive generalization. Our findings suggest that the transferred adaptation may be a higher-order modification within the central nervous system, which in turn may account for its generalizability. The results also point to the need of further examining individual differences in the rate of adaptation. Some people may be more prone to simulation sickness than others, and therefore, identifying the traits for "adaptability" would have several practical implications for space adaptation syndrome and other situations entailing perceptual adjustment. Notably, an adaptation training program in the form of a virtual environment or vection drum may help alleviate several of the motion sickness-induced found in other visual–vestibular conflict environments. For example, Vanderploeg, Stewart, and Davis (1985) have previously reported that of the 22 space travelers who have had an opportunity for more than one flight, 11 were sick in various degrees on their first flight and 11 were not, and subsequently were symptom-free on their second exposure. These findings clearly indicate the need for preadaptation training of those who are prone to simulation sickness-type symptoms for a variety of applications including NASA astronauts.

In summary, our results showed that preadaptation training in the form of simulated rotary Purkinje stimulation produce reduced levels of simulation sickness in both the virtual and vection (OKN) drum environments. The significant differences in dizziness, nausea, oculomotor, and other related simulation sickness symptoms found between the control and experimental groups are a clear indication of perceptual adaptation. These results are consistent with the relatively enduring adaptation to prism-displaced vision demonstrated even months after the initial prism exposure. It is not well understood whether the adaptation training can be sustained and maintained over a prolonged period of time. In addition, the transfer of adaptation from one situation of visual–vestibular conflict to another situation warrants further investigation. Also, the dichotomy of simulated rotary stimulation task (Coriolis versus pseudo-Coriolis) is an important dimension in examining individual differences in adaptation to perceptual rearrangement and space syndrome. Further research is needed to address these issues through a series of interlocking empirical experiments.

ACKNOWLEDGMENTS

We would like to thank Paul Huchens, Dan Compton, and Cecelia Grizzard for the data collection and technical assistance. Also, we would like to thank Drs. Norm Lane and Bob Jones for their insightful comments during the course of this research. This research was supported by a NASA contract (NAS2-02016). Charles DaRoshia was the technical monitor.

REFERENCES

Benson, A. J., 1978. Motion sickness. In Dhenin, G., & Ernsting, J (Eds.), *Aviation medicine: Physiology and human factors* (pp. 468–493). London, UK: British Crown Copyright.

Benson, A. J., & Bodin, M. A., 1966. Interaction of linear and angular accelerations on vestibular receptors in man. *Aerospace Medicine, 37*, 144–154.

Boynton, R. M., & Das, S. R., 1966. Visual adaptation: Increased efficiency resulting from spectrally distributed mixtures of stimuli. *Science, 154*, 1581–1583.

Cohen, J., 1977. *Statistical power analysis for the behavioral sciences.* New York: Academic Press.

Collins, E., 1974. Habituation of vestibular responses and visual stimulation. In Kornhuber, H. H. (Ed.), *Handbook of sensory physiology.* Vol. V1/2, *Vestibular systems.* Berlin: Springer–Verlag.

Crawshaw, M., & Craske, B., 1976. Oculomotor adaptation to prisms: Complete transfer between eyes. *British Journal of Psychology, 67(4)*, 475–478.

Dichgans, J., 1977. Optically induced self–motion perception. *Proceedings of the Symposium of Life Sciences Research in Space* (pp. 109–112). Paris, France: European Space Agency (ESASP–1 30).

Dichgans, J., & Brandt, T., 1973. Optokinetic motion sickness as pseudo-Coriolis effects induced by moving visual stimuli. *Acta Otolaryngologica, 76*, 339–348.

Dobie, T. G., & May, J. G., 1990. Generalization of tolerance to motion environments. *Aviation, Space, and Environmental Medicine, 61(8)*, 707–711.

Dobie, T. G., May, J. G., Fischer, W. D., & Elder, S. T., 1987. A comparison of two methods of training resistance to visually–induced motion sickness. *Aviation, Space, and Environmental Medicine, 58(9, Sect 2)*, 34–41.

Dobie, T. G., May, J. G., Gutierrez, C, & Heller, S. S., 1990. The transfer of adaptation between actual and simulated rotary stimulation. *Aviation, Space, and Environmental Medicine, 61(12),* 1085–1091.

Dolezal, H. F., 1982. *Living in a world transformed.* New York: Academic Press.

Festinger, L., Burnbham, C. A., Ono, H., & Bamer, D., 1967. Efference and the conscious experience of perception. *Journal of Experimental Psychology Monograph, 74(4),* 1–36.

Fineberg, M. L., 1977. The effects of previous learning on the visual perception of velocity. *Human Factor, 19,* 157–162.

Fregly, A. R., & Kennedy, R. S., 1965. Comparative effects of prolonged rotation at 10 RPM on postural equilibrium in vestibular normal and vestibular effective human subjects. *Aerospace Medicine, 36(12),* 1160–1167.

Fried, C., 1962. *Studies on the perceptual threshold for motion. II. Effects of induced motion on threshold velocity* (Technical Memorandum No. 18–62). Aberdeen Proving Ground, MD: Army Human Engineering Laboratories.

Goodenough, F. L., & Tinker, M. A., 1931. The retention of mirror reading ability after two years. *Journal of Educational Psychology, 22,* 503–504.

Graybiel, A., & Lackner, J. R., 1983. Motion sickness acquisition and retention of adaptation effects compared in three motion environments. *Aviation, Space and Environmental Medicine, 54,* 307–311.

Guedry, F. E., Jr., 1965. Habituation to complex vestibular stimulation in man: Transfer and retention of effects from twelve days of rotation at 10 RPM. *Perceptual and Motor Skills, 21,* 459–481.

Guilford, J. P., 1954. *Psychometric methods.* New York: McGraw-Hill.

Harlow, C. S., 1959. Learning set and error factor theory. In Koch, S. (Ed.), *Psychology: A study of a science* (Vol. 2). New York: McGraw-Hill.

Harm, D. L., & Parker, D. E. 1993. Perceived self-orientation and self-motion in micro-gravity, after landing and during preflight adaptation training. *Journal of Vestibular Research: Equilibrium and Orientation, 3(3),* 297–305.

Harm, D. L., & Parker, D. E. 1994. Preflight adaptation training for spatial orientation and space motion sickness. *Journal of Clinical Pharmacology, 34(6),* 618–627.

Harris, C. S., 1965. Perceptual adaptation to inverted, reversed, and displaced vision. *Psychological Review, 72,* 419–444.

Harris, C. S., 1980. Insight or out of sight? Two examples of perceptual plasticity in the human adult. In Harris, C. S. (Ed.), *Visual coding and adaptability.* Hillsdale, NJ: Lawrence Erlbaum Associates.

Hein, A., 1972. Acquiring components of visually guided behavior. In Pick, A. D. (Ed.), *Minnesota symposia on child psychology.* Minneapolis, MN: University of Minneapolis Press.

Held, R., 1965. Plasticity in sensory–motor systems. *Scientific American, 213,* 84–91.

Held, R., 1968. Dissociation of visual functions by deprivation and rearrangement. *Psychologische Forschung, 31,* 338–348.

Homick, J. L., Reschke, M. F., & Vanderploeg, J. M., 1984. Space adaptation syndrome: Incidence and operational implications for the space transportation system program. *Proceedings of AGARD Conference, Motion sickness: Mechanisms, prediction, prevention and treatment* (AGARD–CP–372). Neuilly–Sur–Seine, France: Advisory Group for Aerospace Research and Development.

Ishii, M., 1993. Space and vertigo: In relation to space motion sickness. *Japanese Journal of Aerospace and Environmental Medicine, 30(1),* 41–45.

Jell, R. M., Ireland, D. J., & LaFortune, S., 1985. Human optokinetic after nystagmus. *Acta Otolaryngology, 99,* 95–101.

Jones, G. M., & Gonshor, A., 1972. Extreme vestibular habituation to long-term reversal of vision during natural head movements. *Preprints of the Aerospace Medical Association Annual Scientific Meeting* (pp. 22).

Jones, M. B., 1970. A two-process theory of individual differences in motor learning. *Psychological Review, 77(4),* 353–360.

Jones, P., & Holding, D. 1975. Extremely long-term persistence of the McCullough effect. *Journal of Experimental Psychology: Human Perception and Performance, 4,* 323–32.

Katz, D. I., & Lackner, J. R., 1977. Adaptation to delayed auditory feedback. *Perception and Psychophysics, 22(5),* 476–486.

Kennedy, R. S., 1970. *Visual distortion: A point of view* (Monograph No. 15). Pensacola, FL: Naval Aerospace Medical Institute.

Kennedy, R. S., 1972. *The relationship between habituation to vestibular stimulation and vigilance: Individual differences and subsidiary problems.* Doctoral dissertation, University of Rochester, NY. (Also NAMRL Monograph No. 20, Naval Aerospace Medical Research Laboratory, Pensacola, FL.)

Kennedy, R. S., Berbaum, K. S., & Frank, L. H., 1984. Visual distortion: The correlation model. *Proceedings of the SAE Aerospace Congress and Exhibition* (Paper No. 841595). Long Beach, CA: Society of Automotive Engineers.

Kennedy, R. S., Berbaum, K. S., Williams, M. C., Brannan, J., & Welch, R. B., 1987. Transfer of perceptual–motor training and the space adaptation syndrome. *Aviation, Space, and Environmental Medicine, 58* (9 Suppl.), A29–A33.

Kennedy, R. S., Fowlkes, J. E., Berbaum, K. S., & Lilienthal, M. G., 1992. Use of a motion sickness history questionnaire for prediction of simulator sickness. *Aviation, Space, and Environmental Medicine, 63,* 588–593.

Kennedy, R. S., & Frank, L. H., 1986. *A review of motion sickness with special reference to simulator sickness.* Paper presented at the 65th Annual Meeting of the Transportation Research Board, Washington D.C.

Kennedy, R. S., Frank, L. H., & McCauley, M. E., 1984. *Simulator sickness: Reaction to a transformed perceptual world II. Sourcebook and suggested readings* (NAVTRAEQUIPCEN 81–C–0105–7). Orlando, FL: Naval Training Equipment Center.

Kennedy, R. S., Hettinger, L. J., Harm, D. L., Ordy, J. M., & Dunlap, W. P., 1996. Psychophysical scaling of circular vection (CV) produced by optokinetic (OKN) motion: Individual differences and effects of practice. *Journal of Vestibular Research, 6*(5), 331–341.

Kennedy, R. S., Jones, M. B., & Harbeson, M. M., 1980. *Assessing productivity and well-being in Navy workplaces.* Proceedings of the 13th Annual Meeting of the Human Factors Association of Canada. Rexdale, Ontario, Canada: Human Factors Association of Canada, pp. 108–113. Also, Naval Biodynamics Laboratory, New Orleans, LA: November 1981, pp. 8–13. (Research Report No. NBDL–82R004). (NTIS No. AD A111180).

Kennedy, R. S., Jones, M. B., Stanney, K. M., & Compton, D. E., 2001. *Getting control of the stimulus: Equipment features and individual differences in VR induced cybersickness.* Phase I Final Report to National Eye Institute, NIH: Washington D.C.

Kennedy, R. S., Lane, N. E., Berbaum, K. S., & Lilienthal, M. G., 1993. Simulator Sickness Questionnaire (SSQ): A new method for quantifying simulator sickness. *International Journal of Aviation Psychology, 3(3),* 203–220.

Kennedy, R. S., Lilienthal, M. G., Dutton, B., Ricard, G. L., & Frank, L. H., 1984, December. Simulator sickness: Incidence of simulator aftereffects in Navy flight trainers. *Proceedings of the SAFE Symposium* (pp. 299–302). Las Vegas, NV.

Kennedy, R. S., Stanney, K. M., Compton, D. E., Drexler, J. M., & Jones, M. B., 1999. *Virtual environment adaptation assessment test battery.* Phase II Final Report, Contract No. NAS9–97022. Houston, TX: NASA Lyndon B. Johnson Space Center.

Kennedy, R. S., Stanney, K. M., Drexler, J. M., Compton, D. E., & Harm, D. L., (in press). Configural scoring of simulator sickness, cybersickness, and space adaptation syndrome: Similarities and differences? In Hettinger, L., & Haas, M. (Eds.), *Psychological issues in the design and use of virtual and adaptive environments.* Mahwah, NJ: Lawrence Erlbaum Associates.

Kennedy, R. S., Stanney, K. M., & Rolland, J., 2001. *Optokinetic studies of the relationship between vection and cybersickness* (Report No. N61339–00–C–0054). Orlando, FL: Naval Air Warfare Center, Training Systems Division.

Kinney, J. A. S., Luria, S. M., Weitzman, D. O., & Markowitz, H. 1970. *Effects of diving experience on visual perception under water* (NSMRL Report No. 612). Groton, CT: U.S. Naval Submarine Medical Center.

Kinney, J. A. S., McKay, C. L., Luria, S. M., & Gratto, C. L., 1970. *The improvement of divers' compensation for underwater distortions* (NSMRL Report No. 633). Groton, CT: U.S. Naval Submarine Medical Center.

Klapp, S. T., Nordell, S. A., Hoekenga, K. C., & Patton, C. B., 1974. Long-lasting aftereffect of brief prism exposure. *Perception and Psychophysics, 15,* 399–400.

Kottenhoff, H., 1957. Situational and personal influences on space perception with experimental spectacles. *Acta Psychological, 12,* 79–87.

Lackner, J. R., & DiZio, P., 1998. Adaptation in a rotating artificial gravity environment. *Brain Research Review, 28(1–2),* 194–202.

Lackner, J. R., & Graybiel, A., 1984. Influence of gravitoinertial force level on apparent magnitude of Coriolis cross-coupled angular accelerations and motion sickness. *Proceedings of AGARD Conference, Motion sickness: Mechanisms, prediction, prevention and treatment* (AGARD–CP–372). Neuilly–Sur–Seine, France: Advisory Group for Aerospace Research and Development.

Lackner, J. R., & Lobovits, D., 1977. Adaptation to displaced vision: Evidence for prolonged aftereffects. *Quarterly Journal of Experimental Psychology, 29,* 65–69.

Lentz, J. M., 1984. Laboratory tests of motion sickness susceptibility. *Proceedings of AGARD Conference, Motion sickness: Mechanisms, prediction, prevention and treatment* (AGARD–CP–372). Neuilly–Sur–Seine, France: Advisory Group for Aerospace Research and Development.

Lentz, M., & Guedry, F. E., 1978. Motion sickness susceptibility: A comparison of laboratory tests. *Aviation, Space, and Environmental Medicine, 49,* 1281–1288.

Luria, S. M., & Kinney, J. A. S., 1970. Underwater vision. *Science, 167,* 1454–1461.

Luria, S. M., Kinney, J. A., & Weissman, S., 1967. Estimates of size and distance underwater. *American Journal of Psychology, 80,* 282–286.

Mack, A., 1967. The role of movement in perceptual adaptation to a tilted retinal image. *Perception and Psychophysics, 2,* 65–68.

McCauley, M. E., 1984. (Ed.). *Simulator sickness: Proceedings of a workshop.* Washington D.C.: National Academy of Sciences/National Research Council/National Academy of Sciences, Committee on Human Factors.

McGonigle, B. O., & Flook, J., 1978. Long-term retention of single and multistate prismatic adaptation by humans. *Nature, 272,* 364–366.

McLaughlin, S. C., & Webster, R. C., 1967. Changes in straight-ahead eye position during adaptation to wedge prisms. *Perception and Psychophysics, 2,* 37–44.

Melamed, L. E., Beckett, P. A., & Halay, M., 1979. Individual differences in the visual component of prism adaptation. *Perception, 8,* 699–706.

Money, K. E., Watt, D. G., & Oman, C. M., 1984. Preflight and postflight motion sickness testing of the Spacelab I crew. *Proceedings of AGARD Conference, Motion sickness: Mechanisms, prediction, prevention and treatment* (AGARD–CP–372). Neuilly–Sur–Seine, France: Advisory Group for Aerospace Research and Development.

Monrad-Krohn, G. H., 1926. *The clinical examination of the nervous system* (3rd ed.). New York: Paul B. Hoeber.

Nguyen, T., 1996. Space sickness. *Proceedings of the 5th International Conference on Space '96, Vol. 2.* Albuquerque, NM, June 1–6.

Oman, C. M., Lichtenberg, B. K., & Money, K. E., 1984. Space motion sickness monitoring experiment: Spacelab 1. *Proceedings of AGARD Conference, Motion sickness: Mechanisms, prediction, prevention and treatment* (AGARD–CP–372). Neuilly–Sur–Seine, France: Advisory Group for Aerospace Research and Development.

Oman, C. M., 1991. Sensory conflict in motion sickness: an Observer Theory approach. In Ellis, S. R., Kaiser, M., & Grunwald, A. (Eds.), *Pictorial communication in virtual and real environments* (pp. 362–376). London: Taylor & Francis.

Parker, D. E, Reschke, M. F., Arrott, A. P., Homick, J. L., & Lichtenberg, B. V., 1985. Otolith tilt–translation reinterpretation following prolonged weightlessness: Implications for preflight training. *Aviation, Space, and Environmental Medicine, 56,* 601–606.

Peterson, J., & Peterson, J. K., 1938. Does practice with inverting lenses make vision normal? *Psychological Monographs, 225,* 12–37.

Reason, J. T., 1970. Motion sickness: A special case of sensory rearrangement. *Advancement of Science., 26,* 386–393.

Reason, J. T., & Graybiel, A., 1972. Factors contributing to motion sickness susceptibility: Adaptability and receptivity. *Proceedings of AGARD Conference: Predictability of motion sickness in the selection of pilots* (AGARD–CP–109). Neuilly–Sur–Seine, France: Advisory Group for Aerospace Research and Development.

Redding, G. M., 1973a. Simultaneous visual adaptation to tilt and displacement: A test of independent processes. *Bulletin of Psychonomic Society, 2,* 41–42.

Redding, G. M., 1973b. Visual adaptation to tilt and displacement: Same or different processes? *Perception and Psychophysics, 14,* 193–200.

Redding, G. M., 1975a. Simultaneous visuomotor adaptation to optical tilt and displacement. *Perception and Psychophysics, 17,* 97–100.

Redding, G. M., 1975b. Decay of visual adaptation to tilt and displacement. *Perception and Psychophysics, 17,* 203–208.

Reschke, M. F., Bloomberg, J. J., Harm, D. L., Paloskli, W. H., Layne, C., & McDonald, V. 1998. Posture, locomotion, spatial orientation, and motion sickness as a function of one space flight. *Brain Research Review, 28,* 102–117.

Reschke, M. F., Homick, J. L., Ryan, P., and Mosely, E. C., 1984. Prediction of the space adaptation syndrome. *Proceedings of AGARD Conference, Motion sickness: Mechanisms, prediction, prevention and treatment* (AGARD–CP–372). Neuilly–Sur–Seine, France: Advisory Group for Aerospace Research and Development.

Savreau, D., 1979. Persistence of simple and contingent motion aftereffects. *Perception and Psychophysics, 26(3),* 187–194.

Slotnick, R. S., 1969. Adaptation to curvature distortion. *Journal of Experimental Psychology, 81,* 441–448.

Snyder, F. W., & Snyder, C. W., 1957. Vision with spatial inversion: A follow-up study. *Psychological Record, 7,* 20–30.

Stanney, K. M., Kennedy, R. S., Drexler, J. M., & Harm, D. L., 1999. Motion sickness and proprioceptive after-effects following virtual environment exposure. *Applied Ergonomics, 30(1),* 27–38.

Stanney, K. M., Mourant, R. R., & Kennedy, R. S., 1998. Human factors issues in virtual environments: A review of the literature. *Presence, 7(4),* 327–351.

Taub, E., & Goldberg, I. A., 1973. Prism adaptation: Control of intermanual transfer by distribution of practice. *Science, 180,* 755–757.

Thornton, W. E., Pool, S. L., Moore, T., & Vanderploeg, J., 1987. Clinical characterization and etiology of space motion sickness. *Aviation, Space, and Environmental Medicine, 58(9, Suppl.),* A1–A8.

Vanderploeg, J. M., Stewart, D. F., & Davis, J. R., 1985. *Space motion sickness.* Houston, TX: NASA (NASA Report NASA–S–85–02963).

von Holst, E., 1968. Relations between the central nervous system and the peripheral organs. In Haber, R. N. (Ed.), *Contemporary theory and research in visual perception* (pp. 497–503). New York: Holt, Rinehart, and Winston.

Warren, D. H., & Platt, B. B., 1974. The subjects: A neglected factor in recombination research. *Perception 3,* 421–438.

Welch, R. B., 1978. *Perceptual modification: Adapting to altered sensory environments.* New York: Academic Press.

Welch, R. B., 2000a. Adapting to virtual environments. In Stanney, K. M. (Ed.), *Handbook of virtual environments: Design, implementation, and applications.* Mahwah, NJ: Lawrence Erlbaum Associates.

Welch, R. B., 2000b. *Adapting to telesystems.* In Hettinger, L., & Haas, M. (Eds.), *Psychological issues in the design and use of virtual and adaptive environments.* Mahwah, NJ: Lawrence Erlbaum Associates.

Welch, R. B., Bridgeman, B., Williams, J. A., & Semmler, R., 1998. Dual adaptation and adaptive generalization of the human vestibulo-ocular reflex. *Perception and Psychophysics, 60(8),* 1415–1425.

Welch, R. B., Choe, C. S., & Heinrich, D. R., 1974. Evidence for a three-component model of prism adaptation. *Journal of Experimental Psychology, 103,* 700–705.

Wolfe, J., 1985. Fatigue and structural change: Two consequences of visual pattern adaptation. *Investigative Ophthalmology and Visual Science (Supplement), 24,* 215.

Wooster, M., 1923. Certain factors in the development of a new spatial coordination. *Psychological Monographs, 32(4),* 1–96.

14 Civil Aviation
*Flight Simulators and Training**

Ronald J. Lofaro and Kevin M. Smith

CONTENTS

---

* The views and opinions expressed in this chapter are solely those of the authors. They do not necessarily represent those
  of any governmental, public, or private organizations.

INTRODUCTION

The use of flight simulators for civil pilot/crew training and performance evaluation has evolved to the point where they have become key and indispensable tools for air carrier education—and will continue to be so. This is due to a conjunction of factors: safety, cost, simulator fidelity, and fairly recent changes and additions to the federal aviation regulations (FARs). A short bit of explanation on the Federal Aviation Administration (FAA) and FARs follows. The FAA regulates aviation in the United States, from air traffic to civil aviation security, the operation of air carriers, pilot training, and more. The federal regulations covering aviation are all found in Combined Federal Regulations (CFR), Title 14, Aeronautics and Space; these are commonly referred to as the FARs. The FARs are divided into parts (1 through 199) and each part has a descriptive title and is a specific and detailed regulation. For example, CFR 14, Part 121 is the FAR titled Operating Requirement: Domestic Flight and Supplemental Operations. The FARs are usually referred to by part number; this one would just be called Part 121.

As an aid to aviation, the FAA normally published advisory circulars (ACs) that relate to specific FARs. The ACs are designed to provide assistance and guidelines in complying with FARs. In fact, these ACs, which often are longer than the length of the FAR, are written in meticulous detail and serve as a "how to" template. The ACs are titled, numbered, and grouped by such areas as air traffic control, civil and general aviation security, pilot training, and so on. For example, AC 120-45A is the AC titled Airplane Flight Training Device Qualification. The 120 specifies the general area of air carrier and commercial operations and helicopters, whereas the 45 refers to the fact that this is the 45th AC under the 120 area. The "A" means it is the first revision.

For the remainder of the chapter we will refer to the FARs by part number only, and the same for ACs. A caveat: We will, somewhat extensively, cite from FARs and ACs. As these are large documents, and we have space limitations, we will sometimes omit sentences within a relevant portion of a citation. We may, occasionally, rather than use a long citation, synopsize what we are referring to. (For the interested reader, the complete FARs and ACs can be found on the FAA website: http://www.faa.gov.)

We will begin this chapter with an overview of flight simulators (FS) and their use in the air carrier arena. From there, this chapter will proceed to a brief look at the human factors issues and problems in civil aviation's use of flight simulators. These are, in the main, the same issues and problems of flight simulator use in any environment: fidelity, part-task trainers, transfer of training, motion axes, transition training and the like. In addressing the human factors of civil aviation, we recognize that the hexapod axial motion bases and the veridicality of the FS to the actual flying environment are what have led to the use of the FS as the major pilot/crew training, evaluation and certification tool. As one example, flight simulators today have assumed such an important place in air carrier training that an aircraft-type rating can be obtained (almost) entirely in a flight simulator. Advances in the capabilities of this generation of flight simulator has led to modified FAA classification schemas (levels) for airplane flight simulators and flight training devices (FTDs) and to the first new pilot/crew training effort in over 30 years, the Advanced Qualification Program (AQP).

Our human factors focus will be on training, and the models for training and evaluating the skills we see as paramount for the pilot/crew in accomplishing risk identification and risk management. Thus, the chapter will deal extensively with the use and maximization of line-oriented flight training (LOFT). The Air Transport Association of America (ATA) and the FAA have worked on the best ways to design, develop, and implement LOFT and line-oriented evaluation (LOE) in flight simulators, as shown by the relevant FARs and ACs. The result is that LOFT, which is done entirely in a flight simulator, has become, over the past 15 to 17 years, what could be called the "crown jewel" of air carrier pilot/crew training. LOFT and LOE received initial impetus from their use in crew resource management (CRM) training. However, CRM in the mid-1990s encountered problems, with one result being the "Big Three" U.S. flag air carriers (American, Delta, and United) almost completely revamping and renaming their CRM programs (*Aviation Week and Space Technology*, 1996).

LOFT, always recognized as the key element in CRM, has thus become more and more recognized as the independent and indispensable training and evaluation tool for pilot/crew performance. The FAA's emphasis on air carrier crews going to a new training and certification paradigm, the above-mentioned AQP as spelled out in (Special FAR) SFAR 58, has further enhanced the role of LOFT and LOE.

Lastly, this chapter will deal with LOFT design, development, and use in crew performance and evaluation, using the mission performance model (MPM) and the operational decision making (ODM) paradigm. We will lay out the use of LOFT for learning/practice in operational decision making, which results in risk assessment and reduction. This, the authors have long considered as the key functions for any airline captain and crew.

AN OVERVIEW OF CIVIL AVIATION TRAINING, FLIGHT SIMULATORS, AND THE HUMAN FACTORS THEREIN

INTRODUCTION

There are three somewhat obvious benefits from the use of a flight simulator in training. These are the underpinning of the now-extensive use of flight simulators in general aviation, civil aviation, and military aviation. Briefly put, they are:

1. Cost reduction and increased efficiency by replacing the real system, the plane, with the flight simulator.
2. Reduction in the hazards of training in the plane. The loss of life and injuries that result from training accidents and incidents are well documented.
3. The ability to train skills and performances that cannot be trained in the aircraft, such as malfunctions and adverse conditions and, more important, missions/tasks that may never be performed in real-world operations but are essential components of the operational mission profile of the aircraft (cf. Flexman and Stark, 1987).

The extensive use of flight simulators in the civil aviation world has resulted from both recognizing these benefits and a confluence of other causes. The first, as said, is that the flight simulator is a safe environment, putting neither crew nor planes at risk. However, although crew and aircraft safety is foremost, looking further we see the following set of converging vectors: In the formative years, and continuing well into the late 1980s and early 1990s, both civil aviation and the FAA relied on ex-military members (mainly active-duty personnel who left after fulfilling their commitment, but also some retirees in their 40s) for a source of experienced manpower. In civil aviation, these former military members included pilots and aviation maintenance technicians (AMT). The same was true in the FAA, where there was, perhaps, a higher emphasis placed on the ex-military pilot, who could be placed in the flight standards, aircraft, and pilot certification areas without missing a beat. The rationale for the aviation industry seeking (and welcoming) military personnel is both obvious and subtle. It is obvious that the military was a source of highly trained and qualified personnel. Plus, their training was both extensive and standardized. It is also true that there is a "brotherhood of airmen," where inclusion is highly dependent on airmen background, experiences, training and even common acquaintances. Add to these factors a common "language," one that is technical, acronym-laden and replete with idiomatic expressions. All of the above are still active (albeit to a lesser degree) today. One result of the influx of military personnel was the use of the flight simulator as the major training tool for aircrew.

In passing, it must be remembered that the earliest flight simulator, with replicated cockpit instrumentation, controls, and most aspects of flight built by Edward A. Link in 1929, was a generic flight simulator for General Aviation (GA) use. This Link trainer, whose picture we have all seen (it looks like a child's drawing of a plane mounted on a base), soon evolved into an instrument flight trainer as a result of WWII. From there, the great advances in flight simulators had to do with its use in military training. The history of the early flight simulator development of both capability and capacity for training was for use in training military pilots/aircrew. It was natural, as many of the early air carrier and FAA personnel had military backgrounds, that the use of the flight simulator in training and certification became paramount. Add to this a piece of reality that is often overlooked: the air carriers simply do not have enough planes to take significant or even small item numbers out of service for pilot training. As one example, the largest U.S. flag carriers own/lease less than 300 planes each. Unlike the military, which has large numbers of aircraft that are dedicated only to training pilots, the air carriers must use their planes, in the main, to generate income. Considering that the air carrier's run 24/7 schedules, it is apparent that the flight simulator is, must be, and will continue to be the training and certification tool in civil aviation.

To resume: This military use of the flight simulator drove much of early flight simulator technology as aircraft became more complex, more automated, and achieved higher performance. On the civil aviation front, the air carriers began to insist that the delivery of a flight simulator for a new type of aircraft be simultaneous, or even before, the new aircraft was put in everyday service. Similarly, the civil side of aviation demanded more and more simulator capability (fidelity and veridicality). The major air carriers used their pilot and crew training facilities to house a growing number of flight simulators. Companies that made flight simulators worked closely with both the airframe manufacturers and the air carriers to design and deliver flight simulators that met the changing needs of pilot training and certification. Today, for example, we have civil aviation flight simulators for the B-757/767 and 777, which cost upward of $35 million and cost in the thousands of dollars per hour when in operation. These operational costs include maintenance, the simulator operator, and the air conditioning needed to maintain the temperature in the flight simulator faculty at a level that does not impact the highly sophisticated computers that drive the flight simulator.

The final vector, or piece, of the equation has been the technological advances in flight simulator capability during the 1980s and '90s. The advances in the fidelity of the visual scene presented to the crew, as well the fidelity of the response of flight simulator instruments (be they "glass" or "steam") to inputs by the crew are outstanding examples of this fidelity.

In summation, through a convergence of causal vectors, the period from approximately 1970 to today has seen the emergence of the flight simulator as the essential tool for pilot training and certification in the civil area.

FLIGHT SIMULATOR BASICS

The primary functions of any flight simulator (i.e., the functional definitions, as it were) are:

1. To present information that the real system would present for the purpose of training
2. To provide a practice environment that facilitates and enhances the skills and knowledge of the pilot and thus provides learning that enhances performance in the real system, the airplane

Put into other terms, a flight simulator is a system designed to "imitate" the functions of another system (a plane) in a real operational environment and to be a realistic substitute that responds realistically to flightcrew inputs. The key here is that a flight simulator can be programmed to offer varied experiences to a flightcrew, but experiences that are safe, in that if you "crash" in a simulator, there is no injury, save to your pride. (We will return to the role of experience in flight training and flying later in this chapter.) Basically, a flight simulator is a training device that is safer, less expensive, capable of quick modification, and can operate in all weather and for all or any part of a 24-hour day. The flight simulator presents accurate cockpit displays to the flightcrew and accurately (except for complete motion capability) responds to control and avionics inputs—all the time processing and storing data on the crew's control inputs, etc.

The characteristics of a flight simulator are that it:

1. Stores data that can be replayed and analyzed on crew input/crew response
2. Stores data that can be used to generate a realistic "environment"/mission or portion; control and other responses to crew inputs
3. Displays such data/info both to the flightcrew and to the flight simulator operator
4. Responds to crew inputs accurately as to their effects on both system and environment
5. As would the actual plane, has accurate/valid displays of the status of onboard systems/components (e.g., EPRs) that are so vital for the crew to see and monitor
6. Provides two-way training interfaces for the flight simulator instructor and the flightcrew being trained

There are research applications of different types of flight simulators. The *engineering development flight simulator* is used in the cockpit/flight control systems design phase. This flight simulator makes system design easier because it is quickly reconfigurable, so that one can conduct system experiments on changes and reconfigurations without having to build or tear down a real system.

The *research/engineering simulator* is a system used to help with basic R&D and applied research on system operations (to look at differences in various flight-control systems; e.g., fly by wire vs. manual vs. fly by light). This flight simulator has many of the capabilities mentioned for the engineering development flight simulator. It can also evaluate human performance limits in the system and evaluate system interaction with other systems (data-link, dispatch, ATC). And lastly, the research/engineering flight simulator can be used to train personnel in the operation of the system.

Although, as mentioned, there are several types of flight simulators, the focus in this chapter will be what is often termed the "full-up" flight simulator. Simply put, a "full-up" flight simulator has:

1. Three-axis motion base (pitch/roll/yaw) in two directions each (hexapod motion, six degrees of freedom)
2. Computer-generated graphic displays for the "out the windows" visual scene; these include most types of weather and environments, as well as night scenarios
3. A complete cockpit that is the same as in the aircraft type that the flight simulator models
4. Tremendous computer memory, which allows for superb capability in realistic flight simulation

In short, the flight simulator has ultra-realism, except damping as to the motion bases. These flight simulator capabilities are the component parts of the team *fidelity*—the closeness to which the flight simulator mimics actual flight. What may be of more import is the flight simulator's veridicality (see following subsection).

HUMAN FACTORS AND FLIGHT SIMULATORS

The human factors training functions that a flight simulator can address are many and varied. We will simply list many of them. Such a list must include briefings and demonstrations, practice, performance analysis, learning enhancement, providing knowledge of results of actions, providing supplementary cues to the flightcrew, building cognitive structures, performance assessment, and, finally, providing a safe environment for introducing adverse conditions, malfunctions, and outright mechanical and other failures (cf. Flexman and Stark, 1987).

Human factors training as a major component of pilot training became possible with the advent of AQP. This was the first time that a complete review of traditional training became possible. No longer were air carriers tied to the existing FARs, but were allowed to build programs to meet more specifically targeted needs. This training usually included CRM, but more accurately, allowed curricula development that addressed complex problem-solving events that a flightcrew would encounter operating under adverse conditions. Thus, one saw an explosion of "line-oriented" training and certification events as part of this new emphasis on human factors.

There are many issues, human factors being a major one, in the building and use of flight simulators for the training and evaluation of pilot/crew performance. We have briefly mentioned some, although we did not identify them as issues, in the preceding subsection. These issues cluster around the level of flight simulator fidelity necessary for training and/or evaluating a pilot/crew task. This is not to say that other concerns do not exist. But, in the main, the use in training and evaluations of a flight simulator deals what is called fidelity (of the flight simulator to the aircraft) in terms of (a) the motion bases, (b) the out–the-windscreen/window visuals, and (c) the simulator response to control inputs. All these issues can be subsumed under the more general question of "How veridical to actual flight does a flight simulator have to be in order to insure training that fully prepares a pilot/crew for actually flying the plane?"

Veridicality is the closeness of the correspondence of the knowledge structures formed by using the flight simulator (learning and using controls/input responses/instrument responses/visual scene/motion, etc.) to the information environment it represents, that is, the actual aircraft type. Because the flight simulator is used in training to build knowledge structures in the crew that will be used in actual flight, it is obvious that veridicality is the primary factor in flight simulator design and use. The higher the fidelity of a flight simulator, the more veridical the knowledge structures built in the flight simulator are—making the flightcrew optimally prepared for actual flight.

To be sure, we do not want to give the impression that other issues do not exist and could include incorrect control inputs, incorrect sequencing, poor or incorrect decision making, and more. However, these are beyond the scope of this chapter.

We will, however, look at one basic human factors/training assumption: The use of any flight simulator for training tasks and skills results in the skills gained transferring to the actual cockpit, called "transfer of training." The assumption is that the knowledge structures and information acquired previously on one task affects (neutrally) the ability to be trained on another/other tasks. Although we are talking of tasks here, the intent is that the learning of tasks trained in the flight simulator will aid the learning (performance) of a new task in the plane. Confusing as this may sound, the task learned in the flight simulator, when performed in the plane, is referred to as a new task. Why? Because the task in the plane, even though it is the same as the task in the flight simulator, is being done now in the plane; therefore, it is called a new task. Note: Transfer of training also occurs from plane to flight simulator.

There are two types of training transfer that occur. The desired one is called positive transfer where previous training/experience aids "learning" of new tasks. However, there also exists negative transfer where previous experience interferes with learning new tasks or performing the trained, "old" task in new environment. It is important again to note that positive and negative transfer can occur in either direction: flight simulator to plane or plane to flight simulator. There are some examples of skills gained in flying that are not transferrable to the cockpit. This would seem to have to do with the veridicality of the flight simulator to the aircraft and can present some difficult problems. It would also seem to have to do with how the flight simulator was certified for use.

As one component of transfer of training, there has been great emphasis on the need for and value of the flight simulator having the capability for hexapod axial motion. At this writing (2006), the FAA, NASA, and the DOT/Volpe Transportation Center were conducting sophisticated experiments on the benefits and need for hexapod motion for the platform on which the airline flight simulator is mounted. The ultimate goals of these experiments (Burki-Cohen, Go et al., 2003) are to provide information for a possible FAA AC and to develop information for a possible FAA policy on flight simulator motion requirements in airline pilot training and evaluation. A brief overview of the research findings to date is that hexapod platform motion has a significant positive effect for flight-crew evaluation, but no significant benefit for training. Further, certain enhancements to the motion washout filters (lateral side force and heave motion) seem to be beneficial in all cases. However, for more complete information, the reader is referred to the works cited above, as it is not our purpose here to engage in a lengthy discussion of flight simulator motion issues and research.

Another problem is that of "simulator sickness": a phenomenon in which a pilot becomes sick (vertigo, nausea) in the flight simulator. This has been handled in several ways. It now seems clear that it is caused by a complex interaction that involves conflicting visual and kinesthetic cues. Another part of the interaction seems to be the time duration between flying and using the flight simulator.

It would appear that, for some individuals, use of the flight simulator in close proximity to having actually flown can cause simulator sickness. This is (usually) easily remedied by specifying a minimum time duration that must pass between flight and flight simulator. In some cases, there has been a reverse "simulation sickness" reaction whereby the pilot becomes sick in the aircraft. Obviously, this is dangerous, as well as possibly career ending. To the author's knowledge, this has been handled via specifying (as before) minimum time duration between flight simulator and flight. Although medication, ranging from over-the-counter motion sickness pills to prescription anti-vertigo drugs can be used, it would seem to be only a one-time or short-term remedy. The rationale here seems obvious.

We now will leave the above issues as we are quite sure that they are well covered in other chapters of this text and, the issues/problems that we mention in passing are not the focus of the chapter.

MAJOR DRIVERS IN CIVIL AVIATION PILOT/CREW TRAINING

Aircrew training for air carrier pilots (Part 121) has evolved over the years due to five main drivers. They are:

1. Technical advancements in aircraft systems and simulation realism
2. Engine out operations
3. Mission critical alerts and warnings
4. Adverse condition operations
5. Human factors

Technical advancements in aircraft systems have, for obvious reasons, driven pilot training programs. The features of a new system and how it should be used operationally have always been built into the curriculum. A good example of this is terrain collision avoidance system, version II (TCAS II), a hard/software system that provides the aircrew with alerts for terrain collision avoidance.

Although TCAS I was initially introduced with a part-task trainer, it is now an important feature of full-mission simulators, and collision avoidance training is now possible.

Engine out operations as a major driver of pilot training is not quite so obvious. With the advent of multiengine aircraft, engine out training had always been important to pilot certification. However, with the advent of swept-wing turbojet aircraft, this training took center stage. This was due to the unique aerodynamic properties of swept-wing aircraft, more specifically, asymmetrical thrust and axis coupling. During asymmetrical thrust operations, the swept-wing turbojet aircraft experiences pronounced axis coupling, manifested in a rapid roll off or wing drop along with an equally pronounced yaw. Increased pilot skill was and is the only counter tactic to this potentially fatal condition.

In 1968 a DC-8 training accident involving asymmetrical thrust led to the effort to conduct all training in simulators. Such an effort was successful, prompting, among other things, advancements in simulator realism.

Although often overlooked, the third major pilot training and certification driver has and continues to be mission critical alerts and warnings. This area includes such maneuvers as stalls and steep turns, wind shear recovery, and ground proximity warning recovery. Recent additions include CAT III auto land system failure recovery maneuvers. It is important to note that all of these recovery maneuvers require the aircraft to be "hand-flown" by the pilot.

This last statement brings to the surface what we think is the major challenge facing training managers today: the tension line between increasingly sophisticated autopilot systems and the continuing and pressing need for a high degree of basic "stick and rudder" pilot skills. Pilots therefore need to demonstrate proficiency in (1) adverse conditions (which include engine out operations), (2) low visibility operations, (3) mission critical alerts and warnings, and (4) system and human limitations. We shall later show how these four conditions form the boundaries for the pilot's worldview and how they can be incorporated into a training/operation model to manage/reduce risk.

FLIGHT SIMULATORS AND FLIGHT TRAINING DEVICES

Before we begin this and following sections, we again feel pressed to make the following caveat. Much of the following is from FAA documents: SFAR 58 and its accompanying AC (AC 120-AQP); AC 120-40B; AC 120-45A; AC 120-35B; and AC 1210-45B. For brevity, "ease of flow," and resultant clarity, we have condensed some of the material in these; we omitted portions not pertinent to this chapter and often deleted references to other FARs and ACs; on some occasions, there is paraphrasing. As has been said, the complete documents are online if the reader wants to see the entirety of any of the FAR and AC cited.

Overview

The availability of advanced technology has permitted greater use of flight simulators for training and checking of flightcrew members. The complexity, costs, and operating environment of modern aircraft also have encouraged broader use of advanced simulation. Simulators can provide more in-depth training than can be accomplished in airplanes and provide a very high transfer of learning and behavior from the simulator to the airplanes. The use of simulators in lieu of airplanes results in safer flight training and cost reductions for the operators. It also achieves fuel conservation and reduction in adverse environmental effects.

As technology progressed and the capabilities of flight simulation were recognized, FAR revisions were made to permit the increased use of simulators in approved training programs. Simulators have been used in training and some checking programs since the middle 1950s. Various FAR amendments gradually permitted additional simulator use in training and checking aircrews. A significant recognition of simulator capability has occurred since the early 1970s. In December 1973, FAR Amendments 61-62 and 121-108 permitted additional use of visual simulators. In the early 1990s, various ACs and SFAR 58 further recognized simulator capability and use in training and evaluating flightcrews.

Of importance is the fact that the FAA makes a distinction between an airplane (flight) simulator and an airplane flight training device. The FAA AC that deals with airplane simulators is FAA AC 120-40B, and AC 120-45B deals with FTDs.

The term FTD covers everything from a PC with training specific software to a mock-up of an instrument panel, to a complete cockpit. However, what air carrier pilots/crew use for our focal point, LOFT, is a full-up, hexapod axial motion-based, high quality visual scene flight simulator, often called the "box" or the "sim." Although FTDs are used as part-task trainers, it is the sim alone that is used for LOFT. The box has full mission capabilities to include ATC chatter/instructions as well as day/night and various weather and wind conditions. The simulator operator can program a mission (a flight from point A to point B) that introduces the full spectrum of conditions and problems gleaned from the experiences and reports of other pilots who have flown that particular route. The mission simulation also introduces conditions and problems that have been encountered or reported on other flights/routes.

FLIGHT SIMULATORS AND TRAINING

An Airplane Simulator [commonly called a flight simulator] is a full size replica of an airplane's instruments, equipment, panels, and controls in an open flight deck area or an enclosed airplane cockpit, including the assemblage of equipment and computer software programs necessary to represent the airplane in ground and flight operations, a visual system providing an out-of-the cockpit view, a force [motion] cueing system with provides cues at least equivalent to that of a three degree of freedom motion system; and is in compliance with the minimum standards for a Level A simulator specified in AC 120-40, as amended.

The airplane simulators are placed, graded as it were, into 4 levels, A through D; the FTDs are similarly ordered, except the classification scheme of levels 1 through 7 is used. In both cases, the levels refer to the capabilities and complexities (hard and soft ware) of the training equipment. In both cases, all equipment are placed in a matrix, by level, that indicates what flight tasks can be trained at each level.

The new designations and their relationships with the simulator definitions used and in FAR Part 121, Appendix H are:

Level A—Visual
Level B—Phase I
Level C—Phase II
Level D—Phase III

While trying not to oversimplify this distinction, the main difference is that a "full-up" airplane simulator has axial motion capability whereas an FTD does not. This will become clearer next as we give the FAA definitions of both types of flight training equipment.

FLIGHT TRAINING DEVICES AND TRAINING

An airplane flight training device is a full scale replica of an airplane's instruments, equipment, panels, and controls in an open flight deck area or an enclosed airplane cockpit, including the assemblage of equipment and computer software programs necessary to represent the airplane in ground and flight conditions to the extent of the systems installed in the device. An FTD does not require a force (motion) cueing or visual system and meets the criteria outlined in the AC for a specific flight training device level. In an FTD, any flight training event or flight checking event can be accomplished

Nonvisual simulators are now grouped with Level 6 training devices, but must meet the requirements, except for visual, of a Level A simulator. There is no other change in their characteristics or description; just their name. Alphabetic designations were chosen for simulators to maintain a distinction from the numerically designated training devices.

In coordination with a broad cross section of the aviation industry, the FAA has defined seven levels of flight training devices as Level 1 through Level 7. Level 1 is currently reserved. Levels 2 and 3 are generic in that they are representative of no specific airplane cockpit and do not require reference to a specific airplane. Levels 4 through 7 represent a specific cockpit for the airplane represented. Within the generic or specific category, every higher level of flight training device is progressively more complex. Because of the increase in complexity and more demanding standards when progressing from Level 2 to Level 7, there is a continuum of technical definition across those levels. (Note: For complete matrices of flight simulator and FTD/levels and the tasks that can be trained and/or checked in each device, see AC120-40B and AC120-AQP.)

FLIGHT SIMULATOR AND FTD ASSESSMENT

The need for standard flight simulator and FTD assessment and qualification criteria was necessitated by the use of simulators for training and checking. The evolution of the simulator technology and the concomitant increase in permitted use has required a similar evolution of the criteria for simulator qualification. A listing of known simulator criteria should be, therefore, informative. The qualification basis for a given simulator may be any of the past criteria, depending on when the simulator was first approved or last upgraded.

The training and checking credits for nonvisual and visual simulators were delineated in FAR Part 61, Appendix A, and FAR Part 121, Appendices E and F. Four levels of simulators were addressed; Basic (nonvisual and visual simulators), Phase I, Phase II, and Phase III. (These designations have since been replaced by levels A through D as seen in Subsection A.) Each of the four levels is progressively more complex than the preceding level and each contains all the features of preceding levels plus the requirements for the designated level. As the technology has advanced, so has the qualification guidance. Efforts to keep the criteria updated are, therefore, ongoing with active participation from both industry and government resources

Any FTD or airplane flight simulator must be assessed in those areas that are essential to accomplishing airman training and checking events. The assessment requirements and guidelines are, essentially, the same for both FTD and flight simulator. This includes climb, cruise, descent, approach, and landing phases of flight. Crew member station checks, instructor station functions, checks, and certain additional requirements depending on the complexity of the device (i.e., touch-activated cathode ray tube instructor controls; automatic lesson plan operation; selected mode of operation for "fly-by-wire" airplanes, etc.) must be thoroughly assessed. Should a motion system or visual system be contemplated for installation on any level of flight training device, the operator or the manufacturer should contact the network services project management (NSPM) for information regarding an acceptable method for measuring motion and/or visual system operation and applicable tolerances. The motion and visual systems, if installed, will be evaluated to ensure their proper operation.

The FAA's intent is to evaluate flight simulators and FTDs as objectively as possible. Pilot acceptance, however, is also an important consideration. Therefore, the flight simulator or FTD will be subjected to validation tests listed in the relevant ACs. These tests include a qualitative assessment by an FAA pilot who is qualified in the respective airplane or set of airplanes. Validation tests are used to objectively compare flight simulator or FTD data and airplane data (or another approved reference data) to assure that they agree within a specified tolerance. Functions tests provide a basis for evaluation of the flight simulator or FTD capability to perform over a typical training period and to verify correct operation of the controls, instruments, and systems.

The above subsections should suffice as an introduction to the FARs and ACs as they apply to defining flight simulators and FTDs, as well as to the concept of "levels" of flight simulators and

FTDs. When we deal with LOFT later in this chapter, it will be LOFT as done in a Level D flight simulator.

SFAR 58 AND AQP

HISTORY

In 1975, the FAA began to deal with two issues: hardware requirements needed for total flight simulation and the redesign of training programs to deal with increasingly complex human factors problems. At the urging of the air transportation industry, the FAA addressed the hardware issue first. This effort culminated in 1980 in the development of the Advanced Simulation Program. Since then, the FAA has continued to pursue approaches for the redesign of training programs to increase the benefits of advance simulation and to deal with the increasing complexity of cockpit human factors. A joint government–industry task force was formed on flightcrew performance issues. On September 10, 1987, the task force met at the Air Transport Association's headquarters to identify and discuss flightcrew member performance issues. Working groups in three major areas were formed, and the recommendations to the joint task force were presented to the FAA administrator. Some of the substantive recommendations to the FAA administrator from the flightcrew member training group were the following:

a. Provide for a Special Federal Aviation Regulation (SFAR) and Advisory Circular to permit development of innovative training (SFAR 58)
b. Require all training to be accomplished through a certificate holder's training program
c. Provide for approval of training programs based on course content and training aids rather than specified programmed hours (SFAR 58)
d. Require Cockpit Resource Management (CRM; 121.404, SFAR 58) training and encourage greater use of line-oriented flight training (LOFT)

SFAR/AQP: OVERVIEW AND SYNOPSIS

In this subsection, we will show how the relevant FAR (SFAR 58) on AQP came into being, the portions of it that directly impact the use of flight simulator, and finally, why and how SFAR 58 and the accompanying extensive AC have changed civil pilot training (the most significant change being the enhanced role of flight simulator and LOFT). We will now present a brief look at the aspects of SFAR 58 that pertain to training and to the use of flight simulators and other training devices.

Note: Any Special FAR (SFAR) expires within 5 years unless extended or made into an FAR. In the case of SFAR 58, it would have expired in late 1995, but has been extended until October 2, 2005. It is interesting to note that the original AQP AC accompanying SFAR 58 was published in 1990. It has been updated and is in the process of finalization to be reissued in its newest version. It was expected that this would occur in early 2004, or some 14 years since the original AC was published.

In response to the recommendations from the joint government–industry task force and from the National Transportation Safety Board (NTSB), the FAA put forward SFAR 58, Advanced Qualification Program (AQP), in October 1990. AQP was also established to permit a greater degree of regulatory flexibility in the approval of innovative pilot training programs. Based on a documented analysis of operational requirements, an airline (FAA certificate-holder) under AQP may propose to depart from traditional training practices and requirements for pilot/crew with respect to what, how, when, and where training and testing is conducted. This is subject to FAA approval of the specific content of each proposed program. SFAR 58 requires that all departures from traditional regulatory requirements be documented and based upon an approved continuing data collection process sufficient to establish at least an equivalent level of safety. AQP provides a systematic basis for matching technology to training requirements and for approving a training program with content based on relevance to operational performance.

SFAR 58

SFAR 58 provides for approval of an alternate method, AQP, for qualifying, training, certifying, and otherwise ensuring competency of crew members, aircraft dispatchers, other operations personnel, instructors, and evaluators who are required to be trained or qualified under parts 121 and 135 of the FAR or under this SFAR. For pilots in command, seconds in command, and flight engineers, a proficiency evaluation—a portion of which may be conducted in an aircraft, flight simulator, or flight training device as approved in the certificate holder's curriculum—must be completed during each evaluation period.

Each AQP qualification and continuing qualification curriculum must include approved training on and evaluation of skills and proficiency of each person being trained under an AQP to use their cockpit resource management skills and their technical (piloting or other) skills in an actual or simulated operational scenario. (The integrated assessment of CRM and technical flight skills will be discussed later.) For flightcrew members this training and evaluation must be conducted in an approved flight training device or flight simulator.

A person enrolled in an AQP is eligible to receive a commercial or airline transport pilot, flight engineer, or aircraft dispatcher certificate or appropriate rating based on the successful completion of training and evaluation events accomplished under that program if the applicant shows competence in required technical knowledge and skills (e.g., piloting) and cockpit resource management knowledge and skills in scenarios that test both types of knowledge and skills together. (Note: There are other requirements, but, as said, we are focusing on the flight simulator in AQP.)

As has been said, any flight simulator or FTD that will be used in an AQP for one of the following purposes must be evaluated by the FAA administrator for assignment of a flight training device or flight simulator qualification level:

(i)   Required evaluation of individual or crew proficiency
(ii) Training activities that determine if an individual or crew is ready for a proficiency evaluation
(iii) Activities used to meet requirements for recent experience
(iv) Line operational simulations (LOS, and to include LOFT)

AQP, LOS/LOFT, and Simulators

The capabilities and use of simulators and other computer-based training devices in training and qualifications activities have changed dramatically. SFAR 58 and AC 120-AQP allow certificate holders that are subject to the training and evaluation requirements of Part 121 and Part 135 to develop innovative training and qualification programs that incorporate the most recent advances in training methods and techniques. SFAR 58 and the AC also apply to training centers under Part 142, which intend to provide training for eligible certificate holders. AQP emphasizes crew-oriented training and evaluation. These training and evaluation applications are now grouped under the general term of line operational simulations (LOS), including line-oriented flight training (LOFT), special purpose operational training (SPOT), and line operational evaluation (LOE). Due to the role of crew resource management (CRM) issues in fatal accidents, it has become evident that LOS is the most appropriate environment to train and evaluate both technical and CRM skills. Consequently, a structured LOS design process is necessary to specify and integrate the required CRM and technical skills into line-oriented LOS scenarios. These should provide the opportunity for training or evaluation, as appropriate, in accordance with approved AQP qualification standards. All of the above can be done in an FAA-approved flight simulator.

LINE-ORIENTED FLIGHT TRAINING (LOFT)

BACKGROUND

LOFT emphasizes an orientation on events that could be encountered in line operations ("flying the line"). Thus, mission realism—making the LOFT session correspond as closely as possible to event sets that could or would be encountered in flying one or more point A to point B legs—becomes the major driver in LOFT design. In other words, events that make up a LOFT scenario should pass the test of mission realism where it is reasonable to assume that this "could" happen in the real world. The use of flight training devices and flight simulators has become increasingly important in training flightcrew members. As the level of sophistication in simulators increased, air carriers have come to rely on simulators for part or all of their flight training programs. Since the mid-1970s, some FAR Part 121 and Part 135 operators have implemented alternative simulator training (now LOFT) to train crew members. LOFT is training in a simulator with a complete crew using representative flight segments that contain normal, abnormal, and emergency procedures that may be expected in line operations.

This FAA AC specifies the multiple types of line operational simulations, of which LOFT is one. The AC also specifies the types of LOFT and line operational evaluation (LOE). In this AC, the FAA provides guidelines for LOFT content, LOFT use, LOE use, and LOFT/LOS instructor qualifications. We will briefly show some relevant portions of this AC because LOFT and LOS are done in a flight simulator, and because LOFT is the vital venue for pilot training and evaluation.

(Excerpt from FAA AC 120-35B 58, Line Operational Simulators/LOS, with our usual caveat.)

LOFT is a useful training method because it gives crewmembers the opportunity to practice line operations (e.g., maneuvers, operating skills, systems operations, and the operator's procedures) with a full crew in a realistic environment. Crewmembers learn to handle a variety of scripted real-time scenarios, which include routine, abnormal, and emergency situations. They also learn and practice cockpit resource management skills, including crew coordination, judgment, decision-making, and communication skills. The overall objective of LOFT is to improve total flightcrew performance, thereby preventing incidents and accident during operational flying.

The types of LOFT are:

1. Qualification LOFT—An approved flight simulator course of LOFT to facilitate transition from training using flight simulation to operational flying. Qualification LOFT meets other requirements of FAR Part 121, Appendix H.
2. Recurrent LOFT—An approved flight simulator course of LOFT which may be used to meet [yearly] recurrent flight training requirements and to substitute for alternate proficiency checks.
3. Line Operational Evaluation (LOE)—An evaluation of crewmembers and crews in a flight training device or flight simulator during real-time Line Operational Simulations.

LOE is primarily designed for crewmember evaluation under an Advanced Qualification Program (AQP). LOE is conducted in a flight simulator or flight training device and is designed to check for both individual and crew competence. [Authors: Such competencies should be demonstrated in a mission-realistic environment.] LOE may also be used to evaluate a specific training objective. Operators conducting LOE may be approved to use any level of flight simulator or flight training device, depending on the objective of the evaluation and the capability of the device. The level of the flight simulator of flight training device required to support evaluation in LOE will depend upon the evaluation objectives and the device's capability to support the objectives.

Special Purpose Operational Training (SPOT) is an approved course of operationally oriented flight training, conducted in a flight simulator or flight training device, which may be used to learn, practice, and accomplish specific training objectives, for example, training in variant aircraft or special aircraft equipment.

LOFT is "no-jeopardy" training, that is, the instructor does not issue a passing or failing grade to a participating crew member. As a LOFT scenario progresses, it is allowed to continue without interruption so crew members may learn by experiencing the results of their decisions. Decisions that produce unwanted results do not indicate a training failure, but serve as a learning experience. If the LOFT instructor identifies crew member performance deficiencies, additional training or instruction will be provided. This training or instruction may be in any form, including additional LOFT. Before the crew member may return to line operations, the performance deficiencies will be corrected and the instructor will document the training as satisfactorily completed. The "no-jeopardy" concept allows crew members to use their full resources and creativity without instructor interference. At the end of a LOFT session and after debriefing, the instructor certifies that the training has been completed. (We will return to jeopardy versus nonjeopardy in LOFT later; it has both a history and problematic aspects.)

To iterate: Each AQP qualification and continuing qualification curriculum must include approved training on and evaluation of skills and proficiency of each person being trained under an AQP to use their cockpit resource management skills and their technical (piloting or other) skills in an actual or simulated operations scenario. For flightcrew members this training and evaluation must be conducted in an approved flight training device or flight simulator.

The reader may feel, at this point, that what has been presented has been an overabundance of FAA definitions, regulations, policies and guidance. This is only somewhat true and if the reading of what has come before may have been somewhat dry and/or tedious, a point must be made again. All of civil aviation's activities come under the purview of the FAA. It is not possible to completely or clearly understand the role and functions of flight simulation (whether in flight simulator or FTD) in civil aviation without the information so far presented.

MAXIMIZING LOFT: THE MISSION PERFORMANCE MODEL AND THE OPERATIONAL DECISION MAKING PARADIGM

LOFT: CURRENT AND FUTURE

We have described the initial development of LOFT, and its current form and content. We have stated that LOFT is the major training and check tool in an AQP. LOFT and LOE, as performed in the flight simulator, simply put, are both the optimal training/testing environment and the "court of last resort," as it were. Upon successful completion of LOFT/LOE, the pilot/crew has earned new ratings or certifications or are "good to go" for another year.

However, the current LOFTs and LOEs need to be strengthened for exactly the reasons cited above; they are the best and safest methods for cutting edge, realistic training and evaluation, and they provide a final stamp of approval in an AQP—as well as a more traditional Part 121-based training program. We have set the stage to present how our earlier statements about the tremendous potential and existing use-value of LOFT can be merged and realized via the MPM and the ODM models.

RISK IDENTIFICATION AND MANAGEMENT: TRAINING AND EVALUATION WITH MPM AND ODM PARADIGM

The end result of all civic pilot training should be to prepare a pilot to identify, assess, and manage risk. The primary role of the pilot as a risk manager has been emphasized multiple times over the past 10 years by the authors (Lofaro, and Smith, 1993, 1998, 1999, 2000, 2001, 2003). LOFT is simply the preeminent tool, as well as test situation, for training and evaluating civil captains/crews. Over the years, two major models have been developed by which LOFTs can be designed and crew performance enhanced as well as evaluated. The first is the Mission Performance Model (MPM) as developed by Captains Kevin Smith and William Hamman of United Airlines, with some input from Jan DeMuth and Ron Lofaro of the FAA. The MPM came from the recognition that the CRM skills must be integrated with a corresponding set of technical skills (flight control skills) in an interactive matrix in order to fully evaluate overall crew proficiency. Further, such an integrated CRM approach would serve as a training tool—in LOFT design and in specifying where the CRM/flight control skill linkages existed. An approach to integrated CRM, along with both human factors and flight control/technical skill evaluation scales, was partially developed during an FAA-hosted workshop in 1992. Dr. Lofaro was the designer and facilitator of this workshop and Smith, along with several training captains from NW, DL, United Airlines, the chief pilot for Boeing, 2 FAA personnel, an aviation psychologist for the USN Postgraduate School, and a research psychologist under contract to the FAA were the participants. The results of that workshop are in Report DOT/FAA/RD-92/5: Workshop on Integrated Crew Resource Management (Lofaro 1992).

The integration, and assessment, of crew resource management (CRM) and flight control skills had received considerable attention—and a fair share of concern and skepticism—in the 1980s and early 1990s. As one response, the ATA formed a joint air carrier/FAA/academic working group to deal with this and other CRM issues in 1990; both Smith and Lofaro were on that group. Dr. Robert Helmreich, in conjunction with several major air carriers, developed a complete set of flightcrew CRM performance markers (he termed them "CRM behavioral markers") with behaviorally-anchored rating scales. In a NASA/FAA/University of Texas project, Helmreich worked with several air carriers on research that involved the use of these markers in LOFT.

In 1991, Smith and DeMuth developed an initial set of performance markers for the technical/flight control skills. Both the CRM and the technical sets of markers were used in the next step of CRM integration: the attempt at developing an analytic paradigm. Smith created the framework for a model that demonstrated that the CRM human factors skills and the technical/flight control skills are interrelated, interdependent, and often simultaneous in execution—that, for safe and efficient flight, CRM can sometimes be integral to flight control, and vice versa. This model is called the Mission Performance Model (MPM). Smith worked with Hamman and others to develop exemplars of the application of the MPM to actual flight maneuvers, such as an engine-out at V1, with a turn procedure required by the terrain.

MISSION PERFORMANCE MODEL

The model is based on these concepts:

1. Flying is an integrated, mission-orientated activity and must be evaluated as such.
2. The crew's performance is not adequately captured by totaling the sum of the component tasks/subtasks/elements. The focus must be on crew function—usually at the task and critical subtask levels.
3. Flight proficiency skills/knowledge are interwoven, interdependent, and necessarily interact with the CRM skills/knowledge differentially across tasks and conditions. These interactions can be identified/specified by a matrix-type crew mission performance model using the tasks, which comprise a mission/flight leg. (This is what we term *integrated CRM*.)
4. The model can capture these interactions and can be sensitive to changes in both task and mission—for example, show that, for different tasks and conditions, the technical/flight proficiency skills, the CRM skills, and their interactions will vary. This is an indication that the model has a measure of discriminatory power or "sensitivity" to changes in task and conditions.
5. Helmreich's behavioral markers can adequately delineate CRM skills and provide one basis for the (flightcrew) Mission Performance Model, as can the technical markers capture the flight control skills and form the other MPM basis (see below).

Finally, the bases for the technical proficiency evaluation currently exist in a behavioral marker-type format with scales. Both the marker and their scales can be validated/modified for evaluation of all these proficiencies, which will be called "crew performance markers—technical factors." This arena focuses on the crew as a unit and how well they discharge the technical aspects of the mission. It specifically addresses precision maneuvers across these areas:

1. Flight maneuvers and attitude control
2. Propulsion/lift/drag control
3. System operations
4. Malfunction warning and reconfiguration
5. Energy management

Another rationale for the MPM, and later, ODM, is that pilot/crew performance has often been seen as series of discrete tasks, where each task was further decomposed to reveal a set of subtasks combined with the requisite knowledge and skills necessary for subtask completion. For many applications, such as aircrew training, this produces a large collection of task, knowledge, and skill data. In most traditional pilot or crew training programs, these are taught individually as isolated knowledge components. Consequently, the trainee is left with the responsibility of combining these isolated knowledge components into integrated wholes (Merrill, 1989). However, the linear decomposition of individual tasks does not address integrated functioning nor does it reveal how tightly coupled teams (flightcrews) perform, thus an analytical process other than the traditional task analysis approach is considered necessary. Therefore, the MPM uses the functional modeling approach.

The Mission Performance Model has embedded within it the concept of functions. It is proposed that the model, as constructed, represents all significant functions necessary for the successful completion of an air transport mission. This model views crew performance as consisting of system level functions that represent the mechanisms used to perform a mission activity. The importance of a model that is founded on a set of systems level functions cannot be overstated. Moreover, the model delineates crew performance at a level of abstraction that is significantly different than the current descriptions of individual performance.

The MPM consists of a set of functions that can be activated by inserting an instance/example—in other words, asking the function to specify/describe a particular activity or situation in the mission. If a particular function such as workload management was asked to "spin out" the components of a particular mission activity, such as takeoff with an engine failure at V_1, then the function should be able to organize, sequence, distribute, and coordinate key crew actions so that a successful outcome could be assured.

This workload management function, then, can be viewed as a generic performance statement that

a. Can be applied to many mission activities/situations, and
b. Can be activated for the application to, and specification of, any one of these activities/situations.

The Mission Performance Model specifies the components of flightcrew "effectiveness" (effective performance). That the model represents effectiveness is important to understand since, if the crew is really engaging in the set of functions that are both germane and linked to the problem at hand, and if these functions are the prerequisites for a successful outcome, then effectiveness has been demonstrated.

Similarly, the model is prescriptive; it prescribes what needs to be accomplished for the crew to perform effectively. For example, we can specify, during the LOFT design process, what are very likely to be the necessary crew behaviors.

In summary, in the MPM, human factors as well as technical performance clusters are specified along with the applicable markers under each cluster. For example, under workload management and situational awareness, key markers include preparation, planning, vigilance, workload distribution, and distraction avoidance. Similarly, under the cluster titled "propulsion/lift/drag control," the key makers include instrument interpretation, energy management, power control, lift control, and drag control. When all these markers are combined into a matrix array with their various categories, the MPM emerges.

FROM CRM/MPM TO ODM

Upon completion of the 1992 Integrated CRM Workshop, a new set of issues and concerns became apparent to Smith and Lofaro. The Integrated CRM concept and the MPM were well received by the workshop participants. However, due to many factors—such as a lack of FAA interest for follow-on efforts and a CRM "establishment" that was not open to taking CRM to either another level or in new directions, along with the jeopardy issue—it was clear that Integrated CRM and the MPM had become dead issues. Of much more import was the realization that CRM was not the human factors silver bullet. Captain Hal Sprogis asked, "Is the Aviation Industry Experiencing CRM Failure?" (Sprogis, 1997). Captain Daniel Maurino had written "Crew Resource Management: A Time for Reflection" (Maurino, 1999). Both indicate that we may have expected too much from CRM; that the relationship between CRM and safety, which was and is the prime rationale offered for teaching CRM, has not been proven; that CRM is a process, not an outcome, and certain efforts to assess outcomes (i.e., individual performance) may be misguided. In July of 1996, American Airlines decided to totally revamp their CRM training program. Its reason was that flightcrews had valid objections to, and concerns about, CRM: "CRM is too often viewed as a number of interpersonal issues that simply do not define the problems that we face in aviation .... CRM training will most likely always be defined and suffer in terms of the first generation of courses…which were seen as 'touchy-feely,' 'getting along,' and 'managing human relations or resolving personality conflicts' rather than dealing with truly important concerns" (Ewell and Chidester, 1996). American's new focus is on preparing flightcrews for the daily challenges of normal and abnormal operations encountered flying the line. Delta Airlines, in the same timeframe, revamped its "CRM for New Captains" course and now calls it "In Command." As with American, Delta emphasized leadership, responsibility, and performance. So, in 1996–97, we see these two major carriers eschewing overemphasis on communication and interpersonal relations in their CRM training. Lastly, United Airlines' version of CRM was and is, called C-L-R, where the C is for "command" and the L is "leadership," indicating that United wanted to bypass the interpersonal with C-L-R and move on to the performance issues. Yet, even United changed aspects of its CRM in 1997.

Further, "common wisdom" was that pilots made good decisions easily and almost naturally, aided by (some) increase in experience. The facile assumption that additional experience will teach pilots to make better decisions has proven to be a dangerous fallacy. Experience can be a nasty teacher, often giving the test before, or without, giving the lessons and materials needed for the test. Experience can also reinforce poor decisions and behaviors that seemingly "worked" in the past (the "not your day to die" phenomenon). There was also the commonly accepted view that decision making is but one of the components of CRM. This was, and is, a gross error.

CRM, with its emphases on communications and team function, is but one enabler of good decisions. As such, it is a part of decision making, not vice versa. CRM is, simply put, an enabler of decision making. Decision making is the primary tool to be used by the pilot and crew with their primary functions: risk identification and risk reduction. In short, risk management.

It also became apparent that aeronautical decision making was greatly different that decision making on the ground, and that a new paradigm was necessary that both articulated the differences and had a new set of decision making (DM) techniques specific to what pilots and crew encounter. Another realization was on the primacy of LOFT in pilot training. As one result of this Hamman,

Seamster, Lofaro and Smith wrote an interrelated set of papers on LOFT design and delivery, that later formed a session at the 1993 International Symposium of Aviation Psychology biennial meeting in Columbus, Ohio.

As another result, Lofaro designed and held a FAA/Industry/DoD/Academe Workshop in Denver (1992) which had some of the CRM workshop participants and added others from the decision-making world. The two-volume FAA report on this workshop (DOT/FAA/RD-92, Vols. I, II; Lofaro and Adams) initiated the efforts for what has become the operational decision making (ODM) model of Smith and Lofaro (Lofaro and Smith, 2000, 2001, 2003)

THE ODM

OPERATIONAL DECISION MAKING: NEW WINDOW OF OPPORTUNITY

In the new millennium, there seems to be a heightened level of recognition of both the role and the importance of decision making in aviation safety. In July of 2000, *Aviation Week and Space Technology* printed four somewhat interrelated articles on pilot/crew errors and decision making in aviation safety. These articles presented audit information, research, and analyses along with current "fixes." Some findings include flightcrews ignoring increased evidence that the original flight plan was no longer appropriate; tactical DM (what we could call operational DM) errors, which are the second most prevalent crew errors in crew-involved accidents; and pilot perception of risk, a key factor in safety. Several other vital points were that (1) it is a fallacy that crew error can be eliminated via sufficient vigilance, and (2) there is a need to emphasize managing the consequences of error. The proposed "fixes" that were offered encompass risk and error management training as well as new decision-making training. All in all, these articles showed us that many of the components of ODM we have developed and published since 1992 were on target. However, we believe that there were critical components missing, as well as a coherent structure, or model embedding the components.

In addition to the above problems, we sought to address such things as the "common wisdom" referred to above and some training issues that follow.

INTRODUCTION TO THE ODM PARADIGM

Over the past 12 years, we (Smith and Lofaro) have zeroed in on decision making in the operational air carrier environment and developed a paradigm called operational decision making (ODM). During that period, we have introduced and published on such concepts as event sets in LOFT (1993); the pilot as risk manager (1992, 1993, 1998, 1999, 2000, 2001); the primacy of decision making over CRM (1998, 2000, 2001). The focus of ODM is on enabling the pilot's primary role, that of risk manager, by using the model; this essentially redefined the role and activities of the pilot. Safety becomes the operational aspect of successful mission completion through risk management; ODM is the key to successful risk management and good decision-making skills are the primary tool in a pilot's safety arsenal. We see decision making as the key pilot activity. How can a captain command and lead if he or she is not prepared (trained and practiced) to make the best decision possible? This must be the focus for developing, then training, captains to use an operational decision-making process. Any ODM process must function in real-time, and the ODM training must enable a captain and crew to both identify and mange risk. The need for operationally oriented decision-making training is vital for pilots and crews of major carriers, with their highly complex, automated craft and their responsibility for hundreds of lives each time they fly.

Further, in developing our ODM model, we sought to address what we see as a shortfall in current aircrew training. Air carrier training today is built around (1) a sequence of discrete events and/or conditions and whether or not these are, separately, within what is termed "legal limits" (as per FARs); and (2) the pilot's responses to these events. However, it seems clear to us that all too often there exist interactions and interplay of seemingly discrete events and conditions. Although any one or all of a group of events and conditions might be within limits, the interactive resultant (cumulative effect) of them may place the aircraft and mission at risk. We are not aware of air carrier training that uses this perspective. We believe that our ODM model directly addresses this gap in aircrew training.

In summary, ODM deals with the complex issues and methods for the pilot/crew identification and evaluation of risk factors as the necessary skills for managing such risk and thereby achieving mission success. The ODM should be embedded in either qualification on recurrent training as the apex of CRM and should be taught immediately after CRM.

COMPONENTS OF THE ODM MODEL

Integrated throughout the model is the pilot's role as risk manager. The other components are:

1. The operational envelope
2. Situational knowledge/risk location
3. The critical mission impact areas; the critical mission factors that comprise the impact areas/risk location
4. The rising risk continuum/risk location cumulative effect (a concept whose use is embedded throughout all the above components)

It must be strongly noted that all of these components are so intertwined that any separation or sequencing of them is artificial, because it will become apparent that to speak of any one component brings in the others. Actually, there is no sequence per se. Rather, there is a constant interplay and branching across the components; perhaps a continuously rotating circle best describes the process the pilot is involved in. However, for the purposes of presentation, we will treat each one separately.

RISK MANAGEMENT: RISK, RISING RISK, AND FLYING THE LINE

Mission completion and risk management involve completing the mission of flying the public because of its economic benefits, but in a way that does not place people or equipment at undue risk; these should be the goals of any airline pilot. By risk, we mean specific risk or danger to the aircraft, passengers and crew, and the corporation. There are three levels of risk in the paradigm. High risk is defined as the likelihood or high probability of injury, damage, or death. Moderate risk, if left unchecked, could continue to rise and/or likely result in significant flight trajectory deviations. Low risk, finally, is a normal situation where routine, normal procedures are sufficient. Rising risk refers to the facts that (1) if some, or any, problems went unnoticed and/or (2) the decisions were not accurate, timely, and appropriate, then (3) the risk to the successful completion of the flight could rise to the point where the flight is truly endangered. We will return to these later. If the level of risk rises, effective risk reduction strategies need to be employed to keep that risk within manageable limits. Risk management is critical to the retention of the flying public customer base and the long-term viability of the industry. Risk management is the key operational activity that works hand in glove with mission execution skills. Central to a completed and safe mission is the pilot as risk manager, an operational responsibility that undergirds the model.

RISK MANAGEMENT: THE OPERATIONAL ENVELOPE, RISK LOCATION, AND CUMULATIVE EFFECT

We will work from the center of the model outward, then return to the inside. The first—and last—component in the spiral-like process is a graphical representation of the boundary conditions in a mission. This is the pilot's "world," and we term it the operational envelope, as does the military. It gives, to use a hackneyed phrase, the big picture; the "ops envelope" is the context in which all the ODM paradigm's components are activated. The operational envelope gives a rather straightforward way to grasp the pilot's task universe. The ability to locate oneself within the ops envelope results from the pilot's situation knowledge and ability to do accurate risk location. It would seem

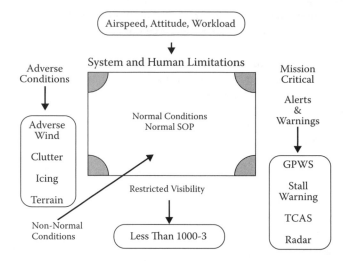

FIGURE 14.1 Operational envelope.

that civil aviation has never taken this larger view of the envelope because it has focused on discrete data points instead of on the big picture. Even today, we find that Airbus and Boeing are working on software for flight control computers that are aimed at keeping the aircraft from exceeding a predetermined flight envelope (*Aviation Week and Space Technology,* August 28, 2000). However, these efforts focus on alarms and/or software to stop overstress, possibly dangerous pitch angles and over banking; in essence, these deal with a small, specific set of discrete flight control errors, not decision making.

The ops envelope can be visualized as a four-sided figure, composed of sides that intersect at right angles to each other. These sides—"boundaries"—are adverse conditions; restricted visibility; mission critical alerts and warnings; and system and human limitations, as shown in Figure 14.1. However, what we show in this figure is a flat cross section. The actual envelope is three-dimensional as the plane cannot only fly any direction on the compass rose, but can also climb and descend. Although this seems obvious, we remind the reader not to lose sight of the fact that we are using a linear representation for a 3-D world.

Figure 14.1 illustrates the operational envelope and shows some sample conditions that are embedded in each boundary/side. The first risk management aspect of the operational envelope is that, at the very center, there is an area of normal flight conditions. Within this inner area, normal SOPs will suffice. However, a single event such as freezing rain, or event sets, such as contamination plus strong crosswinds, encountered during flight may drive a pilot and crew out of that inner area and toward the edges/boundaries. If that happens, there may still be guidelines on what to do. But, the second risk management aspect is that, although each event or factor may be able to be handled by itself, and keep the aircraft inside the edges/boundaries of the envelope, how do we handle the combined or cumulative effect, that is the result of multiple events and factors? If the cumulative resultant of combined factors in the event set drives us toward any corner, we first encounter what we termed a "gray zone" where we are still within the envelope, but close to a corner. If near a corner, in a gray zone, there exists no SOPs or procedures. Certainly, cumulative effects will effect one's position in the ops envelope and, thereby, impact risk. We will return to this later.

RISK MANAGEMENT: CRITICAL MISSION IMPACT AREAS AND THEIR COMPONENTS

Critical to mission success is the ability to operate in adverse conditions while simultaneously executing the mission plan and managing risk. The need to have the capability to operate under adverse conditions and thus provide reliable transportation is self-evident. But this leaves unanswered what events/factors cause a (rising) risk: What are some of the "risk drivers"? We must first look to identifying, defining, and understanding the mission-critical impact areas (MCIA) that engender risk. A mission impact area, if encountered, denotes some level of risk and, if action is not taken, will cause the risk to rise.

BOUNDARY CONDITIONS AS MISSION CRITICAL IMPACT AREAS

We posit the boundaries/sides of the ops envelope function as the critical mission impact areas. Table 14.1 shows the boundary conditions of the ops envelope, with their subareas and critical mission components.

Note: As one rule of thumb, any factor encountered on a mission will cause the risk to rise; two factors generally will result in moderate risk; an interplay of three or more factors usually results in a high-moderate to high-risk situation.

RISK MANAGEMENT: SITUATION KNOWLEDGE AND RISK LOCATION

The continuous task of the pilot is risk identification by using situation knowledge and consequently, accomplishing (ever-changing) risk location. Accurate and timely risk location is the only way to achieve both an accurate and timely action response to risk. Situation knowledge and risk location are interrelated concepts. Situation knowledge is that part of the ODM structure that consists of the continually changing set of elements (knowledge bits) comprising the pilot's awareness of (1) the area of the ops envelope in which the captain believes the aircraft is located and (2) which of the critical components of the ops envelope boundaries are in play. The result of these components "tells" the pilot what is the cumulative effect of the critical factors that are in play. By using the result of a cumulative effect, the pilot can relocate the aircraft in the operational envelope. This enables the pilot to use the rising risk continuum as a decision tool for action response. As said, accurate risk location is the key, when in a (rising) risk situation, to making the optimal selection of a course of action—for example an action response that is an alternative to the original mission plan; we will return to this later.

RISK MANAGEMENT: RISING RISK, RISK LOCATION, AND RESPONSE ACTION

We view rising risk as a teaching concept and the decision-making tool that enables the crew action responses needed for optimum risk management. The teaching aspect of rising risk is in engendering the awareness that, as issues and problems arise, the risk will rise. As risk will rise under virtually any set of adverse conditions, risk management demands that the crew execute, in a timely fashion, specific mitigation procedures to prevent "risk migration to the right" into the moderate and high-risk areas. Rising risk also is the decision tool for response actions, based on the rising risk continuum. If risk is low, the original plan can be executed to completion. When the risk rises to a moderate level, modifications to the original plan must be implemented in order to maintain an acceptable "location" in the risk dimension. When the risk rises further to some critical threshold, the original flight plan needs to be discontinued and the mission is aborted. In summary, if the risk rises, the captain, working with dispatch and other crew members, either (1) continues with the mission as originally planned for low risk situations, (2) modifies the mission plans as needed in moderate risk situations, or (3) abandons the mission altogether in high-risk situations.

However, it can be seen that the pilot must, in order to have an accurate perception of risk location, have an awareness of any cumulative effect on the plane and any adverse factors that are in play. In short, the pilot's perception of the risk must be consonant with the reality of the plane's location in the ops envelope. We now return to cumulative effects and their impact on risk location in the ops envelope.

TABLE 14.1

Boundary Conditions of the Operational Envelope

Adverse Conditions	Mission Critical Alerts and Warnings
Adverse weather	Stall warning
Slippery	Predictive windshear
Clutter	Actual windshear
Contamination	Predictive terrain
Icing aloft	Actual terrain
Freezing precipitation	TCAS RA
Volcanic ash	Improper configuration
Convective activity	PRM breakaway
Adverse wind	Radar Doppler return
Headwind	Convective return w/ hook
Crosswind	Wing contamination
Tailwind	Any severe conditions
Severe gust	Upset
Windshear	Wake turbulence
Nonnormal operations	**System and Human Limitations**
Nonprecision approach	Performance limited ops
ICAO takeoff	Clutter
Circling approach	Weight/fuel
Day-only restrictions	Flaps
Cold temperatures	Packs
Extreme latitudes	Delayed VR
Raw data	Cruise/speed altitude
Unfamiliar	Landing
Engine out operations	Missed approach
Takeoff alternate	MEL
T-procedure	Human limitations
V-1 cut	Memory saturation
V-2 cut	Task demand and overload
EO approach	Channel saturation
EO landing	Information overload
EO missed approach	Fatigue
ETOPS divert	Activity prioritization
	Risk awareness
Restricted Visibility	Multitasking
Below 1000/3	Task interference
Below circling minimums	
Below CAT 1	
Below CAT 2	
Below CAT 3	
Takeoff below landing minimums	
Blowing snow	
Blowing sand	
Patchy fog	
Night mountainous	

A DISTINCTION: CUMULATIVE EFFECT RESULTANT VERSUS ADDITIVE EFFECT RESULTANT

We have discussed the cumulative effect that results from the interaction of factors that come from any two contiguous sides of the ops envelope. In this, we have relied, albeit loosely, on vector/tensor mathematics; our cumulative effect vector is somewhat analogous to the resultant vector that can be computed from two or more forces at right angles to each other. The key points here are: (1) The cumulative effect resultant (CER) has a new and different direction than either/any of the forces that comprise it, (2) the CER drives the plane toward a corner, and (3) the CER changes the shape and position of the corner the plane is being driven toward. As the cumulative resultant of combined factors in the event set drives us toward a corner, we first encounter what we termed a "gray zone" where we are still within the envelope, but close to a corner. If near a corner, in a gray zone, there exists no SOPs or procedures. The same is true if forced out of the envelope (see Figure 14.2).

As said, the CER of an event set, composed of critical mission (and boundary) factors can drive a pilot toward one of the four corners (pun intended, as you are really "cornered"). The closer to a corner, the more the risk has risen. However, the corner of the ops envelope has also changed shape; it has become a triangle, with the (45°) hypotenuse of the two sides being the new boundary line. Thus, the corner boundary lines are replaced by the new line (the hypotenuse), termed a "special boundary." This special boundary is closer in than the former corner so that before you would get to the former corner, you have actually crossed this new (special) boundary line and are outside of the envelope (see Figure 14.3). A typical set of conditions that cause a change in the position and shape (becoming a new boundary line) of what once was a corner could be low ceilings and visibility (restricted visibility) with a reduced braking effectiveness due to a slippery runway and strong crosswind (adverse conditions).

There is another effect that comprises more than one factor and which can act in a way to drive the aircraft either out of the ops envelope area of normal operations or out of the envelope entirely; we will term this the additive effect resultant (AER). The difference here is that an AER is composed entirely of factors that do not give the resultant a new direction. This is to say that all the factors in play come from one and only one particular mission impact area or set of boundary factors. These factors combine, additively, to produce an effect larger than any of the factors. However, the AER pushes the plane toward a boundary of the envelope, rather than a corner. One simple example would be a series of adverse conditions such as icing aloft, clutter on the way down, and slippery runways on arrival. Pilots seem to be able to recognize that these linked factors do raise the risk and, usually, take the necessary actions. Still, we are surprised at the level of stress engendered when more than one factor is encountered.

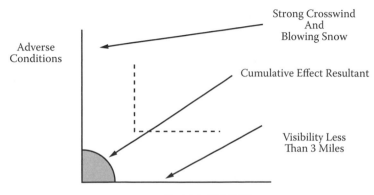

FIGURE 14.2 Cumulative CER.

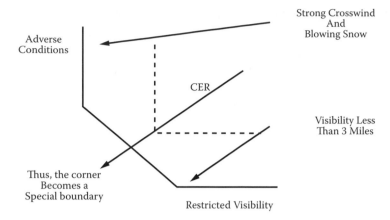

FIGURE 14.3   Formation of a special boundary.

Operational Envelope and Rising Risk Continuum: Relationship

There is no simple isomorphic relationship between the aircraft's position in the ops envelope and its position on the rising risk continuum. However, by looking again at the ops envelope, we can develop a loose mapping to take us from a position on the ops envelope to the risk continuum. What follows is somewhat rough, but seems intuitively obvious. This aspect needs refinement and clarification. Once again, the authors are working on it.

Clearly, if a plane is in the normal ops zone of the ops envelope, that is roughly equivalent to being at low risk. The nonnormal ops zone is, then, roughly equivalent to at least moderate risk. Penetration of any boundary, or special boundary, of the ops envelope puts the aircraft at high risk. The gray areas, where an aircraft is nearing a corner due to a CER, we term as high-moderate, bordering on high-risk.

Putting It All Together: Risk Location and Risk Management in the Operational Envelope

We return to the ops envelope and the risk location within it—in other words, the big picture, or in some current phraseology, maximal situation awareness. As was said, all the paradigm's components are intertwined, and the pilot is using them by a constant process of mentally rotating through them; a process that, as it deals with three axes, is a spiral one. The pilot must always ensure that his risk location encompasses not only the critical mission factors but the plane's location in—or, more dangerous—outside the ops envelope, and the risk factors in play due to that position as well. This is what we have termed *cumulative effects*. By returning to the ops envelope focus, the pilot can accurately place the plane on the rising risk continuum, then take the needed action. Risk location in/out of the ops envelope, translated into risk location on the rising risk continuum, followed by response actions are the keys to successful risk management.

The challenge is to use our situation knowledge to accurately develop the result of the combined critical factors and locate ourselves (risk location) in or outside the ops envelope. Next, we must translate our ops envelope location into our location on the risk continuum. Once we locate ourselves accurately on the risk continuum, taking into account the cumulative effect of being in, or very near, a corner, with all the factors that are in play, we can formulate and execute optimum decisions. Again, when we encounter this phenomenon of cumulative effect and rising risk (gray zones; new, special, boundary lines), the needed decisions cannot be made by simply following procedures.

ODM AND MPM IN LOFT DESIGN, DEVELOPMENT, AND EVALUATION

INTRODUCTION

We must deal with major issues before we go into LOFT design using ODM and MPM. The first is that CRM training was first developed in the late 1970s/early 1980s after a series of disastrous and fatal air carrier accidents—accidents where perfectly functioning planes crashed. Human-factor errors by pilot/crew were seen as the cause of these accidents. As a result, the FAA wanted the air carriers to implement new, human-factors-oriented training—for example, CRM. Rather than append existing FARs to make CRM mandatory, the FAA chose another path. (Of interest here is that in SFAR 58, the FAA decided, after many years, to make CRM mandatory in AQP training.) To return to the situation at hand, the FAA, in order to make CRM training costs palatable to air carriers, offered to waive some hours of pilot recurrency training in lieu of CRM training. As training is a "big buck" item for air carriers, this allowed the carriers to save (not spend additional funds) and give CRM. It also allowed the FAA to ensure the CRM training would, to a great extent, be given, thus silencing some critics who, understandably, wanted new human factor training to counter the rash of accidents.

However, there was a sticking point: jeopardy. Simply put: As a further inducement to carriers to give CRM, the FAA and ALPA agreed that CRM would be "no jeopardy" training. When CRM skills were evaluated in a LOFT, neither pilot nor crew could fail or be given a "down," which requires additional training and checking. Therefore, the evaluation of a LOFT such as the CRM, consisted of videotaping the LOFT and a critique/debrief given to the crew upon completion of the LOFT. The videotape is then erased.

Our view is that LOFTs built around the MPM and ODM must be evaluated as a jeopardy LOFT session. The MPM and ODM must be evaluated as a jeopardy LOFT session. The MPM has technical markers that encompasses actions and skills normally evaluated in a check ride (flight simulator or actual flight), which can be failed. These include attitude management, course deviation, power management, etc. In short, the full panoply of flight skills that are usually evaluated in sessions/flights can be included, so it would seem that failure should be an option. Added to this, we would have LOFT scenarios that enable ODM, and both pilot and crew must be allowed to succeed or fail.

We have postulated ODM as the primary tool for training pilots and crew to do risk identification and management—and that risk identification and management are the primary functions of a flightcrew. The common fallacies about decision making were discussed earlier in the chapter. We add this: One of the authors (Smith) functioned as a "line check airman" during the late 1990s. He was checking fairly senior pilots transitioning to a large (250-plus passenger capacity), highly automated aircraft. He was saddened (and both angry and frightened) to see the number of times pilots either did not recognize a decision point in time to stay ahead of the power curve; did not recognize a decision and action point at all; and made poor decisions—decisions that raised the risk for having an unsafe and unsuccessful flight. In conversations, the authors became even more convinced of the absolute need for ODM.

What LOFT not only lends itself to evaluation but is actually designed for evaluation? A LOFT that uses event sets with embedded decision points carefully designed to force decisions on a risk continuum, and a LOFT that is designed with event sets partitioned into the MPM matrix, thus showing both CRM and flight skills. The evaluations of these carry with them the possibility of failure, without which they are meaningless.

LOFT: ODM AND MRM

In designing and developing LOFT scenarios, the basic unit, as proposed in 1993 (viz. Hamman, Smith, Lofaro, and Seamster, 1992) is the event set. The LOFT scenario is a set of event sets selected from real-world ops reports or made from amalgams of events and incidents as reported, or actually put together from the experiences of the LOFT design team. (An aside: NTSB accident reports can also be used.) It should be clear that superior LOFT design is a team effort, and the team should be carefully selected. The LOFT design team must consist of senior pilots with extensive flight time in the aircraft type the LOFT scenario is being created for. These pilots should also have experience in the air carriers' training complex. It is also somewhat desirable to have a person from the training department with ISD credentials, as will be shown later. One LOFT design team member should be a flight simulator operator to ensure that the event sets selected can be replicated in the flight simulator. Finally, it is truly preferable if one or more LOFT design team members have been line check airmen.

Having selected the team, the next step would be to layout an overview of the LOFT mission/ flight leg(s). This overview would include the basics, such as Wx, time-of-the-year ops (i.e., winter), and departure and destination airports, as well as alternatives. Into this skeletal framework, the team will select the event sets for each phase of flight (takeoff, cruise, descent, landing) as well as any pretakeoff event sets that may impact the flight leg.

The next steps are the crucial ones: Carefully select the problems that you want the flightcrew to encounter: mechanical, system malfunctions, etc. Then, plan the sequence into which you want to embed the problems. Remember that the overall goal is not to create the fabled "LOFT from hell"—one which cannot be successfully flown but must result in a loss of flight control.

In both the sequencing of the event sets and the selection of the problems to be embedded in the LOFT, the MPM and the ODM are to be used as the structural underpinnings. It is done in this manner:

1. Upon selection of the problems and the phases of flight that these problems are to occur in, the ODM is used to build a sequence that results in a rising risk. The decision points are identified. (A "decision point" is a point in the flight where if no decision and resultant action is taken, or if a wrong decision is made, the risk rises from low to moderate or from moderate to high.) Upon identifying the decision points, the basic sequence is modified to add the various outcomes from no decision/wrong decision; that is to say, the sequence now contains branches that are dependent upon the decisions made/unmade. Each branch or node will also need to have any changes in conditions and systems (again; Wx, en route or at destination, systems malfunctions, etc.) built in.
2. Next, the MPM is integrated with ODM. The concept here is to make the consequences of following a no decision/wrong decision model such that the risk continues until it reaches the high level and crew action must be taken in order to regain any possibility of successful flight completion. The "successful completion" may evolve ATB or diversion to the/an alternate airfield where "success" simply means landing the plane.

This integration is a two-step process. The first involves taking the selected event sets and identifying the critical tasks that are to be performed during those times. These high-level critical tasks (e.g., V1 "cut" on takeoff) are then decomposed, using the ISD process, into the complete list of subtasks involved. In the second step, the MPM is then used to further identify which of the critical tasks track to which of the relevant CRM and lift control functions necessary for successful task performance. The set of MPM functions will organize, sequence, distribute, and coordinate the actions key to successful performance.

Looked at another way: On the V1 "cut" at takeoff, as an examplar, we find that the needed CRM function is workload management. The MPM, with ISD decomposition, will spin out the specifics of the critical actions and flight control skills embedded in the workload function. The flight control tasks for this example include propulsion/lift/drag, operational integrity, and altitude control—with such subtasks as disconnecting the auto throttle at 400' AGL, setting airspeed to xyz knots, checking flap setting, and so on. The MPM will also spool out the crew performance markers for each subtask—both the CRM and flight technical markers. Not only that, but the functions and actions of both the pilot flying (PF) and the pilot not flying (PNF) will be clearly spelled out. These, as said, will be spelled out at the subtask level. In fact, this is true CRM integration—the place where both CRM and flight control actions are presented as a unified whole. However, space and scope preclude further explication, and there is a CRM integration document (Lofaro, 1992).

Because the necessary performances are specified, the performance markers can be used not only to track the crew's actions but, if desired, to evaluate them. This evaluation can be done simultaneously using a flight simulator operator and a check airman, or done post hoc using the videotapes that are normally part of LOFT sessions. Again, scope precludes going further into the evaluation area.

In summary, we see that the LOFT design has been driven by using the ODM to do initial event set selection and sequence design. Then, the MPM was used to generate the task and subtask breakouts for selected events within the event sets. The MPM further sequenced the events selected (as an example, CRM and flight control integration was performed at the subtask level, with optional evaluation procedures).

The LOFT design can be seen as embedding event sets into the LOFT scenario that can take the crew and plane into the moderate and even the high risk areas of the rising risk continuum, thus:

1. If the conditions causing the risks are either not identified or their interactions are not recognized.
2. If the decision points are either missed or result in an incorrect decision(s).
3. As a result of 1 and or 2, no actions are taken or incorrect actions are taken.

So far, we have shown the LOFT design process as one where the event sets, as well as initial and changing conditions, are used to generate decision points. The decision points, if missed or responded to incorrectly, cause a rise in the mission risk. The MPM is overlaid to give a level of detail whereby an analysis will determine where the errors were made: in flight control, in CRM, or in CRM and flight control. The MPM also offers an evaluative framework. However, LOFT design could be done in the other direction.

LOFT Design: Another Approach

We have discussed selecting event sets that have built-in, as it were, decision points. Put another way, events/event sets can be selected that require decisions (and actions) to prevent risk from rising—to prevent the aircraft's position in the ops envelope from approaching a corner or a boundary. As an example, the event set could include deteriorating Wx en route or at the destination airport, perhaps with braking advisories or crosswinds on approach/landing. From there, the MPM would be used to develop the flightcrew tasks and functions for PF and PNF. An initial bifurcation could be made: one path of event sets following the correct identification of rising risk and attendant risk reduction actions; the second path based on nonidentification of rising risk. Now, there would also be subpaths, for example, showing the correct identification of rising risk but incorrect response(s). The branching process can be repeated as needed. Thus, the ODM is the driver and the MPM is the method used to develop functionality.

However, LOFT can be developed in a different way, still using the MPM and ODM. A series of event sets (based on incident reports, "hangar talk," experiences, etc.) can be selected, linked, and the PF/PNF functions identified. These event sets we will term "expanded event sets" or "fully articulated event sets." By analyzing these sets, the decisional points can be identified. In fact, "identified" is not the exact term; "selected" is more appropriate. This is because it seems clear that, in any flight, new conditions or changes in conditions (Wx, flight system problems, etc.) will result in changes in the aircraft's position both in the ops envelope and on the rising risk continuum.

With the initial set of fully articulated functions and actions developed via the MPM, changes are introduced using the ODM's boundary conditions as guidelines. That is to say, an initial set of boundary conditions will be specified and used as a basis for carefully selecting changes to them that result, if left unidentified and/or unchecked, in additive or cumulative interaction, such interactions driving the aircraft toward a corner or side in the ops envelope. Of course, this means that the risk has risen to moderate or high-moderate—even to high.

The changes to the boundary conditions should be introduced at different points in flight so that the risk does not rise suddenly. The rationale here is that one goal of the LOFT is to keep situation awareness high by the introduction of an ongoing series of changes, rather than a compressed set of events that lead to an immediate abnormal ops or emergency, with limited options for the flightcrew. If the changes in the boundary conditions are introduced over the first 1 to 1½ hours of the LOFT session, their additive and/or cumulative interactions and impact will be sequences so that the flightcrew's ODM skills are tested. Thus, ODM skills are tested rather than skills at handling an overt and immediately apparent abnormal or emergency situation, which are often trained in other venues.

An aside: This is not to say that missed decision points as well as incorrect decisions and actions may not lead to an abnormal or emergency situation. If that occurs, then the LOFT can also demonstrate flightcrew skills in the emergency arena. However, as said, the training, to include recurrent or special-item training of flightcrews does provide for certain emergency training. As one example, recently some air carriers have instituted upset recovery training (recovering the aircraft from unusual or abnormal attitudes).

To resume: By carefully introducing boundary condition changes into the event sets, the risk can be caused to rise from additive or cumulative interactions. As before, when we indicated how to use the ODM to MPM LOFT design methodology, there will be a branching effect, contingent on decisions (made, unmade, correct, incorrect) and resultant actions (taken, not taken). The LOFT scenario must be designed to include the various pathways, so that the flight simulator can be preprogrammed for the contingencies.

It would seem that, optimally, the OPM to MPM and the MPM to ODM methods would operate simultaneously or in an intertwined manner. It may be fairly said that the use of the MPM and the ODM is actually a necessary and sufficient condition of effective LOFT design

At this point in time, we believe that we have presented the ODM in sufficient detail and with useful examples. The same can be said for the MPM. We have given references for the reader who wants more information and exposition of either model. We have presented the framework for developing ODM/MPM-based LOFT scenario(s). The evaluation of the flightcrew in the LOFT training session has been discussed.

It is of import to now clearly state that neither the ODM, the MPM, nor any LOFT developed using them need have an evaluative aspect. Further, if evaluation is to be an aspect of the LOFT session, it need not be a jeopardy situation. However, we still hold to our original view that LOFT should have a jeopardy component.

Training

Although we have not mentioned or emphasized the training aspects of the MPM or the ODM, it is clear that there are necessary training considerations for both. However, the MPM needs little, if any, training in terms of flightcrew. The reason is that the CRM components are already included as part of either initial or recurrent training. The flight-control maneuvers components are all included in flight training/type training—and many of the flight control aspects are used in recurrency training. Additionally, these flight control tasks/subtasks are all part of the handbooks used by pilots for each type of aircraft. Put another way, from the task through the subtask level of flight control, pilots are familiar with and have been trained in all of it. Of more importance, the performance of these flight control tasks, and the FAA and carrier standards to which they must be performed, are already known to the flightcrew—they have learned and been tested in them on the ground and been evaluated on their ability to perform the standard in the air. Therefore, for any critical task decomposition used in a LOFT, the flightcrew is well aware of the subtasks required to perform the task. Where, then, is any training needed for understanding and use of the MPM? It would seem that a single presentation and explanation of the MPM would suffice. There are the CRM and flight control behavior marks to consider. However, these are only of concern if the LOFT is to be evaluated for "jeopardy." If not, the markers and scoring scales can be distributed and explained; this process could be incorporated into the presentation and explanation of the MPM. Two hours would suffice.

Such is not the case with the ODM. This model would require dedicated training time. Again, there is a "however": The boundary conditions are well known to pilots. Although it is true that the flightcrew may never have seen the way ODM structures the boundaries, no training time is really needed for that aspect. The rising risk continuum and the concepts of interaction among boundary conditions/functions (with resultants that can exceed the impact of the single factors involved) can be easily trained in a 2 to 4 hour class, with pencil-and-paper exercises. At this point in time, the optimum use of the ODM for safety would be to automate some or all of it, and make it a call-up part of a display. Perhaps the best concept would be to have the display come up when two or more boundary conditions, from either the same boundary side or contiguous sides, have become active. Such an endeavor, or any discussion of it, is far beyond the scope of this chapter.

REFERENCES

Burki-Cohen, J., Go, T. H. et al., 2003, Simulator fidelity requirements for airline pilots training and evaluation continued: An update on motion requirements research. *Proceedings of the Twelfth Annual International Symposium on Aviation Psychology,* Dayton, OH.

Cannon-Bowers, J. A., Salas, E., and Converse, S. A., 1995. Shared mental models in expert decision making teams. In N. J. Castellan, Jr. (Ed.), *Current Issues in Individual and Group Decision Making.* Hillsdale, NJ: Lawrence Erlbaum Associates.

Ewell, C. D. and Chidester, T., 1996. American Airlines Converts CRM in Favor of Human Factors and Safety Training, The Flightdeck, July/August, 1996. Flight Department, American Airlines; DFW Airport). *Aviation Week and Space Technology,* September 6, 1996, p. 15.

Flexman, R. H. and Stark, E. A., 1987. Training simulators. Chapter in *Handbook of Human Factors.* Salvendy, Gavriel, Ed.

Go, T. H., Burki-Cohen, J., et al., 2003, The Effects of Enhanced Hexapod Motion on Airline Pilot Recurrent Training and Evaluation, AIAA-2003-5678.

Hamman, W. R., Seamster, T. L., Lofaro, R. J. and Smith, K. M., 1993. The future of LOFT scenario design and validation. *Proceedings of the Seventh International Symposium of Aviation Psychologists.* R. S. Jensen, Ed. Columbus, OH.

Lofaro, R. J. and Smith, K. M., 2003. The finalized paradigm for operational decision-making (ODM) paradigm: Components and placement. *Proceedings of the 12th International Symposium on Aviation Psychology.* Dayton, OH.

Lofaro, R. J. and Smith, K. M., 2001. Operational decision making: integrating new concepts into the paradigm. *Proceedings of Eleventh International Symposium on Aviation Psychology.* R. S. Jensen, Ed. Columbus, OH.

Lofaro, R. J. and Smith, K. M., 2001. A paradigm for developing operational decision-making (ODM). *Proceedings of 2001 SAE World Aviation Congress (WAC) Conference.* Various articles in *Aviation Week and Space Technology,* Vol. 15, No. 3, July 17, 2000, pp. 58–63.

Lofaro, R. J and Smith, K. M., 1999. Operational decision-making (ODM) and risk management: Rising risk, the critical mission factors and training. *Proceedings of the Tenth International Symposium of Aviation Psychologists.* R. S. Jensen, Ed. Columbus, OH.

Lofaro, R. J. and Smith, K. M., 1998. Rising risk? Rising safety? The Millennium and Air Travel special issue of the *Transportation Law Journal,* Vol. 25, No. 2, University of Denver Press, Denver, CO.

Lofaro, R. J. and Smith, K. M, 1993. The role of LOFT in CRM integration. *Proceedings of the Seventh International Symposium of Aviation Psychologists.* R. S. Jensen, Ed. Columbus, OH.

Lofaro, R. J., Adams, R. J., and Adams, C. A., 1992. Workshop on Aeronautical Decision-Making (ADM) DOT/FAA/RD-92/14; Vol. I, II. National Technical Information Service: Springfield, VA.

Maurino, D., 1999. Crew resource management: A time for reflection. Chapter in *Handbook of Aviation Human Factors.* Garland, Daniel, Wise, John, and Hopkin, V. David, Eds.

North, D. M., Finding common ground in envelope protection systems. *Aviation Week and Space Technology,* Vol. 153, No. 9, August 28, 2000.

Seamster, T. L., Hamman, W. R., Smith, K. M., Lofaro, R. J., and McDougall, W., 1993. CRM assessment and instructor knowledge structures. *Proceedings of the Seventh International Symposium of Aviation Psychologists.* R. S. Jensen, Ed. Columbus, OH.

Sprogis, H., 1997. Is the aviation industry expressing CRM failure? *Proceedings of Ninth International Symposium on Aviation Psychology.* Rakovan and Jensen, Eds. Columbus, OH.

FEDERAL AVIATION ADMINISTRATION ADVISORY CIRCULARS (AC) AND REGULATIONS

AC 120-35B: Line Operation Simulations (9/6/91)

AC 120-40B: Airplane Simulator Qualification (7/29/91)

AC 120-45A: Airplane Flight Training Device Qualification (2/5/92)

AC 120-AQP: Advanced Qualification Program (8/9/91). Note: This AC has been revised and will be reissued in early 2004.

SFAR 58: Advanced Qualification Program (5/29/03). Note: This is an extension of the original SFAR of 1991.)

15 Distributed After-Action Review for Simulation-Based Training

Emily E. Wiese, Jared Freeman, William J. Salter,
Emily M. Stelzer, and Cullen Jackson

CONTENTS

INTRODUCTION

In this introduction, we begin by defining "distributed after-action review (AAR) for simulation-based training" and deriving a few implications from the definition. We then touch on several issues that seem general across distributed AARs for simulation-based training, although we note that the diversity of such training means that exceptions might well be found. Finally, we briefly outline the balance of this chapter.

DEFINITIONS

"Distributed" means geographically dispersed, which can range from being in separate rooms to thousands of miles of separation. An "after-action review" (also "AAR," "debrief," or "debriefing") is a facilitated discussion of training performance in which the basic goal is to enhance subsequent trainee performance,* generally conducted soon after the training event. (We discuss AAR functions in more detail in the next section.) It is important to note that by "distributed AAR" we mean that the AAR itself (and, typically, the instructors) will be distributed, not only the learners. That is a vital constraint, as it means that all instructors cannot observe the same aspects of training or meet face-to-face to discuss what happened. They must use collaborative technology of some sort, which can range from simple teleconferences to sophisticated computer systems.

"Simulation-based training" means that learners use simulators rather than engaging in live exercises. Such simulators are typically highly technological and range from simple desktop flight simulators to submarine control rooms identical to real ones except for the lack of a surrounding submarine and ocean. For the purposes of this chapter, we assume that the simulators involve computers and that the computers collect data on what is occurring during the exercise and how trainees respond to events during the exercise. Of course, the quantity and utility of such data can vary widely, and this can greatly affect the detail and coverage provided in the debrief.

AARs for distributed simulation-based training are growing in importance largely because distributed simulation-based training is increasing in prevalence. This increase is in turn driven by several factors. First, more missions are coalition and/or joint, and the heterogeneous participants in such missions tend to be more geographically distributed, and thus harder and more expensive to coordinate for co-located training, than participants from one service. This, in part, reflects the broadening of missions beyond those traditionally handled by the military. Note that the broadening of missions and their joint/coalition emphasis also tend to require that a wide range of skills be trained, specifically including teamwork and coordination skills, and implies that one overall (often called "community" or "mass") debriefing may not address all training requirements. We will return to this point.

Second, cost pressures more broadly are making it harder to support the (often considerable) expense of bringing people together for the purposes of simulation-based training. And third, rapid advances in enabling technologies make it relatively easy to use existing simulators for distributed simulation. High levels of network reliability, bandwidth, and speed are dropping in price far more quickly than new simulation technologies are being introduced, making the basic technology infrastructure needed for distributed simulations more available. In particular, DIS (distributed interactive simulation) and HLA (high level architecture)—the two communications standards used for almost all military simulations—can run over wide-area networks as long as those networks have adequate performance characteristics, which means that simulators that often had to be in adjacent rooms to interoperate effectively can now be separated by hundreds or thousands of miles.

Distributed simulation-based training will involve multiple simulators. And typically, multiple platforms, weapons systems, and/or elements will be involved. (This is not always true; for example,

---

* AARs are frequently conducted for actual missions as well. These can be very valuable for enhancing tactics, gathering intelligence ("intell"), and improving procedures and performance, but they are not the subject of this chapter.

a strike lead and a wingman could participate in a coordinated mission using simulators in different locations.) There will also typically be at least an implicit hierarchy of training objectives, some for the individual elements, some across elements, and some for the mission as a whole.* Debriefings for distributed simulation-based training generally reflect two levels of the basic hierarchical structure of objectives: separate debriefs for each element or platform and a community or mass AAR that addresses coordination across elements and mission objectives.

SOME ISSUES IN DISTRIBUTED AARS FOR SIMULATION-BASED TRAINING

Different information is required for each element or platform and for the community debrief, and different expertise is generally required to deliver the debriefs. This creates several complexities. First, *it is desirable that an instructor (or a designated participant-instructor) be physically present for each separate "cell" or team of the distributed simulation.* Because some important actions (or lack of actions) may not be recorded in sufficient detail for immediate postexercise analysis by automated components of the distributed simulation, humans can provide a level of detail that can be quite valuable. For example, if participants communicate by voice, even if all voice communications are recorded, language processing software is not currently adequate to support pedagogically useful analysis. Furthermore, replay of all communications for postexercise analysis requires too much time and must be synchronized with replay during the review in order to be meaningfully linked with other actions.

Second, identifying cross-platform issues to be addressed in the community debrief, and deciding how to characterize those issues, requires *information fusion across the distributed simulation platforms.* By definition, those issues will involve interaction, coordination, and/or communication across platforms or elements. The identification of problems of that sort can be difficult, and the diagnosis and suggested remediation for problems will tend to be more so. This fusion must be addressed via procedures, technology, and preparation of the instructors.

Thus, more elaborate debrief preparation is generally needed, both because instructors must gain insight into events and actions that they did not observe and because issues to cover in debriefs must be divided among elements or platforms and between element debriefs and the community debrief. We believe that *more formal and more extensive use of computer-supported debrief preparation tools is needed* to effectively conduct AARs for distributed simulation-based training than for traditional co-located training. This is true to a lesser but still significant extent even if a single element or platform is being trained, because distributed instructors must share insights and build up reasonably extensive shared situation awareness.

Computer-supported methods of rapidly moving through and analyzing performance can be of particular value in distributed training, because more cognitive processing will tend to be required by distributed instructors than in co-located training. Importantly, while fully shared situation awareness may *not* typically be possible, even for distributed training of a single element, it is needed to understand the complete mission timeline and the ways in which trainee performance propagate across time and elements. Well-designed computer-supported AAR tools should assist in sharing the debriefing workload across instructors, allowing each to address what he or she has observed in detail, thus facilitating a more global awareness of performance across the exercise participants.

Ideally, these analysis and debriefing technologies will also function as *collaboration tools for distributed instructors,* because they operate under considerable time and task pressure. The time pressure is obvious; AARs typically take place within an hour of completing the training exercise, while experiences are fresh in participants' and instructors' minds. Task pressure comes from the

---

* Designing and implementing scenarios for distributed simulation can be more complex for more specialized training. And the AAR obviously has crucial dependencies on the scenario. However, the important topics of training objective development and scenarios design are beyond the scope of this chapter.

fact that failing to address important aspects of the training in the AAR can result in seriously impaired learning, which, of course, attenuates the entire purpose of the exercise.

TRADITIONAL DEBRIEFING TECHNIQUES

In the next section we discuss traditional debriefing techniques in some detail. We outline the goals and functions of AARs and characterize the strength and weaknesses of the methods employed. We then go into more detail on the *challenges and opportunities* afforded by the increasing importance of distributed AARs. We operationalize the previous discussion by addressing the *requirements* for distributed AARs, and then discuss *current methods* for conducting them. Finally, we conclude with a more speculative discussion of *the future of distributed AARs*.

FUNCTIONS AND CURRENT METHODS OF AAR

AARs fulfill diagnostic, instructional, and social functions. We define these functions here, then turn to a brief review of the current after-action review techniques and technologies that attempt to support them.

FUNCTIONS OF AAR

The principle function of AARs is instructional: they must convey the right lesson to the right people at the right time. In more mechanistic, cognitive terms, an AAR must help the learner recall from the recent training specific episodes of *correct* performance in context, and generalize this knowledge so that it can drive performance in similar (but not identical) future circumstances. An AAR must also help the learner recall specific instances of *incorrect* performance, discourage repetition of that performance in the future, cue recall of correct performance knowledge, and associate it with similar circumstances. These activities should be targeted only at trainees who need to learn and who have the capacity and motivation to do so.

An AAR is not just a process for delivering lessons, it is also helps participants to discover those lessons. That is, AARs help trainers and trainees discover performance failures (and successes) and diagnose their causes.

Finally, AARs serve a social function. For all involved, they are an opportunity to show and assess technical competence (the ability to discriminate good from bad performance and diagnose its cause) and social competence (the ability to convey critiques of oneself with candor, and of co-participants or trainees with diplomacy).

In sum, AARs support diagnosis of performance (D1), recall of performance in training (I1), understanding of expert performance (I2), generalization to future situations (I3), and assessment and display of competence (S1).

METHODS OF AAR

Techniques and technologies for AARs have evolved to support these functions more or less completely, more or less well.

Simulators typically support the instructional function of AAR through replay. Platform simulators, such as flight simulators, and large-unit simulator systems, such as Joint Semi-Automated Forces (JSAF), commonly record the course of selected simulation events, enable trainers to tag or bookmark instructive moments in that event stream, and replay those events using standard video controls (play, fast forward, etc.). Serial replay should have strong effects on learning. It conforms to the serial structure of the episode in memory and thus serial replay should ease recall (I1). It should reinforce memory for normative sequences of events (e.g., mission phases; Schank, 1982) and thus it should help trainees to generalize from the specific episode to its class (I3). Finally, serial replay should help trainees recognize actions that snowball into disaster (or success) as a scenario evolves and thus serial replay should support the diagnosis function (D1) of AAR and the skills underlying diagnosis and, one hopes, prognosis.

The devil is in the details, however. Replay is often implemented in ways that help trainees to recall and learn the whole but not the parts, the progress of their unit but not their vehicle, and the flow of the mission but not its parts. For example, replay is often implemented as a set of icons moving over a tactical map (see http://www.tadil.net/netscape/images/jsaf.jpg for an example). This is a useful representation for cueing recall of the tactical state of forces and tactical actions of units. However, many simulators don't help individuals recall the situation by, for example, presenting the scene as a pilot, tank driver, or other operator perceived it. Replay systems rarely record and represent operators' displays and instruments, nor do they support recall of *responses* because the systems generally do not record and represent the trainee's use of controls. Still fewer simulators will record all or some of these viewpoints. Rare exceptions, mainly in the field of aviation training, include an F-16 distributed debriefing system developed by the Air Force Research Laboratory (AFRL) that combines a central tactical view with instrument displays on each side (Sidor, 2002). Similarly, the Dismounted Infantry Virtual After-Action Review System (DIVAARS, developed by the Army Research Institute and the University of Central Florida) provides multiple viewpoints of the simulation space during replay. These systems encourage operators to have detailed discussions about how they perceived the environment and the actions they took in it.

Above, we noted that replay may help trainees learn the course of an overall mission, but not its parts. If an AAR is to help trainees generalize parts of the current scenario to future scenarios (I3, mentioned previously), it may be useful to show them multiple instances of a class of situation and of response. Astute trainers can use the bookmark features of simulator AARs to tag similar situations and responses. In our experience, this is rarely done, however. AARs more often proceed from the first scenario to the last, rather than jumping between like events. AAR technology rarely helps trainers identify and navigate from one instance of a class of events to the next because simulation systems are rarely instrumented with measurement systems that can categorize events and human responses to them. One exception (Salter et al., 2005) categorizes events, assesses performance in those events, displays those categories and assessments, and links each instance directly to its replay. This design gives trainers random access to multiple instances of a given class of events and thus supports trainees as they attempt to generalize from instances to the larger class.

If AARs are to help trainees learn expert alternatives to their incorrect performance (I2, mentioned before), they must present them in some way. Few, if any, high-end simulators (e.g., flight simulators and driving simulators with physical cockpits) are capable of generating examples of expert performance because they do not incorporate computational models of expert behavior. Thus, AARs raise alternative behaviors to the attention of trainees largely through discussion; alternatives are said, not shown. This may be sufficient in some circumstances. However, recent empirical research (Shebilske et al., in press) demonstrates that describing expert solutions to complex problems (e.g., team planning and execution of military air missions) produces learning outcomes that are reliably inferior to describing and "playing" solutions using visual animations. In this research, expert solutions were generated by an optimization model. In traditional intelligent tutoring systems, these solutions are generated by heuristic or rule-based models of expertise.

The diagnostic function of AARs typically is supported by debriefing techniques, not technology. These techniques encourage trainers and trainees to identify and analyze strengths and shortcomings in performance. The Navy and the Air Force, for example, decompose AARs for large simulated and live exercises into independent debriefs of small elements or packages and overall debriefs involving the entire training audience (community or mass debriefs). The element debriefs typically identify specific performance failures that support diagnosis in the community debrief. The Army has codified its method in a set of questions that soldiers explore in AARs: What was supposed to happen? What happened? What accounts for the difference? (Dixon, 2000). A set of AAR guidelines (e.g., "Call it like you see it," "No thin skins") encourages participants to think critically and to be candid in their review of events. Similarly, the commercial aviation community espouses AAR methods that engage trainees in identifying and diagnosing performance failures. Studies of these methods and their impact on diagnostic quality are rare. However, one analysis of AARs in commercial aviation (Dismukes et al., 2000) found that instructors often failed to engage trainees in diagnostic (or any) discussions during AAR, and instead dominated these sessions with monologues concerning their own observations. When techniques fail in this way, trainers and trainees cannot fall back on diagnostic technologies. AAR systems are generally incapable of generating diagnoses because they do not incorporate expert behavioral models against which to compare trainee performance. Nor do most AAR systems record data concerning trainee performance or compute measures that summarize that performance, attribute effects to individual performers, or relate causes to effects.

Finally, AAR techniques (but not the technologies) support the social processes (S1) by which participants assess the competence of their colleagues and assert their own. The Army AAR procedures encourage participation, as do the commercial aviation techniques mentioned above. However, current AAR technologies do not provide any features that support assessment and assertion of competence. Technologies that might provide this support include polling and group decision support tools that elicit or require input from all participants, and AAR authoring tools with which participants could focus attention on key events. The lack of tool support is particularly troublesome in distributed AARs, where reliance on teleconferencing may even hinder this social function by anonymizing participants or excluding some trainees from full participation due to technology difficulties (e.g., poor audio quality).

The functions of AAR—instructional, diagnostic, and social—are partially supported by AAR technologies. AAR techniques help trainers to address some of the remaining functions, particularly diagnostic and social functions. However, trainers have a spotty record of applying these AAR techniques well, and the advent of distributed debriefings may make it even more difficult for them to use these methods, as we discuss next.

CHALLENGES OF DISTRIBUTED AARs

Recent advances in technology have allowed for the development of coordinated simulation tools, which can be used to simultaneously train groups of individuals who are dispersed across several geographical locations. As outlined earlier, these distributed training exercises can be conducted with less cost and risk than traditional live training events, allowing diverse groups of individuals to collaboratively train whole mission exercises more frequently than was ever before possible (e.g., Dwyer, Fowlkes, Oser, and Salas, 1996). Although distributed training exercises can produce more effective and routine training events, this new approach to training can complicate debriefs that follow those events. We discuss the potential challenges that distributed training can pose to debriefing within the framework of the five key functions of an AAR outlined earlier, namely diagnosis of performance (D1), recall of performance in training (I1), understanding of expert performance (I2), generalization to future situations (I3), and assessment and display of competence within the social setting of a debrief (S1).

PERFORMANCE DIAGNOSIS

The effectiveness of a debrief hinges on an instructor's ability to support trainees in diagnosing the underlying causes of mission failure (or success), and attributing those causes directly to individual or team behavior (D1). As noted earlier, serial mission replay capabilities are usually provided as a global representation of mission performance, which trainees observe to recall and learn the general flow of the mission. Traditionally, such replays do not include views of specific displays or instruments that can provide the needed context of individual constraints and reasoning in diagnosing mission performance. When the training environment is extended to include multiple, diverse, and distributed training groups, the limitations of this training approach become increasingly apparent.

Because distributed training exercises eliminate the logistics and cost issues associated with live training events, more diverse trainees (or more trainee groups) can participate. For example, a distributed Naval training event may include an E2-C Hawkeye aircraft, designed to provide surveillance coordination, and a set of F/A-18 Hornets, to provide suppression of enemy air defenses and strike missions, as well as ground control and intelligence support. The diversity of the participants in the training exercise, represented in this example by the two air platforms and the supporting ground elements, generates complexity in the type of mission that is executed, the data that is generated from the mission, and the interdependencies between actions in mission performance. With current procedures and technologies, instructors and trainees must diagnose successes and failures, and the interdependencies of actions to support these outcomes, using the replay of a simple common operational picture. Because this technology cannot capture the subtle details of actions and communications between remotely located elements, the diagnosis of performance is likely to be hindered.

The AAR process can be structured to encourage instructors and trainees to collaboratively identify performance shortcomings and strengths, for which instructors are an essential guide in the diagnosis process. Under a distributed training process, however, trainees and instructors will likely not all be co-located, thus inhibiting the element instructors from observing and integrating performance information in real-time across the package. In these cases, measures of performance may be collected automatically through the training simulation or remotely by observing performance through global views of mission performance. By distributing trainees and instructors across locations, instructors will also face challenges in diagnosing performance and ultimately may be less helpful in supporting performance diagnosis in trainees.

In order to support these diagnostic processes and leverage that diagnosis to improve future performance, it is critical that trainees and instructors are successful in recalling mission performance (I1), comparing that performance to expert behavior (I2), and extrapolating behaviors to future situations (I3). Each of these key processes can be inhibited by the dispersion of trainees across geographical locations, as we note next.

PERFORMANCE RECALL, COMPARISON, AND EXTRAPOLATION

Traditional replay techniques can have great utility in supporting memory for the sequence of mission events (Schank, 1982) in traditional training events. Distributed training exercises can compromise this recall by increasing the load placed on instructor and trainee memory through two independent mechanisms. First, because distributed training exercises can involve richer interactions with heterogeneous training groups, the data and behaviors associated with these interactions increase in number and complexity. For example, communications in nondistributed training events may be limited to radio communications from a strike pilot to ground control. In distributed events, these same communications will occur, but may also be augmented with calls to pilots in supporting platforms. Second, distributed training exercises rely upon simulation systems that have evolved into sophisticated data collection tools, which can exponentially increase the amount of data that is collected (Jacobs, Cornelisse, and Schavemaker-Piva, 2006), and possibly recalled, by instructors. Although all of these data may not be conventionally discussed in traditional debriefing processes, they may be included in distributed debriefs, thus increasing the demand on trainee memory and reducing the likelihood of recalling these granular data.

The comparison of these data, particularly for performance failures, to expert alternatives is further complicated by the complexity of the interactions between trainees. As the number of individuals involved in the training exercise increases, the predictability of their interactions and the ability to optimize or simulate these interactions in visual animations also becomes complex. Finally, the grouping of similar performance data becomes an essential component to understanding performance trends and extrapolating those trends to assessing future behavior. Because the distributed training environment provides more frequent opportunities for data collection, this training approach can reveal rich, informative patterns in trainee behavior. As in each of the critical AAR processes discussed thus far, the sheer quantity of data and the heterogeneity of behavior categories can complicate this process beyond that encountered with traditional training events.

ASSESSMENT AND DISPLAY OF COMPETENCE

The final function that the AAR provides is to support the social processes through which trainees can evaluate the competence of their colleagues, as well as assert their own expertise. Whereas distributed debriefing processes can influence the AAR functions described earlier by generating more complex and diverse performance data, the distribution of trainees and instructors during debrief constrains the social mechanism of appraisal quite differently.

Distributed debriefing, and the tools that are used to support communication during these processes, can affect social appraisal and display of competence in three key ways. First, information sharing tools (e.g., collaborative desktops) and communication channels (e.g., video teleconference) can be useful in exchanging knowledge across disparate locations; however, these tools can still constrain the type of information that is readily shared. These tools are especially useful at exchanging text-based or pregenerated spatial content, but are not highly effective at facilitating the interaction between trainees who are co-located at a whiteboard and sketch out mission developments and aircraft formations. Second, the microphones and sound quality associated with teleconferences or video teleconferences can limit the ease with which discussion can readily take place, even with the most advanced systems. These communication technologies are also poor at transmitting radio communications that are replayed during a mission review. Finally, these communication devices cannot capture the gestures and nonverbal communications that can be used to effectively assess and display competence. While traditional training processes can rely on nonverbal information exchange such as eye contact, distributed training environments strip this form of communication from the essential social interactions that occur between individual trainees, as well as between trainees and their instructors.

REQUIREMENTS FOR DISTRIBUTED AARs

In the preceding section, we identified several challenges that distributed debriefings might, and frequently do, encounter. However, standard procedures for conducting effective distributed debriefing with collaborative technologies have not yet been defined. Although a range of processes could be used to prepare and deliver debriefs in the distributed environment, the utility of these approaches depends both on the context in which they are being used and the design of the training technology to support the instructor. It is tempting to discuss the technical and procedural requirements for distributed AARs separately. However, due to their very nature, distributed AARs combine both technology and process in a way that is difficult, if not impossible, to separate. To ensure that the technologies and the processes interact seamlessly, it is important to address the design of these pieces simultaneously and collaboratively. We discuss distributed AAR requirements next, relating them to the previously defined AAR functions (diagnosis of performance [D1], recall of performance training [I1], understanding of expert performance [I2], generalization to future situations [I3], and assessment and display of competence [S1]). Importantly, although these requirements may be met by a single technology, it is perhaps more likely that a series of AAR tools and institutional processes will ultimately fulfill distributed AAR needs.

COMMUNICATION

A distributed AAR must support communication between the various locations involved, during both the preparation and delivery phases. At a minimum, voice communication should be supported. Ideally, videoconferencing will be supported across all sites. This is no small technological feat, particularly across multiple locations. Although current technology exists that supports this requirement, there are numerous technical issues that almost always pose some issues. Naturally, the frequency of technical issues increases with more distributed sites. Aside from technical issues, each distributed exercise must decide on and follow a few ground rules for using these communication technologies, beginning with the start of the communication (i.e., who calls who) and including turn-taking, tips on reducing extraneous noise, and how electronic information will be shared. This is a critical requirement of any distributed AAR, which supports all of the previously defined AAR functions.

COLLABORATION

Closely tied to communication is collaboration. The distributed AAR must allow sites to coordinate on the content that should be debriefed, the strategy for debriefing, and the actual delivery. Thus, any performance data, simulator replay feeds, or other supporting information available must be shared across sites. Collaboration technologies that allow all participants to view the same information reduce confusion and facilitate the creation of common ground between all instructors and trainees. Optimally, the collaboration technology will allow each site to take control of the information, manipulating it ways that help illuminate the results of the training exercise. Here again, ground rules on effective use of the collaboration technology are imperative. Confusion in turn-taking can quickly lead to a chaotic AAR, both in the preparation and delivery phases. As with communication, without collaboration mechanisms, none of the AAR functions can be fulfilled in a distributed fashion.

AUTOMATED DATA CAPTURE

Distributed exercises run on a very tight schedule. Instructors are not given much time to develop an AAR; 20–30 minutes is fairly standard. Any distributed AAR technology must facilitate rapid AAR development, part of which is accessing available performance data and simulator feeds. Allowing instructors to view performance data specific to their element and common across all exercise participants supports diagnosis, recall, understanding, generalization, and, ultimately, overall performance assessment. The distributed AAR technology should accept and process performance data and simulator feeds automatically or semiautomatically (in the case of observer measures), with little direction on the part of the instructor.

DATA PRESENTATION

Any performance data (i.e., performance measurements) collected during the exercise have two potential presentation audiences: the instructors (during AAR preparation) and the students (during AAR delivery). How this performance data is presented can greatly facilitate or hinder the instructors' and students' ability to diagnose, understand, and, subsequently, assess their performance during the exercise. The distributed AAR technology should allow the performance data to be presented at varying levels of detail, as it relates to the community, the package, and each element. Drill down capabilities are key, as are the methods by which performance data are presented (e.g., on a timeline, by event, textual representations, graphs, etc.).

DATA SELECTION

Not all performance data is relevant for every element. Not all performance data is relevant for the entire group of exercise participants. In order to facilitate diagnosis and understanding of performance, instructors must be able to easily select the relevant performance data and simulator feeds or displays. Thus, the instructors must be allowed to identify key aspects of the exercise that are indicative of both good and poor performance. Subsequent review of performance during these key events can facilitate debriefs at the element, package, and community levels.

REPLAY PERSPECTIVE

Although viewing performance data is important, replaying exercise events is equally critical. Showing these events from multiple points of view can greatly facilitate diagnosis, recall, understanding, generalization, and assessment of trainee performance. Viewing events on a tactical map (or from a God's eye view), from a first-person view, or a third-person view can provide context and perspective to participants that would, otherwise, be difficult to obtain. Similarly, it may be useful to display gauges and instrument panels in order to provide a more common understanding of element capabilities across trainees. The distributed AAR technology must allow instructors to replay selected exercise events from these multiple points of view, to the extent they are available. Additionally, the distributed AAR technology must allow instructors to choose when and how these viewpoints are presented, in order to best fit in with the overall AAR.

EXPERT MODELS OF PERFORMANCE

Viewing and analyzing performance in comparison to defined standards or models of expert performance can greatly assist instructors in diagnosing trainee performance. Discussing how the trainees' performance compared to these standards can help the trainee understand what went well or poorly and understand why. The distributed AAR technology should present alternative or expert models of performance for each platform, either in the form of quantitatively modeled behavior or in the form of performance categories.

FLEXIBLE DELIVERY STYLE

The way in which an AAR is conducted varies according to the institution sponsoring the training exercise, the domain(s) being trained, and the instructors conducting the training. It is therefore important that any distributed AAR technology not unduly constrain or force instructors into presenting feedback to trainees in a specific style. This requirement can be tricky to fulfill. Certainly, some instructional strategies may be more effective than others. And indeed, some instructors may be more effective than others. However, all other things being equal, instructors should be allowed to tell the performance story in the manner that best suits their needs. For example, it may be appropriate to conduct the AAR in a way that tells a story, while allowing the instructor to drill down to specific training objectives and aspects of performance when appropriate. In this way, the AAR can be tailored to each trainee audience, thereby maximally supporting trainee learning.

POSTEXERCISE REVIEW

Once the distributed training exercise is complete, the AAR should be available for offline review by each site. Additionally, each participant should receive an AAR takeaway report after the exercise is complete. This can facilitate a variety of postexercise analysis activities, such as a more in-depth review of that site's performance, evaluation of training effectiveness, evaluation of instructor effectiveness, and evaluation of AAR effectiveness.

STORE LESSONS LEARNED

Distributed exercises accomplish much more than teaching individual trainees. Each exercise results in a variety of lessons learned (e.g., about trainees, about training materials and scenarios, etc.) to be used when planning the next distributed exercise, in local training by units and squadrons, and during real-world missions when deployed. Retaining and using institutional knowledge is a difficult process in any environment. The distributed AAR technology must facilitate institutional learning by providing a mechanism to accumulate these lessons learned, distribute them, and use them when developing the performance assessment plan for the next exercise.

SCALEABLE

Distributed simulation training exercises come in all shapes and sizes. At their simplest, they involve two different elements, each located at a different geographic location. The elements may or may not be similar. At the other end of the spectrum, large-scale distributed simulation exercises, such as the Air Force's Virtual Flag, may involve up to 25 different sites, involving activities at the operational and tactical levels. Adding to the complexity, some sites may host a variety of different types of simulators. Distributed AAR technology must be scaleable to many locations of the same or different platforms. It must work equally well with two sites (as in a package debrief) as with 25 sites (as in a mass or community debrief). Given the limitations in resources, it is simply not feasible for sites to learn and maintain multiple technologies and processes for conducting distributed AARs.

EASE OF USE

Instructors may be involved in a distributed exercise a couple of times a year—if they're lucky. Time spent immediately prior to the exercise typically focuses on reviewing the relevant techniques, tactics, and procedures; becoming familiar with the scenario being executed during the exercise; and ironing out any kinks in the distributed technology. There is typically little time to become familiar with *how* the distributed technology works. Therefore, any distributed AAR technology must be very easy to use, allowing the instructors to quickly learn (or relearn) the technology with minimal hassles or instruction.

CURRENT TECHNIQUES FOR DEBRIEFING DISTRIBUTED TEAMS

Many existing simulation environments provide the technical building blocks upon which many of the distributed AAR requirements can be fulfilled. Although some of these requirements have been fulfilled by existing technologies, no fully implemented distributed AAR system addresses all of these requirements.

STATE OF THE ART IN DISTRIBUTED DEBRIEFING

Today's distributed simulation training has come a long way. Both the U.S. Navy and the Air Force regularly conduct complex virtual training exercises that involve a variety of simulated platforms and locations (e.g., the Navy's Operation Brimstone and the Air Force's Virtual Flag Exercises). Research and development efforts across all of the U.S. military services are continuing to develop additional simulation environments for use locally and in a distributed manner.

LARGE-SCALE DISTRIBUTED SIMULATION TRAINING EXERCISES

During large scale virtual training exercises hosted by the Air Force and Navy, the distributed AARs heavily rely on common tools found throughout the services. Standard video teleconferencing (VTC) applications are used to connect sites during briefs and debriefs. What formal data collection occurs is generally presented to all trainees in slide show form. During the debrief, collaboration technology (such as Information Workspace) is used to share these slide shows across the network and saved to commonly accessible shared network drives. The diagnosis of performance and delivery of the AARs is typically left up to the individual instructors, although some overall guidance on areas of good and poor performance may be provided from an internal assessment team. The slide shows largely contain textual information, with some still images as applicable.

This method of developing and conducting distributed exercises certainly has its benefits. The use of commonly available applications minimizes the maintenance required by each site and minimizes the need to learn yet another application by already busy instructors. Additionally, the free-form nature of the slide show allows the instructors to add whatever content is desired. On the other hand, these commonly available tools do not allow instructors to take advantage of the plethora of simulation data available to them. To do so would involve much more time than instructors currently have. A technology more focused on providing instructors with immediate data and feedback regarding the trainees' performance may help them develop the AAR more rapidly, covering more instructional points than they are currently able to.

Small-Scale Distributed Simulation Training Exercises

Small-scale distributed AARs are experimenting with distributed AAR technologies a bit more. Distributed AAR technologies such as the Navy's DDSBE AAR (developed by Aptima, Inc.) and AFRL's Distributed Mission Training Collaborative Briefing and Debriefing System are two such examples, primarily used to conduct a distributed AAR across two sites (Salter et al., 2005; Sidor, 2002). Both systems support communication and collaboration across sites, replay of events using a tactical map, interaction with that map, and view of various instrument gauges. In addition, the DDSBE AAR (Salter et al., 2005) collects and presents formal performance data collected during the training exercise. Instructors are able to select specific performance data points for discussion and presentation during the AAR. To facilitate this task, the performance data are color-categorized into good performance (green), poor performance (red), and average performance (yellow).

These small-scale distributed AAR tools are certainly on the right track for becoming a scaleable solution that can be used during large-scale distributed training exercises as well. Additional work needs to be done to ensure that collaboration methods are scaleable across multiple sites, to incorporate multiple viewpoints in replay capability, to ensure that formal performance data are collected and available for all trainees, and to support use of the data after the exercise is over.

SUMMARY

Currently, most developers of distributed AARs focus either on the technology or on researching academic issues surrounding debriefing processes. Little information is publicly available describing efforts to combine these two strands in meaningful ways. In order to be truly successful, distributed training exercises must conduct AARs that rigorously and formally promote trainee learning. We believe that, by considering the current challenges to these issues and the requirements presented above, distributed AAR technologies and techniques can begin to meet this lofty goal.

REFERENCES

Dismukes, R. K., McDonnell, L. K., & Jobe, K. K., 2000. Facilitating LOFT debriefings: instructor techniques and crew participation. *International Journal of Aviation Psychology,* 10, 35.

Dixon, N. M., 2000. *Common knowledge: How companies thrive by sharing what they know.* Cambridge: Harvard University Press.

Dwyer, D. J., Fowlkes, J., Oser, R. L., & Salas, E., 1996. Case study results using distributed interactive simulation for close air support training. In *Proceedings of the 7th International Training Equipment Conference* (pp. 371–380). Arlington, VA: ITEC Ltd.

Jacobs, L., Cornelisse, E., & Schavemaker-Piva, O., 2006. Innovative debrief solutions for mission training and simulation: Making fighter pilots training more effective. In *Proceedings of the Interservice/ Industry Training, Simulation, and Education Conference (I/ITSEC).* Orlando, FL.

Salter, W. J., Hoch, S., & Freeman, J., 2005. Human factors challenges in after-action reviews in distributed simulation-based training. *Proceedings of the Human Factors and Ergonomics Society 49th Annual Meeting.*

Schank, R. C., 1982. *Dynamic memory: A theory of reminding and learning in computers and people.* New York: Cambridge University Press.

Shebilske, W., Gildea, K., Freeman, J., & Levchuk, G., (in press). Optimizing instructional strategies: A benchmarked experiential system for training (BEST). *Theoretical Issues in Ergonomics Science.*

Sidor, G. J., Capt. 2002. Distributed mission training collaborative briefing and debriefing system (electronic version). *AFRL Horizons.* Retrieved August 6, 2007.

16 Performance Measurement Issues and Guidelines for Adaptive, Simulation-Based Training

Phillip M. Mangos and Joan H. Johnston

CONTENTS

INTRODUCTION

Simulation-based training has become an increasingly versatile method for enhancing adaptive performance in a variety of complex task domains. Military settings rely heavily on simulation-based training for tasks ranging from command and control, air defense warfare, ship and aircraft maintenance, and damage control in dismounted combat and urban warfare. One reason for the emergence of simulation as a dominant training paradigm in the U.S. military is the increased technological sophistication and computing power of modern simulators, which permits the use of a number of advanced instructional capabilities. For example, modern military simulations leverage enhanced networking capabilities to allow for multiple, physically distributed team members to participate in a common training exercise. Furthermore, many simulations have the additional capability of adapting scenario content or performance feedback to address the skill deficiencies of individual trainees or teams.

Two emerging trends in the technological evolution of training simulators are the enhanced levels of automation and customization. Many systems are capable of automating various aspects of scenario or feedback generation, reducing the workload of instructors while providing a tailored training experience. These trends highlight the critical role of individual assessment and performance measurement in the context of adaptive, simulation-based training. Modern simulations, driven by increased computing power, afford a number of advanced assessment and measurement opportunities, allowing for a staggering number of variables to be recorded in the course of an exercise. The challenge is to be able to reduce the information to a comprehensive and unbiased picture of how an individual performed with respect to individual training objectives. This challenge is compounded by the fact that the manner in which individual performance is conceptualized and measured has critical implications for how training is structured, organized, and delivered, and for how raw performance information can be reduced and organized into meaningful performance feedback for the trainee.

The purpose of this chapter is to provide a critical analysis of the role of performance measurement in light of these emerging trends, drawing from the perspective that it provides the foundation for automated, adaptive training content and feedback delivery. A wide variety of techniques are used in practice to measure performance and diagnose skills underlying observable performance. However, the proliferation of data analysis methods available to extract meaningful patterns from the abundance of available performance data affords the possibility of reverting to ostensibly sophisticated but ad hoc measurement strategies. These strategies lack a confirmatory framework necessary to draw causal inferences regarding relations among training objectives, the psychological constructs targeted during training, and observable performance.

We begin by providing an example of current and emerging performance measurement trends. We describe a U.S. Navy research program that developed a coherent set of performance measurement, assessment, diagnosis, and debriefing tools for distributed teams performing simulation-based training exercises. Next, we describe the characteristics of a theory-driven, confirmatory performance measurement framework in light of emerging trends in adaptive training. We then discuss several dimensions along which performance measures can vary, describe desirable characteristics of measures along each dimension, and introduce a set of principles articulating how individual performance measures can be used to support adaptive training.

We emphasize throughout this discussion the potential benefits to be gained by applying psychometric principles to the development of simulation-based performance measures. We propose that the *training* potential of simulation systems be increased by focusing on their *assessment* potential. That is, by treating a simulation-based training system as a vehicle for generating customized training content around a core of embedded, potentially high-fidelity assessment "items," one can achieve a number of critical training outcomes. First, one has an enhanced ability to diagnose the causes of suboptimal performance. Second, a higher proportion of training time may be focused on correcting the unique skill deficiencies of an individual learner. Third, desired performance levels may be achieved and maintained in less time. Finally, trained skills may generalize better and be maintained longer when transferred to real-world job settings.

ILLUSTRATION OF FUTURE SIMULATION-BASED TRAINING CAPABILITIES AND TRENDS

The Debriefing Distributed Simulation-Based Exercises (DDSBE) project is a U.S. Navy research effort that developed a set of integrated performance assessment tools for distributed teams performing simulation-based training exercises. The DDSBE research effort improved upon current practices that involve (1) coordination of disparate simulation and instructional tools (including both automated or computer-based and instructor-led assessment methods) to accomplish assessment and debriefing objectives, (2) multiple participants hierarchically organized in physically distributed, multitiered team settings, (3) highly complex, data-rich scenarios that afford a wide variety of measurement opportunities with respect to training objectives, and (4) logistic challenges inherent in assimilating and aggregating performance data within the limited range of observational opportunities for instructor-led assessments (Johnston, Radtke, Van Duyne, Stretton, Freeman, and Bilazarian, 2004).

The DDSBE system is composed of a set of interdependent software architectures that perform five specific functions in support of the objectives previously described: exercise planning, scenario generation, briefing, assessment, and debriefing. Exercise planning, scenario generation, and briefing functions collectively support mission planning, including selection and generation of training material, and the preparation and delivery of briefs concerning mission objectives. The assessment function supports data collection and data reduction (the transformation of raw performance data into diagnostic information useful for assessment). It performs operations relevant for (1) detecting meaningful performance patterns in raw performance data based on automatic collection of data from the simulation system and the assimilation of instructor observations, ratings, and remarks; (2) defining expert responses to scenario events (i.e., expertise representation) for comparison to trainee responses; (3) identifying discrepancies between observed and expected (i.e., expert) performance; and (4) diagnosing the root causes of performance failures. The debriefing function translates assessment information into a meaningful debrief customized to address skill strengths and weaknesses of the individual trainee as they relate to team performance.

The DDSBE configuration exemplifies several important trends for future training systems that have implications for performance measurement. First, the system represents a common diagnostic model used to assess and diagnose performance, derived from the logic of intelligent tutoring systems, in which performance data indicative of knowledge or skill constructs to be targeted during training are compared to performance patterns that correspond to an expert model (Everson, 1995; Mangos, 2004; Steele-Johnson and Hyde, 1997). Within intelligent tutoring systems, the student and expert models are repeatedly compared throughout the course of training. Discrepancies between the student and expert models guide subsequent branching of instructional content via access to a third component, the instructional model, which contains relevant domain knowledge. More generally, the existence of the assessment function within the DDSBE architecture emphasizes the critical distinctions between performance *measurement* (i.e., nonevaluative description of relevant behaviors), *assessment* (i.e., use of performance information to make inferences regarding latent knowledge, skills, abilities, or other personal characteristics that drive observable performance), and *diagnosis* (i.e., identifying potential causes of suboptimal performance). An essential feature of future simulation-based training systems will be some form of assessment and diagnostic capabilities that support customization of training content. This requirement highlights the importance of designing a performance measurement framework to support assessment and diagnosis in adaptive training settings.

Additionally, the DDSBE system exemplifies the growing trend underlying many training systems in development, that is, the increasing need to accommodate distributed training missions and the emergence of scenario-based training (SBT) as a dominant paradigm for distributed teams in the U.S. military and in other domains (Dwyer, Fowlkes, Oser, and Lane, 1997; Fowlkes, Dwyer, Oser, and Salas, 1998). There is an increased interest in developing training for distributed team members, in which individual team members operate within specific platforms (e.g., E-2C *Hawkeye* aircraft) that are part of a larger configuration (e.g., air wing). The notion of SBT relies on the use of training scenarios that represent a sample of realistic events that could be experienced in the tactical environment. The underlying logic is that immersion in realistic training scenarios provides a level of psychological fidelity necessary for positive transfer of learned skills to the tactical environment (Smith, Ford, and Kozlowski, 1997). However, there is a lack of theoretical guidance for individualizing instructional events to learners' needs in the context of SBT (Mangos, 2004).

Finally, the DDSBE system exemplifies the trend toward automated, adaptive instruction. In essence, early formulations of SBT were based on the logic that critical events embedded within realistic training scenarios could provide important opportunities for learning and performance measurement (Dwyer et al., 1997; Fowlkes et al., 1998). SBT required a human instructor to identify acceptable responses to scenario events a priori, to plan the insertion of "trigger" events at different points during the scenario, and to code and evaluate the learner's responses to those events. This approach promoted an experimental focus in which hypothesized relationships among training objectives, performance episodes, and outcomes were made explicit and tested directly (Dwyer et al., 1997). The DDSBE system represents the next generation of SBT, in which the instructor's role in customizing scenario content and in measuring, assessing, and diagnosing performance is automated by components of the simulation itself (e.g., intelligent software agents). Performance measurement may be accomplished entirely with objective performance measures embedded within the simulation or by combining objective measures and subjective ratings (Johnston, 2005; Johnston et al., 2004). Furthermore, the use of trigger events is transformed into a continuous stream of adaptive scenario content that is customized to provide the appropriate level of challenge to the evolving training needs of the learner.

A CONFIRMATORY PERFORMANCE MEASUREMENT FRAMEWORK FOR ADAPTIVE, SIMULATION-BASED TRAINING

The trends summarized previously—the use of performance information for diagnosis, use of simulation for distributed training, and increased automation and customization of training content—present a number of challenges for the development of performance measures. The hardware and software technologies contributing to these trends have evolved at a rapid pace. As a result, trainers have the opportunity to extract vast amounts of raw data from a simulation, to employ data mining algorithms to seek out consistencies in the data, or to rapidly reconfigure training scenarios based on an arbitrary notion of the trainee's skill deficiencies. In other words, it is very easy for the trainer to set up an ad hoc training strategy with accompanying ad hoc performance measures and little guidance in terms of defining training objectives, identifying critical skills to be trained, developing valid performance measures that convey individual differences in the critical skills (and allow changes in the skills to be modeled over the course of training), and evaluating training effectiveness.

In an effort to provide such guidance, we propose a comprehensive measurement framework useful for guiding the development and evaluation of performance measures in adaptive, simulation-based training contexts (see Figure 16.1). Specifically, we define the criteria for a performance measurement framework and use it to provide specific principles and guidelines for the development and use of performance measures. The essential characteristic of performance measures conforming to this framework is that they support a *confirmatory* strategy to measuring and evaluating performance in adaptive training contexts, supporting sound inferences regarding hypothesized relationships among training objectives, performance episodes, and outcomes.

Similar representations of the training process, its phases, and the role of performance measures have been proposed in other research and development efforts. For example, Zachary, Cannon-Bowers, Bilazarian, Krecker, Lardieri, and Burns (1999) proposed a model of embedded training systems that describes the cycle through which (1) historical training data and job performance standards are combined to create performance objectives, (2) training objectives are used to script scenario events and derive performance measures, and (3) performance measures are used as the basis for performance diagnosis, feedback, and revision of trainee performance history. Our model augments and extends this framework. Within the proposed model, (1) knowledge, skills, abilities, and other personal characteristics (KSAOs) necessary for effective job performance are derived from job/task analytic data, rated on independent dimensions (e.g., importance and criticality), and linked empirically to specific tasks; (2) critical KSAOs are used to define performance standards and drive the development of performance measures embedded within scenario content; (3) performance standards are used to determine instructional objectives, which in turn are used to script and generate training scenarios with embedded performance measures; (4) observed performance on the embedded measures provides estimates of the underlying KSAOs represented by the measures; (5) performance standards and KSAO estimates jointly determine performance feedback and

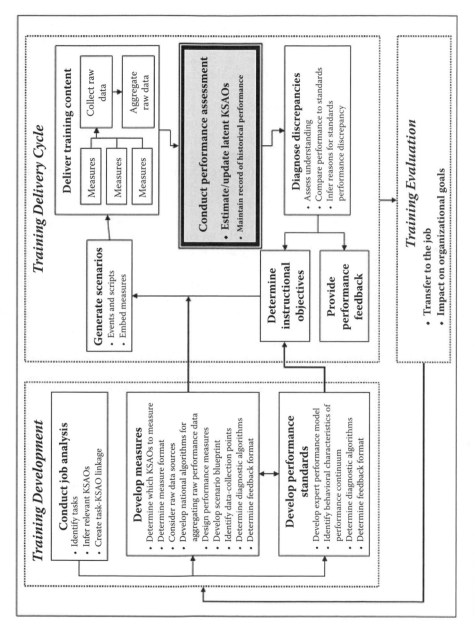

FIGURE 16.1   Performance measurement framework for simulation-based training.

subsequent training objectives; (6) revised training objectives drive the generation of new training content targeting deficient KSAOs; and (7) performance measures obtained throughout training are used to evaluate the training system itself, allowing inferences regarding transfer of training and providing feedback for new instructional methodologies.

A number of features of the framework should be noted. First, a feedback loop is integrated into the training delivery cycle portion of the model, emphasizing two critical notions: (1) performance measures are error-prone indicators of latent KSAOs, and (2) the training delivery cycle reflects an ideographic approach by iteratively assessing relevant KSAOs and strategically inserting scenario elements designed to evoke learning throughout training. We propose that KSAOs can be estimated indirectly via repeated performance measurement under changing scenario conditions. The confirmatory process of repeatedly exposing trainees to varying training content follows the logic of adaptive testing and allows for repeated, increasingly accurate measurements of latent KSAOs (Embretson and Reise, 2000). The resulting KSAO measurements drive subsequent generation of scenario content tailored to the learner's deficient KSAOs and permit the possibility of modeling performance changes throughout training. Second, the model emphasizes the complementary roles of deliberate practice and performance feedback. Performance feedback provides a mechanism for highlighting specific gaps in the learner's knowledge structure, correcting misconceptions, and guiding students through effective solutions to specific problems. However, we believe that a complementary mechanism should serve the express purpose of generating training content that targets specific skill deficiencies. SBT can provide such a capability by allowing for focused, deliberate practice within a realistic simulation environment, a necessary capability to support expert performance (Ericcson, Krampe, and Tesch-Römer, 1993). Although the focus of our discussion is on performance measurement issues in adaptive training, it should be noted that the same issues are relevant for the development of tailored feedback. Third, the model assumes that training content will be customized to target the KSAOs of a single trainee. This limitation stems from the fact that the theory and methods necessary to develop tailored training are still in early stages of development. Thus, it would be difficult to generate training content that is simultaneously tailored to the needs of multiple individuals, each with unique skill deficiencies, performing interdependent tasks in a team setting (although research has pointed to the potential use of intelligent agents to simulate the actions of teammates, resulting in a simulated team environment and allowing practice of critical teamwork behaviors (Zachary, Santorelli, Lyons, Bergondy, and Johnston, 2001).

DIMENSIONS AND ESSENTIAL CHARACTERISTICS OF PERFORMANCE MEASURES

Simulation-based training systems have been maturing at such a rapid rate that little attention has been directed toward identifying desirable characteristics of performance measures (Johnston et al., 2004). To address this gap, we identify six dimensions—validity, criterion relevance, reliability, measure invariance, objectivity and intrusiveness, and diagnosticity—along which performance measures in adaptive training systems can vary. This provides a basis for identifying desirable characteristics of performance measures and recommendations for improving measurement practices.

Validity

Performance measurement refers to the process through which behaviors observed within a job or training environment are translated into a summary statement of an individual's performance in the particular setting, providing the foundation for subsequent performance evaluation, management, or prediction. Performance measures are commonly referred to as *criteria* because they provide a basis for arriving at evaluative judgments about individual job performance and often serve as the dependent variable in validity research. The concept of a set of interrelated, observable behaviors that are relevant for accomplishing higher-order job or training objectives is consistent with the notion of a psychological construct, a conceptual term used heuristically to articulate, describe, and predict a set of related, covarying behaviors associated with a phenomenon of theoretical interest (e.g., intelligence, personality, anxiety, and expertise; Binning and Barrett, 1989; Cronbach and Meehl, 1955; Edwards and Bagozzi, 2000). A measure, in contrast, is an observed score recorded using some measurement method (e.g., self-report, interview, observation, and objective measurement) that represents an empirical analog of a construct (Edwards and Bagozzi, 2000).

Discussions of the difference between constructs and measures in the context of personnel selection, training, and performance appraisal, though limited, have distinguished between an ideal, hypothetical criterion construct (i.e., the domain of all behaviors important for attaining organizational, job, or training objectives), and the actual measures used to representatively sample this domain of behaviors (Binning and Barrett, 1989; Borman, 1991). Stated more precisely, the behavioral domain comprising the hypothetical criterion construct can be considered an expression of the collective KSAOs important for organizational, job, or training effectiveness, often derived from job/task analyses, and formalized in explicit training or learning objectives. However, despite the performance criterion/measure distinction, there is no explicit unifying model useful for articulating the meaning of the validity of a performance measure. Validity studies have emphasized the predictive, criterion-related validity of a selection system or training intervention, that is, the degree to which performance on a selection test or during training predicts subsequent real-world performance. Less attention has been paid, however, to what is meant by the validity of the criterion measure in and of itself.

Discussions of a measure's construct validity often invoke the idea of a nomological network, an expected pattern of relationships among constructs and between constructs and empirical observations (e.g., measures). Traditionally, evidence for a measure's construct validity has been provided in the form of significant correlations, with measures purporting to measure the same or similar construct (i.e., convergent validity), and nonsignificant correlations, with measures purporting to measure dissimilar constructs (i.e., discriminant validity). Such evidence can be derived using analytical techniques such as the multimethod-multitrait matrix (Campbell and Fiske, 1959), and the resulting pattern of relationships has been termed the *nomological network* for the target measure. The traditional approach to construct validity has focused primarily on the degree of empirical support for a nomological network and the resulting quality of the inferences that may be drawn from it (Cronbach and Meehl, 1955). However, reliance on a nomological network as a foundation for assessing the validity of a measure introduces a potential problem that may be especially pronounced with respect to the validity of performance measures, specifically, that the meaning of a construct and its measures emerge as a result of their configuration within the nomological network (Borsboom, Mellenbergh, and van Heerden, 2004). This introduces the tautological fallacy of using the network to implicitly define the constructs of which it is composed strictly in terms of their relationships with each other and without reference to theoretical terms (Borsboom et al., 2004).

An alternate view of validity, proposed by Borsboom and colleagues (2004), poses two criteria for a valid measure: (1) the construct exists in the real world, and (2) variations in the construct cause analogous variations in the measure. This view transfers the locus of evidence for validity from the observed relationships among measures to the response processes that convey the causal effect of a psychological construct on its measure (i.e., substantive validity; Messick, 1995). Consider measures used in the natural sciences—a common thermometer may be considered a "valid" measure of temperature because thermal energy exists in the ambient environment, which transfers the energy to the thermometer and causes the mercury to rise to a degree that depends completely on the amount of energy transferred. No allusion to a nomological network is necessary, because evidence for the validity of the instrument lies entirely in the causal sequence of events linking variations in the construct with variations in the measurement instrument.

This view has yet to gain traction within mainstream validity research, possibly as a result of the general lack of detailed theories of response processes associated with psychological constructs (Borsboom et al., 2004). We argue, however, that such a perspective is especially relevant to and necessary for the development of performance measures for adaptive, simulation-based training.

First, this conception of validity requires a detailed theory of response processes with respect to a set of KSAOs. That is, one must explicitly describe the behaviors associated with a given KSAO, and the specific behaviors that are indicative of various levels of effectiveness with respect to that KSAO. This constraint is often satisfied in simulation-based training and intelligent tutoring system research, because both require the articulation of an expert performance model that describes the ideal behavioral patterns to be expected with respect to critical KSAOs vis-à-vis the training scenario content. Thus, by adopting a detailed theory of response processes, users can maximize the diagnostic potential of SBT by articulating responses to scenario content that are associated with various effectiveness levels of specific KSAOs. Second, it may be difficult to "build" nomological networks for performance measures, that is, to predict relationships between the target measures and other measures that target similar and dissimilar constructs, which are useful for construct validity inferences. We believe this to be especially true because, ideally, performance measures should be developed to target specific, nonredundant sets of behaviors such that no two measures assess the same constructs. In such cases, a performance measure's nomological network would be composed exclusively of other measures with which one would not expect significant relationships. Third, it would be difficult to examine patterns of covariance among performance measures under dynamic scenario conditions because this could confound inferences regarding (1) the validity of the individual performance measures and (2) the effects of scenario modifications on changes in targeted KSAOs. Finally, researchers have noted the potential utility of response processes to support validation of measures assessing complex, multidimensional constructs (Ployhart, 2006). In order to understand whether a performance measure captures the latent construct it is designed to measure, one must understand the response processes associated with the underlying construct. This is especially true for complex constructs such as situational awareness, multitasking performance, dynamic workload management, and team communications assessed in adaptive, simulation-based training systems.

A validation strategy that considers the response processes associated with relevant KSAOs is likely to support the development and refinement of performance measures consistent with the proposed measurement framework. Valid performance measures accurately represent the latent KSAOs driving observable training performance by capturing essential KSAO-specific response processes. This allows for comparison of observed performance against theory-driven benchmarks of expert performance, accurate estimation of latent KSAOs, and fine-grained customization of subsequent training content.

Criterion Relevance

Another critical issue is the degree to which performance measures comprehensively, yet efficiently, capture the domain of behaviors they represent. This notion invokes the concepts of criterion relevance, deficiency, and contamination (Borman, 1991). Criterion relevance refers to the idea that performance measures should correspond to the actual performance demands of the training situation. Measures should accurately assess only the KSAOs they represent and not other, irrelevant sources of variance. Two potential problems that may compromise criterion relevance are criterion contamination and deficiency. Criterion contamination refers to the degree to which a performance measure taps variance unrelated to performance demands. Drawing from the DDSBE example, contamination might occur if one used an automated speech recognition capability to assess the quality of team communications but the program required users to memorize keywords not typically used in the training scenario in question. In this case, the measure tapped an irrelevant construct (i.e., working memory) rather than the intended construct (i.e., communication quality). Criterion deficiency occurs when a performance measure fails to sample important training behaviors. Deficiency might occur if one intended to measure the quality of the trainee's communications during a simulation but the scenario content was designed such that too few or only a limited variety of team communication opportunities were offered.

Although criterion relevance is implicitly defined as the absence of criterion contamination and deficiency, an additional consequence is enhanced parsimony and efficiency of measurement. A measurement strategy conforming to the proposed framework will include a suite of uncorrelated measures, each measuring a unique, relevant aspect of performance, that collectively provide a comprehensive, representative sample of the hypothetical criterion domain. Additionally, it is possible to maximize criterion relevance by ensuring that training objectives are based on thorough, accurate job analytic results. A comprehensive job analysis methodology will provide the blueprint detailing which KSAOs should be included in the training context, by providing empirical estimates of KSAO importance and task–KSAO linkages. Consequently, training objectives based on thorough job analysis results will help ensure that only relevant criteria are included in training scenarios.

Reliability

Adoption of a perspective in which performance measures are characterized as error-prone surrogates of a hypothetical performance domain encourages examination of the sources of unsystematic variance. In the language of classical test theory, validity usually refers to measurement accuracy, whereas reliability refers to consistency in measurement (e.g., consistency across test items, measurement intervals, or raters). The two concepts usually go hand in hand, emphasizing the notion that reliability is a necessary, but not sufficient, condition for validity. The logic underlying this notion is that measurement error in the form of unreliability must be minimized to assess the true magnitude of the statistical relationship between variables when provided as evidence for validity (Crocker and Algina, 1986; Nunnally, 1978). A related concept, method variance, refers to measurement error associated with using different methods to measure a construct, often in the context of construct validation (e.g., multitrait-multimethod matrices; Bagozzi and Yi, 1990; Coovert, Craiger, and Teachout, 1997).

In the context of adaptive, simulation-based performance measurement, a number of methodological issues challenge traditional notions of measurement error and methods of reliability assessment. Most importantly, method variance takes on new meaning for performance measures in adaptive training contexts, given the fact that individuals are observed in continuously changing measurement contexts, because the performance construct itself is changing. That is, the latent KSAOs represented by performance measures are expected to improve (hopefully) over the course of training, driving subsequent scenario modifications. Thus, the traditional conception of reliability as consistency across performance measures or measurement opportunities may not be sufficient as an indicator of measurement error in the context of adaptive training.

As with any performance measurement system, reliability is a prerequisite to validity. Classical test theory notions of internal consistency as reliability may be useful in adaptive training contexts if one could establish the dimensionality of the performance measures. However, this may be limited by the fact that the performance constructs of interest in adaptive training contexts are often complex and multidimensional. Additionally, test–retest reliability cannot be meaningfully computed when the latent construct influencing test scores changes over time (as with adaptive training). It is possible, however, to develop and test covariance structures (e.g., latent growth curve models) that model performance changes over time and allow for the inclusion of scenario events as time-varying covariates (Bollen and Curran, 2006). Such analyses may provide useful insight into how reliably performance measures are functioning across time and contexts. However, such analyses have intense statistical power requirements (highlighting the need for adequate numbers of subjects) and can be employed only when there are repeated opportunities to observe performance (reiterating the requirement for multiple observational opportunities).

Measure Invariance

According to the proposed measurement framework, one must observe a trainee's behavior across measurement contexts in order to make meaningful, reliable inferences about his or her latent

KSAOs. Given that adaptive training entails continuous modification of the training environment, an essential property of performance measures is the ability to assess critical training behaviors across a range of varying scenario content. Measure invariance refers to the degree to which performance measures retain their essential measurement properties and thus can be used to make meaningful comparisons across observations and under transient scenario contexts. Psychological measures usually contain multiple assessment items varying in content and along critical psychometric parameters (e.g., difficulty, discrimination). Consistent with the notion of a psychological construct as a theory of behavioral consistency over varying contexts (Cronbach and Meehl, 1955), the specific pattern of responses across items allows observation of behavioral consistency and, consequently, inference of the individual's standing on the latent construct (Embretson, 2006).

As Embretson (2006) has noted, in response to the ongoing search for nonarbitrary metrics in psychological research, a number of innovative psychometric theories and methodologies have emerged from the psychological and educational assessment domains. It is possible to draw from these theories and methods to develop performance measures that provide meaningful information about the performance construct across changing task or scenario conditions. Computerized adaptive testing, for example, is an assessment methodology that customizes the content and sequence of assessment items to the individual being assessed (Olson-Buchanan and Drasgow, 1999). A notable advantage of assessment methods such as computerized adaptive testing is the use of psychometric models derived from modern test theory (i.e., item response theory) to produce trait score estimates that do not depend on population distributions (Embretson and Reise, 2000). In contrast to traditional, normative assessment strategies, in which test scores are norm referenced via classical test theory analyses (Crocker and Algina, 1986), trait scores derived from adaptive tests gain meaning by direct comparison of estimated trait levels to item parameters (e.g., the item's difficulty level). This enhances diagnosticity and retains desirable psychometric properties of the test while reducing the length of test administrations, and allows meaningful performance comparisons across individuals who received different item sets.

The same standards are relevant for adaptive, simulation-based training. Use of normative performance scores (e.g., mean performance across a scenario) does not allow direct observation of what specific elements of a scenario influenced performance, and thus prevents unequivocal inferences of the individual's standing on the latent KSAO's driving performance. That is, it does not allow one to measure which specific aspects of the scenario posed the greatest level of difficulty for the trainee. The logic of modern test theory demands that test items be scaled according to their difficulty—test performance makes sense only after taking into account the difficulty levels of the specific items that were passed or failed. Analogously, one may scale scenario content according to its difficulty level, or more specifically, one may define the minimum level of the underlying skill the trainee must possess to successfully handle the demands of a specific scenario element. Subsequently, performance measures can be constructed around statistical models that allow aggregation of individual performance observations across performance episodes of varying difficulty. However, for performance measures to be useful in such a context, it would be necessary for them to sensitively capture critical behaviors across the spectrum of difficulty levels and across a wide range of scenario content. Similar endeavors have been attempted, with some evidence of success, to model learner performance in complex problem-solving domains, using item response theory and other probabilistic models, such as Bayesian networks (Embretson, 1997, 1998; Levy and Mislevy, 2004; Mislevy, 1995; Mislevy and Wilson, 1996; Pirolli and Wilson, 1998). Such a process, if applied to adaptive, simulation-based training would allow for a fine-grained analysis of how individuals respond to specific elements that comprise a scenario, address how behavioral responses correspond to specific skill sets or changes within an individual's knowledge structure, and support scenario generation that adaptively challenges deficient knowledge and skills.

Objectivity and Intrusiveness

Simulation-based training performance measures can differ according to their level of objectivity. Such differences may depend on characteristics of the simulation environment, which can range from realistic, immersive, and automated to artificial and contrived. The level of realism and automation inherent within the simulation can influence whether assessments can be performed passively from within the simulation environment or whether an external intervention is required to observe and record performance. The resulting degree of objectivity has implications for the quality of the inferences to be made regarding the latent KSAOs underlying observable performance. Whereas objective measures afford direct observation and measurement of specific behaviors useful for assessing and evaluating performance, subjective measures introduce an additional source of error variance in the form of rater error, potentially undermining the quality of the inferences to be drawn regarding an individual's performance (Borman, 1991; Landy and Farr, 1980). Additionally, obtrusive measures can create a source of criterion contamination by distracting the trainee's attention away from scenario content in order to attend to the performance measure.

It is possible to create opportunities for direct, naturalistic performance measurement when measures are embedded directly into the simulation environment. There is a current trend toward enhanced physical fidelity in simulations, enabling the development of more sophisticated representations of real-world scenarios in which the trainee is immersed with high levels of presence (Draper, Kaber, and Usher, 1998). Automated performance measures embedded in such systems are capable of passively recording critical behaviors without disrupting the training exercise. Often, it is possible to glean raw data (e.g., in DDSBE, the number of radar tracks engaged; the range, altitude or speed of engaged aircraft; and the accuracy of fired weapons) directly from the simulation environment. Such data, when aggregated in a meaningful way, can be used to form direct, unobtrusive performance measures. However, subjective measures are often needed to assess constructs such as situational awareness that are difficult to assess purely with raw performance data. In such cases, a combination of objective and subjective measures can be used to provide a more comprehensive portrayal of performance effectiveness, as is the case with DDSBE. However, this could introduce a number of additional measurement challenges, including the identification of highly skilled subject matter experts (SMEs) to serve as raters, intensive SME training to ensure accurate, reliable ratings of behaviors that often reflect highly specialized skills, and difficulties in attending to all relevant performance information using traditional subjective measurement techniques, potentially leading to criterion deficiency. Use of multiple raters combined with intensive rater training, behaviorally based performance measures, and stringent interrater agreement and reliability criteria can help mitigate such difficulties.

Diagnosticity

Simulation-based training measures can differ further according to their capabilities for translating raw performance information into assessment information useful for diagnosing skill deficits. In some training contexts, a single performance measure can be used as an indicator of the trainee's standing on the latent KSAO it represents (e.g., number of algebra problems completed correctly as a measure of mathematical ability). Such measures are termed *reflective* in that they reflect or represent the manifestation of a single construct. Often, however, we are interested in constructs that represent the composite of multiple component variables. Measures for such constructs are termed *formative,* given that the construct is formed or induced by its measures (Edwards and Bagozzi, 2000). Formative measures are increasingly common in simulation-based training environments because they are commonly used to target more complex constructs, such as situational awareness, teamwork skills, multitasking ability, and communication effectiveness—constructs formed by aggregating measures of more basic constructs (e.g., working memory, performance on a single task dimension, and attention to a single visual/auditory stimulus).

A critical issue with respect to diagnosticity is the extent to which performance measures, whether reflective or formative, provide insights regarding *why* an individual is performing at a suboptimal level. Measures that allow comparison of patterns of responses to a theoretical model of response processes, that is, measures conforming to the Borsboom et al. (2004) validity framework outlined earlier, are likely to be useful from a diagnostic standpoint. Such measures support inferences regarding an individual's skill deficiencies by virtue of the observed pattern of responses. Thus, a measure that is "valid" in terms of its ability to capture KSAO-specific response processes is also likely to be diagnostic. A second issue with respect to diagnosticity is the fact that the use of purely aggregate measures without attention to the composite measures of which they are formed could confound diagnostic inferences. Aggregate measures are useful in adaptive training contexts by providing a summary index of the complex variety of behaviors that occur within the simulation. However, the individual measures of which an aggregate measure is composed can reflect unique constructs or rater perspectives. Aggregation treats meaningful variance associated with unique perspectives or constructs as measurement error, introducing a form of aggregation bias (James, 1982; Morgeson and Campion, 2000; Sanchez and Levine, 2000) and rendering difficult the drawing of inferences regarding why a deficient score on an individual performance measure was observed. Thus, aggregate measures may not provide the diagnostic precision necessary to customize training content to target skill deficiencies. In such cases, aggregate measures may be more useful for providing performance feedback to trainees, whereas narrower, individual performance measures may be necessary for structuring adaptive training content.

MEASUREMENT PRINCIPLES FOR ADAPTIVE TRAINING

In Table 16.1 we summarize the critical dimensions of performance measures, their associated challenges with respect to the proposed confirmatory measurement framework, and the desirable characteristics of measures along each dimension. The primary challenge with respect to validity is to articulate a model of response processes and ensure that the measures are capable of capturing critical responses as specified by the model. With respect to criterion relevance, the challenge is to minimize criterion contamination and deficiency as potential sources of measurement error. For reliability, the challenge is to hypothesize a model of behavioral consistency across scenario contexts and to model changes in the latent KSAOs over time. For measurement invariance, the challenge is to develop performance measures that provide meaningful, interpretable metrics across performance contexts. For objectivity and intrusiveness, the challenge is to employ a measurement strategy that does not interfere with performance and to integrate objective measures with different loci of assessment into a coherent suite of measures. For the diagnosticity dimension, the challenge is to meaningfully aggregate raw performance data into a summary index useful for performance assessment and subsequent diagnosis and scenario modifications.

In addition to the specific guidelines provided for each dimension, we offer an additional set of more general principles relevant for the effective application of performance measures in adaptive training contexts, which are as follows: (1) ensure that performance measure development is guided by a sound theoretical framework, (2) identify and exploit measurement affordances of the adaptive training environment, and (3) consider training evaluation strategies early in the performance measure development process.

PRINCIPLE #1: ENSURE THAT PERFORMANCE MEASURE DEVELOPMENT IS GUIDED BY SOUND THEORY

We believe that the primary ingredient for sound performance measures is grounding in a sound theoretical framework. Substantial theory development in the areas of learning, skill acquisition,

TABLE 16.1
Strategies for Addressing Performance Measurement Challenges

Performance Measure Dimension	Challenges	Measurement Strategies
Validity: The degree to which a performance measure accurately represents a performance construct in the real world (i.e., the latent KSAOs driving observable performance), and variations in the construct cause analogous variations in the measure (i.e., essential KSAO-specific response processes; Borsboom et al., 2004)	• Articulate a model of response processes and ensure measures are capable of capturing critical responses as specified by the model	1. Ensure measures are sensitive to subtle variations in the latent KSAOs driving observable performance, capturing behavioral patterns corresponding to different levels of the latent KSAOs 2. Employ specific performance benchmarks derived from theory-driven expectations about "expert" or optimal performance (e.g., expert performance model)
Criterion relevance: The degree to which the domain of behavior is captured by performance measures	• Minimize criterion contamination and deficiency as potential sources of measurement error	1. Ensure measures comprehensively, accurately, and parsimoniously sample the criterion domain 2. Map measures directly to specific training objectives guided by real-world performance demands (e.g., derived from job/task analyses)
Reliability: The degree to which measurement is consistent across context, raters, and time. Method variance: Variance that is due to using different methods, e.g., observation, multiple raters, self-report	• Hypothesize a model of behavioral consistency across scenario contexts • Model changes in the latent KSAOs over time	1. Ensure repeated performance measurements across multiple observational opportunities 2. Assess internal consistency reliability when the dimensionality of the measures can be established 3. Assess reliability within a latent growth curve modeling approach that incorporates the presence or absence of scenario content as time-varying covariates; ensure adequate levels of statistical power
Measure invariance: The degree to which performance measures provide invariant measurements across transient scenario contexts	• Develop performance measures that provide meaningful, interpretable metrics across performance contexts	1. Use modern test theory as a psychometric framework to scale scenario content according to its difficulty level 2. Ensure performance measures are sensitive to critical behaviors across a wide range of scenario content and difficulty levels
Measure objectivity: The degree to which the measure allows direct versus indirect observation and measurement of specific behaviors. Intrusiveness: The degree to which the trainee is made aware of the measurement process	• Employ a measurement strategy that does not interfere with performance • Integrate objective/subjective measures with different loci of assessment into a coherent suite of measures	1. Use automated, embedded performance measures based on raw or aggregated data that can be obtained directly from simulation environment 2. Combine subjective measures, when it is necessary to use them, with objective measures 3. Employ multiple raters, rater training, behaviorally based performance measures, and stringent interrater agreement and reliability criteria when subjective rater judgments are necessary
Diagnosticity: The process of translating raw performance data into assessment information	• Meaningfully aggregate raw performance data into a summary index useful for performance assessment and subsequent diagnosis and scenario modifications	1. Adopt a validity model that considers response processes 2. Ensure that performance measures have the necessary precision to make diagnostic inferences; use aggregate measures mainly for performance feedback, and narrower, individual measures as a basis for structuring training content

practice, cognitive modeling, and psychometrics has resulted in robust, detailed theories useful for guiding training designs. The decision to customize training content or feedback delivery, automate aspects of scenario generation or performance measurement, or vary the pacing, content, or sequencing of training content should have a clearly defined theoretical rationale drawn from these lines of research. This body of knowledge will be useful for articulating how specific training interventions will influence immediate learning and performance as well as long-term retention and transfer performance.

Individualized instruction in the form of adaptive training and intelligent tutoring systems has a growing theoretical and empirical research base supporting its effectiveness. A major stimulus for this research base emerged from theorizing on the concept of aptitude-treatment interactions (ATIs), which suggest that instructional interventions are effective to the extent they meet the individual needs of the learner (Cronbach and Snow, 1981; Snow and Lohman, 1984; Snow, 1994). Research on ATIs has revealed that the effectiveness of instruction is influenced by specific individual differences, endorsing an idealized model for instruction in which instructional events are customized to challenge, accommodate, or adapt to a given learner's unique skills (Snow, 1994; Snow and Lohman, 1984). This line of research provides a useful theoretical lens for developing adaptive training content and performance measures. The notion that individuals experience the training environment differently depending on latent ability levels suggests that it is possible to systematically measure the latent abilities underlying performance, model their changes throughout training, and customize training to these evolving ability levels using adaptive instruction. Thus, it is possible to consider adaptive training as a tool for inducing a continuous sequence of ATIs throughout training, thereby providing a consistently high level of challenge without compromising motivation or overwhelming the trainee.

The research literature on ATIs emphasizes characteristics of instructional conditions that could differentially influence learning, depending on skills and abilities unique to the learner. Indeed, an early application of ATIs was to inform selection for training or instruction, an application based on the tenuous assumption that the latent skills and abilities underlying training performance remained stable during training. ATI research effectively cast training performance as a *between-subjects* phenomenon—some training interventions are effective for a subpopulation of individuals with certain levels of a requisite skill, whereas other interventions are more effective for other, more or less skilled subpopulations. However, a critical element of adaptive training, as implied by the cyclical representation of training delivery in the proposed measurement framework, is the ability to customize instructional content, and thus model the effects of instruction on a single individual over time. This can complement ATI research by providing the *within-subjects* perspective needed to describe and predict how an individual learner's performance (as an indicator of the latent KSAOs that are being targeted during training) varies throughout training (Alliger and Katzman, 1997).

Research addressing individual patterns of progress through distinct cognitive stages during the learning process can provide additional insight into the mechanisms underlying ATIs (Embretson, 1997; Schoenfeld, Smith, and Arcavi, 1993). Often, the performance changes that occur when learning a complex task do not reflect a single, unitary "instance" of learning. Instead, individuals frequently experience a series of learning events in which they demonstrate effective problem solving after experiencing impasses that emerge in the task environment (Annett, 1991; Van Lehn, 1996). A learning event corresponds to the discovery of a problem's solution after the learner experienced errors or difficulties. Impasses signal faults in the learner's knowledge structures, prompting the learner to divert attention from problem solving to the discovery of new knowledge and questions about domain knowledge itself (Van Lehn, 1996). Paralleling the ATI literature, research has indicated that the nature and timing of learning events depend on idiosyncratic experiences with impasses and on levels of stable individual differences in the requisite KSAOs relevant for learning (Ackerman, 1987; Campbell and DiBello, 1996; Ohlsson, 1996; Seifert and Hutchins, 1992; Snow, 1994).

These theoretical notions hint enticingly at the possibility of structuring adaptive training content to control the occurrence of learning events or to induce a sequence of ATIs throughout training. It is possible to recast the concept of ATIs as a deliberate product of training rather than as an unyielding framework for training assignments, and learning events as a deliberate outcome of training rather than as a chance phenomenon confined to basic cognitive research. However, a critical contingency in applying such promising theoretical concepts to training design is that performance measures must be designed to capture these elusive phenomena, both of which represent, ultimately, subjective experiences (Schoenfeld et al., 1993; Van Lehn, 1996). This emphasizes the key issue that performance measurement is instrumental for the translation of theory into training design. Valid performance measures will be sensitive to response processes indicative of targeted KSAOs, and models of response processes can only be constructed within the framework of a specific theory of learning.

Principle #2: Consider and Exploit Measurement Affordances

Considerable variability exists in the types of performance domains for which adaptive training has been developed and, consequently, in the scenario-generation methods and simulation content used to represent these domains. As stated earlier, whereas a general challenge of job performance measurement efforts has been to identify and exploit objective performance measurement opportunities, the challenge for simulation-based performance measurement has been to reduce the abundance of objective data into meaningful diagnostic patterns. This challenge is complicated further by the need to articulate and test relationships among training interventions, the psychological constructs targeted during training, and observable performance.

The event-based training approach offered a promising solution to these challenges by incorporating "trigger events" into scenario content (Dwyer et al., 1997; Fowlkes et al., 1998). Responses to these events served as indicators of the individual's standing on the relevant skill being trained. This logic provides an interesting parallel to the domain of computerized assessment. As mentioned earlier, computerized adaptive testing is an assessment method that provides iterative estimation of the targeted KSAO (Olson-Buchanan and Drasgow, 1999). Computerized adaptive testing uses the individual's responses to initial test items to provide hypothetical estimates of the underlying ability level. Subsequent items are selected on the basis of the likelihood of their providing additional diagnostic information about the underlying ability, considering both initial ability estimates and item parameters (e.g., item difficulty and discrimination; Embretson and Reise, 2000). This form of testing relies on the logic that assessments represent a form of experimentation in which test items (representing the independent variable) elicit cumulative information about some underlying trait (the dependent variable) that influences test behavior (Embretson and Reise, 2000).

This perspective is equally applicable to simulation-based training research. Initial formulation of the event-based approach treated scenario content as an instrument for embedding individual trigger events. In the context of adaptive training, however, it is possible to reconceptualize the scenario as a palette for generating a continuous stream of simulation-based assessment content useful for iterative estimation of latent skills and subsequent scenario generation. Simulation-based training scenarios are often scripted with the primary objective of realistically recreating real-world tasks or problems. Assessment content is often an afterthought in such a model, and trainers are left to force assessment opportunities out of the resulting scenario content. However, one can maximize the assessment potential of the simulation-based training environment by considering its measurement affordances in advance, and by developing scenario content around these affordances.

Several additional lines of assessment research may provide specific guidance for exploiting the measurement affordances and realizing the assessment potential of the simulation environment. One assessment method—situational judgment tests (SJTs)—provides descriptions of problem situations likely to be experienced in the task environment along with potential solutions ranging in effectiveness as response options. SJTs purport to measure the trainees' expectations of the effectiveness of different performance options, given realistic task cues, essentially treating the quality of these expectations as an indicator of expertise (Chan and Schmitt, 2002). The parallels between SJTs and simulation-based training are obvious; indeed, SJTs were developed as a low-fidelity alternative to more sophisticated assessments at a time when limited computing and simulation capabilities prevented higher-fidelity assessments. It is possible now, however, to draw from SJT methods to develop simulation-based versions of SJT items to make use of the measurement opportunities afforded by SBT.

An additional area of research, on the measurement construct of a "time window," provides useful guidance for measuring and assessing performance in light of the opportunities for trainee actions offered by the simulation task (Rothrock, 2001). A time window is a measurement construct useful for decomposing simulation content according to which specific activities can be performed within a given period of time. For example, in the air defense warfare domain, the presence of task cues (e.g., three unknown radar tracks on the radar screen) and the actions of one team member (e.g., the Air Intercept Coordinator illuminating one track as hostile) can engage a window of opportunity for another team member to perform a variety of actions differing in their effectiveness (e.g., ignore or engage the track). The time window defines the time period bounded by the emergence of cues or operator actions that constrain performance and the execution of some action by the target performer. The development of the time window as a formal measurement construct is based on the premise that a functional relationship exists between action constraints and time availability, a notion grounded further in the theory of situated cognition (Greeno, 1994; Hutchins, 1995; Lave, 1988). By explicitly defining operational and time constraints on performance, the time window construct is likely to be a useful tool for (1) reducing vast amounts of objective simulation data and (2) allowing useful inferences on the meaning of performance in light of task constraints, supporting the confirmatory measurement framework described previously.

A third line of inquiry revolves around research on mathematical modeling of human performance (Campbell and Bolton, 2005; Campbell, Buff, and Bolton, in press; Dorsey and Coovert, 2003). This research focuses on the development of formal mathematical models of human behavior with respect to situational cues and action affordances of the simulation environment. Typically, the mathematical model specifies the relationship between terms reflecting aspects of the environment (e.g., presence or absence of specific cues) and some aspect of performance (e.g., decision making). Recent efforts have compared the effectiveness of various mathematical modeling techniques (e.g., fuzzy logic, multiple regression) and have applied mathematical modeling specifically to the development of customized feedback in simulation-based training (Campbell and Bolton, 2005; Dorsey and Coovert, 2003). Use of mathematical modeling techniques to drive adaptive scenario generation and performance measurement would be a natural extension for this research. Specifically, because mathematical models reflect explicit, quantitative hypotheses about performance under different situational cues, they provide a mechanism for developing expert performance models as a basis for assessing and diagnosing individual performance.

Principle #3: Ensure Usefulness of Measures for Evaluating Training Effectiveness

A final guideline concerns the training and transfer validity of the simulation-based training system as a whole. Ideally, performance measures will allow assessment of performance vis-à-vis specific training objectives, which should reflect real-world performance demands and be derived from job/task analyses. However, a potential limiting factor in the usefulness of performance measures for evaluating training effectiveness is the fact that simulations are often used strictly for training and seldom for generating on-the-job performance criteria. There is often a disconnect in the strategies used to assess simulation-based training performance and those used to assess on-the-job performance. The former often employs finer-grained, objective measures, whereas the latter often uses broader, subjective measures (e.g., supervisor or multisource ratings). The resulting difference in the levels of analysis could limit the magnitude of the training validity coefficients that were observed to be useful for evaluating training effectiveness.

Use of performance measures consistent with the measurement framework described earlier (e.g., invariant to changing scenario contexts) may prove useful as a foundation for evaluating training effectiveness. Performance assessed using scenario-invariant measures takes on evaluative meaning only after considering the difficulty of the scenario content in which performance was observed. Thus, this framework allows for experimental manipulation of the difficulty levels of various situational elements to address how these elements influence immediate and long-term learning and performance. For example, assessment research suggests that highly discriminating test items with moderate (e.g., 50%) difficulty levels give the most diagnostic information about a person's actual trait level. The proposed framework allows for analogous research to address how situational parameters influence performance in the context of training, as well as training evaluation research to support inferences regarding long-term outcomes.

SUMMARY AND CONCLUSION

The purpose of this chapter is to describe the role of performance measurement in adaptive, simulation-based training contexts in light of emerging technological and methodological innovations. We have presented criteria for a confirmatory measurement framework to emphasize the necessity of sound performance measurement as the foundation for automated, adaptive training content and feedback delivery in simulation-based training. Additionally, we have identified a number of dimensions along which performance measures can vary and the desirable characteristics of performance measures along each dimension to support the criteria for confirmatory performance measurement.

Performance measures that conform to this framework are likely to provide high utility as a result of their diagnosticity, objectivity, unintrusiveness, comprehensiveness, and efficiency. However, perhaps the greatest advantage of implementing such measures is the ability to draw sound, causal inferences regarding relationships among scenario content, the latent psychological constructs targeted during training, and observable performance. The use of "valid" performance measures— that is, measures capable of transmitting the causal influence of the latent performance construct on observable performance—provide a necessary foundation for adaptive scenario modifications useful for iteratively assessing and correcting deficient skills as they change over the course of training. One effect of the rapid evolution of simulation-based training systems has been the tendency to resort to ad hoc measurement strategies to reduce the large amounts of objective performance data resulting from these systems. We believe that this measurement framework provides a useful set of specific, quantifiable standards to counteract this trend, providing a key mechanism for improving long-term learning and retention.

REFERENCES

Ackerman, P. L., 1987. Individual differences in skill learning: An integration of psychometric and information processing perspectives. *Psychological Bulletin, 102,* 3–27.

Alliger, G. M., & Katzman, S., 1997. When training affects variability: Beyond the assessment of mean differences in training evaluation. In Ford, J. K., Kozlowski, S. W. J., Kraiger, K., Salas, E., & Teachout, M. S., (Eds.), *Improving training effectiveness in work organizations* (pp. 223–246). Mahwah, NJ: Lawrence Erlbaum Associates.

Annett, J., 1991. Skill acquisition. In Morrison, J. E. (Ed.), *Training for performance: Principles for applied human learning* (pp. 13–52). Chichester, England: John Wiley and Sons.

Bagozzi, R. P., & Yi, Y., 1990. Assessing method variance in multitrait-multimethod matrices: The case of self-reported affect and perceptions at work. *Journal of Applied Psychology, 75,* 547–560.

Binning, J. F., & Barrett, G. V., 1989. Validity of personnel decisions: A conceptual analysis of the inferential and evidential bases. *Journal of Applied Psychology, 74,* 478–494.

Bollen, K. A., & Curran, P. J., 2006. *Latent curve models: A structural equation perspective.* Hoboken, NJ: John Wiley and Sons.

Borman, W. C., 1991. Job behavior, performance, and effectiveness. In Dunnette, M. D., & Hough, L. M. (Eds.), *Handbook of industrial and organizational psychology: Vol. 2* (2nd ed., pp. 271–326). Palo Alto, CA: Consulting Psychologists Press.

Borsboom, D., Mellenbergh, G. J., & van Heerden, J., 2004. The concept of validity. *Psychological Review, 111,* 1061–1071.

Campbell, D. T., & Fiske, D. W., 1959. Convergent and discriminant validation by the multitrait-multimethod matrix. *Psychological Bulletin, 56,* 81–105.

Campbell, G. E., & Bolton, A. E., 2005. HBR validation: Integrating lessons learned from multiple academic disciplines, applied communities, and the AMBR project. In Gluck, K. A., & Pew, R. W. (Eds.), *Modeling human behavior with integrated cognitive architectures: Comparison, evaluation, and validation* (pp. 365–396). Mahwah, NJ: Lawrence Erlbaum Associates.

Campbell, G. E., Buff, W. L., & Bolton, A. E., (in press). Viewing training through a fuzzy lens. In Kirlik, A. (Ed.), *Adaptation in human-technology interaction: Methods, models, and measures.* Oxford, England: Oxford University Press.

Campbell, R. L., & DiBello, L., 1996. Studying human expertise: Beyond the binary paradigm. *Journal of Theoretical and Experimental Artificial Intelligence, 8,* 277–293.

Chan, D., & Schmitt, N., 2002. Situational judgment and job performance. *Human Performance, 15,* 233–254.

Coovert, M. D., Craiger, J. P., & Teachout, M. S., 1997. Effectiveness of the direct product versus confirmatory factor model for reflecting the structure of multimethod-multirater job performance data. *Journal of Applied Psychology, 82,* 271–280.

Crocker, L., & Algina, J., 1986. *Introduction to classical and modern test theory.* New York: Holt, Rinehart, and Winston.

Cronbach, L. J., & Meehl, P. E., 1955. Construct validity in psychological tests. *Psychological Bulletin, 52,* 281–302.

Cronbach, L. J., & Snow, R. E., 1981. *Aptitudes and instructional methods: A handbook for research on interactions.* New York: Irvington.

Dorsey, D. W., & Coovert, M. D., 2003. Mathematical modeling of decision making: A soft and fuzzy approach to capturing hard decisions [Special issue]. *Human Factors, 45,* 117–135.

Draper, J. V., Kaber, D. B., & Usher, J. M., 1998. Telepresence. *Human Factors, 40,* 354–375.

Dwyer, D. J., Fowlkes, J. E., Oser, R. L., & Lane, N. E., 1997. Team performance measurement in distributed environments: The TARGETs methodology. In Brannick, M. T., Salas, E., & Prince, C., (Eds.), *Team performance assessment and measurement: Theory, methods, and applications* (pp. 137–154). Hillsdale, NJ: Lawrence Erlbaum Associates.

Edwards, J. R., & Bagozzi, R. P., 2000. On the nature and direction of relationships between constructs and measures. *Psychological Methods, 5,* 155–174.

Embretson, S. E., 1997. Multicomponent item response models. In Van der Linden, W. J., & Hambleton, R. K. (Eds.), *Handbook of modern item response theory* (pp. 305–322). New York: Springer-Verlag.

Embretson, S. E., 1998. A cognitive design system approach for generating valid tests: Approaches to abstract reasoning. *Psychological Methods, 3,* 300–396.

Embretson, S. E., 2006. The continued search for nonarbitrary metrics in psychology. *American Psychologist, 61,* 50–55.

Embretson, S. E., & Reise, S. P., 2000. *Item response theory for psychologists.* Mahwah, NJ: Lawrence Erlbaum Associates.

Ericcson, K. A., Krampe, R. T., & Tesch-Römer, C., 1993. The role of deliberate practice in the acquisition of expert performance. *Psychological Review, 100,* 363–406.

Everson, H. T., 1995. Modeling the student in intelligent tutoring systems: The promise of new psychometrics. *Instructional Science, 23,* 433–452.

Fowlkes, J. E., Dwyer, D. J., Oser, R. L., & Salas, E., 1998. Event-based approach to training (EBAT). *International Journal of Aviation Psychology, 8,* 209–221.

Greeno, J. G., 1994. Gibson's affordances. *Psychological Review, 101,* 336–342.

Hutchins, E., 1995. How a cockpit remembers its speeds. *Cognitive Science, 19,* 265–288.

James, L. R., 1982. Aggregation bias in estimates of perceptual agreement. *Journal of Applied Psychology, 67,* 219–229.

Johnston, J. H., 2005. Methods for assessing and debriefing team and multiteam performance in distributed simulation-based training. Symposium presented at the 49th Annual Conference of the Human Factors and Ergonomics Society, Orlando, FL.

Johnston, J. H., Radtke, P. H., Van Duyne, L., Stretton, M., Freeman, J., & Bilazarian, P., 2004. Team training in distributed simulation based exercises. *Proceedings of the Human Factors and Ergonomics Society 48th Annual Meeting* [CD-ROM, pp. 2557–2561]. Santa Monica, CA.

Landy, F. J., & Farr, J. L., 1980. Performance rating. *Psychological Bulletin, 87,* 72–107.

Lave, J., 1988. *Cognition in practice: Mind, mathematics and culture in everyday life.* Cambridge: Cambridge University Press.

Levy, R., & Mislevy, R. J., 2004. Specifying and refining a measurement model for a computer-based interactive assessment. *International Journal of Testing, 4,* 333–369.

Mangos, P. M., 2004. A psychometric framework for intelligent scenario generation. In Buff, W. L., & Campbell, G. E. (Chairs), *Expanding and Incorporating Approaches from Traditional Intelligent Tutoring Systems into Scenario-Based Training Systems.* Symposium presented at the 48th Annual Conference of the Human Factors and Ergonomics Society, New Orleans, LA.

Messick, S., 1995. Validity of psychological assessment. *American Psychologist, 50,* 741–749.

Mislevy, R., 1995. Probability-based inference in cognitive diagnosis. In Nichols, P., Chipman, S., & Brennan, R. (Eds.), *Cognitively diagnostic assessment* (pp. 43–71). Hillsdale, NJ: Lawrence Erlbaum Associates.

Mislevy, R. J., & Wilson, M., 1996. Marginal maximum likelihood estimation for a psychometric model of discontinuous development. *Psychometrika, 61,* 41–71.

Morgeson, F. P., & Campion, M. A., 2000. Accuracy in job analysis: Toward an inference-based model. *Journal of Organizational Behavior, 21,* 819–827.

Nunnally, J. C., 1978. *Psychometric theory.* New York: McGraw-Hill.

Ohlsson, S., 1996. Learning from performance errors. *Psychological Review, 103,* 241–262.

Olson-Buchanan, J. B., & Drasgow, F., 1999. Beyond bells and whistles: An introduction to computerized assessment. In Olson-Buchanan, J. B., & Drasgow, F. (Eds.), *Innovations in computerized assessment* (pp. 1–6). Mahwah, NJ: Lawrence Erlbaum Associates.

Pirolli, P., & Wilson, M., 1998. A theory of the measurement of knowledge content, access, and learning. *Psychological Review, 105,* 58–82.

Ployhart, R. E., 2006. The predictor response process model. In Weekly, J. A., & Ployhart, R. E. (Eds.), *Situational judgment tests: Theory, measurement, and application* (pp. 83–106). Mahwah, NJ: Lawrence Erlbaum Associates.

Rothrock, L., 2001. Using time windows to evaluate operator performance. *International Journal of Cognitive Ergonomics, 5,* 1–21.

Sanchez, J. I., & Levine, E. L., 2000. Accuracy or consequential validity: Which is the better standard for job analysis data? *Journal of Organizational Behavior, 21,* 809–818.

Schoenfeld, A. H., Smith, J. P., & Arcavi, A., 1993. Learning: The microgenetic analysis of one student's evolving understanding of a complex subject matter domain. In Glaser, R. (Ed.), *Advances in instructional psychology* (Vol. 4, pp. 55–177). Hillsdale, NJ: Lawrence Erlbaum Associates.

Seifert, C. M., & Hutchins, E. L., 1992. Error as opportunity: Learning in a cooperative task. *Human-Computer Interaction, 7,* 409–435.

Smith, E. M., Ford, J. K., & Kozlowski, S. W. J., 1997. Building adaptive expertise: Implications for training design. In Quinones, M. A., & Dudda, A. (Eds.), *Training for a rapidly changing workplace: Applications of psychological research* (pp. 89–115). Washington D.C.: APA Books.

Snow, R. E., 1994. Abilities in academic tasks. In Sternberg, R. J., & Wagner, R. K. (Eds.), *Mind in context: Interactionist perspectives on human intelligence.* Cambridge: Cambridge University Press.

Snow, R. E., & Lohman, D. F., 1984. Toward a theory of cognitive aptitude for learning from instruction. *Journal of Educational Psychology, 76,* 347–376.

Steele-Johnson, D., & Hyde, B. G., 1997. Advanced technologies in training: Intelligent tutoring systems and virtual reality. In Quinones, M. A., & Ehrenstein, A. (Eds.), *Training for a rapidly changing workplace: Applications of psychological research* (pp. 225–248). Washington D.C.: American Psychological Association.

Van Lehn, K., 1996. Cognitive skill acquisition. *Annual Review of Psychology, 47,* 513–53.

Zachary, W., Cannon-Bowers, J., Bilazarian, P., Krecker, D., Lardieri, P., & Burns, J., 1999. The Advanced Embedded Training System (AETS): An intelligent embedded tutoring system for tactical team training. *International Journal of Artificial Intelligence in Education, 10,* 257–277.

Zachary, W., Santorelli, T., Lyons, D., Bergondy, M., & Johnston, J. H., 2001. Using a community of intelligent synthetic entities to support operational team training. In *Proceedings of the Computer Generated Forces Conference* [CD-ROM], Orlando, FL.

17 Decision Making under Crisis Conditions

A Training and Simulation Perspective

Tiffany Nickens, Dahai Liu, and Dennis A. Vincenzi

CONTENTS

INTRODUCTION

Humans make decisions every day. These range from life-planning decisions, such as whether to take a job after college or go to graduate school, to quotidian decisions about what to eat for lunch. Decision making is a task in which "a person must select one option from a number of alternatives" with "some amount of information available" and under the influence of "time frame" and context uncertainty (Wickens, Lee, Liu, and Becker, 2004). For decisions such as what to eat for lunch, humans can take enough time to consider all the available options, and even if a bad decision is made, the consequence is not significant. Unfortunately, this is not the case when making a decision during a crisis. Decision making in a crisis situation involves time stress and uncertain information and can be an issue of life or death, such as navigating an airplane through severe weather or deciding when to deploy a parachute if the airplane malfunctions in such a situation. Indeed, as Orasanu and Connolly (1993) noted, for crisis decision making, "the stakes are often high and the effects on lives are likely to be significant."

    A crisis can best be described as a "rare and unique" event (Sniezek, Wilkins, and Wadlington, 2001), bringing with it an "unexpected, life-threatening, and time-compressed" (McKinney, 1993) sequence of events. The characteristics of a crisis include the following (Sniezek et al., 2001):

- Uncertainty—Not understanding enough about the event or situation to know how to carry out an appropriate action or to know what the corresponding outcome(s) of that action would be.
- Threat to property/life—A chance that possessions and/or human life "could be lost, or soon will be" (Sniezek et al., 2001).

- Quick occurrence—Resulting effects of crisis quickly spread out to other areas (i.e., panic, supplies shortage, potential for violence, etc.). Immediate actions are critical in restricting the magnitude of damage.
- Uncontrollability—Many of the crisis' outcomes can be "partially influenced" (Sniezek et al., 2001), but not completely controlled.

These characteristics make coherent decision making under crisis nearly impossible. Nevertheless, even during this time of uncertainty, high stress levels, and time pressure, the individual or team knows that "not making a decision is not an option" (Flin and Arbuthnot, 2002). One individual or all people involved must take control of the situation and not only prevent it from getting worse, but not "fan the flames" either. This set of actions is known as *crisis management.* As Sniezek et al. (2001) explain, crisis management can be compared to risk management, only the situation is "real, not potential." Good and accurate decision making under time pressure and uncertainty is what makes crisis management effective. In this chapter, we will summarize the research findings in this area. Firstly, we will briefly highlight some of the background information on time stress and uncertainty, particularly the effect they have on decision makers. This will be followed by decision-making theories as related to crisis decision making. In the final section, we will discuss the training and simulation issues for crisis decision making.

EFFECTS OF TIME STRESS AND UNCERTAINTY ON DECISION MAKING

Research has shown that time pressure can reduce the quality of decision making because limited time is available for thinking through various possible actions (Edland and Svenson, 1993; Maule, Hockey, and Bdzola, 2000). Time pressure as a task characteristic has different meanings for different tasks. Some researchers use the terms *time urgency* or *time stress* (Rastegary and Landy, 1993) and *time window* (Rothrock, 2001). Time urgency refers to an accelerated pace of activities that results from striving to finish more and more tasks in a decreasing period of time, whereas time pressure is defined as "the difference between the amount of time available and the amount of the time required to solve the task" (Rastegary and Landy, 1993). In most cases, crisis decision making requires humans to respond within an appropriate time interval. For example, pilots must decide whether to proceed or turn back when encountering severe weather conditions. Such decisions should be made within the appropriate time window—neither too early, nor too late (Rothrock, 2001). As a result, the decision maker must decide what actions to take within a finite amount of time, as well as determine when to implement the chosen actions (Brehmer, 1992).

As for uncertainty, many definitions exist. Related terms include *vagueness, incompleteness, ambiguity, conflict,* and *randomness* (Davis and Hall, 2003). Definitions can be classified into two categories: (1) the variability of a given situation and (2) the characteristics of information regarding the situation (Rastegary and Landy, 1993). Thus, in human decision making, uncertainty can be characterized as the unknown probability (or likelihood) of a possible outcome (Busemeyer, 1985) or the lack of complete information on which to base a decision (e.g., where an incoming hurricane is likely to make landfall and should certain cities be evacuated; Kuipers, Moskowitz, and Kassirer, 1988). Brecke and Garcia (1995) classified uncertainty in a decision problem as "primary" and "secondary" uncertainties. Primary uncertainty is the *action uncertainty* to the decision, whereas secondary uncertainty includes *situation uncertainty, goal uncertainty,* and *option uncertainty.* The information required to end primary uncertainty pertains to secondary uncertainty. Different levels of uncertainty can interact to make the uncertain situation more complex; those emanating from the environment, the organization, or individuals (Rastegary and Landy, 1993). Although many variations of the term persist, what can be agreed upon is that uncertainty plays a significant role in increasing stress in decision-making processes and affects performance (Rastergary and Landy, 1993).

OTHER EFFECTS ON HUMAN DECISION MAKERS UNDER CRISIS CONDITIONS

As a result of the many stressors placed on the human during an emergency situation, many physiological and psychological effects can occur and limit cognitive resources (Mandler, G., 1982; Mandlcr, J. M., 1979). Under normal circumstances, the average person can simultaneously process roughly five to nine concepts (Miller, 1956); however, when a high volume of stimuli is suddenly experienced, thought capacity decreases to two concepts (Waugh and Norman, 1965). Because of the overwhelming amount of stimuli and stressors encountered in a crisis situation, a short-term memory deficit will undoubtedly ensue (Mandler, 1979; Hockey, 1986). As in a domino effect, communication between teammates and/or the command base is often lacking because of short-term memory failure—thereby creating further problems (Stuster, 1996; Wickens, 2005). For obvious reasons, communication is a critical link between not only the team members, but also the team and command base, and is essential for receiving correct and complete information on the crisis incident to achieve a better situational understanding.

Further problems include *attention tunneling,* or when attention is devoted solely to one dilemma at a time, by way of prioritization. Moray and Rotenburg (1989) described this as "cognitive lock-up." With the probability of more than one problem surfacing, limitation of the expanse of damages is greatly compromised by the lack of cognitive processes. Confusion can also be induced in high-stress environments. This is due to the sudden influx of information and the human attempting to receive and process this information as quickly as possible (Horvitz and Barry, 1995). With working memory degrading as a result of the situation, giving each piece of incoming information sufficient amount of time and thought is extremely difficult. In a time of emergency, there is moreover a need to make a decision as quickly as possible, no matter whether all alternatives have been evaluated or not. Hockey (1986) discovered this when participants, under different combinations or by themselves, were placed under noise and anxiety stress; a situation not uncommon to that seen in crises. Unfortunately, premature decision making can be counterproductive and lead to additional problems, especially if the situation was not understood correctly to begin with.

Crisis situations can have many stressors associated with them that will limit the human's decision-making ability. To further understand the effect of decision making under crisis conditions, special decision-making theories are needed. In the next section, we will discuss some of the theories associated with decision making and how these theories address the effects produced by time stress and uncertainty.

DECISION-MAKING THEORIES

To improve human decision-making skills in crisis situations, researchers have striven to find the best strategies and models to describe, predict, and aid human decision-making processes. Early efforts, now known as the "classical" normative model, utilized probability and statistical theories. These included subjective expected utility (SEU) theory and multiattribute utility (MAU) theory (Wickens et al., 2004). These theories assumed every decision maker to be a complete rational entity. Combining this assumption with probability models (such as Bayesian models and the Markovian model), researchers argued that optimal behavior could be expressed by using quantitative measures. This normative model is based on the assumptions that (1) the human decision maker has complete and valid information available for each decision and (2) the decision maker has unlimited time to put all the information into the normative model, compare the outcomes of each alternative, and make the right decision. The decision-making process is assumed to proceed through a linear series of steps, i.e., the DECIDE model (Jensen, 1988).

Despite the wide application of the normative model, the assumptions underlying these rational models are often violated in crisis situations. Consider an aeronautical weather-related decision-making (WRDM) scenario (Wiggins and O'Hare, 1995). When approaching a weather condition, a pilot must decide whether to continue proceeding to the original destination, to divert the plane to a new destination, or to cancel the flight and return to the departure point. The pilot's decision, which has to be made within the appropriate and very short time frame (neither too early nor too late), is based on limited and uncertain information such as the present state of aircraft, the current performance characteristics of the aircraft, meteorological conditions, aerodrome specifications, and topological maps. Each of these pieces of information has unquantifiable effects on future events. That is, according to the rational normative model, the pilot has neither the time nor the information to decide what to do. Instead, the pilot must decide what to do in a more intuitive manner. The pilot's decision will probably be based on his or her prior experiences. In an emergency situation, humans typically make decisions without formally quantifying each information cue and all outcome alternatives into probabilities (Beach and Lipshitz, 1993).

Therefore, researchers have argued that during a crisis, humans tend to make decisions more "naturally" or "intuitively" rather than completely "rationally" (Klein, 1997, 2000; Orasanu and Connolly, 1993; Zsambok, 1997). In naturalistic descriptive models, from Klein's Recognition-Primed Decision Making (RPD; Klein, 1989) to Rasmussen's Skill-, Rule-, and Knowledge-based (SRK) behavior in decision making (Rasmussen, 1983), the belief that experience and extensive practice within a particular domain is the only way to improve decision-making skills has become widely accepted. According to Klein's (1989) RPD model, decision making is *primed* by the decision maker's *recognition* of the situation based on his or her experience with this task-specific domain. If an unfamiliar situation is encountered, this RPD model will not work (Orasanu, 1997); a person must have some previous experience or familiarity with a situation to develop any sort of valid hypothesis about the current situation. Take for example the difference in decision making between a novice and an expert. At the novice level, decision making is slow, analytical, unreliable, effortful, and disjointed (Brecke and Garcia, 1995). At the expert level, decision making is intuitive, fast, reliable, effortless, and parallel. Researchers who identified these characteristics in decision-making tasks include Deitch (2001); Kirlik, Fisk, Walker, and Rothrock (1998); Klein (2000); Means, Salas, Crandall, and Jacobs (1993); Mosier (1997); Shanteau (1995); and Wiggins and O'Hare (1995).

DECISION-MAKING PERFORMANCE MEASURES

Decision making in dynamic environments such as crises lacks a single valid performance measure to assess its effectiveness. Decision making differs from other skills such as perceptual skills or psychomotor control skills. The latter two can be objectively measured and the measurement outcomes directly reflect skill level. One major problem with measuring decision making is that the outcomes from decision making in uncertain environments are relatively random. That is, even if the decision maker applied perfect decision-making strategies, the outcome might not be successful due to unpredictable interventions of chance, whereas conversely, a lucky guess could produce a successful outcome. Although basing performance on the outcome does greatly simplify things, it does not identify "training needs or provide trainees with feedback" (Johnston, Cannon-Bowers, and Smith-Jentsch, 1995; Johnston, Smith-Jentsch, and Cannon-Bowers, 1997). This implies that for assessing decision-making efficiencies under uncertainty, an individual outcome is not a direct measure. Therefore, "measures of performance" (or processes) and "measures of effectiveness" (or outcomes; Smith-Jentsch, Johnston, and Payne, 1998) are needed to understand the whole picture of decision-making effectiveness.

Examples of measuring both decision-making processes and outcomes exist in the literature. For example, Cohen, Freeman, and Thompson (1997) used several different measures to assess decision-making efficiency, including the number of issues considered, amount of evidence identified, number of explanations of conflict generated, number of alternatives generated, accuracy of assessment, consensus and confidence in assessment, and frequency of contingency planning. Johnston et al. (1997) developed a framework to measure outcomes and processes at both the individual and team level.

In attempting to find evidence of internal thought processes, Woods (1993) applied a "process-tracing" or "protocol analysis" methodology. Verbal protocol, behavior protocols, walkthroughs, and interviews are the most common techniques for process tracing. In naturalistic decision-making studies, retrospective self-reports such as these as well as other interview techniques are widely used (Boreham, 1989; Doherty, 1993). One drawback in these approaches is the reliance on human recall of past events, which can substantially limit the reliability and validity of the measures. Other research has used regression techniques, such as the Lens model, to measure relationships between environmental cues and human decisions (Bisantz, Kirlik, Gay, Phipps, Walker, and Fisk, 2000; Hammond, 1993; Jha and Bisantz, 2001; Rothrock and Kirlik, 2003). Although the research on measuring decision-making processes and outcomes has been enlightening, much work remains to be done.

With the measurement of decision-making effectiveness, the efficacy of decision-making training can be determined. Traditional measures of training effectiveness apply a transfer-of-training paradigm (Liu, Blickensderfer, Vincenzi, and Macchiarella, 2006; Liu and Vincenzi, 2004). Transfer of training can be measured in many ways; both as an outcome or process.

For example, as one of the most popular process measures, transfer of training can be measured by making comparisons between the durations of the training needed to perform a task at a certain skill level (time to standard; Liu et al., 2006). Learning-curve techniques have been used in some transfer-of-training studies (Damos, 1991; Liu et al., 2006; Spears, 1985; Taylor, Lintern, Hulin, Talleur, Emanuel, and Phillips, 1999) and may be useful in assessing decision-making skill development. Raw data obtained by decision-making performance measures (e.g., accuracy of assessment) can be used in developing a learning curve and determining just how effective the training program is. The learning-curve-fitting methods provide a much more detailed analysis of data, and the three aspects of performance, i.e., beginning, asymptotic, and rate of improvement, can be examined separately (Liu, Nickens, and Wang, 2006).

CRISIS DECISION-MAKING TRAINING

The next question is, exactly how do we train for a rare and abrupt situation occurring in a crisis environment that requires humans to decide on efficacious actions in a short span of time with ambiguous information? Due to the dynamic nature of crises, which makes training extremely difficult, little research has been conducted in this area. In this section, we will discuss what needs to be involved in the training program, the problems experienced with traditional training processes, and what unconventional training processes could be beneficial in ensuring a successful crisis management training program.

GENERAL AND STRESS TRAINING

One current method of training for high-stress environments involves two separate aspects: general training and stress training. General training ensures that "required knowledge, skills, and abilities" are acquired by means of classroom training or simulation under predictable conditions (Driskell and Johnston, 1998). This training content should extensively cover, from beginning to end, all mission goals, depending on the particular mission and domain. Even with crises being as unique as they are, set procedures should be learned and exercised on a multitude of possible scenarios and system malfunctions. Research has shown that as long as the individual understands the relationships between symptoms and causes (Dienes and Fahey, 1995) and the "dependencies between all system components" (Kersholt, 1997), control of the situation can be obtained.

If there is specific information needed that has not been made available, they must be able to use their knowledge of the system to find this information (Gonzalez, Vanyukov, and Martin, 2005). One result, other than the sheer knowledge that will be required to work with complex system interdependencies, is that the individual will undoubtedly face "unintended consequences" of their decisions (Gonzalez et al., 2005). This may result from hasty or forced decision making, lack of complete information, or even from the dynamic environment itself. Another consequence is that of goal conflicts (Gonzalez et al., 2005). In many instances, the available resources (i.e., human-power, time, supplies, etc.) are simply not enough to sustain the situation. A decision must be made that will prioritize these needs and determine what resources will be focused where. The trainee also needs to learn what side effects will be produced as a result of his or her decisions in this dynamic system and how to make trade-offs when certain goals are threatened. One increasingly popular method of learning the intricate system relationships and how the individual's decisions affect the system as a whole is through microworld (or scaled-world) simulations (e.g., Controller Teamwork Evaluation and Assessment Methodology [CTEAM] or Networked Fire Chief [NFC]). More will be discussed on this type of simulation further on in the chapter. Therefore, and perhaps not surprisingly, it is imperative that each individual have exposure in dealing with nearly every possible situation, whether it is a planned part of the mission or something outside of that, and how to respond accordingly (Cohen, Freeman, and Thompson, 1997); thereby rendering multiple tasks less novel.

Stress training, on the other hand, is used solely to prepare someone on how to cognitively and behaviorally respond in a high-stress environment. This means that the majority of the training is performed outside of the classroom, without "normal" or expected conditions (Driskell and Johnston, 1998). These stress-training tasks involve uncertain cues and time pressure that are extremely critical in ensuring transfer of training; so that when the real event happens, effective actions occur "naturally." Much research has been conducted on the viability of exposing trainees to stress and how it later affects task performance (Ivancevich, Matteson, Freedman, and Phillips, 1990; Johnston and Cannon-Bowers, 1996; Meichenbaum, 1985; Novaco, Cook, and Sarason, 1983; Smith, 1980; Zakay and Wooler, 1984). For example, one such stress exposure training (SET) program (Driskell and Johnston, 1998) follows these steps:

1. Information provision: An introduction to the symptoms of stress and how stress influences performance. Allows the trainee to become familiar with sensory information, procedural information, and instrumental information associated with a stressful environment, giving them a sense of greater control over the situation.
2. Skills acquisition: Provides exposure to "attentional focus, overlearning, and decision-making skills" training.
3. Application and practice: The application of knowledge and critical-thinking skills obtained by the effects of stress to scenarios similar to those that could probably be experienced, with the stress level being gradually increased over time.

Stress training provides a number of advantages applicable to a high-stress situation that traditional or general training cannot, the first of which is that it gives a better understanding of stressful environments (Driskell and Johnston, 1998; Johnston and Cannon-Bowers, 1996). This allows the trainee to learn to "form accurate expectations" concerning crisis situations, thereby allowing for better "predictability" (Driskell and Johnston, 1998). Furthermore, skills are acquired to overcome anxiety and other stress effects produced by high-stress levels that hinder performance. When trained on what to expect and how to respond, individuals will be skilled in acknowledging and then "cognitively controlling" (Driskell and Johnston, 1998) or suppressing these stress effects to perform appropriately and efficiently. Lastly, this type of training builds performance confidence (Driskell and Johnston, 1998; Johnston and Cannon-Bowers, 1996). Those who learn to approach tasks in a positive or confident manner are found to be less likely to become distracted by extraneous variables in the environment and focus instead on the task at hand.

SIMULATION

Crisis situations are nearly impossible to replicate in training and it is not safe to expose trainees to them. Traditional training (i.e., instructor, classroom, etc.) has typically been deemed insufficient for all spheres of crisis management training. Sniezek et al. (2001) identified the following issues in developing a crisis management training program through traditional training methods: expert selection and recruitment, determining training content, effectiveness assessment, feedback, interactions with trainer, scheduling, cost, realism, and transfer of training. As a result, the best training program to overcome these traditional training concerns would be through the use of simulations— a training method that produces a wide range of scenarios, with an "immersive interface," complete experimental control, and a performance feedback system (Sniezek et al., 2001).

There are many advantages to using simulation over the traditional training techniques. According to Sniezek et al. (2001), for effective crisis management, humans need to train "under acute stress" or at least under a combination of "arousal, time pressure, and anxiety"; conventional training methods, unlike simulation, simply cannot provide this. If a simulated training program can successfully produce these results by accurately replicating the natural environment with sequences likely to be experienced, trainees will become "immersed" and approach each scenario as though it were real, as opposed to only "managing a simulated event" (Crego and Spinks, 1997). The level of realism produced is an important key in promoting transfer of training, and if deficient in any way, can greatly hinder training transfer (Zakay and Wooler, 1984).

Other advantages include the ability of the trainee to understand the effects and side effects of his or her chosen actions. As mentioned previously, it is extremely important for the trainee to learn and understand inputs and outputs of the system to know what decisions to make and to begin to gain control of the situation. Simulation incorporates these complex interdependent relationships of the system into the training. Other benefits include the training of multiple trainees at any given time. This is especially beneficial in situations where individuals may be inactive for periods of time before the action (e.g., military personnel being transported over long distances to a war zone) and can use the system for refreshing or recurrent training. Trainees will also be able to interact with one another on the same task, even if they exist in different domains (e.g., air traffic control [ATC] trainees communicating with student pilots in separate simulated environments), an essential in team decision-making training.

The automated feedback system in simulation programs also assists in satisfying a few of the traditional training issues addressed previously. As Kirlik et al. (1998) noted, there are four areas that would strengthen the individual's training experience if implemented in the feedback system: timeliness, standardization, diagnostic precision, and presentation mode.

Timeliness: An automated feedback system allows trainees to receive instant information at the end of the trial, or even during the trial if requested. Often, feedback is obtained too late to be of any use to the trainee (Kirlik et al., 1998). Habit breaking can also be achieved if the system has been programmed to intervene when the trainee commits an error during the simulation (Sniezek et al., 2001).

Standardization: Although expert trainers can provide individualized performance feedback to the trainee, it is labor intensive (Sniezek et al., 2001) and can be "highly idiosyncratic" (Kirlik et al., 1998). The trainer must be able to identify the processes used by the trainee to achieve the outcome. Unfortunately, this is not always possible or feasible. As has been already established, the process is as important as the outcome in identifying where improvements are needed. Additionally, trainers tend to have their own preferences in training, and what is deemed important by one may differ from other trainers' viewpoints, or even differ from the training program itself. With numerous trainers involved in the program, each trainee could receive variations in training; this in turn could hinder future team interactions.

Diagnostic precision: Following a training session, the trainee must be informed as to where and how errors occurred, not just that x number of errors were committed. An automated feedback system would be able to diagnose the exact failure and provide an explanation about what went wrong, as well as offer suggestions on how to improve or prevent it from happening again. Explanations are essential in ensuring that the trainees not only understand the feedback (Sniezek et al., 2001), but that they do not "attribute the error to the particular events in the scenario" and instead take away from it a more generalized lesson (Kirlik et al., 1998).

Presentation mode: Kirlik et al. (1998) found that verbal feedback from trainers during the training session resulted in more interference by creating a "secondary task." The presentation mode used in their study implemented a text-based "real-time, embedded feedback" system. In a study by Kersholt et al. (1996), participants were supplied with an additional computer screen containing information about the system and the relationships between subsystems; 20% more problems were solved by participants who used this technique than those who did not.

Currently, simulations are being used widely in decision-making training, but more specifically are being used for dynamic decision making. As will be described next, one form of simulation gaining popularity in dynamic decision-making research is microworld simulation.

Microworld

Although training in the field does provide the highest level of fidelity and allows trainees to replicate real-world tasks, it is extremely difficult to manipulate and control training scenarios, especially when incorporating time stress and uncertainty. Microworld (or scaled-world) simulations, on the other hand, offer a "compromise between experimental control and realism" (Gonzalez et al., 2005). This type of simulation has become an increasingly useful educational and dynamic decision-making research tool over the past three decades (Granlund, Johansson, Persson, Artman, and Mattson, 2001). It enables trainees to operate in a "scaled" version of the environment, thereby giving the users a top-down view of how their decisions and actions made in real time affect the system as a whole.

Microworld simulations show the system/environment as it changes autonomously and when each decision or action is enforced. If the user hesitates in decision making or makes no decision at all, the simulation incorporates this time of inactivity into the current scenario. In addition, this type of simulation gives the researcher the capability to shape the training session to precisely meet the needs of the trainee and the researcher. It ensures that trainees receive a "deeper and more integrated understanding" of the system and environment in which they are immersed—especially of the "environmental inputs and behavioral outputs" (Ehret, 1998). Some of the current microworld simulation programs that have been evaluated and shown to incorporate relatively high dynamics and complexity are NEWFIRE, Fire Chief, Duress II, Moro, and Water Production Plant (Gonzalez et al., 2005). Although this method of training has been deemed useful in dynamic decision-making studies, further research is needed on its true advantages and disadvantages when applied in crisis training.

Overall, although the benefits of simulation far outweigh conventional training methods in crisis training, a huge barrier faced when implementing simulation into the training program is the initial cost. This cost must cover the "research and development costs" associated with a system such as this (Sniezek et al., 2001). The simulation end results are only as good as the model; therefore, an extensive amount of time and effort must be committed to the development of the design.

CONCLUSION

In this chapter, characteristics of a crisis and the effect they have on the human decision maker have been discussed, as well as problems associated with relying solely on traditional training methods to develop effective decision-making skills during a crisis. Although traditional training methods are adequate for acquiring general domain knowledge and skills, its use otherwise is relatively limited.

Crisis training involves much more complicated requirements. During a crisis, individuals face time pressure, high risk, and ambiguous information in a dynamic environment. Research has shown that SET can assist in mitigating many of these effects mentioned. Therefore, the crisis training program relies heavily on simulation to meet these needs not satisfied by traditional methods.

REFERENCES

Beach, L. R., & Lipshitz, R., 1993. Why classical decision theory is an inappropriate standard for evaluating and aiding most human decision making. In Klein, G. et al (Eds.), *Decision making in action: Models and methods* (pp. 21–36). Norwood, NJ: Ablex.

Bisantz, A. M., Kirlik, A., Gay, P., Phipps, D. A., Walker, N., & Fisk, A. D., 2000. Modeling and analysis of dynamic judgment tasks using a lens model approach. *IEEE Transactions on Systems, Man, and Cybernetics, 30*(6), 605–616.

Boreham, N. C., 1989. Modeling medical decision-making under uncertainty. *British Journal of Educational Psychology, 59,* 187–199.

Brecke, F. H., & Garcia, S. K., 1995. Training methodology for logistic decision making. *USAF-AMRL-Technical-Report (Brooks).* October 1995; AL/HR-TR-1995-0098: iii–vii, 1–94.

Brehmer, B., 1992. Dynamic decision making: Human control of complex systems. *Acta Psychologica, 81,* 211–241.

Busemeyer, J. R., 1985. Decision making under uncertainty: A comparison of simple scalability, fixed-sample, and sequential-sampling models. *Journal of Experimental Psychology: Learning, Memory and Cognition, 11*(3), 538–564.

Cohen M. S., Freeman, J. T., & Thompson, B. T., 1997. Integrated critical thinking training and decision support for tactical anti-air warfare. In *3rd International Command and Control Research and Technology Symposium Proceedings.*

Crego, J., & Spinks, T., 1997. Critical incident management simulation. In Flin, R., Salas, E., Strub, M., & Martin, L. (Eds.), *Decision making under stress: Emerging themes and applications* (pp. 85–94). Burlington, VT: Ashgate.

Damos, D. L., 1991. Examining transfer of training using curve fitting: A second look. *The International Journal of Aviation Psychology, 1*(1), 73–85.

Davis, J. P., & Hall, J. W., 2003. A software-supported process for assembling evidence and handling uncertainty in decision-making. *Decision Support System, 35,* 415–433.

Deitch, E., 2001. Learning to land: A qualitative examination of pre-flight and in-flight decision-making processes in expert and novice aviators. Dissertation, Virginia Polytechnic Institute and State University.

Dienes, Z., & Fahey, F., 1995. Role of specific instances in controlling a dynamic system. *Journal of Experimental Psychology: Learning, Memory and Cognition, 21*(4), 848–862.

Doherty, M. E., 1993. A laboratory scientist's view of naturalistic decision making. In Klein, G. et al. (Eds.), *Decision making in action: Models and methods* (pp. 362–389), Norwood, NJ: Ablex.

Driskell, J. E., & Johnston, J. H., 1998. Stress exposure training. In Cannon Bowers, J. A., & Salas, E. (Eds.), *Making decisions under stress: Implications for individual and team training.* Washington D.C.: American Psychological Association.

Edland, A., & Svenson, O., 1993. Judgment and decision making under time pressure: Studies and finding. In Svenson, O., & Maule, A. (Eds.), *Time pressure and stress in human judgment and decision making,* (pp. 27–40). New York: Plenum Press.

Ehret, B. D., 1998. Scaled worlds as research tools: A demonstration. *Human Factors and Ergonomics Society 42th Annual Meeting* (p. 1157). Santa Monica, CA: Human Factors and Ergonomics Society.

Flin, R., & Arbuthnot, K., 2002. *Incident command: Tales from the hot seat.* Aldershot: Ashgate.

Gonzalez, C., Vanyukov, P., & Martin M. K., 2005. The use of MicroWorlds to study dynamic decision making. *Computers in Human Behavior, 21,* 273–286.

Granlund, R., Johansson, B., Persson, M., Artman, H., & Mattson, P., 2001. Exploration of methodological issues in micro-world research—Experiences from research in team decision making. Presented at a workshop on the use of micro-worlds in research. Granada, Spain. Retrieved online at http://www.nada.kth.se/~artman/Articles/Misc/MIKRO_GRANADWORKSHOP.pdf

Hammond, K. R., 1993. Naturalistic decision making from a Brunswikian viewpoint: Its past, present, future. In Klein, G. et al. (Eds.), *Decision making in action: Models and methods* (pp. 205–228). Norwood, NJ: Ablex.

Hockey, G. R. J., 1986. Changes in operator efficiency as a function of environmental stress, fatigue and circadian rhythms. In Boff, K. R., Kaufman, L., & Thomas, J. P. (Eds.), *Handbook of perception and human performance* (pp. 1–49). New York: Wiley.

Horvitz, E., & Barry, M., 1995. Display of information for time-critical decision making. *Proceedings of the 11th Conference on Uncertainty in Artificial Intelligence,* San Francisco, CA: Morgan Kaufmann.

Ivancevich, J., Matteson, M., Freedman, S., & Philips, J., 1990. Worksite stress management interventions, *American Psychologist, 45,* 252–261.

Jensen, R. S., 1988. Creating a '1000 Hour' pilot in 300 hours through judgment training. *In Proceedings of the Workshop on Aviation Psychology.* Newcastle, Australia: Institute of Aviation, University of Newcastle.

Jha, P., & Bisantz, A. M., 2001. Modeling fault diagnosis in a dynamic process control task using a multivariate lens model. In *Proceedings of the Human Factors and Ergonomics Society 45th Annual Meeting,* Minneapolis/St. Paul, Minnesota.

Johnston, J., & Cannon-Bowers, J. A., 1996. Training for stress exposure. In Driskell, J. E., & Salas, E. (Eds.), *Stress and human performance* (pp. 223–256). Mahwah, NJ: Lawrence Erlbaum.

Johnston, J. H., Cannon-Bowers, J. A., & Smith-Jentsch, K. A., 1995. Event-based performance measurement system for shipboard command teams. *Proceedings of the First International Symposium on Command and Control Research and Technology* (pp. 274–276). Washington D.C.: Institute for National Strategic Studies.

Johnston, J., Smith-Jentsch, K. A., & Cannon-Bowers, J. A., 1997. Performance measurement tools for enhancing team decision-making training. In Brannick, M. T., Salas, E., & Prince, C. (Eds.), *Team performance assessment and measurement: Theory, methods, and applications* (pp. 311–327). Mahwah, NJ: Lawrence Erlbaum Associates.

Kerstholt, J. H., 1997. Dynamic decision making in non-routine situations. In Flin, R., Salas, E., Strub, M., & Martin, L. (Eds.), *Decision making under stress: Emerging themes and applications* (pp. 185–192). Burlington, VT: Ashgate.

Kerstholt, J. H., Passenier, P. O., Houttuin, K., & Schuffel, H., 1996. The effect of *a priori* probability and complexity on decision making in a supervisory control task. *Human Factors, 38*(1), 65–98.

Kirlik, A., Fisk, A. D., Walker, N., & Rothrock, L., 1998. Feedback augmentation and part-task practice in training dynamic decision-making skills. In Cannon-Bowers, J. A., & Salas, E. (Eds.), *Making decisions under stress* (pp. 91–113). Washington D.C.: American Psychological Association.

Klein, G. A., 1989. Recognition-primed decisions. In Rouse, W. (Ed.), *Advances in man-machine systems research,* (pp. 47–92), Greenwich, CT: JAI Press.

Klein, G., 1997. An overview of naturalistic decision-making applications. In Zsambok, C., & Klein, G. (Eds.), *Naturalistic decision making* (pp. 48–61), Mahwah, NJ: Lawrence Erlbaum Associates.

Klein, G., 2000. How can we train pilots to make better decisions? In O'Neil, H., & Andrews, D. (Eds.), *Aircrew training and assessment* (pp. 165–194), Mahwah, NJ: Lawrence Erlbaum Associates.

Kuipers B., Moskowitz, A. J., & Kassirer, J. P., 1988. Critical decision under uncertainty: Representation and structure, *Cognitive Science, 12,* 177–210.

Liu, D., Blickensderfer, E., Vincenzi, D., & Macchiarella, N., 2006. Transfer of training. To appear in Vincenzi, D., & Wise, J. (Eds.), *Human factors and simulation.* Accepted for publication.

Liu, D., Nickens, T., & Wang, Y., 2006. *Modeling decision-making learning process under crisis situations.* Paper presented at the 10th Annual Fall Simulation Interoperability Workshop, Orlando, FL.

Liu, D., & Vincenzi, D., 2004. Measuring simulation fidelity: A conceptual study. *Proceedings of Human Performance, Situation Awareness and Automation Conference,* Daytona Beach, FL.

Mandler, G., 1982. Stress and thought processes. In Goldberger, L., & Breznitz, S. (Eds.), *Handbook of stress: Theoretical and clinical aspects.* New York: Free Press.

Mandler, J. M., 1979. Categorical and schematic organization in memory. In Puff, C. R. (Ed.), *Memory organization and structure* (pp. 259–299). New York: Academic Press.

Maule, A. J., Hockey, G. R., & Bdzola, L., 2000. Effects of time-pressure on decision-making under uncertainty: Changes in affective state and information processing strategy, *Acta Psychologica, 104,* 283–301.

McKinney, E. H., 1993. Flight leads and crisis decision making. *Aviation, Space, and Environmental Medicine, 64,* 359–362.

Means, B., Salas, E., Crandall, B., & Jacobs, T. O., 1993. Training decision makers for the real world. In Klein, G. et al. (Eds.), *Decision making in action: Models and methods* (pp. 306–327). Norwood, NJ: Ablex.

Meichenbaum, D., 1985. Teaching thinking: A cognitive-behavioral perspective. In Segal, J. W., Chipman, S. F., & Glaser, R. (Eds.), *Thinking and learning skills, 2: Research and open questions.* London: Lawrence Erlbaum Associates.

Miller, G., 1956. The magical number seven plus or minus two: Some limits on our capacity for processing information. *Psychological Review, 63,* 81–97.

Moray, N., & Rotenberg, I., 1989. Fault management in process control: Eye movements and action. *Ergonomics, 32,* 1319–1342.

Mosier, K., 1997. Myths of expert decision making and automated decision aid. In Zsambok, C., & Klein, G. (Eds.), *Naturalistic decision making* (pp. 319–331). Mahwah, NJ: Lawrence Erlbaum Associates.

Novaco, R., Cook, T., & Sarason, I., 1983. Military recruit training: An arena for stress-coping skills. In Meichenbaum, D., & Jaremko, M. (Eds.), *Stress reduction and prevention* (pp. 377–418). New York: Plenum.

Orasanu, J., 1997. Stress and naturalistic decision making: Strengthening the weak links. In Flin, R., Salas, E., Strub, M., & Martin, L. (Eds.), *Decision making under stress: Emerging themes and applications* (pp. 43–66). Burlington, VT: Ashgate.

Orasanu, J., & Connolly, T., 1993. The reinvention of decision making. In Klein, G., Orasanu, J., Calderwood, R., & Zsambok, C. (Eds.), *Decision making in action: Models and methods* (pp. 3–20). Norwood, NJ: Ablex.

Rasmussen, J., 1983. Skills, rules, and knowledge; Signals, signs, and other distinctions in human performance models. *IEEE Transactions on Systems, Man, and Cybernetics, 13,* 257–266.

Rastegary, H., & Landy, F., 1993. The interaction among time urgency, uncertainty and time pressure. In Svenson, O., & Maule, A. (Eds.), *Time pressure and stress in human judgment and decision making,* New York: Plenum Press.

Rothrock, L., 2001. Using the time windows to evaluate operator performance, *International Journal of Cognitive Ergonomics, 5*(1), 1–21.

Rothrock, L., & Kirlik, A., 2003. Inferring rule-based strategies in dynamic judgment tasks: toward a non-compensatory formulation of the lens model. *IEEE Transactions on Systems, Man, and Cybernetics,* Part A, *33*(1), 58–72.

Shanteau, J., 1995. Expert judgment and financial decision making. In Green, B. (Ed.), *Risky business: Risk behavior and risk management.* Stockholm University. Retrieved July 2005 online from http://www.ksu.edu/psych/cws/pdf/financial_experts95.PDF.

Smith, R. E., 1980. A cognitive/affective approach to stress management training for athletes. In Nadeau, C. H., Halliwell, W. R., Newell, K. M., & Roberts, G. C. (Eds.), *Psychology of motor behavior and sport—1979* (pp. 54–73). Champaign, IL: Human Kinetics.

Smith-Jentsch, K. A., Johnston, J. H., & Payne, S. C., 1998. Measuring team-related expertise in complex environments. In Cannon-Bowers, J. A., & Salas, E. (Eds.), *Decision making under stress: Implications for training and simulation* (pp. 61–87) Washington D.C.: American Psychological Association.

Sniezek, J. A., Wilkins, D. C., & Wadlington, P. L., 2001. Advanced training for crisis decision making: Simulation, critiquing, and immersive interfaces. *Proceedings of the 34th Hawaii International Conference on System Sciences,* Maui, HI: IEEE Computer Society.

Spears, W., 1985. Measuring of learning and transfer using curve fitting. *Human Factors, 27,* 251–266.

Stuster, J., 1996. *Bold endeavors: Lessons from polar and space exploration.* Annapolis, MD: Naval Institute Press.

Taylor, H. L., Lintern, G., Hulin, C. L., Talleur, D. A., Emanuel, T. W., Jr., & Phillips, S. I., 1999. Transfer of training effectiveness of a personal computer aviation training device. *International Journal of Aviation Psychology, 9*(4), 319–335.

Waugh, N., & Norman, D., 1965. Primary memory. *Psychological Review, 72,* 89–104.

Wickens, C. D., 2005. Attentional tunneling and task management. *Proceedings of the 13th International Symposium on Aviation Psychology.* Dayton, OH: Wright-Patterson AFB.

Wickens, C., Lee, J. D., Liu, Y., & Becker, S., 2004. *An introduction to human factors engineering.* Upper Saddle River, NJ: Prentice Hall.

Wiggins, M., & O'Hare, D., 1995. Expertise in aeronautical weather-related decision-making: A cross-sectional analysis of general aviation pilots. *Journal of Experimental Psychology: Applied, 1*(4), 305–320.

Woods, D. D., 1993. Process-tracing methods for the study of cognition outside of the experimental psychology laboratory. In Klein, G. et al. (Eds.), *Decision making in action: Models and* methods (pp. 228–252), Norwood, NJ: Ablex.

Zakay, D., & Wooler, S., 1984. Time pressure, training and decision effectiveness. *Ergonomics, 27,* 273–284.

Zsambok, C. E., 1997. Naturalistic decision making: Where are we now? In Zsambok, C., & Klein, G. (Eds.), *Naturalistic decision making* (pp. 3–16). Mahwah, NJ: Lawrence Erlbaum Associates.

18 Augmented Reality as a Means of Job Task Training in Aviation

Nikolas D. Macchiarella, Dahai Liu, and Dennis A. Vincenzi

CONTENTS

Historically, the aviation industry expends significant amounts of time and resources training and retraining its workforce to perform psychomotor and cognitive maintenance tasks necessary to keep aircraft safely flying (Ott, 1995). The industry continues to dedicate a substantial amount of its effort and capital ensuring that its workforce is prepared to maintain modern and complex aircraft systems. Despite the rapid advances in computer-based training technologies (e.g., augmented reality [AR]), aviation maintenance workers presently participate in job task training in traditional face-to-face settings that would be familiar to aviation maintenance workers from generations past. Changing the manner in which aviation maintenance workers are trained, with the goal of capturing the positive effects associated with computer-based training technologies, has the potential to optimize training.

Airframe and Powerplant (A&P) certified mechanics are serving as the primary workers in the nation's aviation industry. The United States General Accounting Office (2003) completed a study that highlights the need for curriculum reform by the Federal Aviation Administration (FAA) for the training and certification of A&P mechanics. A relatively large number of workers in the aviation maintenance field possess an A&P license. The number of A&P mechanics in the U.S. labor market is not forecasted to meet the industry's needs by 2010 (U.S. General Accounting Office, 2003). A panel convened by the U.S. General Accounting Office (2003) cited the current curriculum for being "obsolete geared to smaller less complex aircraft ..." (p. 1). Within the next several years, institutions training future aviation maintenance workers will receive a new curriculum for training A&P mechanics. This new curriculum will address the modern complexities of systems and materials being used in aircraft. This change of curriculum, combined with significant cost in resources and time necessary to train and retrain aviation maintenance workers, creates an opportunity to change the fundamental nature of instructional delivery systems (IDS) being used in the aviation maintenance training field. AR has the potential to help the aviation industry meet its training need due to its visual-spatial dynamic that is analogous to a spatial graphical user interface (GUI) (Majoros and Boyle, 1997; Majoros and Neumann, 2001; Neumann and Majoros, 1998).

Several key factors are associated with training aviation workers: aviation maintenance work tasks require a high level of knowledge in the field, from entry level (i.e., novice) to the highly skilled level (i.e., expert); the FAA rigidly regulates training curriculum and certification of workers; workers perform work tasks at irregular intervals (e.g., replacing an oil pump on a turbine engine may only occur once in 5 years); and when workers fail to perform work tasks properly, the consequences could be dire. Aviation accidents in general, often result in the loss of human life and large-scale destruction of property. Highlighting the consequences of improper maintenance, the National Transportation Safety Board (NTSB) determined that the crash of Alaska Airlines Flight 261 in January 2000 was due to maintenance irregularities (U.S. General Accounting Office, 2003). The FAA licenses and regulates aviation maintenance workers as part of its effort to ensure safe aviation operations and protect the public in general.

The FAA originally developed its core curriculum for repairing and maintaining aircraft over 50 years ago (U.S. General Accounting Office, 2003). Aviation maintenance workers inspect and repair engines, landing gear, instruments, pressurized sections, and other parts of the aircraft. Additionally, they conduct routine maintenance and replacement of parts; repair surfaces for both sheet metal and composite materials; and inspect for corrosion, distortion, and cracks in the fuselage, wings, and tail. While performing maintenance, A&P mechanics test parts and equipment to ensure that they are working properly and then certify that the aircraft is ready to return to service. Aviation maintenance workers often work under time pressure to maintain flight schedules. The majority of them obtain an A&P license through certification by the FAA. Those who do not possess an A&P license can only perform maintenance tasks under the direct supervision of an A&P-licensed mechanic. Candidates for the A&P license must successfully complete a minimum of 1900 hours of classroom instruction at any of the 175 FAA-approved aviation maintenance technician schools or acquire documented evidence that they have at least 30 months of on-the-job training (e.g., service as an aviation mechanic in the military), or show evidence detailing work experience with aircrafts' engines and bodies. After meeting the requisites for licensing, A&P candidates must pass written and oral tests and demonstrate through a practical test that they can perform maintenance tasks (U.S. General Accounting Office, 2003). Any instructional delivery system or new learning paradigm that has a significant positive effect on aviation maintenance workers during their initial training or retraining after receiving an A&P license could reduce training time and costs, helping to meet the industry's need for trained workers.

AUGMENTED REALITY (AR)

AR presents a visual-spatial dynamic that may elicit efficiencies during aviation maintenance training (Macchiarella, 2004; Neumann and Majoros, 1998; Valimont, 2002). AR applications that deliver composite virtual and real scenes during aviation maintenance training are analogous to the spatial GUI that now dominates human–computer interaction, and may aid attention, memory, and recall (Neumann and Majoros, 1998). However, AR is an emerging technology, and essentially very little research regarding its effectiveness as a training paradigm has been conducted. Consequently, new research is constantly expanding the body of knowledge of the technologies necessary to bring AR into the real world for application (Azuma, 2004).

HISTORICAL OVERVIEW: AR AND TRAINING

Essential to understanding the concept of AR is the need to distinguish between real objects, virtual objects, and objects that display characteristics of both reality and virtuality. Milgram and Kishino (1994) effectively defined AR and placed it into a mixed-reality continuum (see Figure 18.1). Milgram's virtuality continuum is useful for categorizing surroundings as perceived by the human mind. On one end of the continuum is the real environment. It is comprised of real objects that have an actual existence. The virtual environment at the other end of the continuum comprises objects

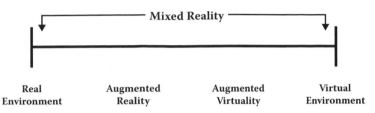

Mixed Reality

Real   Augmented   Augmented   Virtual
Environment   Reality   Virtuality   Environment

FIGURE 18.1 Milgram's reality–virtuality continuum. (Adapted from Milgram, P., and Kishino, F., 1994. A taxonomy of mixed reality visual displays. *IEICE Transactions Information Systems, E77-D*(12), 1321–1329.)

that exist in essence or effect but not in a formal or actual state of being. Between these two ends lies the world of mixed-reality (Azuma, 1997; Azuma et al., 2001; Billinghurst, Kato, and Poupyrev, 2001; Milgram and Kishino, 1994). The distinction between varying degrees of reality and virtuality are not significant in terms of human interaction with the mixed-reality world. However, from a technical perspective for creating a mixed-reality world, varying degrees of reality and virtuality are significant. It is more difficult to bring virtual elements into real environmental settings (viz., outside a laboratory setting) than it is to bring a real environment object into a computer-generated virtual environment scene (e.g., using one's hand, fitted with a haptic input device, to grasp a virtual object). Effectively, AR is any scene or case in which the real environment is supplemented by using computer-generated graphics.

Azuma's (1997) monograph defines AR as a variation of virtual environments (VEs) and provides detailed information on all key aspects of AR-based systems. VEs are more commonly referred to as virtual reality (VR). Users of VE technologies are fully immersed in a synthetic environment. An AR system supplements the real world with virtual (i.e., computer-generated) objects that appear to coexist in the same space as the real world. Azuma (2001) defines AR systems as having the following properties: combines real and virtual objects in a real environment, runs interactively, runs in real-time, and registers (i.e., aligns) real and virtual objects with each other. AR is a machine vision and computer graphics technology that merges real and virtual objects into unified, spatially integrated scenes. Azuma (Azuma, 1997; Azuma et al., 2001) deconstructs all AR systems into three subsystems: scene generator, display device, and tracking–sensing device. He clearly defines AR as its own field of study due to AR's unique blending of computer-generated worlds and the real world to form a new world for humans to function within.

AR systems fall into either one of two categories (Feiner, MacIntyre, and Hollerer, 1997; Kalawsky, Stedmon, Hill, and Cook, 2000). The categories are: optical-based technologies (see Figure 18.2) and video-based technologies (see Figure 18.3). Optical-based systems typically employ a head-mounted display (HMD) that is comprised of see-through lenses that enable the user

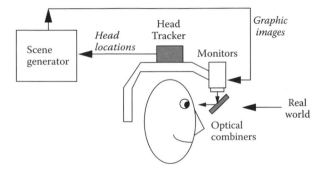

Head
Tracker
*Head
locations*   *Graphic
images*
Scene
generator   Monitors
Real
world
Optical
combiners

FIGURE 18.2 Simple schematic of an optical see-through HMD AR system. (Adapted from Azuma, R. T, 1997. A survey of augmented reality. *Presence, 6*(4), 355–385.)

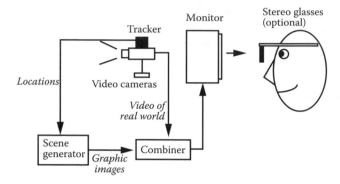

FIGURE 18.3 Simple schematic of a monitor-based AR system. (Adapted from Azuma, R. T., 1997. A survey of augmented reality. *Presence, 6*(4), 355–385.)

to see the real world with the virtual world projected on combiner lenses positioned in front of the eye. The combiner lenses are partially transmissive, enabling the user to look directly through them to see the real world. The user sees the virtual world superimposed over the physical view of the real world. Video-based systems use video cameras that provide the user a view of the real world. Video from these cameras is combined with the graphic images created by a scene-generating computer to blend the real and virtual worlds. The result is sent to the monitors in front of the user's eyes in a closed-view HMD or to a traditional computer monitor.

Fishkin, Gujar, Harrison, Moran, and Want (2000) propose that AR-like systems have the potential to transform human–computer interaction as drastically as the GUI-transformed computing. They state that "the physical configuration of computational devices is a major determinant of their usability" (p. 75). The authors highlight that traditional physical interaction with computers is limited. Humans primarily interact with computers through a pointing device, display, buttons, or keys. This means that the human–computer interaction is identified as the windows, icons, menus, and pointing devices (WIMP) approach (Shneiderman, 1998). Applying the uses of a piece of paper by humans as a metaphor for the human–computer interaction, humans use paper in numerous and varying ways while recording data, including writing, flipping, thumbing, bending, and creasing. Humans have developed dexterity, skills, and practices that are not brought fully to bear on computational device interfaces; human interaction with paper is more varied than typical human–computer interaction.

Billinghurst and Kato (2002) provide an overview of the technologies associated with creating AR and some of the possible applications for enhancing collaborative work in educational settings. The authors use scenes from the movie *Star Wars* as a metaphor. In *Star Wars,* characters communicate with each other, across great distances, while observing computer-generated and projected three-dimensional (3-D) life-size virtual images. These images are superimposed on the real world. The authors cite these scenes as foreshadowing collaborative AR. They state that the long-term goal of AR research is to make it possible for the real world and virtual world to blend seamlessly together; real and virtual worlds would become indistinguishable from one another.

Billinghurst, Kato, and Poupyrev (2000) discuss a technology and its implications for collaborative learning through the use of AR. The authors developed "The MagicBook" to explore the use of AR to bring text-based books to life with virtual animations. The reader, or readers when used in a collaborative learning environment, read the book while looking through a handheld see-through display. The handheld see-through display is similar to a heads-up display in a fighter aircraft. As the reader observes pages, virtual 3-D avatars and images appear on the book page and act out scenes that are described in the text. This article illustrates the stunning technology available to transform two-dimensional (2-D) books into the "third dimension."

Neumann and Majoros (1998) provide a review of cognitive studies and analyses relating to how AR interacts with human abilities. They describe how these AR-enhanced human abilities may benefit manufacturing and maintenance tasks. The authors describe possible applications for AR and a prototype system designed to facilitate aviation worker training and performance of aviation maintenance tasks. They state that AR has a considerable effect on recall by establishing to-be-recalled items in a highly memorable framework; by using AR to develop scenes in an easy-to-remember framework, AR can complement human information processing. This complement can reveal itself in training efficiency applicable to a wide variety of maintenance tasks. The authors provide a list of potential AR uses and state that the possible applications of AR are nearly limitless.

Majoros and Neumann (2001) propose that AR can complement human information processing during the performance of aviation maintenance tasks (e.g., on-orbit maintenance procedures). They provide analysis of cognitive models that suggest that scenes merging real and synthetic features (i.e., AR) will complement human information processing by controlling attention, supporting short- and long-term memory, and aiding information integration. They state that applications of AR enable immediate access to information; immediate access to information is akin to an expert's retrieval from short-term memory or well-encoded long-term memory. Easy interaction with the design interface should allow rehearsals and stable links between graphics and the real world.

Yeh and Wickens (2001) report their findings regarding an application of AR as a means of providing "intelligent cueing." Intelligent cueing is the application of AR to a scene assumed to be important by a computer-based optical searching assistant. In their experiment, the authors used 16 participants actively serving in the U.S. Army or U.S. Marine Corps. Participants were presented with a high-definition virtual-reality scene of a desert environment. Virtual targets were placed into the scene and were observable by the participant and the computer-based optical searching assistant. Reliability of cueing was manipulated between 100% and 75% reliability to help the authors develop inferences regarding cue reliability and detection behavior (i.e., detection distance and accuracy). The researchers defined reliability as the degree of accuracy the cue provided to the participant as it pointed to the virtual object in the desert scene (e.g., cueing that is 75% reliable accurately points to the virtual target three out of four times). Unreliable cueing was found to induce the cognitive response of *disuse* of the cue. Reliable cueing was found to induce user reliance on the cue, or in some cases, *overuse*.

Kalawsky, Stedmon, Hill, and Cook (2000) provide a brief background of AR to define terms and provide information on psychological and physiological aspects associated with AR. They highlight that AR does not have to be a purely visual augmentation; additionally, it may encompass the use of other sensory modalities. One of the sensory modalities highlighted is the use of 3-D sound to provide enhanced spatial awareness. The authors do make a key point that AR is not widely used due to technical problems associated with registering the virtual world to the real world. Registration is the process of creating one coherent scene. It is a difficult process outside static settings such as those found in laboratories.

Poupyrev et al. (2002) report on their development of a "tile" system approach to implementing an AR environment. Each tile has a unique marker that a computer-based AR system can recognize and then use to render a virtual image as an overlay on a real-world scene. The authors positioned the tiles on a magnetic whiteboard to demonstrate an application for the rapid prototyping of an aircraft instrument panel. In addition to tiles replicating aircraft instruments, the authors included tiles with the functionalities of delete, copy, and help. These "functionality" tiles enabled the user to manipulate the AR environment in a manner similar to the way icons interact with the common GUI found on personal computers.

Several studies identify that the development of AR environments for training purposes is an inherently interdisciplinary pursuit (Macchiarella, 2004, 2005; Macchiarella, Gangadharan, Liu, Majoros, and Vincenzi, 2005; Vincenzi et al., 2003). The design of an effective AR environment entails incorporating theories of computer design, empirical research in several fields, the nature of human perceptual and cognitive systems, reasoning with diverse forms of information, human learning under varying situations, technology for presenting information to the human user, and getting information to and from the user and the computer in an effective manner. Developing an understanding of human abilities and complementary applications of AR to create mixed-reality worlds is an essential element in the design of any AR learning environment that complements human cognitive activity. Vincenzi and Gangadharan (2001) identify distinctive human abilities as being able to:

- Detect meaningful stimuli and patterns
- Integrate information within and between sensory modalities (e.g., sight, sound, and smell as indicators of condition)
- Compare information/events to standards
- Perform qualitative judgments

They identify complementary applications of AR annotations as follows:

- Tethering virtual annotations to real-world work pieces minimizes the need to search for information.
- Virtual images can provide examples of correct conditions.
- Markers or flags can direct attention to specific real-world work piece features.
- Virtual annotations can influence the users' anticipation, (e.g., knowledge of possible defects with the real-world work piece.
- With input options, users can obtain the desired level of information detail for the work task.
- Virtual objects offer an easy-to-use interface for recording work task steps.

AR is a relatively new field within the computer science field of study, and its nature is inherently interdisciplinary. The concept of augmenting an observer's perception of reality has age-old roots (Stapleton, Hughes, Moshell, Micikevicius, and Altman, 2002). Reality alteration or augmentation was, and still is, used by magicians and entertainers in the form of illusions and other gimmicks to bewilder, amaze, and entertain. The desired goal is to make people perceive ordinary objects in extraordinary ways. The modern development of computer-based AR has the ability to bewilder, amaze, and entertain. However, commercial applications of AR designed with the goal of improving education, training, and work task performance can create a new mixed-reality world inconceivable just a few decades ago. AR requires connecting reality with imagination to make people perceive ordinary objects in extraordinary ways.

COGNITION AND AR

ELABORATION AND RECALL

Ormrod (1999) and Haberlandt (1997) identify key aspects of elaboration and recall. The manner in which information is encoded and retained determines how easy it will be to retrieve for future use. Cues can be used to aid this retrieval immediately and for the long term from memory. Although not yet thoroughly tested, researchers have theorized that AR-based learning may inherently possess a great potential for facilitating retention of learned material to be retrieved later for real-world application during work tasks (Macchiarella, 2004; Majoros and Neumann, 2001; Valimont, 2002). AR-based learning can affect many more modalities of human senses than present learning paradigms. By complementing human associative information processing, and aiding information integration through multimodal sensory elaboration by the use of visual-spatial, verbal, proprioceptive, and tactile memory while the learner is performing a knowledge acquisition task, AR can enable increased elaboration during the time the learner participates in an AR-based learning environment

(Bjork and Bjork, 1996; Majoros and Neumann, 2001; Vincenzi et al., 2003). Hypothesizing that the uses of text labels in AR scenes serve as cues for retrieval is consistent with the Tulving and Osler (1968) study. The study found that, when subjects studied a list of words with an associated mnemonic aid (i.e., cue word), they had a significantly higher level of recall as compared to a group that did not use a cue word. Applying the same principle to the AR environment, virtual text labels appearing on real-world objects serve as a word cue, or mnemonic, for the object.

Elaboration is the process by which one expands upon new information by creating multiple associations among the incoming information. Stein, Littlefield, Bransford, and Persampieri (1984) conducted research to determine the effectiveness of elaboration on immediate recall. They found that, when the elaborative cue was closely related to the to-be-recalled material (e.g., information to-be-recalled, the *strong* man read a book; the cue, about *weight lifting*), the learners displayed a significantly higher level of recall. With regard to educational practice and cues, Reigeluth (1999) defines four key elements of elaboration: selection, sequencing, synthesizing, and summarizing of the subject-matter content. It draws from different sensory inputs and past information already held in long-term memory. In terms of learning procedural tasks, the learner focuses on sequential steps to help select and sequence acquisition of knowledge in a manner that will optimize attainment. Elaboration has been shown to greatly improve the encoding and retention of newly acquired information. When precise cues are applied in AR scenes (i.e., virtual text annotations naming functions and components of a real-world object) higher levels of recall can be anticipated.

Mayer (1992) provides a brief monograph of psychology theory and research. He begins with E. L. Thorndike's work (1905) and concludes by citing contemporary authors who address the application of cognitive psychology in educational practice. He ties together developments in the fields of psychology and learning theory to show the origins of recent educational practice. The author concludes that the behaviorist influences in educational practice are waning, and educational practice based on cognitive psychology is prevailing.

Research has shown that retrieval and recall of learned information is most effective when the similarities between the learning environment and the task environment are maximized. Meaningful learning occurs when the learner has relevant prior knowledge to form a frame of reference from which to draw (Bjork and Bjork, 1996; Knowles, 1984; Stein, Littlefield, Bransford, and Persampieri, 1984). Elaboration, within domains of knowledge the users are familiar with, may be one of the key strengths associated with using AR in learning settings. In terms of elaboration and recall, AR may have the ability to facilitate the sequencing of ideas that will assist in learning cognitive and complex psychomotor tasks (e.g., isolating a fault in an aircraft electrical system).

Spatial Relations

Spatial cognition (i.e., cognitive functioning that enables the ability to process and interpret visual information regarding the location of objects in an environment—often referred to as visual-spatial ability) relates the representation of spatial information (e.g., location) in memory. Spatial information has been found to be an extremely powerful form of elaboration for establishing associations in memory that facilitate recall. Researchers have found that spatial information is automatically processed when visual scenes are encoded into long-term memory (Lovelace and Southall, 1983; Neumann and Majoros, 1998; Pezdek and Evans, 1979).

Pezdek and Evans (1979) conducted four experiments to assess the role of verbal and visual processing in memory for aspects of a simulated, real-world spatial display. Participants viewed a 3-D model of a city with 16 buildings that were placed on the display. The buildings were represented on the model with, or without, an accompanying name label on each building. The participants studied the display and subsequently were tested on recall and recognition of the building names, picture recognition of the buildings, and spatial memory for where the buildings were located within the model. Overall, picture recognition accuracy was low, and the presence of a name label on each building significantly reduced picture recognition accuracy but improved location recognition accuracy. The authors concluded that spatial location information was not encoded independently of verbal and visual identity information. In this study, labeling facilitated location identification accuracy. It did not significantly affect visual recognition. The authors' real-world spatial display (i.e., 3-D model) in several ways is comparable to the AR environment. AR environments are inherently 3-D in nature. The real-world objects occupy three dimensions of space, and the virtual component of the scene can be rendered to present a 3-D appearance.

Saariluoma and Kalakoski (1997) conducted four experiments to test the effects of imagery on the long-term working memory of skilled chess players. The purpose of their experimentation was to gain insights on effects of visual and auditory inputs on game play. The authors hypothesized that the visual modality would have the most significant effect on how chess players form mental images of game play. The authors concluded that skilled imagery is built on long-term working-memory retrieval structures and that effective transformation of information between these retrieval structures and visual working memory is required to construct complex mental images. Expert chess players are better able to construct complex mental images of task-specific materials than less skilled chess players. Regardless of modality of information transmission, the chess move is transformed into visuospatial code and stored as such by the chess player. Participants in AR learning environments view scenes that contain both the real-world object being studied and the corresponding virtual overlay. It is reasonable to believe that these mixed-reality scenes are encoded into long-term memory as one integrated scene and, when the scene is recalled, a transformation to long-term working memory is required to construct mental images in the visual working memory. Should this effect prove true, participants in AR-based learning would demonstrate significantly higher levels of recall when compared to participants using traditional forms of learning.

Nakamura (1994) describes research conducted to measure the effect, on recall, of different types of spatial relations. The spatial relations are grouped into three categories: scene-expected, scene-unexpected, and scene-irrelevant. The author's findings contribute to the body of knowledge dealing with spatial relations with regard to attention and recall. When spatial scenes incorporate elements that are not naturally associated with the scene, viewer attention is drawn to the scene. When the scene contains multiple surprising but naturally occurring elements, the viewers demonstrate higher levels of recall. Application of these findings can facilitate learner recall in various training and educational settings.

Phaf and Wolters (1993) report on four experiments they conducted to examine the processes that determine the effectiveness of rehearsal on long-term memory. They cite previous research that divided rehearsals into one of two categories: maintenance rehearsal and elaborative rehearsal. Maintenance rehearsal involves rote repetition of an item's auditory representation. Elaborative rehearsal involves deep semantic processing of to-be-remembered items, resulting in the production of durable memories. The authors' experiments led them to several conclusions. First, the effectiveness of a rehearsal depends on the degree of attentional processing applied to the material being rehearsed. Second, an important criterion for attentional processing seems to be the "novelty" of stimuli being rehearsed. Third, attention may result in faster learning because novel patterns may enable the development of new associations. These findings may affect instructional design; increasing attention during rehearsals could lead to higher levels of recall.

Pham and Venkataramani (1997) report on their investigation of the processes of source identification and its effect on effectual communication. The authors propose a framework that identifies four types of source identification processes: semantic cued retrieval, memory-trace refreshment, schematic inferencing, and pure guessing. They hypothesize that these processes are sequential in nature. The authors report on two experiments. They support their position that these processes occur in a contingent manner; their experimental cases all supported this position and were statistically significant. Additionally, the authors hypothesized that cued retrieval was the dominant process.

Moreno and Mayer (1999) review previous research and report on their research regarding the learning effects associated with multimedia instructional designs that employ varying combinations of text, narration, images, and animation. They elaborate upon the contiguity principle that states:

"The effectiveness of multimedia instruction increases when words and pictures are presented contiguously in time and space" (Moreno and Mayer, 1999, p. 385). The authors refine the contiguity principle into the temporal-contiguity effect and spatial-contiguity effect. The spatial-contiguity effect occurs when text and images are integrated into one visual scene. The temporal-contiguity effect occurs when visual and spoken materials are temporally synchronized. They conclude that, when learners are presented with a visual presentation that incorporates text or narration, narration has a more significant effect on the learner. The authors qualified their findings by calling for more research. In this experiment, they did not factor in individual differences in spatial ability, coordination ability, and experience.

Waller (2000) conducted a multivariate study of relationships between several factors and the ability to acquire and transfer spatial knowledge from a VE. The author bisects spatial ability into related dimensions: spatial visualization and spatial orientation. Spatial visualization is the ability to manipulate figures mentally. Spatial orientation is the ability to account for changes in viewpoint. When both factors are psychometrically assessed as being higher in an individual, that individual demonstrated an increased ability to acquire spatial information from a VE. Additionally, proficiency with the VE's interface was found to significantly affect performance measures of spatial knowledge. The author postulates that a likely explanation for this finding centers on user attention while engaged in spatial learning (i.e., effortful processing of the interface interferes with the user's ability to learn in the environment). Waller's research empirically demonstrates that measured spatial abilities correlate to the ability to learn from a VE, and additionally, that the degree of attention or level of difficulty associated with the user interface detracts from one's ability to learn spatially. Replication of this study with an AR environment would quantitatively substantiate the position that AR inherently leads to efficiencies while learning due to its low-effort interface and attentional nature that creates spatial scenes for learning.

Several studies have found that gender affects spatial ability, and males tend to have higher levels of spatial ability (Cutmore, Hine, Maberly, Langford, and Hawgood, 2000; Czerwinski, Tan, and Robertson, 2002; Hamilton, 1995; Waller, 2000). Cutmore et al. (2000) conducted research into cognitive factors affecting virtual navigation performance, while navigating within a desktop-computer-generated VE clearly describes the differences in spatial ability between males and females. Various cues were used as treatments to experimental groups (e.g., compass pointers, icons for association with locations, and icons for association with landmarks). Males acquired route knowledge from landmarks quicker than females. The specific cause of this difference is speculative. However, multiple studies substantiate its existence. Cutmore et al. (2000) make an important point that gender should be a factor when designing VE training environments. Further research into gender differences with regard to spatial ability is necessary for mixed-reality worlds. However, postulating that it exists is prudent.

By its inherent nature, AR presents a visual-spatial dynamic that can be expected to enable learning advantages associated with spatial cognition that helps effective encoding of information into memory and facilitating recall. Virtual text labels, or virtual overlays in general, become associated with the real-world object and encoded into memory as one visual image. Spatial cognition is an integral element of AR and human learning (Majoros and Neumann, 2001; Neumann and Majoros, 1998).

MEMORY CHANNELS AND AR

AR interfaces affect more modalities of human senses than present learning paradigms (Bjork and Bjork, 1996; Macchiarella, 2004; Neumann and Majoros, 1998). AR is believed to complement human associative information processing by aiding information integration through multimodal sensory elaboration. Multimodal sensory elaboration occurs by utilizing visual-spatial, verbal, proprioceptive, audio, and tactile memory while the learner is encoding the information into long-term memory. This elaboration on the subject material may occur due to an increase of memory channels, enabling a greater chance for information to be encoded properly and retained in long-term memory. Effective encoding is key to the learner's ability to recall information for application in a real-world environment.

Mania and Chalmers (2001) studied the effects of immersion in a VE on recall and spatial perception. Several of their findings were inconclusive, but they did find a significant correlation between recall and environments that presented multimodal sensory elaboration as found in three different environments with corresponding inherent levels of immersion. The environments for the research comprised the real world and a virtual world, in which the subjects were fully immersed, and a virtual world created with a desktop computer, in which subjects were partially immersed. Their research found overall that relevant multimodal stimuli enhanced recall.

Gamberini (2000) studied groups of subjects who were exposed to a fully immersive VE or a nonimmersive VE (i.e., a virtual world depicted within a real-world setting on a desktop computer). The researcher found that subjects in the nonimmersive group scored higher in the areas of recall for spatial and visual memories. He postulated that several factors affected this outcome. His key factor for consideration was that the nonimmersive environment is more familiar to subjects because they see both real-world and virtual-world objects. In an AR learning environment, real-world objects (e.g., turbine engine aircraft oil pump) are presented to learners, and the learners can engage in learning in a multimodal sensory fashion.

Multimodal sensory elaboration can create a framework of associations that aid recall and learning (Majoros and Neumann, 2001; Neumann and Majoros, 1998). Each association of a virtual object (e.g., virtual text label) with a real-world object serving as a work piece is the basis for a link in memory that might not otherwise exist. Together these links (e.g., a visual arrangement of text callouts in an AR work piece scene) may form a framework like that created when subjects use a classic mnemonic technique to remember a list of items. With this method, a subject associates items to-be-remembered with invented places or landmarks on an imaginary path (Neumann and Majoros, 1998; Yates, 1984). During recall, the subject "mentally walks" on the path, encounters a mental *landmark,* visualizes the item associated with the landmark (e.g., to-be-recalled item on a real-world work piece), and then processes the to-be-recalled item into working memory. AR has the potential to expand these mental landmarks to include multimodal sensory input that establishes multiple channels to the memory. Users of AR are provided a framework (i.e., the real world) that holds the items that will be recalled. This association and multimodal elaboration does not necessarily happen intentionally; it can occur as a by-product of the use of enhanced work piece scenes (Neumann and Majoros, 1998).

KNOWLEDGE DEVELOPMENT AND TRAINING TRANSFER

Reduced costs and increasing capabilities of computer-based technologies have initiated dramatic increases in the application of computer-delivered instruction such as computer-based training, Web-based training, multimedia learning environments (Brown, 2001), virtual reality (Stone, 2001), and augmented reality (Majoros and Neumann, 2001). Computer-based training has become ubiquitous throughout the government, military, and commercial training associated with the aviation field. It typically gives the learner the loci of controls over instruction. Learner-controlled environments offer learners choices regarding practice level, time on task, and attention.

Transfer of training refers to how well learned skills and information can be applied in a different work setting. In the case of AR-based training, skills first acquired in a mixed-reality work setting would serve as training for subsequent skill application in the real world. Application of these skills could involve cognitive or psychomotor work tasks. In the future, the new mixed-reality world may redefine how workers are trained (Kalawsky, Stedmon, Hill, and Cook, 2000; Majoros and Neumann, 2001). The traditional training paradigm employs some form of training (e.g., computer-based tutorials, face-to-face instruction, self-study with printed manuals) prior to licensing or assignment to a work task. In this future mixed-reality world, AR may make some forms of training unnecessary or at least reduced in time and scope (Macchiarella, 2005; Macchiarella, Gangadharan, Liu, Majoros, and Vincenzi, 2005; Majoros and Neumann, 2001; Vincenzi et al., 2003). Cognitive tasks normally associated with training could be performed for the human by the AR system. This characteristic of AR may enable *just-in-time* training functions that occur simultaneously with work task performance. As an example, AR could provide scenes that are annotated with types of information that is customarily learned through training. This presentation of information could support humans in inspection tasks or enable them to perform work tasks that are rarely encountered and with little prior training.

AR scenes, in the same manner as VR scenes, have the ability to direct learner attention and facilitate the acquisition of spatial knowledge regarding a real world or virtual world (Witmer, Baily, and Knerr, 1996). Virtual environments provide direct natural feedback that symbolic media (e.g., a map or photograph) cannot provide. Witmer, Baily, and Knerr (1996) conducted a study using undergraduate students at the University of Central Florida in conjunction with the U.S. Army. Selected test participants rehearsed navigation through a building either using VE or photographs and maps. The participants using the VE rehearsal were significantly more accurate in their navigation of the real building. Additionally, the authors postulated that additional VR cues, tactile or aural, would enhance the participants' gained knowledge and improve navigation through the building. The creation of an AR-based mixed-reality world, where the positive transfer information occurs with users, could enhance training environments.

Waller, Knapp, and Hunt (2001) conducted research involving the effects of visual fidelity and individual differences on the ability to learn in a virtual environment, and subsequently transfer the learned knowledge to a real-world use. They found that the fidelity of the VE is less important when used to train tasks that do not require higher-level cognitive processes. Additionally, the authors found individual differences, such as cognitive abilities and level of computer-use experience, did impact the transfer of training for virtual-to-real and real-to-virtual environments more than the fidelity of the simulation. Two possible positive effects can be inferred regarding AR and this research. First, AR can be designed to deliver information that normally is obtained through training, in effect reducing cognitive load and helping to mitigate differences in cognitive abilities while training. Second, the AR interface is intuitive, and typically does not require an interface device (i.e., trackball, joystick, etc.). The intuitive interface of AR may help mitigate differences in levels of computer use skills. The users of AR look at a real-world object, and virtual scenes of information are automatically presented for use.

Self-efficacy (i.e., people's judgments of their capabilities to organize and execute courses of action necessary to attain designated types or levels of performances; Bandura, 1986, 1997) is central to the success or failure that learners experience as they engage the tasks necessary to attain knowledge in a given field. High self-efficacy helps create feelings of serenity or "peace of mind" as learners approach difficult tasks and activities that comprise decision-making and complex work tasks. Neumann and Majoros (1998) postulate that AR scenes may support self-efficacy by creating an environment where the learner, or user of AR, has the loci of controls over their learning environment. A high level of individualized control for the learning situation has a positive effect on learning (e.g., allow users to invoke an AR scene with virtual "paste and copy" to keep information accessible while conducting a real-world work task; Ormrod, 1999).

With regard to concurrent training and performance, AR enables learning experiences where users train for tasks in a manner that identically replicates performance of the task in the real-world environment; this type of a "real-world" training environment has shown to provide advantages regarding transfer of knowledge and training (Majoros and Neumann, 2001). Rose et al. (2000) empirically ascertained that VEs do transfer training as effectively as real-world training. They also highlight that three main factors influence interference between concurrent task learning: task similarity, practice, and task difficulty. Regarding task similarity, the authors concluded that the extent of interference between two separate tasks is dependent on the degree they share a stimulus modality (e.g., visual, auditory, and tactile) and whether they rely on the same memory coding processes (e.g., verbal and visual). Rose et al. (2000) cite research by Sullivan (1976) as corroborating their position that concurrent tasks are impaired when the difficulty of the tasks is increased. They differentiate between performance that is resource limited (i.e., dependent on the mental processing resources available to devote to the task) and data limited (i.e., dependent on external stimulus quality—instructions, notes, cues, etc.). In both cases of performances, both resource limited and data limited, AR has the potential to enhance concurrent training by delivering annotated work scenes that reduce mental workloads through virtual text callouts, equipment diagrams, and instructions with step-by-step sequencing.

As AR training environments mature, creation of just-in-time or concurrent training may be feasible (Majoros and Neumann, 2001). One objective of future applications of AR may be to provide annotated visual scenes that supplant the need for certain aspects of training. This substitution for training would occur by providing AR-delivered information to the user, during work task performance, in lieu of the user recalling work task steps from long-term or working memory.

WHAT IS THE FUTURE OF JOB TRAINING—TRAINING ON THE JOB LITERALLY?

Applications of AR can enable learning environments embedded in the real world and make the real world part of the computer interface (see Figure 18.4). Future applications of virtual environments can take the form and function of a mixed-reality world with hypertext linking to vast resources of information and instructional content. The visual nature of the AR scenes is, in many ways, analogous to a GUI in the mind's eye. AR may have a positive effect on recall by enticing elaboration through the creation of multiple associations between the real-world object being studied and the to-be-learned virtual information (Macchiarella, 2004; Valimont, 2002).

In this new mixed-reality world, multimodal sensory elaboration can create a framework of associations that aid recall and learning. Each association of a virtual object (e.g., virtual text label) with a real-world object could serve as a basis for a link in memory that might not otherwise exist. Together these links (e.g., a visual arrangement of text callouts in an AR work piece scene) may form a framework like that created when students use a mnemonic technique to remember a list of items (see Figure 18.5). With this method, in the mind's eye, a student would associate items to be remembered with places or landmarks after viewing mixed-reality images of the studied item. During recall, the student "mentally walks" on the path; encounters a mental landmark, visualizes the item associated with the landmark (e.g., to-be-recalled aspect of a real-world work piece), and

FIGURE 18.4   AR-aided inspection of an aircraft elevator.

FIGURE 18.5   AR scene with instructions for servicing a turbine engine oil pump.

then processes the to-be-recalled item into working memory. AR has the potential to expand these mental landmarks to include multimodal sensory input that establishes multiple channels to the memory. Users of AR are provided a framework (i.e., the real world) that holds the items that will be recalled. This association and multimodal elaboration does not necessarily happen intentionally; it can occur as a by-product of the use of enhanced work piece scenes.

Transfer of training refers to how effectively learned skills and information can be applied in a work setting. In the case of AR-based training, skills first acquired in a mixed-reality work setting would serve as training for subsequent skill application in the real world. Application of these skills could involve cognitive or psychomotor work tasks. In the future, the new mixed-reality world may redefine how workers are trained (Kalawsky, Stedmon, Hill, and Cook, 2000; Majoros and Neumann, 2001). The traditional training paradigm employs some form of training (e.g., computer-based tutorials, face-to-face instruction, self-study with printed manuals) prior to licensing or assignment to a job task. In this future mixed-reality world, AR may make some forms of training unnecessary or at least reduced in time and scope (Macchiarella, Gangadharan, Liu, Majoros, and Vincenzi, 2005a; Macchiarella and Haritos, 2005). Cognitive tasks normally associated with training could be performed for the human by the AR system. This characteristic of AR may enable just-in-time training functions that occur simultaneously with job task performance. As an example, AR could provide scenes that are annotated with types of information that is customarily learned through training. This presentation of information could support humans in inspection tasks or enable them to perform job tasks that are rarely encountered and with little prior training.

AR has the potential to transform computing as drastically as the GUI transformed computing (Fishkin, Gujar, Harrison, Moran, and Want, 2000; Vincenzi et al., 2003). Physical configuration of computational devices is a major determinant of their usability. Despite the rapid advances in computing technology afforded by exponential increases in computational power, humans still interact with computers in a very limited manner. The mode of interaction available for humans with computers primarily consists of a keyboard and a pointing device. In most cases, the pointing device is a mouse, and humans are limited to pointing, dragging, and drawing. When contrasting the various ways humans interact with each other (e.g., speaking—actual meaning of words, speaking—use of tone, listening, touching, gesturing, etc.), human interaction with computers is relatively simple (Alessi and Trollip, 2001). As researchers, computer scientists, and practitioners of AR solve the technological issues associated with using AR in real time and in the real world, AR-based human and computer interaction can become more like human-to-human interaction and engage more human modalities. The movie *Minority Report* (Frank and Cohen, 2001) portends human interactions with computers in an insightful and powerful way. The film depicts numerous applications of AR. Police officers interact with computer-generated images from human minds through a wall-sized interface device they manipulate with speech and touch. The officers can tear virtual media from the display, move media around, change view aspects, and generally use the virtual media in the real world as if it were a real-world object. Another interesting application of AR in the movie is for marketing and sales purposes. Pedestrians walk past scanners and receive an iris scan that positively identifies them. This application of biometric identification enables a computer to generate a holographic 3-D salesperson that is implanted into the real world as an AR feature. The 3-D salesperson makes a personalized sales presentation to the pedestrian. The movie presents many other innovative examples for applications of AR.

CONCLUSION

As the computational power of computers continues its rapid advance, as prophesied by Moore (1965), developers of AR-based training, during the upcoming decades, will have the opportunity to create AR workstations that are portable and powerful. These portable and powerful workstations can enable AR in the real-world work settings of the aerospace industry. AR has the potential to positively affect training by enabling higher levels of recall and just-in-time training functions. Training could occur in the actual work setting and at times simultaneously with job task performance. The net positive effect resulting from the use AR as a learning medium may derive from the learners' ability to mentally match augmented information directly with the work piece in front of them; future research is required to fully ascertain these effects on the cognitive activities associated with job tasks.

REFERENCES

Alessi, S. M., & Trollip, S. R., 2001. *Multimedia for Learning: Methods and Development* (3rd ed.). Boston: Allyn and Bacon.

Azuma, R. T., 1997. A Survey of Augmented Realty. *Presence, 6*(4), 355–385.

Azuma, R. T., 2004. Overview of Augmented Reality. *Proceedings of the Conference on SIGGRAPH 2004, Los Angeles, CA.*

Azuma, R. T., Baillot, Y., Behringer, R., Feiner, S., Julier, S., & MacIntyre, B., 2001. Recent Advances in Augmented Reality. *IEEE Computer Graphics and Applications, 21*(6), 34–47.

Bandura, A., 1986. *Social Foundations of Thought and Action: A Social Cognitive Theory.* Englewood Cliffs, NJ: Prentice Hall.

Bandura, A., 1997. *Self-Efficacy: The Exercise of Control.* New York: Freeman.

Billinghurst, M., & Kato, H., 2002. Collaborative Augmented Reality. *Communications of the ACM, 45,* 64–70.

Billinghurst, M., Kato, H., & Poupyrev, I., 2000. *ARToolKit User's Manual.* Seattle, WA: University of Washington.

Billinghurst, M., Kato, H., & Poupyrev, I., 2001. The MagicBook—Moving Seamlessly between Reality and Virtuality. *Computer Graphics and Applications, 21*(3), 2–4.

Bjork, R. A., & Bjork, E. L. (Eds.), 1996. *Memory.* San Diego, CA: Academic Press.

Brown, K. G., 2001. Using Computers to Deliver Training: Which Employees Learn and Why. *Personnel Psychology, 54*(2), 271–296.

Cutmore, T. R. H., Hine, T. J., Maberly, K. J., Langford, N. M., & Hawgood, G., 2000. Cognitive and Gender Factors Influencing Navigation in a Virtual Environment. *International Journal of Human-Computer Studies, 53,* 223–249.

Czerwinski, M., Tan, D., & Robertson, G., 2002. *Women Take a Wider View.* Paper presented at the ACM, SIGCHI, Conference on Human Factors and Computing Systems [Spatial Cognition], Minneapolis, MN.

Feiner, S., MacIntyre, B., & Hollerer, T., 1997. A Touring Machine: Prototyping 3D Mobile Augmented Reality Systems for Exploring the Urban Environment. *Proceedings of the International Symposium on Wearable Computing,* 74–81.

Fishkin, P., Gujar, A., Harrison, B., Moran, T., & Want, R., 2000. Embodied User Interfaces for Really Direct Manipulation. *Communications of the ACM, 43*(9), 75–80.

Frank, S., & Cohen, J. (Writers), 2001. *Minority Report* [motion picture]. Hollywood: Twentieth Century Fox and Dreamworks LLC.

Gamberini, L., 2000. Virtual Reality as a New Research Tool for the Study of Human Memory. *CyberPsychology and Behavior, 3*(3), 337–342.

Haberlandt, K., 1997. *Cognitive Psychology* (2nd ed.). Needham Heights, MA: Allyn and Bacon.

Hamilton, C., 1995. Beyond Sex Differences in Visuo-Spatial Processing: The Impact of Gender Trait Possession. *British Journal of Psychology, 86*(1), 1–20.

Kalawsky, R., Stedmon, A. W., Hill, K., & Cook, C., 2000. *A Taxonomy of Technology: Defining Augmented Reality*. Paper presented at the Human Factors and Ergonomics Society Annual Meeting, Santa Monica, CA.

Knowles, M., 1984. *The Adult Learner: A Neglected Species* (3rd ed.). Houston TX: Gulf Port Publishing.

Lovelace, E. A., & Southall, S. D., 1983. Memory for Words in Prose and Their Locations on the Page. *Memory and Cognition, 11*(5), 429–434.

Macchiarella, N. D., 2004. Effectiveness of Video-Based Augmented Reality as a Learning Paradigm for Aerospace Maintenance Training. *Dissertation Abstracts International, 65(09)*, 3347A, (UMI No. 3148420).

Macchiarella, N. D., 2005. Augmenting Reality as a Medium for Job Task Training. *Journal of Instruction Delivery Systems, 19*(1), 21–24.

Macchiarella, N. D., Gangadharan, S. N., Liu, D., Majoros, A. E., & Vincenzi, D. A., 2005. Augmenting Reality as a Training Medium for Aviation/Aerospace Applications. *Proceedings of the Human Factors and Ergonomics Society 49th Annual Meeting,* Orlando, FL, 2174–2178.

Macchiarella, N. D., Gangadharan, S. N., Liu, D., Majoros, A. E., & Vincenzi, D. A., 2005a. Application of Augmented Reality for Aerospace Maintenance Training. *Proceedings of the 11th International Conference of Human Computer Interaction,* Las Vegas, NV, CD-ROM, 1–5.

Macchiarella, N. D., & Haritos, T., 2005. A Mobile Application of Augmented Reality for Aerospace Maintenance Training. *Proceedings of the 24th Digital Avionics Systems Conference, Avionics in a Changing Market Place: Safe and Secure,* Washington D.C., 5.B.3–1—5.B.3–9.

Majoros, A., & Boyle, E., 1997. Maintainability. In G. Salvendy (Ed.), *Handbook of Human Factors and Ergonomics* (2nd ed., pp. 1569–1592). New York: John Wiley.

Majoros, A., & Neumann, U., 2001. *Support of Crew Problem-Solving and Performance with Augmented Reality*. Galveston, TX: Bioastronautics Investigators' Workshop.

Mania, K., & Chalmers, A., 2001. The Effects of Levels of Immersion on Memory and Presence in Virtual environments: A Reality Centered Approach. *CyberPsychology and Behavior, 4*(2), 247–264.

Mayer, R., 1992. Cognition and Instruction Their Historic Meeting Within Educational Psychology. *Journal of Educational Psychology, 84*(4), 405–412.

Milgram, P., & Kishino, F., 1994. A Taxonomy of Mixed Reality Visual Displays. *IEICE Transactions Information Systems, E77-D*(12), 1321–1329.

Moore, G. E., 1965. Cramming More Components Onto Integrated Circuits. *Electronics, 38*(8), 1–4.

Moreno, R., & Mayer, R., 1999. Cognitive Principles of Multimedia Learning: The Role of Modality and Contiguity. *Journal of Educational Psychology, 91*(2), 358–368.

Nakamura, G., 1994. Scene Schemata in Memory for Spatial Relations. *American Journal of Psychology, 107*(4), 481–497.

Neumann, U., & Majoros, A., 1998. Cognitive, Performance, and System Issues for Augmented Reality Applications in Manufacturing and Maintenance. *Proceedings of IEEE the Virtual Reality Annual International Symposium (VRAIS),* 4–11.

Ormrod, J., 1999. *Human Learning* (3rd ed.). Upper Saddle River, NJ: Prentice-Hall.

Ott, J., 1995. Maintenance Executives Seek Greater Efficiency. *Aviation Week and Space Technology, 142,* 2.

Pezdek, K., & Evans, G. W., 1979. Visual and Verbal Memory for Objects and Their Spatial Locations. *Journal of Experimental Psychology: Human Learning and Memory, 5*(4), 360–373.

Phaf, R., & Wolters, G., 1993. Attentional Shifts in Maintenance Rehearsal. *American Journal of Psychology, 106*(3), 353–382.

Pham, M., & Venkataramani, J., 1997. Contingent Processes of Source Identification. *Journal of Consumer Research, 24*(3), 249–266.

Poupyrev, I., Tan, D., Billinghurst, M., Kato, H., Regebrecht, H., & Tetsutani, N., 2002. Developing a Generic Augmented-Reality Interface. *Computer Magazine, 35*(3), 44–50.

Reigeluth, C. M., 1999. The Elaboration Theory: Guidance for Scope and Sequence Decisions. In C. M. Reigeluth (Ed.), *Instructional-Design Theories and Models: A New Paradigm of Instructional Theory* (Vol. II). Hillsdale, NJ: Lawrence Erlbaum Associates.

Rose, F. D., Attree, B. M., Brooks, D. M., Parslow, D. M., Penn, P. R., & Ambihaipahan, N., 2000. Training in Virtual Environments: Transfer to Real World Tasks and Equivalence to Real Task Training. *Ergonomics, 43*(4), 494–511.

Saariluoma, P., & Kalakoski, V., 1997. Skilled Imagery and Long-Term Working Memory. *American Journal of Psychology, 110*(2), 177–202.

Shneiderman, B., 1998. *Designing the User Interface, Strategies for Effective Human-Computer Design* (3rd ed.). Reading, MA: Addison-Wesely.

Stapleton, C., Hughes, C., Moshell, M., Micikevicius, P., & Altman, M., 2002. Applying Mixed Reality to Entertainment. *Computer, 35*(12), 122–124.

Stedmon, A. W., Hill, K., Kalawsky, R. S., & Cook, C. A., 1999. Old Theories, New Technologies: Comprehension and Retention Issues in Augmented Reality Systems. *Proceedings of the 43rd Annual Meeting of the Human Factors and Ergonomics Society,* Santa Monica, CA, 1050–1054.

Stein, B., Littlefield, J., Bransford, J., & Persampieri, M., 1984. Elaboration and Knowledge Acquisition. *Memory and Cognition, 12*(5), 522–529.

Stone, R., 2001. Virtual Reality for Interactive Training: An Industrial Practitioner's Viewpoint. *International Journal of Human–Computer Studies, 55*(4), 699–711.

Sullivan, L., 1976. Selective Attention and Secondary Message Analysis: A Reconsideration of Broadbent's Filter Model of Selective Attention. *Quarterly Journal of Experimental Psychology, 28*, 167–178.

Thorndike, E. L., 1905. *The Elements of Psychology.* London: Routledge and Kegan.

Tulving, E., & Osler, S., 1968. Effectiveness of Retrieval Cues in Memory for Words. *Journal of Experimental Psychology, 77*(4), 593–601.

U.S. General Accounting Office. 2003. *FAA Needs to Update the Curriculum and Certification Requirements for Aviation Mechanics.* Washington D.C.: United States General Accounting Office.

Valimont, B., 2002. *The Effectiveness of an Augmented Reality Learning Paradigm.* Daytona Beach, FL: Embry-Riddle Aeronautical University.

Vincenzi, D. A., & Gangadharan, S., 2001. *Project Proposal Collaborative Research on Augmented Reality.* Daytona Beach, FL: Embry-Riddle Aeronautical University.

Vincenzi, D. A., Valimont, B., Macchiarella, N. D., Opalenik, C., Gangadharan, S., & Majoros, A., 2003. The Effectiveness of Cognitive Elaboration Using Augmented Reality as a Training and Learning Paradigm. *Proceedings of the Human Factors and Ergonomics Society 47th Annual Meeting,* Denver, CO, 2054–2058.

Waller, D., 2000. Individual Differences in Spatial Learning from Computer-Simulated Environments. *Journal of Experimental Psychology, 6*(4), 307–321.

Waller, D., Knapp, D., & Hunt, E., 2001. Spatial Representations of Virtual Mazes: The Role of Visual Fidelity and Individual Difference. *Human Factors, 43*(1), 147–158.

Witmer, B., Baily, J., & Knerr, B., 1996. Virtual Spaces and Real World Places: Transfer of Route Knowledge. *International Journal of Human–Computer Studies, 45*(4), 413–428.

Yates, F. A., 1984. *The Art of Memory.* London: Routledge and Kegan Paul.

Yeh, M., & Wickens, C., 2001. Display Signaling in Augmented Reality: Effects of Cue Reliability and Image Realism on Attention Allocation and Trust Calibration. *Human Factors, 43*(3), 355–365.

19 Simulation Research in the Command and Control of Air Operations
Implications of the Network-Centric Concept

Robert S. Bolia, Michael A. Vidulich, and W. Todd Nelson

CONTENTS

THE COMMAND AND CONTROL ENVIRONMENT

Command and control (C2) is defined by the United States Department of Defense (DoD, 2004) as "the exercise of authority and direction by a properly designated commander over assigned and attached forces in the accomplishment of the mission." The lexicographers note further that this exercise and direction are "performed through an arrangement of personnel, equipment, communications, facilities, and procedures employed by [the] commander in planning, directing, coordinating, and controlling forces and operations" designed to accomplish that mission. Although this definition may not conjure a distinct image of the day-to-day job of a military commander, it certainly offers at least a hint of the complexity inherent in the phrase "command and control."

If the vision supplied is not exceptionally detailed, it is at least partially because it is context-free. Some of the relevant perspective is of course provided by recalling that this chapter is restricted to a discussion of the C2 of *air* operations, although this alone is insufficiently illuminating. Further clarification may be gained by distinguishing between the "levels of war" traditionally considered by military theorists. There are three such levels: strategic, operational, and tactical.

The strategic (Greek στρατηγος, "general, commander of an army") level of war is defined as "the level of war at which a nation, often as a member of a group of nations, determines national or multinational (alliance or coalition) security objectives and guidance, and develops and uses national resources to accomplish these objectives" (DoD, 2004). C2 at this level is typically the responsibility of the political leadership of nations and their military chiefs of staff. Strategic command transcends the bounds of both service (Air Force, Army, Navy) and component (air, ground, maritime), and as such will not be considered here.

The operational (Latin *operare,* "to work") level represents a step down from the strategic level in terms of scope—both spatial and temporal—and responsibility. It is characterized by the DoD (2004) as "the level of war at which campaigns and major operations are planned, conducted, and sustained to accomplish strategic objectives within theaters or other operational areas." For air operations, operational-level C2 is conducted at air and space operations centers (AOCs).

The tactical (Greek τακτικος, "fit for ordering or arranging") level of war is that "at which battles and engagements are planned and executed to accomplish military objectives assigned to tactical units or task forces" (DoD, 2004). Tactical C2 of air operations may be carried out by an airborne platform, such as the United States Air Force's E-3 Airborne Warning and Control System (AWACS) or E-8 Joint Surveillance Target Attack Radar System (JSTARS), or the United States Navy's E-2C Hawkeye; in the combat information center of a ship; or from a ground-based battle control station (see Vidulich, Bolia, and Nelson, 2004, for a more thorough enumeration of the tasks of tactical air battle managers).

Common to all tactical and operational C2 environments is their characterization as teams of teams. The AWACS mission crew, for example, may be composed of a weapons team, a surveillance team, and a communications team, all responsible to the mission crew commander. These teams work together to accomplish the mission, while also functioning, in whole or in part, as members of other teams. A weapons controller, for instance, serves as part of the weapons team on the AWACS, but is also part of the strike package he or she controls. Although AWACS has been drawn on as a case in point, the team of teams concept applies equally to all of the systems under consideration, as it will likely apply to any future C2 system.

NETWORK-CENTRIC OPERATIONS

The future of C2 is being driven by a concept of operations dubbed network-centric warfare (NCW),* which seeks to generate increased speed of command by means of enhanced situation awareness and self-synchronization, characteristics that advocates of NCW claim follow naturally from the dense networking of sensors and shooters (Cebrowski and Garstka, 1998; Alberts, Garstka, and Stein, 2000). For its adherents, NCW represents a revolution in military affairs (RMA), which will create for its practitioners an advantage akin to that obtained by Wal-Mart in the commercial world, allowing them to operate inside of the enemy's decision cycle and hence "lock out" the possibility of defeat. Its detractors foresee a number of difficulties with this vision.

On the one hand, there are those who believe in some of the tenets of NCW, but not all. Theorists in the United Kingdom and the United States Marine Corps have a philosophical problem, for example, with the *centricity* of the network, and prefer a term like "network-enabled capability," which stresses that the network is not what is fundamental in the equation, and that it should be treated as a capability, just as an aircraft or submarine is treated as a capability.

On the other hand, there are those who are completely at ease with the concept of NCW, but believe rather that its novelty is overstated, and that its articulation by Cebrowski and his colleagues is no more than an abuse of "buzzwords" (Havig, Aleva, Reis, and McIntire, 2007). Indeed, the concept of self-synchronization can easily be linked to Moltke's conception of *Auftragstaktik,* which suggests that field commanders who share the same mental model—presumably inculcated by means of training—as their commanding officer will self-synchronize automatically (van Creveld, 1985; Hughes, 1993; Fitz-Gibbon, 1995). In naval circles, this idea goes back at least to the days of Nelson,

---

* Alternative nomenclatures, driven by national, organizational, or semantic differences, abound, e.g., network-centric operations (NCO), network-enabled capability (NEC), network-enabled operations (NEOps).

whose subordinates had no difficulty interpreting his command intent—even in the absence of reliable communications—at the Battle of the Nile (Lavery, 1998; Hughes, 2000). Moreover, the idea of networked tactical forces is far from new; Woodward (1997), for example, provides a view of a networked air defense system in use by the Royal Navy in the Falklands War.

Finally, there are those skeptics who simply believe that NCW will not work as advertised. NCW devotees enjoy calling attention to Metcalf's law, which states that the power of a network is proportional to the square of the number of nodes in the network (Alberts and Hayes, 2003). What they fail to point out is that such an increase in "power" comes only with a concomitant increase in complexity, which may lead to unpredictable behaviors and even instability (Waldrop, 1992). Anyone who has ever used a networked computer has experienced times at which the network appears sluggish or is "down" for unspecified reasons. If a maximally connected network is envisioned as a force multiplier, shouldn't a disconnected network be regarded as a force divider?

Thus far, only the complexity issue has arisen. It should also be clear that networks may fail for other reasons. Proponents of NCW generally disregard—at least in their writings—the possibility of countermeasures, although these have proven the undoing of other RMAs (Bolia, Vidulich, Nelson, and Cook, 2007). One recalls the words of Italian airpower theorist Giulio Douhet, once thought prophetic: *Tutto ciò che l'uomo può fare sulla superficie non tange l'aereo capace di muovere lungo la terza dimensione* (Douhet, 2002, p. 19).* Clearly, Douhet failed to predict the development of the surface-to-air missile.

Yet it is not only by means of technological failures—enemy-induced or otherwise—that NCW may fail to achieve its full potential. The employment of technology in the absence of appropriate tactics and doctrine has been implicated in numerous military disasters (see, e.g., Bolia, 2004). It is not difficult to imagine the empowerment of the common soldier with situation awareness leading to decisions being made at a level incommensurate with the required authority or expertise. It is equally easy to forecast commanders-in-chief using their knowledge of the situation to micromanage the tactical level of war. Indeed, any implementation of NCW will no doubt lead to a blurring of the levels of war, with untold consequences for typical command relationships.

C2 SIMULATION RESEARCH

To fairly consider the future of simulation-based C2 research, it may be worthwhile to look back and examine the history of C2 human factors research. Although it has been pointed out that C2 of one sort or another probably dates back as far as the Stone Age (van Creveld, 1985), the most appropriate precursor to NCW applied to C2 arguably date back to the application of electronic sensing (i.e., radar) and modern communications (i.e., telephone and radio). For example, Alberts et al. (2000) employ the coevolution of technology and C2 doctrine during the Battle of Britain as a laudatory example of how NCW applications must be developed. Although modern human factors and engineering psychology are also often considered to have been born during World War II, the bulk of the research of this era was aimed at improving the performance of pilots (Roscoe, 1997).

Nevertheless, the quantity of C2 human factors research increased dramatically following World War II. The recently deceased Henry McIlvane Parsons (Krueger, 2004) conducted an extensive review of large-scale investigations conducted from the late 1940s to the mid 1960s (Parsons, 1972). Parsons identified that radar, the production of high-performance aircraft, and advanced communications and computers in military systems all encouraged a greater emphasis on large-scale human–machine systems. He carefully reviewed 43 major human–machine research programs, most of which concerned air defense systems. As a part of the review, Parsons identified several key areas that appeared important in the conduct of large-system, human–machine, human factors research:

---

* "Nothing that man can do from the surface can interfere with the capacity of an airplane to move along in the third dimension." (Translation by the first author.)

management (e.g., planning, acquisition and administration of resources, and staffing), design, simulation, subjects, and measurement.

Today, NCW has been identified as both a challenge and a promise for future C2 systems. Needless to say, it has also presented challenges to the human factors research community, though in many ways the research challenges of today are the same as those identified by Parsons (1972). Consequently, it should be instructive to evaluate the current NCW C2 human factors research programs with respect to how well they meet the Parsons standards. In particular, how do current programs confront the issues of design simulation and measurement as outlined by Parsons? As exemplars of current C2 human factors research, programs conducted by the U.S. Army, U.S. Navy, and U.S. Air Force will be reviewed.

U.S. Army Future Combat Systems (FCS) Program

Much of the U.S. Army's C2 human factors research has been conducted to support the Future Combat Systems (FCS) program. According to the Government Accounting Office (GAO), the goal of the FCS program is to create a transformational force called the Objective Force (Francis, 2003). The Objective Force is intended to be light enough to be agile, flexible, deployable and mobile, yet remain as powerful as current generation Army heavy forces. To accomplish this, the FCS program is developing a family of 18 systems for the Objective Force. These systems will be smaller and lighter and supported by new technologies (e.g., munitions, unmanned sensors, robotics) to increase effectiveness. Of particular note, the FCS program is charged with creating a C2 network that will substitute synchronized operations for traditional military mass. This synchronization is expected to demand and support delegating greater decision-making authority to commanders closer to the action.

Lickteig, Sanders, Shadrick, Lussier, Holt, and Rainey (2002) have reviewed the human–system research requirements for supporting the FCS program. Their first step was to identify four overarching C2 human engineering research issues: allocation (how best to allocate human–machine functions?); authority (who is in command, human or machine?); autonomy (who is in control?); and awareness (how to maintain human awareness of the big picture?). To attack these research issues, Lickteig et al. (2002) suggested that two complementary simulation approaches would be needed: mid-scale and small-scale. Large-scale environments, particularly those that were multiservice, were not ignored, but a concern was raised that such environments may be too expensive and too unwieldy to provide efficient learning.

Army researchers have been very concerned with methodological issues associated with conducting effective C2 simulation research. For example, Sanders (2003) explored how to improve measurement of verbal communications, human–computer interaction (HCI) behaviors, and subjective assessment. Sanders used data from previous warfighter-in-the-loop battle simulation experiments. Due to time constraints, the data analysis of these experiments was unable to evaluate the frequency and duration of verbal communications among the C2 teams; neither were the duration of the HCI actions available. Sanders developed procedures to produce word counts of verbal communications and time values for the communications based on the word count. These data were tracked over 10-minute segments during the simulated battles and analyzed to provide an estimate of how verbal communication demands vary across the performance of a battle for individual command groups. These data could then be used to guide decisions about whether some tasks might be able to be reallocated to another crew member during periods of high task load. The HCI data were similarly analyzed to identify the task load inflicted on each crew member during different parts of the mission to guide possible task reallocations. Overall, Sanders concluded that the research had supported previous suggestions by Cannon-Bowers and Salas (1997) that process measures of decision making and teamwork would be more useful than outcome measures to investigations of collective decision making.

Lickteig, Sanders, Durlach, Lussier, and Carnahan (2003) expanded on Sanders' (2003) methodology and results. They combined subjective measures, verbal interaction recordings, HCI evaluation and prototype automated measures to examine four members of a command group in four simulated exercises of proposed FCS technology. The four members of the command team were equipped with a prototype C2 display designed to facilitate their situation awareness and control of simulated reconnaissance and combat assets. The command team was composed of four distinct duty positions: commander, battlespace manager, information manager, and effects manager. Each duty position was equipped with a prototype C2 interface. The interface had four windowed features: the Battlefield Assistant that provided individually tailored alerts when predesignated tactical events occurred; an Image Viewer that displayed potential targets for human target recognition or battle damage assessment; a Target Catalog that allowed the user to input or revise information associated with enemy targets; and a Resource Availability display that was used to access and revise information on friendly assets including operational status, available fuel, and current speed and location.

Due to the extremely limited sample size—one basic team with occasional substitutions—Lickteig et al. (2003) did not perform traditional inferential statistical analysis. Instead, they focused on analysis of trends and interpretation of the trends regarding future research needs. This policy was also used in several reports that presented different subsets of the data from the same set of four experiments using the experienced command team. In these studies Army researchers focused on the need to develop better metrics of C2 team communication and HCI activities (e.g., Durlach, Bowens, Neumann, and Carnahan, 2004; Lickteig, Sanders, Durlach, and Carnahan, 2004), as well as the implications of the emerging trends for the FCS C2 system on training requirements (e.g., Campbell, Throne, Black, and Lickteig, 2003; Carnahan, Lickteig, Sanders, Durlach, and Lussier, 2004).

The work reported in this series of reports did not generally investigate interface concepts for the C2 operators, although the prototype C2 display used in the studies most likely represented the feature set expected in future interfaces. Nevertheless, many of the features of the map controls and other interface features were anticipated by earlier Army evaluations of C2 interface requirements and guidelines (e.g., Lickteig, 1986, 1988; Lickteig and Collins, 1995). In addition to the in-house work, the Army has funded some outside studies of C2 interface issues. For example, Morrison, Konya, Toth, Turnbaugh, Gunzelman, and Gilson (2003) conducted an independent literature review to produce interface requirements and design guidelines. The authors first reviewed relevant literature in three domains: contemporary philosophies of design; specific published guidance from military, academic, and industrial sources; and current interface practices for command, control, communications, computer, intelligence, surveillance, and reconnaissance (C4ISR) functions. Based on the review, a model incorporating the interactions among operational variables, the battlespace, and the C2 operator's sensory modalities was developed. This model was then used to generate design guidelines, such as the appropriate use of auditory and visual displays to increase C2 team performance. The guidelines were not instantiated in an interface and tested, but presumably this remains a possibility.

U.S. NAVY C2 HUMAN FACTORS RESEARCH PROGRAMS

The U.S. Navy has supported two major research efforts that have involved simulation research to aid their C2 operations: the Tactical Decision Making Under Stress (TADMUS) and the Space and Naval Warfare (SPAWAR) research program.

The TADMUS program was initiated in the aftermath of the mistaken destruction of Air Iran Flight 655 over the Persian Gulf on July 3, 1988, by the U.S. Navy's cruiser, the USS *Vincennes* (Collyer and Malecki, 1998). The incident investigation concluded that stress, task fixation, and unconscious biases may have played important roles in producing the fatal mistake. As befits its name, TADMUS was founded to investigate decision making under stress in combat situations, with the hope that mistakes like the *Vincennes* incident could be eliminated or at least dramatically reduced in probability.

Johnston, Poirier, and Smith-Jentsch (1998) reported that to execute effective research, the TADMUS team developed two simulation test beds: the Decision Making Facility for Tactical Teams (DEFTT) and the Tactical Navy Decision Making (TANDEM) system. DEFTT was designed to achieve a higher level of cognitive fidelity for use with experienced naval personnel, whereas TANDEM was designed for use with novice naval trainees and naïve participants. In both simulation facilities the need to generate useful scenarios was a challenge. Johnston et al. (1998) assert that although much of the data collected during the TADMUS program had been from the higher-fidelity DEFTT simulator, the availability of the TANDEM simulator and shipboard evaluations were essential to drawing stronger conclusions and making more robust recommendations.

Much of the research conducted in the DEFTT test bed concerned training issues. For example, Kirlik, Fisk, Walker, and Rothrock (1998) reported on experiments conducted in a Georgia Institute of Technology modification of the DEFTT simulation called the Georgia Tech Anti-air warfare coordinator Simulation Platform (GT-ASP). In these experiments it was demonstrated that part-task simulations designed to develop cognitive automaticity in the performance of task components could produce more efficient and less costly training. Similarly, Cohen, Freeman, and Thompson (1998) used the DEFTT simulator to demonstrate that critical thinking skills could be targeted for training and that such training improved the C2 teams' decision processes and outcomes.

In addition to training research, the TADMUS program conducted studies of interface design and decision aiding technology. Rummel (1995) carried out a subjective evaluation of a proposed HCI design for a decision support system (DSS) in the DEFTT facility. The prototype interface being evaluated combined seven windows (Alerts, Track Profile, Comparison to Norms, Template, Situation Assessment by Explanation-Based Reasoning [SABER], Response Manager, and Task Priority List). The subjective evaluations were highly variable across participants, demonstrating the need for considerable development of the interface concepts. On the other hand, the comments from the participants provided considerable insight about possible improvements. In a similar DEFTT-based research, Morrison, Kelly, Moore, and Hutchins (1998) reported that displays that are consistent with naturalistic decision-making strategies provided the most useful support to the commanders in the simulations by facilitating the rapid and accurate assessment of the situation.

The SPAWAR research program overlaps the TADMUS program in some areas, such as decision support, but has had a different research emphasis and used different research facilities. The SPAWAR research program varied dramatically from basic human engineering studies to operational evaluations of complex systems. On the more basic side of the program, there were several studies of display options for air battle management displays. Perspective displays to give the battlespace a 3-D appearance and realistic icon designs were evaluated in several studies. Smallman, Schiller, and Mitchell (1999) examined the use of perspective displays to give the battlespace a 3-D appearance and realistic icon designs as potential improvements for the displays used by air defense operators. A mixed group of naive and trained participants monitored a simulated display of an air defense scenario. The scenario froze periodically and the participant answered probe questions about the situation just before the freeze. A traditional 2-D top-down display with nonrealistic symbols provided superior situation awareness within the first few minutes. However, with more time the 3-D perspective displays with realistic icons provided superior situation awareness for altitude, attitude, and heading. Smallman, St. John, Oonk, and Cowen (2000b) also investigated the performance of participants using nonrealistic symbols versus realistic 3-D icons in a simplified air battle management task. The results demonstrated that the unrealistic 2-D symbols were identified faster and more accurately than the realistic 3-D icons regardless of the air battle experience of the participants. This conclusion was also supported by Smallman, Oonk, St. John, and Cowen (2001a, 2001b).

Another series of studies (e.g., St. John and Cowen, 1999; Smallman, Schiller, and Cowen, 2000; St. John, Harvey, Smallman, Oonk, and Cowen, 2000; St. John, Oonk, and Cowen, 2000; St. John, Smallman, Bank, and Cowen, 2001) compared the typical god's eye, 2-D view of the battlespace to a perspective view display that gave the battlespace display a 3-D appearance. In general, the 2-D

The AWACS aircraft was originally built and fielded in the 1970s (Hirst, 1983; Armistead, 2002). Despite several upgrades AWACS operators still use an interface that is relatively unsophisticated by modern standards (Vidulich, Bolia, and Nelson, 2004). A research program has been undertaken at the Air Force Research Laboratory to evaluate modern interface technologies for possible use in the AWACS.

One notable feature of the AWACS operator's environment is the heavy communications load. An AWACS operator wears headphones that are connected to several radios and an internal intercom system. This results in several simultaneous conversations that the operator must participate in or at least monitor. Air Force researchers (Bolia, 2003a, 2003b; Nelson and Bolia, 2003) evaluated the use of spatialized audio to separate multiple streams of speech in headsets for AWACS operators. The overall finding in several studies was that the spatialized audio increased speech intelligibility for AWACS operators monitoring several speech sources while performing a simulated air battle management task in the laboratory (Nelson and Bolia, 2003) or performing a laboratory task on a laptop in the aircraft during a training mission (Bolia, 2003b).

Another commonality about air battle management displays, including displays on the AWACS, is that they typically include a prominent geospatial display of the current battlespace (Vidulich et al., 2004). The geospatial display provides the information that is at the heart of the air battle manager's task, yet on computer displays it is often occluded by pop-up displays and menus providing additional information or functionality. Bolia, Nelson, and Vidulich (2004) evaluated the utility of two visual display tools to determine their effectiveness in alleviating the negative impacts of display occlusion. One software tool that held promise was to make the occluding text or menu box "transparent" by blending the box with the background display; the other was a multilayer display that could separate the occluding text box or menu in physical depth away from the background display. In these experiments, a multiple-element tracking task was used to simulate the cognitive demands of the air battle manager's geospatial battlespace display and a mental arithmetic decision task appeared on periodic occluding displays. The transparency and depth of the occluding task were varied. Significant benefits were demonstrated for the transparency, but overall the depth manipulation failed to show reliable benefits in these studies.

Current AWACS operators are limited to a computer keyboard and a trackball to communicate with the AWACS computers (Hirst, 1983; Armistead, 2002). Researchers (Nelson, Vidulich, and Bolia, 2004; Vidulich, Nelson, Bolia Guillams, McLaughlin, Donnelly, Collier, Fix, Miller, Brown, and Poole, 2006) investigated speech recognition as an alternative control modality for AWACS air battle managers. Nelson, Vidulich, and Bolia (2004c) implemented a version of the next-generation AWACS interface software on a laptop computer and enabled speech recognition controls for several functions. These laptop simulations were then used to collect performance data from skilled air battle managers. Performance was significantly improved and operator opinions overwhelmingly supported the development of speech recognition controls for the AWACS. Vidulich et al. (2004) examined this conclusion further by using speech controls in a laboratory simulation with a constructive simulation providing dynamic friendly and enemy aircraft. Operators monitored the dynamic battlespace, and retargeted aircraft under their control as needed. Again, both the performance results and operator opinions favored the application of speech controls in the AWACS.

Air Force researchers remain interested in the question of how to properly evaluate performance in an air battle management simulation. Vidulich and Fix (2003) evaluated the global implicit measure (GIM; Vidulich and McMillan, 2000; Vidulich, 2003) as a means to assess air battle management performance of participants performing a generic unmanned combat aerial vehicle (UCAV) supervisory control task. The integrated measure was sensitive to the display manipulation used in the experiment. However, although such a measurement approach could be very useful for gauging performance of relatively procedural tasks, it would by its very nature be unable to cope with assessing the operator's reaction to novel situations. In fact, great decisions by military commanders often seem to break the normal procedural rules (Bolia, Nelson, Vidulich, and Taylor, 2004). This raises the issue of whether the quality of a decision made by a warfighter can be disambiguated from the outcome of that decision (Nelson, Bolia, and Vidulich, 2004). Galster and Bolia (2004a, 2004b) attempted to distinguish between decision quality and mission effectiveness in their study of battle management in a simulated battlespace control task. However, even in this simplified combat management environment, the variability of operator actions and the resulting outcomes proved daunting. The best method for evaluating the decision effectiveness of air battle managers remains elusive and will require more work.

Despite all of the different researchers, task, and target environments involved in the C2 human engineering research of the three U.S. military services, there is considerable commonality in their grand research strategies and needs. For example, all the services make use of simulations of varying levels of fidelity to real-world tasks. The Army researchers distinguished between small-scale and mid-scale research environments, the Navy researchers conducted relatively basic research on icon design with part-task simulations and also supported evaluations in deployed forces, and the Air Force researchers used tasks that were very generic for nonspecialized participants as well as studies conducted in relatively high-fidelity-distributed simulations. Clearly matching the size and complexity of the simulation to the research question being asked is commonplace.

All three services' researchers also shared an interest in trying to optimize the interfaces used by the C2 operators. The Army developed interface guidelines, the Navy explored different icon and display formatting, and the Air Force evaluated spatialized audio, depth displays, and speech controls. There is obviously a consensus that the C2 interfaces used by battle managers can be improved and the variety of technologies being explored suggests that there are many ways readily available to accomplish improvements.

Another area of agreement among the researchers of the three services is in the area of metrics. The Army is developing automated measures of communications and HCI, the Navy researched real-time measures of task load and performance, and the Air Force also explored real-time measures of performance along with situation awareness. The Air Force has also been wrestling with the challenges of distinguishing decision quality from outcomes, and with the extension of individual metrics to teams of operators (Bolia, Nelson, Vidulich, and Taylor, 2004; Bolia, 2005; Bolia and Nelson, 2007). Certainly, better metrics are needed by all researchers in these fields.

Interestingly, there is also a common gap in research across the services. Although the future network-centric battlefield with ubiquitous communication and information flow among manned and unmanned platforms will invariably increase the criticality of real-time battle managers, there is no major program in any of the three services to develop personnel selection tools to identify the individuals that would be best suited for these tasks (Bolia, et al., 2006). Given the great effort and progress that was made in developing selection tools for pilots (Carretta and Ree, 2003), it is surprising that similar efforts to select battle managers are not prominent.

Simulation and Its Utility for C2 Systems

Before entering into a discussion of the technical challenges associated with simulation of network-centric air operations, it makes sense to discuss the uses of simulation in the context of C2, as it is only within this framework that the discussion will attain any significance. This is true at least in part because the motivation for the simulation drives the technological requirements thereof, and thus needs to be made explicit a priori. For example, in simulating a JSTARS environment to a certain degree of fidelity, one needs to know how many of the consoles on the jet one wants to simulate and how many communications channels will be required.

There are a number of potential uses for simulation in the C2 domain, although the most common will doubtlessly be the one that is most common in nearly every domain in which simulation is employed: training. In military environments, simulation training has at least two major advantages over training on real platforms: cost and safety. An AWACS sortie costs thousands of dollars in fuel alone, not to mention the wear and tear on the airframe. Moreover, every time the jet takes off, the lives of both the flightcrew and the mission crew are placed at risk. Both cost and personnel risk are significantly reduced by training mission crews in the simulator instead, and, because the hardware and software in the simulator are the same as that being flown on the platform, the transfer of training should be nearly perfect. What is more, simulation will allow crews to train for situations seldom discussed by NCW disciples, i.e., scenarios involving the degradation of the network.

The benefits of simulation training are most clearly manifested in the concept of DMT, which goes a step beyond the simulation of a single platform (Crane, Robbins, and Bennett, 2001, 2006). Under DMT, multiple simulated assets are linked together in a common simulated environment, allowing strike and C2 assets from geographically distributed bases to train together as they will fight together in wartime. Although most of the DMT research done to date has centered on fighter aircraft, scientists at the Air Force Research Laboratory have begun to conduct studies involving tactical air battle management assets (Schiflett, Elliott, Dalrymple, Tessier, and Cardenas, 2000). Moreover, DMT is regarded as the future of simulation training by several U.S. allies (McIntyre, Smith, and Bennett, 2002; Anonymous, 2004; Lawrie et al., 2004).

Simulation may also be employed for the formation and evaluation of novel tactics. One of the most likely motives for the development of new tactics is the introduction of new technology, the integration of which often predates tactical or doctrinal governance for its employment. Appropriate insertion of the technology, or a simulated version thereof, into a simulated C2 environment may allow operators to elaborate new techniques in a natural way that in the real world might involve casualties. As an example, simulation might be employed to consider the practicality of the control of unmanned combat air vehicles by a weapons director aboard an AWACS or JSTARS (Nelson and Bolia, 2006). Likewise simulation may be used for the development and testing of countermeasures.

For the foreseeable future, interoperability will remain an issue for both tactics and technology integration. Recent air campaigns have been neither unilateral nor single-service. Instead, they have involved operations with major joint and coalition elements, which were not always able to operate together seamlessly. Although often touted as a major success with respect to joint warfare, the air campaign of Operation Desert Storm suffered major failures in technology interoperability (Marolda and Schneller, 2001), and many of the issues identified have not been resolved in the ensuing decade and a half. It is possible that some of them might be resolved, or means discovered for their circumvention, through joint and coalition simulation.

The Air Force has also invested heavily in the concept of simulation-based acquisition, by which the design, development, and fielding of new platforms is guided by the results of simulation exercises. These can be used to determine, among other things, how well a prototype platform might perform on a particular mission, a C2 platform's optimal crew composition and structure, or how a novel or modified concept of operations (CONOPS) might be integrated into a platform's mission.

The evolution of new CONOPS will be a major issue for NCW, as high-fidelity network-enabled simulations should afford the opportunity to look at how technology, tactics, or training applied at one node can affect performance at nodes further down the kill chain. This should allow for visualization of the phenomena of increased speed of command and self-synchronization, as well as measurement of the effects thereof on tactical and operational performance, providing the supporters of NCW with a quantitative measure of its advantages.

Finally, it should be noted that there are a number of uses of simulation relevant to C2 that are not considered here. This arises from the fact that simulation can be accomplished at a variety of levels. For example, it is possible to construct a simulated air battle by creating a digital environment—representations of terrain, man-made structures, and weather—and placing within it a set of entities, each of which has been programmed with its own characteristics and behaviors. If the information about the systems engaged is realistic enough, this type of simulation might be used to explore the effects of a new type of weapon on the outcome of a tactical engagement. However useful this may be, it is not this type of simulation that motivates the present discussion.

This chapter is dedicated instead to questions vis-à-vis *operator-in-the-loop* simulation of network-centric tactical and operational air battle management. Needless to say, this assertion fails to resolve all the ambiguity indicated above—for example, which operators will be in the loop, and which will be simulated—but it does provide a focus: the operator, or, more appropriately, the decision maker. In the end, the purpose of this variety of simulation is to measure and eventually to augment the decision-making performance of an operator or team of operators working in a complex C2 environment.

TECHNICAL CHALLENGES

Although the evolution of the NCW concept has been driven by advancements in technology, a number of technical and technological challenges stand in the way of its full implementation. These obstacles will be no less important for the *simulation* of network-centric operational environments.

Two major concerns are the linked concepts of processing speed and bandwidth. The former refers to the speed at which a computer's processor is able to perform mathematical operations, whereas the latter may be viewed as the diameter of the "pipe" through which data is sent and received. Both are likely to come up in any discussion of network-centric C2, given the requirements for the automated construction, maintenance, and real-time dissemination of a common situational picture.

Many disciples of NCW view the issues of bandwidth and processing speed as solved problems, optimistically citing Moore's law, which alleges that processing power doubles approximately every 18 months (Alberts, Garstka, and Stein, 2000; Owens, 2000). Indeed, Assistant Secretary of Defense John Stenbit has claimed that recent technological advances "will, in the coming decade, eliminate the constraint of bandwidth … unfetter us from the requirement to be synchronous in time and space, and remove the last remaining technological barriers to information sharing and collaboration" (Alberts and Hayes, 2003, p. xiii). Even should this prove true, it will be enabled only by massive allocations of defense spending not typically available to laboratories engaged in simulation research. Moreover, it fails to consider the theory that increases in bandwidth are always accompanied by concomitant increases in available information.

In fact, one of the biggest challenges facing C2 simulation researchers is the sheer size of the environment that needs to be simulated. Consider the simulation of air-to-air or air-to-ground combat. There might be a screen on which the out-of-the-window scene is projected, placed in front of a cockpit shell instrumented with displays and controls, and a series of computers to generate the virtual environment, control the various hardware devices, and collect data. There might also be an intercom, allowing the pilot to talk to the experimenter or trainer, or to a wingman seated in another simulated cockpit. Moreover, the pilot might be flying either against a simulated enemy or, for more realism, against another pilot seated in a comparable simulator.

Consider alternatively the simulation of an airborne tactical air battle management mission. In place of one cockpit and its associated displays and controls, an AWACS or JSTARS has more than a dozen consoles in the mission crew compartment, each of which may need to display a different view of the situational picture. In addition, each console has half a dozen or more voice channels in order to maintain communication with other positions on the platform as well as other tactical and operational assets such as fighters, bombers, and the AOC. Although this dwarfs the fighter simulation in terms of both magnitude and complexity, it is only the tip of the iceberg. Moreover, it raises a number of additional issues, including that of which roles to simulate and which require operators in the loop.

This question depends, of course, on precisely what one wants to achieve by the simulation. For example, in evaluating the effects of spatial intercoms and speech-based control on performance and workload for an AWACS weapons director, researchers at the Air Force Research Laboratory conducted an operator-in-the-loop simulation using a single AWACS operator in the role of weapons director, with two confederates playing the roles of strike lead and senior director (Nelson and Bolia, 2003; Guilliams, McLaughlin, Vidulich, Nelson, Bolia, and Donnelly, 2004). All remaining entities in the simulation were elements of a constructive simulation. On the other hand, a study to measure the effects on mission effectiveness of the types of collaboration technologies proposed by Nelson, Bolia, Vidulich, and Langhorne (2004) requires a more extensive network with more human operators in the loop.

Team communication may present a difficult challenge for C2 simulation. If all of the teammates are present in the experiment, the problem is inconsequential and amounts only to having the number of channels required for the desired network. The difficulty arises when there is a need to simulate one or more of the teammates. Although years of research have led to the construction of software-based speech-to-text systems able to perform continuous large-vocabulary speaker-independent recognition, and of text-to-speech systems able to simulate a human voice with sufficient fidelity, the surface has hardly been scratched on the problem of language representation. Indeed, natural language processing is one of the most complex and demanding problems in computer science; although scientists and engineers have been investigating the area for decades, realistic dialogue systems have been produced for only the most trivial of domains. This is partly due to the difficulty of producing natural speech, given that the exigencies of formal grammar need not—and in many cases *do* not—apply to natural speech. However, the most challenging issue is that of semantic representation. Computers are very good at recognizing speech, and reasonably adept at producing speech, but to date have no idea what the speech means.

To some extent this deficiency represents an inability to extract meaning from the recognized speech. However, the larger problem may be the generation of new meaning in response, which requires that the situational context be encoded in a way that is semantically accessible to a resident model of human reasoning and language. In general, this is the goal of researchers in the field of artificial intelligence (AI), the products of which tend to be rule-based, knowledge-based, or other pattern recognition systems that have consistently failed to demonstrate anything like what humans conceive as "understanding" (Russell and Norvig, 1995). That this echelon of AI is unavailable contributes to the failure to simulate not only one's own teammates but also enemy decision makers. The failure to predict adversarial decisions in complex command environments has been discussed elsewhere in the context of building decision support systems, but is equally relevant to the task of generating such decisions for C2 simulations (Bolia, Nelson, Vidulich, and Taylor, 2004; Bolia, 2005).

COLLABORATION TECHNOLOGIES AND C2 SIMULATION RESEARCH

In future military operations, C2 teams will be increasingly distributed, while continuing to operate in environments characterized by a high communications workload. Collaboration technologies will play an increased role in these operations, and studies on their effects on communication and mission effectiveness, team workload, shared situation awareness, and team decision effectiveness will need to be pursued. There are several commercially available collaboration tools that may have utility for enhancing team SA, information sharing, and overall C2 effectiveness. Collaborative communication tools include video- and teleconferencing, chat and messaging tools, e-mail, and automatic broadcast and alerts. The enhancements provided by these technologies may include virtual face-to-face communications, real-time private and group conversations, and the ability to publish and receive critical information. When combined with file sharing, these technologies will also enable users to collaboratively review and discuss text, images, and video. Additionally, asynchronous communication tools such as bulletin and message boards, and even e-mail, promise to further improve team communication, information exchange, and team decision making.

Shared battlespace visualization may also be enhanced by collaboration technologies. Shared situation displays and customized dashboards, augmented with virtual whiteboards and data capture and replay technologies, may be particularly valuable. Real-time data capture and replay may be effective for mission rehearsal and debriefing, in addition to enriching the shared SA of the C2 team during operations. Frequent and repetitive replay and rehearsal are critical to the development of expert decision-making skills (Salas and Klein, 2001), and as such enhanced training may be a spillover benefit of this technology.

Collaboration technologies involving intelligent agents as collaborators will also likely have their place in future C2 operations. Specifically, decision aids and agents may be used for data mining and knowledge location, content and knowledge management, and automated workflow and scheduling. Given the time-criticality and complexity of network-centric C2, the importance of effective dynamic replanning and rescheduling will continue to increase. To the extent that these technologies support the shared visualization and understanding of the dynamically shifting spatial and temporal landscape of current and future operations, they will promote self-synchronization and result in more efficient prosecution of targets.

Despite the promise of these technologies—and, in some cases, their early adoption—empirical research is needed to determine their most appropriate uses. For example, recent meta-analytic research has suggested that computer-mediated communication (e.g., synchronous and asynchronous text-based messaging) negatively impacts group decision making compared to face-to-face communication in terms of decision time, decision effectiveness, and decision satisfaction (Baltes, Dickson, Sherman, Bauer, and LaGanke, 2002). In fact, the only circumstances under which computer-mediated collaboration was found to equal face-to-face collaboration involved situations in which: (1) no time limit was imposed on group decision-making activities; and (2) absolute anonymity was preserved among group participants. Paradoxically, these are perhaps the two circumstances least likely to be encountered in network-centric C2 operations. Accordingly, although Baltes et al. (2002) recognized the purported advantages of computer-mediated communication for the rapid dissemination of information, they have issued a strong admonition to organizations considering the unbridled adoption of these technologies for group decision-making activities.

Although some researchers have begun to postulate a relation between collaboration technologies and team SA (Bolstad and Endsley, 2005), this issue has seldom been addressed explicitly by means of experimentation. It is imaginable, for example, that technologies such as videoconferencing may promote an increased sense of presence and the verisimilitude of face-to-face teamwork, whereas chat—already used extensively by the U.S. Navy (Jara and Lisowski, 2003)—may reduce verbal communications and improve recall. However, a comprehensive assessment of the effectiveness of these technologies has yet to be completed. Moreover, the success of collaboration technology in the C2 domain will likely be a function of task suitability, technical maturity and usability, and organizational culture, including user acceptance and trust in the technology and an appreciation of its utility for network-centric operations.

To begin to address some of these questions, a survey conducted by researchers from the Air Force Research Laboratory (Nelson, Bolia, Vidulich, and Langhorne, 2004) asked trained U.S. and Australian air battle managers to evaluate which collaboration technologies would be most useful to them in conducting current and future missions. Among these were the technologies described above. Unexpectedly, *all* technologies in the survey were rated as at least potentially useful, but some (e.g., automated workflow and mission timelines, data capture and replay capabilities, file and application sharing) were clearly considered more promising than others (e.g., large-scale displays, automated decision support, videoconferencing), suggesting directions for future work.

In addition to the integration of novel technologies on the interface side, and the introduction of collaborative technologies, proponents of NCW have insinuated that enhanced SA will be a by-product of sensor-netting and data fusion. Future studies should explicitly address this hypothesis, across multiple scenarios, within the context of the NCW CONOPS. This type of research has the potential to influence not only the actualization of NCW, but also the development of tactics and doctrine for the prosecution of time-critical targets by future C2 systems.

To tackle these and other issues, a collaborative technology testbed (CTT) has been designed at AFRL (Figure 19.1). The purpose of the CTT is to allow the systematic evaluation of collaboration technologies and their effects on team performance, communication effectiveness, shared SA, and decision effectiveness in operator-in-the-loop C2 simulations. The CTT is designed to support a program of basic and applied human factors research in the context of network-centric BMC2 work domains, which are characteristically communication-intense, fast-paced, rapidly changing, and replete with information that is often incomplete, inaccurate, and uncertain. One of the principal challenges in supporting the collaborative BMC2 enterprise is the identification of interface

FIGURE 19.1   The Air Force Research Laboratory's Collaborative Technology Testbed (CTT) Laboratory.

concepts and technologies that will enable teams of operators to make effective tactical decisions more efficiently. Most noteworthy are those technologies that facilitate efficient group communication and the rapid acquisition, maintenance, and sharing of tactical SA.

Research in computer-mediated communication has provided some initial guidance for predicting the efficacy of collaborative technologies to support team decision making. As noted by Baltes et al. (2002), two primary dimensions or characteristics of this class of tools are: (1) their degree of synchrony; and (2) the extent to which they support the communication of nonverbal and paraverbal cues. Collaboration technologies that achieve high levels on both dimensions will be most comparable to face-to-face communication and will be expected to result is the highest levels of team decision quality, decision speed, and decision satisfaction. In addition, these notions lead to numerous testable hypotheses that are well suited for operator-in-the-loop simulations of future NCW air battle management scenarios.

The CTT is equipped with a handful of commercially available collaboration software packages, including InfoWorkSpace (IWS) and Microsoft Office Live Communication Server 2005 (LCS2005). Both software suites afford numerous collaboration capabilities including instant messaging (IM) and chat rooms, teleconferencing, videoconferencing, application and file sharing, and shared workspaces such as bulletin boards and virtual whiteboards. Other software packages provide capabilities such as automated workflow, content, knowledge management, advanced data visualization, intelligent agents, data mining utilities and knowledge locators, and opinion polling tools.

Face-to-face collaboration (Figure 19.2A) involves team configurations in which operators are colocated physically and thus able to engage in face-to-face communication with other teammates. This is connoted in the figure by circles: teams working together are those surrounded by the same shade of gray. One advantage of face-to-face communication is that it allows the use of nonverbal cues such as facial expressions, body language, and emotion, which are important for assessing level of common agreement and maintaining team SA.

Local remote collaboration entails communication between operators who are separated by physical distance (i.e., not colocated), but share a common physical environment, e.g., an AWACS or JSTARS aircraft (see Figure 19.2B). Local remote communication will likely be facilitated by collaboration tools such as IM and chat, video- and teleconferencing, shared displays, and interactive virtual whiteboards, as well as file and application sharing. Dynamic work domains that require frequent temporary participation by operators may benefit from these technologies, especially

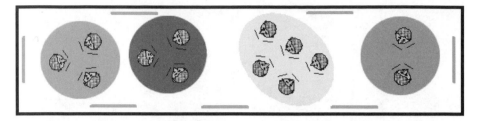

FIGURE 19.2A Face-to-face collaboration. Conceptual layout of generic multimission air battle management platform, in which teams are arranged to leverage face-to-face collaboration and augmented by advanced collaborative interface technology such as instant messaging, workflow management, shared large displays (indicated by thin gray rectangles), and virtual whiteboards.

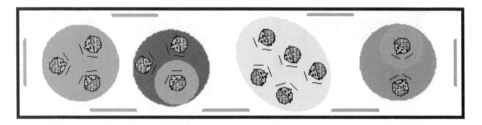

FIGURE 19.2B Local remote collaboration. Local remote collaboration permits operators to remain at their primary workstations while synchronously collaborating with another team. In this case, operators belonging to the second and fourth (from left) teams have temporarily joined the first team.

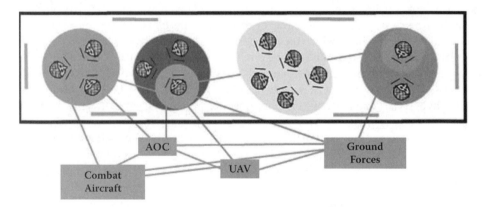

FIGURE 19.2C Distant remote collaboration. Distant remote collaboration enables synchronous, parallel, multiteam communication and information exchange. In this case, collaboration technologies permit shared situation and collaboration decision making across the battlespace constellation (e.g., combat aircraft, unmanned aerial vehicles [UAVs], air operations centers [AOCs], ground forces, etc.) in support of network-centric concepts of operations such as time-critical-targeting.

if primary roles and responsibilities mandate that operators remain at their own consoles. For example, it may be necessary for individuals or teams to temporarily join other collectives to provide assistance in time-critical problem solving or decision making. With reference to Figure 19.2B, operators belonging to the second and fourth (from left) teams temporarily join the first team using collaboration technologies.

Distant remote collaboration denotes communication between geographical distributed teams. This situation is illustrated in Figure 19.2C, which represents a network-centric battlespace scenario, involving real-time synchronous communication and collaboration between teams on the tactical

C2 platform, the AOC, UAVs, and ground forces. Collaboration technologies that will enable such a scenario include automated workflow tools, intelligent agents, decision support aids, automated content and knowledge management systems, IM, video- and teleconferencing, and shared interactive situation displays.

Needless to say, the utility of this taxonomy will only be demonstrated by the results of simulation experiments the likes of which this chapter has set out to delineate. Although there has been a dearth of investigations designed to consider the influence of network-centric warfare on C2, or to study systematically the collaboration technologies which such a CONOPS makes almost obligatory, it is not clear that there is any other way forward. Fortunately, despite the numerous technological challenges outlined in this section, researchers at the Air Force Research Laboratory have developed a laboratory and a framework in which to begin to examine how tactical and operational-level battle managers will perform in a network-centric air battle, and which technologies will best serve them in this undertaking.

EVALUATIONS OF COLLABORATION TECHNOLOGIES

A recent series of investigations conducted in the Air Force Research Laboratory's CTT facility has focused on the efficacy of collaboration technologies in simulated tactical C2 scenarios. In general, the experiments have employed a methodology in which small teams serving as air battle managers, strike operators, and a tanker operator work together to execute challenging tactical air battle management scenarios. Teams typically comprise paid participants, often local college students, who are trained to criterion on the various air battle management tasks. These teams complete a series of experimental trials under various communication conditions, including a voice-only control condition, a collaboration technology-only condition (e.g., virtual whiteboards, IM), and a condition that combines both communication media. The effectiveness of the various communication conditions is then assessed in terms of individual and team performance efficiency, workload, and situation awareness.

For example, a study by Knott, Nelson, Bolia, and Galster (2006) focused on the effects of IM on team performance, workload, and situation awareness in a scenario that required air battle management teams to coordinate attacks, defend friendly airspace, and refuel and rearm fighter aircraft. Teams completed experimental trials under voice-only, IM-only, and combined voice and IM conditions in both high and low workload conditions. As noted by Knott, Nelson, et al. (2006), the IM-only condition was associated with relatively poor team performance, increased mental workload and team process demands, reduced situation awareness, and lower satisfaction with performance compared to the voice-only as well as the combined voice and IM conditions. Knott, Bolia, Nelson, and Galster (2006) replicated these results in a second study that focused more closely on performance metrics such as the number of intercepted targets, time to intercept targets, enemy zone penetration, and lost assets. These researchers pointed out that such findings are consistent with the notion that not all collaboration technologies, even those as popular as IM, are appropriate in all application domains and that tactical C2 environments may require domain-specific collaboration tools, a notion that is consistent with the ideas put forward by Bolstad and Endsley (2005).

Following this line of thought, a domain-specific collaboration tool known as "Picture-Chat" (PC) was designed and evaluated using a similar methodology. The PC interface is an asynchronous collaboration tool that combines whiteboard drawing functionality with an IM interface, permitting operators to share their intent, instructions, and courses of action by sending teammates a visually annotated screen-capture of the tactical display using IM. Using the Knott, Nelson, et al. (2006) tactical air battle management scenario, Finomore, Knott, Nelson, Galster, and Bolia (2007) compared a voice-only condition to a combined voice and PC condition. In addition, the study was designed to more systematically compare three different subject workload scales: the NASA Task Load Index, the Multiple Resources Questionnaire, and the Team Workload Scale. Results indicated that performance efficiency was equivalent between the voice-only and combined voice and PC conditions, and that each workload scale was sensitive to the collaboration tool manipulation.

Collectively, these three studies provide an important "first look" at the effects of collaboration technologies on team performance, workload, and situation awareness in tactical air battle management scenarios. The finding that widely accepted tools such as IM and chat compromise performance efficiency and workload when used in isolation is quite telling and underscores the importance of this type of research rather than simply relying on users' opinions of perceived utility. Additionally, it appears that these initial assessments support the view that collaboration tools tend to be domain- and use-specific and that the full capability of these tools may not be realized unless they are designed with that in mind. Finally, this line of research has revealed a great need for team-based research methodologies and psychometrically validated team metrics of performance efficiency, decision making, workload, and situation awareness. Such research tools would certainly advance the efficiency and reliability of this type of research.

REFERENCES

Alberts, D. S., & Hayes, R. E., 2003, *Power to the Edge: Command ... Control ... in the Information Age,* Washington D.C.: Command & Control Research Program.

Alberts, D. S., Garstka, J. I., & Stein, F. P., 2000, *Network-centric Warfare: Developing and Leveraging Information Superiority,* Washington D.C.: Command & Control Research Program.

Anonymous, 2004, Canada–US collaboration in flight simulation, *Maple Leaf,* 7(16), 4–5.

Armistead, E. L., 2002, *AWACS and Hawkeyes: The Complete History of Airborne Early Warning Aircraft,* St. Paul, MN: MBI Publishing Co.

Baltes, B. B., Dickson, M. W., Sherman, M. P., Bauer, C. C., & LaGanke, J. S., 2002, Computer-mediated communication and group decision making: a meta-analysis, *Organ. Behav. Hum. Decision Processes,* 87, 156–179.

Bolia, R. S., 2003a, Spatial intercoms for air battle managers: does visually cueing talker location improve speech intelligibility? *Proceedings of the 12th International Symposium on Aviation Psychology,* Dayton, OH: Wright State University, pp. 136–139.

Bolia, R. S., 2003b, Effects of spatial intercoms and active noise reduction headsets on speech intelligibility in an AWACS environment, *Proceedings of the Human Factors and Ergonomics Society 47th Annual Meeting,* Santa Monica, CA: Human Factors and Ergonomics Society, pp. 100–103.

Bolia, R. S., 2004, Over-reliance on technology in warfare: the Yom Kippur War as a case study, *Parameters,* 34(3), 46–56.

Bolia, R. S., 2005, Intelligent decision support systems in network-centric military operations, *Intelligent Decisions? Intelligent Support? Pre-proceedings for the International Workshop on Intelligent Decision Support Systems: Retrospects and Prospects,* pp. 3–7.

Bolia, R. S., & Nelson, W. T., 2007, Characterizing team performance in network-centric operations: philosophical and methodological issues, *Aviation, Space, Environ. Med.,* 78, B71–B76.

Bolia, R. S., Nelson, W. T., Summers, S. H., Arnold, R. D., Atkinson, J. L., Taylor, R. M., Cottrell, R., & Crooks, C. L., 2006, Collaborative decision making in network-centric military operations, *Proceedings of the Human Factors and Ergonomics Society 50th Annual Meeting,* Santa Monica, CA: Human Factors and Ergonomics Society, pp. 284–288.

Bolia, R. S., Nelson, W. T., & Vidulich, M. A., 2004, A multi-layer visual display for air battle managers: effects of depth and transparency on performance and workload in a dual-task scenario, *Hum. Factors Aerosp. Saf.,* 4, 181–194.

Bolia, R. S., Nelson, W. T., Vidulich, M. A., & Taylor, R. T., 2004, From chess to chancellorsville: measuring decision quality in military commanders, in *Human Performance, Situation Awareness, and Automation: Current Research and Trends,* Vol. I, Vincenzi, D. A. Mouloua, M., & Hancock, P. A., Eds., Mahwah, NJ: Lawrence Erlbaum Associates, pp. 269–273.

Bolia, R. S., Vidulich, M. A., Nelson, W. T., & Cook, M. J., 2007, The use of technology to support military decision-making and command & control: a historical perspective, in *Decision Making in Complex Systems,* Cook, M. J., Noyes, J. M., and Masakowski, Y., Eds., Aldershot, UK: Ashgate Publishing, pp. 191–200.

Bolstad, C. A., & Endsley, M. R., 2005, Choosing team collaboration tools: lessons from disaster recovery efforts, *Ergonomics in Design,* 13, 7–14.

Campbell, C. H., Throne, M. H., Black, B. A., & Lickteig, C. W., 2003, *Research Observations and Lessons Learned for the Future Combat Systems* (Research Product 2003–4), Alexandria, VA: U.S. Army Research Institute for the Behavioral and Social Sciences.

Cannon-Bowers, J. A., & Salas, E., 1997, A framework for developing team performance measures in training, in *Team Performance Assessment and Measurement: Theory, Methods and Application,* Brannick, M. T., Salas, E., and Prince, C., Eds., Mahwah, NJ: Lawrence Erlbaum Associates, pp. 45–62.

Carnahan, T. J., Lickteig, C. W., Sanders, W. R., Durlach, P. J., & Lussier, J. W., 2004, *Novice versus Expert Command Groups: Preliminary Findings and Training Implications for Future Combat Systems* (Research Report 1821), Alexandria, VA: U.S. Army Research Institute for the Behavioral and Social Sciences.

Carretta, T. R., & Ree, M. J., 2003, Pilot selection methods, in *Principles and Practice of Aviation Psychology,* Tsang, P. S. and Vidulich, M. A., Eds., Mahwah, NJ: Lawrence Erlbaum Associates, pp. 357–396.

Cebrowski, A. K., & Garstka, J. J., 1998, Network-centric warfare: its origin and future, *U.S. Nav. Inst. Proc.,* 124(1), 28–35.

Chaiken, S. R., Barnes, C., Harville, D., Miller, L., Elliot, L., Dalrymple, M., Tessier, P., Fischer, J., & Welch C., 2004, *Do Teams Adapt to Fatigue in a Synthetic C2 Task?* (Tech. Rep. No. AFRL-HE-BR-TR-2004-0041), Brooks City Base, TX: Air Force Research Laboratory.

Chaiken, S. R., Elliot, L. R., Dalrymple, M., Coovert, M. D., Riddle, D., Gordon, T. R., Hoffman, K. A., Miles, D. E., King, T. V., & Schiflett, S. G., 2002, *Weapons Director Intelligent Agent-Assist Task: Procedure and Findings for a Validation Study* (Tech. Rep. No. AFRL-HE-AZ-TP-2001-0006), Mesa, AZ: Air Force Research Laboratory.

Cohen, M. S., Freeman, J. T., & Thompson, B., 1998, Critical thinking skills in tactical decision making: a model and a training strategy, in *Making Decisions under Stress,* Cannon-Bowers, J. A. and Salas, E., Eds., Washington D.C.: American Psychological Association, pp. 155–189.

Collyer, S. C., & Malecki, G. S., 1998, Tactical decision making under stress: history and overview, in *Making Decisions under Stress,* Cannon-Bowers, J. A. and Salas, E., Eds., Washington D.C.: American Psychological Association, pp. 3–15.

Crane, P., Robbins, R., & Bennett, W., Jr., 2001, *Using Distributed Mission Training to Augment Flight Lead Up-grade Training* (Tech. Rep. No. AFRL-HE-AZ-TR-2000-0011), Mesa, AZ: Air Force Research Laboratory.

Crane, P., Skinner, M., Best, C., Burchat, E., Gehr, S. E., Grabovac, M., Pongracic, H., Robbie, A., & Zamba, M., 2006, Exercise Pacific link: coalition distributed mission training using low-cost communications, *Proceedings of SimTecT 2006,* Lindfield, NSW, Australia: Simulation Industry Association of Australia.

Douhet, G., 2002, *Il dominio dell'aria e altri scritti,* Rome: Aeronautica Militare—Ufficio Storico.

Durlach, P. J., Bowens, L. D., Neumann, J. L., & Carnahan, T. J., 2004, *Coding Verbal Interactions in a Prototype Future Force Command and Control Simulation* (Technical Report 1141), Alexandria, VA: U.S. Army Research Institute for the Behavioral and Social Sciences.

Fahey, R. P., Rowe, A. L., Dunlap, K. L., & DeBoom, D. O., 2001, *SynthetictTask Design: Cognitive Task Analysis of AWACS Weapons Director Teams* (Tech. Rep. No. AFRL-HE-AZ-TR-2000-0159), Mesa, AZ: Air Force Research Laboratory.

Feher, B., 2004, *GeoPlot Declutter Interface Usability Evaluation* (Tech. Rep. No. SSC/SD-TR-1917), San Diego, CA: Space and Naval Warfare Systems Center.

Feher, B., Morrison, J. G., & Yturralde, R. F., 2003, *Recommendations for Knowledge Desk Configurations for U.S. Navy Fleet Command Centers* (Tech. Rep. No. SSC/SD-TD-3168), San Diego, CA: Space and Naval Warfare Systems Center.

Feher, B. A., Quinn, M. L., Kelly, R. T., & Smillie, R. J., 1996, *Design and Evaluation of Tools to Support Command and Control Warfare Team Activities* (Tech. Rep. No. NRAD-TR-1726), San Diego, CA: Space and Naval Warfare Systems Center.

Finomore, V. S., Knott, B. A., Nelson, W. T., Galster, S. M., & Bolia, R. S., 2007, The effects of multimodal collaboration technology on subjective workload profiles of tactical air battle management teams, *Proceedings of the 14th International Symposium on Aviation Psychology,* Dayton, Ohio: Wright State University, pp. 190–196.

Fitz-Gibbon, S., 1995, *Not Mentioned in Despatches ... The History and Mythology of the Battle of Goose Green,* Cambridge, UK: The Lutterworth Press.

Francis, P. L., 2003, August 13, *Issues Facing the Army's Future Combat Systems Program* (Report No. GA0-03-1010R), Washington D.C.: U.S. General Accounting Office, downloaded February 12, 2005, from http://www.globalsecurity.org/miltary/systems/ground/fcs-refs.htm.

Galster, S. M., & Bolia, R. S., 2004a, Decision quality and mission effectiveness in a simulated command & control environment, in *Human Performance, Situation Awareness, and Automation: Current Research and Trends,* Vincenzi, D. A., Mouloua, M., and Hancock, P. A., Eds., Mahwah, NJ: Lawrence Erlbaum Associates, pp. 264–268.

Galster, S. M., & Bolia, R. S., 2004b, Exploring the relationship between decision appropriateness and mission effectiveness in a simulated command & control task, in *Proceedings of the Human Factors and Ergonomics Society 48th Annual Meeting,* Santa Monica, CA: Human Factors and Ergonomics Society, pp. 448–452.

Guilliams, N. M., McLaughlin, A. B., Vidulich, M. A., Nelson, W. T., Bolia, R. S., & Donnelly, B. P., 2004, An evaluation of speech recognition technology in a simulated air battle management task, in *Human Performance, Situation Awareness, and Automation: Current Research and Trends,* Vol. II, Vincenzi, D. A., Mouloua, M., and Hancock, P. A., Eds., Mahwah, NJ: Lawrence Earlbaum, pp. 230–235.

Gwynne, J. W., Feher, B. A., Obermayer, R. W., Smillie, R. J., Linville, J. M., & Heacox, N. J. (1996). *Evaluations Collaborative Technologies for Command and Control Teams* (Tech. Rep. No. 1728), San Diego, CA: Naval Command, Control and Ocean Surveillance Center RDT&E Division.

Harville, D., Barnes, C., & Elliot L., 2004, *Team Communication and Performance during Sustained Command and Control Operations: Preliminary Results* (Tech. Rep. No. AFRL-HE-BR-TR-2004-0018), Brooks City Base, TX: Air Force Research Laboratory.

Havig, P., Aleva, D., Reis, G., & McIntire, J., 2007, Putting the science back in C2: what do the buzzwords really mean? *Proceedings of the 12th International Command and Control Research and Technology Symposium,* Washington D.C.: Command and Control Research Program.

Heacox, N. J., Gwynne, J. W., Kelly, R. T., Sander, S. I., & Burns, J. S., 2000, *Cognitive Aspects of Decision Making: Project Summary* (Tech. Rep. No. SSC/SD-TR-1830), San Diego, CA: Pacific Sciences and Engineering Group.

Heacox, N. J., Quinn, M. L., Kelly, R. T., Gwynne, J. W., & Smille, R. J., 2002, *Decision Support System for Coalition Operations* (Tech. Rep. No. SPAWAR-TR-1886), San Diego, CA: Space and Naval Warfare Systems Center.

Hirst, M., 1983, *Airborne Early Warning: Design, Development and Operations,* London: Osprey.

Hughes, D. J., Ed., 1993, *Moltke on the Art of War: Selected Writings,* New York: Ballantine Books.

Hughes, W. P., 2000, *Fleet Tactics and Coastal Combat,* Annapolis, MD: Naval Institute Press.

Jara, T., & Livonski, M. (2003). Don't Silence Navy Chat, *U.S. Naval Institute Proceedings* September 2003, 52–55.

Johnston, J. H., Poirier, J., & Smith-Jentsch, H. A., 1998, Decision making under stress: creating a research methodology, in *Making Decisions under Stress,* Cannon-Bowers, J. A. and Salas, E., Eds., Washington D.C.: American Psychological Association, pp. 39–57.

Kirlik, A., Fisk, A. D., Walker, N., & Rothrock, L., 1998, Feedback augmentation and part-task practice in training dynamic decision-making skills, in *Making Decisions under Stress,* Cannon-Bowers, J. A. and Salas, E., Eds., Washington D.C.: American Psychological Association, pp. 91–113.

Knott, B. A., Bolia, R. S., Nelson, W. T., & Galster, S. M., 2006, Effects of collaboration technology on the performance of tactical air battle management teams, *Proceedings of the Human Factors Issues in Network-Centric Warfare Conference,* Sydney, Australia, 1–3 May 2006.

Knott, B. A., Nelson, W. T., Bolia, R. S., & Galster, S. M., 2006, The impact of instant messaging on team performance and communication effectiveness in air battle management, *Proceedings of the 11th International Command and Control Research & Technology Symposium,* Washington D.C.: Command and Control Research Program.

Krueger, G. P., 2004, Henry McIlvane "Mac" Parsons, 1912–2004, *Human Factors and Ergonomics Society Bulletin,* 47(12), 5–6.

Lavery, B., 1998, *Nelson and the Nile: The Naval War against Bonaparte 1798,* London: Claxton Editions.

Lawrie, G., Capon, S., Cutler, P., Filippidis, A., Iob, M., Pearce, B., Priest, T., Rockliff, A., Skinner, M., Temple, P., Tweedale, J., & White, K., 2004, Wedgetail evolution: soaring to greater heights? *Proceedings of the 11th Australian International Aerospace Congress Meeting,* Melbourne, Australia: The Institution of Engineers.

Lickteig, C. W., 1986, *User Interface Requirements for Battlefield Management Systems (BMS)* (Research Product 86-25), Alexandria, VA: U.S. Army Research Institute for the Behavioral and Social Sciences.

Lickteig, C. W., 1988, *Design Guidelines and Functional Specifications for Simulation of the Battlefield Management System's (BMS) User Interface* (Research Product 88-19). Alexandria, VA: U.S. Army Research Institute for the Behavioral and Social Sciences.

Lickteig, C. W., & Collins, J. W., III, 1995, *Combat Vehicle Command and Control System Evaluation: Vertical Integration of an Armor Battalion* (Technical Report 1021), Alexandria, VA: U.S. Army Research Institute for the Behavioral and Social Sciences.

Lickteig, C. W., Sanders, W. R., Durlach, P. J., & Carnahan, T. J., 2004, *Future Combat Systems Command and Control (FCS C2) Human Functions Assessment: Interim Report—Experiment 3* (Research Report 1819), Alexandria, VA: U.S. Army Research Institute for the Behavioral and Social Sciences.

Lickteig, C. W., Sanders, W. R., Durlach, P. J., Lussier, J. W., & Carnahan, T. J., 2003, *Human Performance Essential to Battle Command: Report on Four Future Combat Systems Command and Control (FCS C2) Experiments* (Research Report 1812), Alexandria, VA: U.S. Army Research Institute for the Behavioral and Social Sciences.

Lickteig, C. W., Sanders, W. R., Shadrick, S. B., Lussier, J. W., Holt, B. J., & Rainey, S. J., 2002, *Human-system Integration for Future Command and Control: Identifying Research Issues and Approaches* (Research Report 1792), Alexandria, VA: U.S. Army Research Institute for the Behavioral and Social Sciences.

Marolda, E. J., & Schneller, R. J., 2001, *Shield and Sword: The United States Navy in the Persian Gulf War,* Annapolis, MD: Naval Institute Press.

McIntyre, H. M., Smith, E., & Bennett, W., 2002, Exploiting high fidelity simulation for aircrew coalition training, *Proceedings of the 2001 Industry/Interservice Training Systems Conference,* Orlando, FL: National Security Industrial Association.

Morrison, J. G., Kelly, R. T., Moore, R. A., & Hutchins, S.G., 1998, Implications of decision-making research for decision support and displays, in *Making Decisions under Stress,* Cannon-Bowers, J. A. and Salas, E., Eds., Washington D.C.: American Psychological Association, pp. 375–406.

Morrison, J. E., Konya, S. H., Toth, J. A., Turnbaugh, S. S., Gunzelman, K. J., & Gilson, D. D., 2003, *Soldier–Machine Interface for the Army Future Combat System: Literature Review, Requirements, and Emerging Design Principles* (IDA Document D-2838), Alexandria, VA: Institute for Defense Analyses.

Nelson, W. T., & Bolia, R. S., 2003, Evaluating the effectiveness of spatial audio displays in a simulated airborne command and control task, *Proceedings of the Human Factors and Ergonomics Society 47th Annual Meeting,* Santa Monica, CA: Human Factors and Ergonomics Society, pp. 202–206.

Nelson, W. T., & Bolia, R. S., 2006, Supervisory control of uninhabited combat air vehicles from an airborne battle management command & control platform: human factors issues, in *Human Factors of Remotely Piloted Vehicles,* Cooke, N. J., Pringle, H., Pedersen, H., and Connor, O., Eds., Mahwah, NJ: Lawrence Erlbaum Associates, pp. 49–58.

Nelson, W. T., Bolia, R. S., & Vidulich, M. A., 2004, Characterizing decision quality in network-centric command and control applications: implications of psychological research, in *Human Performance, Situation Awareness, and Automation: Current Research and Trends,* Vincenzi, D. A., Mouloua, M., and Hancock, P. A., Eds., Mahwah, NJ: Lawrence Erlbaum Associates, pp. 279–282.

Nelson, W. T., Bolia, R. S., Vidulich, M. A., & Langhorne, A. L., 2004, User-centered evaluation of multinational communications and collaborative technologies in a network-centric air battle management environment, *Proceedings of the Human Factors and Ergonomics Society 48th Annual Meeting,* Santa Monica, CA: Human Factors and Ergonomics Society, pp. 731–735.

Nelson, W. T., Vidulich, M. A., & Bolia, R. S., 2004, Designing speech interfaces for command & control applications, *Human Factors and Aerospace Safety,* 4, 195–208.

Oonk, H. M., Schermerhorn, J. H., Glaser, D., & Morrison, J. G., 2003, *Knowledge Desk Limited Objective Experiment (LOE)* (Tech. Rep. No. SSC-TR-1896), San Diego, CA: Space and Naval Warfare Systems Center.

Oonk, H. M., Smallman, H. S., Moore, R. A., & Morrison, J. G., 2001, *Utility and Usability of the Knowledge Wall during the Global 2000 War Game* (Tech. Rep. No. 1861), San Diego, CA: Pacific Sciences and Engineering Group.

Owens, B., with Ed Offley, 2000, *Lifting the Fog of War,* New York: Farrar, Straus, & Giroux.

Parsons, H. M., 1972, *Man-Machine System Experiments,* Baltimore, MD: Johns Hopkins Press.

Roscoe, S. N., 1997, *The Adolescence of Engineering Psychology,* Santa Monica, CA: Human Factors and Ergonomics Society.

Rummel, B. K., 1995, *Subjective Evaluation of Human–Computer Interface Options for a Tactical Decision Support System* (Tech. Rep. No. NCCOSC/RDT/E-TR-1698), San Diego, CA: Naval Command Control and Ocean Surveillance Center.

Russell, S., & Norvig, P., 1995, *Artificial Intelligence: A Modern Approach,* Upper Saddle River, NJ: Prentice Hall.

Salas, E., & Klein, G., 2001. *Linking Expertise and Naturalistic Decision Making.* Mawah, N.J.: Lawrence Erlbaum Associates.

Sanders, W. R., 2003, *Measurement Methods for Human Performance in Command and Control Simulation Experiments* (ARI Research Note 2003-11), Alexandria, VA: U.S. Army Research Institute for the Behavioral and Social Sciences.

Schiflett, S. G., Elliott, L. R., Dalrymple, M., Tessier, P. A., & Cardenas, R., 2000, *Command and Control Team Performance in Distributed Mission Training Exercises,* AFRL-HE-AZ-TR-2000-0085, Brooks, TX: Air Force Research Lab.

Smallman, H. S., Oonk, H. M., Moore, R. A., & Morrison, J. G., 2001, *The Knowledge Wall for the Global 2000 War Game: Design Solutions to Match JOC User Requirements* (Tech. Rep. No. 1860), San Diego, CA: Pacific Sciences and Engineering Group.

Smallman, H. S., Oonk, H. M., St. John, M., & Cowen, M. B., 2001a, *Symbicons: Advanced Symbology for Two-Dimensional and Three-Dimensional Displays* (Tech. Rep. No. SSC-TR-1850), San Diego, CA: Space and Naval Warfare Systems.

Smallman, H. S., Oonk, H. M., St. John, M., & Cowen, M. B., 2001b, *Searching for Tracks Imaged as Symbols or Realistic Icons: A Comparison between Two-Dimensional and Three-Dimensional Displays* (Tech. Rep. No. SSC-TR-1854), San Diego, CA: Space and Naval Warfare Systems.

Smallman, H. S., Schiller, E., & Mitchell, C., 1999, *Designing a Display for the Area Air Defense Commander: The Role of 3-D Perspective Views and Realistic Track Symbols in Achieving Rapid Situation Awareness* (Tech. Rep. No. 1803), San Diego, CA: Pacific Sciences and Engineering Group.

Smallman, H. S., Schiller, E., & Cowen, M. B., 2000, *Track Location Enhancements for Perspective View Displays* (Tech. Rep. No. SSC-TR-1847), San Diego, CA: Space and Naval Warfare Systems.

Smallman, H. S., St. John, M., Oonk, H. M., & Cowen, M. B., 2000, *Track Recognition Using Two-Dimensional Symbols or Three-Dimensional Realistic Icons* (Tech. Rep. No. 1818), San Diego, CA: Pacific Sciences and Engineering Group.

Soltan, P., Lasher, M., Dahlke, W., McDonald, M., & Acantilado, N., 1998, *Improved Second-Generation 3-D Volumetric Display System,* Revision 2 (Tech. Rep. No. SPAWAR-TR-1763-REV-2), San Diego, CA: Space and Naval Warfare Command.

St. John, M., & Cowen, M. B., 1999, *Use of Perspective View Displays for Operational Tasks* (Tech. Rep. No. 1795), San Diego, CA: Pacific Sciences and Engineering Group.

St. John, M., Feher, B. A., & Morrison, J. G., 2002, *Evaluating Alternative Symbologies for Decluttering Geographical Displays* (Tech. Rep. No. 1890), San Diego, CA: Pacific Sciences and Engineering Group.

St. John, M., Harvey, S., Smallman, H. S., Oonk, H. M., & Cowen, M. B., 2000, *Navigating Two-Dimensional and Perspective Views of Terrain* (Tech. Rep. No. SSC/SD-TR-1827), San Diego, CA: Space and Naval Warfare Systems Center.

St. John, M., Oonk, H. M., & Cowen, M. B., 2000, *Using Two-Dimensional and Perspective Views of Terrain* (Tech. Rep. No. 1815), San Diego, CA: Pacific Sciences and Engineering Group.

St. John, M., Smallman, H. S., Bank, T. E., & Cowen, M. B., 2001, *Tactical Routing Using Two-Dimensional and Three-Dimensional Views of Terrain* (Tech. Rep. No. SSC-TR-1849), San Diego, CA: Space and Naval Warfare Systems Center.

United States Department of Defense (DoD), 2004, Joint Publication 1-02, "Dictionary of Military and Associated Terms," as appended 07 October 2004.

van Creveld, M., 1985, *Command in War.* Cambridge, MA: Harvard University Press.

van Orden, K. F., 2001, *Monitoring Moment-to-Moment Operator Workload Using Task Load and System-State Information* (Tech. Rep. No. SSC/SD-TR-1864), San Diego, CA: Space and Naval Warfare Systems Center.

Vidulich, M. A., 2003, Mental workload and situation awareness: essential concepts for aviation psychology practice, in *Principles and Practice of Aviation Psychology,* Tsang, P. S. and Vidulich, M. A., Eds., Mahwah, NJ: Lawrence Erlbaum Associates, pp. 115–142.

Vidulich, M. A., Bolia, R. S., & Nelson, W. T., 2004, Technology, organization, and collaborative situation awareness in air battle management: historical and theoretical perspectives, in *A Cognitive Approach to Situation Awareness: Theory, Measures, and Applications,* Banbury, S. and Tremblay, S., Eds., Aldershot, UK: Ashgate Publishing, pp. 233–253.

Vidulich, M., & Fix, E., 2003, Evaluating an integrated performance measure for simulated control of unmanned combat aerial vehicles (UCAVs), *Proceedings of the 12th International Symposium on Aviation Psychology,* Dayton, OH: Wright State University, pp. 1208–1213.

Vidulich, M., & McMillan G., 2000, The global implicit measure: evaluation of metrics for cockpit adaptation, in *Contemporary Ergonomics 2000,* McCabe, P. T., Hanson, M. A., and Robertson, S. A., Eds., London: Taylor & Francis, pp. 75–80.

Vidulich, M. A., Nelson, W. T., & Bolia, R. S., 2006, Speech-based controls in simulated air battle management, *Int. J. Aviat. Psychol., 16*, 197–213.

Waldrop, M. M., 1992, *Complexity: The Emerging Science at the Edge of Order and Chaos,* New York: Simon & Schuster.

Woodward, S., with P. Robinson, 1997, *One Hundred Days: The Memoirs of the Falklands Battle Group Commander,* Annapolis, MD: Naval Institute Press.

20 Simulation Advances in Medical Training
Laparoscopic Skill Acquisition

Elizabeth A. Schmidt-Panos and Mark W. Scerbo

CONTENTS

BACKGROUND: HARM CAUSED BY MEDICAL ERRORS

Recent research reveals that patients incur an increased risk to their safety when they receive hospital care. In a report issued by the Institute of Medicine (IOM), it was estimated that 98,000 deaths could be attributed to medical errors each year in U.S. hospitals (Kohn, Corrigan, and Donaldson, 1999). Further, it was noted that patient care associated with surgery accounted for 35–48% of all adverse events. Statistics such as these have helped to sharpen the focus on patient safety; however, the fatality estimates have encouraged other researchers to take a closer look at the context in which these deaths occur. Following the publication of the IOM report, Hayward and Hofer (2001) offered a more conservative estimate of deaths due to medical error. In their study, they assessed not only deaths due to medical error, but also the likelihood that the death could have been prevented with better care. Their assessment was based on fatality data from a single year in seven Virginia Veterans Affairs hospitals. The reviewers determined that out of 111 fatalities, death might have been prevented in 23% of cases, and was probably preventable in 6% of cases. The authors noted that these percentages are similar to those reported in other studies of death rates due to medical error (e.g., Brennan et al., 1991; Hayward, McMahon, and Bernard, 1993).

More recently, the HealthGrades organization began studying Medicare data collected from over 5000 hospitals across all 50 states to generate a more accurate count of hospital-related fatalities. In its most recent report (HealthGrades, 2007), covering the years 2002–2005, it found that 284,798 patients had died from safety incidents (e.g., failure to rescue, foreign bodies left during a procedure, infections due to medical care, etc.) with an estimated cost of $8.6 billion. Further, 247,662 of those deaths were potentially preventable. To put this into perspective, if patient death due to medical error was listed as a formal cause of death by the Centers for Disease Control and Prevention, it would rank in the top 10 among all leading causes. More important, the study also found no evidence that the number of deaths due to medical error had decreased from those first published in the IOM report. In fact, they reported that the overall rate of incidents actually *increased* over the interval from 2003 to 2005.

THE APPRENTICESHIP TRAINING MODEL IN MEDICINE

Errors that compromise patient safety may be attributable, in part, to the classic teaching model in medicine. The medical profession has traditionally adhered to an apprenticeship model in which students train under the supervision of a more experienced professional (Kauffman, 2001). Unfortunately, there are many problems associated with this approach to training (Shimada, Nishiwaki, and Cooper, 1998), including: (1) reduced uniformity of learning experiences across students, (2) fewer opportunities for less experienced students to practice uncommon procedures when confronted with very sick patients, and (3) no opportunity to work with patients who refuse to be treated by physicians in training.

Satava (2004) noted that surgical training has never faced a more challenging set of circumstances. Financial reimbursement policies continue to deplete funds needed for training. Further, resident work hours have also been reduced in an attempt to standardize training (American Medical Association, 2005). Unfortunately, these work-hour restrictions have created new training challenges. For instance, residents now have fewer hours in which to learn from patients. Twenty years ago, patients were typically admitted to the hospital for a period of one to two days. Today, however, patients spend substantially less time in the hospital, which limits opportunities for students to encounter the broadest range of pathologies during training and subsequently compromises their ability to recognize and diagnose pathology after they have completed their training (Shimada, Nishiwaki, and Cooper, 1998).

Along similar lines, reductions in work hours also place limits on operating room experiences and can produce residents who are deficient in technical skills (Feldman, Sherman, and Fried, 2004). Surgeons are expected to learn and master many different skills despite the potential inconsistencies associated with their training, such as exposure to different types of surgery, patients, and different curricula. Although the development of procedural skills is a necessity for surgery, the discussion of principles and theories of skill acquisition in the surgical literature has largely been absent. However, with the advent of minimally invasive surgery and the additional burdens it places on surgeons (see following text), there has been a growing interest among surgeons in the fundamentals of skill acquisition.

PSYCHOMOTOR SKILL ACQUISITION

Skills can be described as an individual's learned capability to perform specific acts (Farmer et al., 1999). They reflect a permanent change in the way an action is performed. Psychomotor skills are coordinated muscular movements that follow a motor schema. A motor schema can be thought of as a memory for motor skills that has been well learned and operates independently of perceptual feedback information (Schmidt, 1975). Psychomotor skills can be divided into fine and gross categories (Holding, 1987). Fine psychomotor skills are those that usually involve detailed manipulations of a specific part of the body (e.g., fingers, hands, etc.). Gross motor skills are those that involve whole-body movements.

For an individual to successfully acquire fine psychomotor skills, he or she must practice. Perhaps the most important issue surrounding skill development centers on the nature of practice. Crossman (1959) described motor skill acquisition with respect to performance speed and amount of practice. Performance speed and practice follow a log power function such that initially, performance speed is quite slow when practicing a task. However, with more practice, speed increases. The increase in performance speed is thought to result from decreases in attentional resource demands that allow the skill to be performed in a more automated fashion (Schneider and Shiffrin, 1977; Wickens and Hollands, 2000). However, performance speed does not increase linearly with extended practice. Instead, it increases at a decreasing rate, and eventually, additional practice on the task will result in only minimal gains in speed.

Overlearning is another issue related to practice. Wickens and Hollands (2000) noted that overlearning occurs when an individual continues to practice after he or she has met the performance criterion. Overlearning does not decrease the amount of time it takes to perform a task. However, overlearning can help make skills more automatic by decreasing the attentional resources needed for execution. Wickens and Hollands (2000) suggested that for skills not practiced on a regular basis, overlearning enhances the probability they will be retained over time. However, Ericsson, Krampe, and Tesch-Römer (1993) have argued that thousands of hours of extended, deliberate practice well beyond meeting minimal performance criteria are needed to attain expert levels of performance.

Another important aspect of practice concerns how sessions are structured. Specifically, schedules of practice can be either massed (performed all at one time) or distributed (performed at intervals over a period of time). Farmer et al. (1999) discussed the advantages and disadvantages associated with each schedule of practice. For psychomotor skill acquisition, training sessions that are massed rather than distributed usually result in poorer skill acquisition (Schmidt and Lee, 2005). Also, performance assessed immediately after completion of training is more variable under massed practice (Lee and Genovese, 1988). Farmer et al. (1999) suggest that the poorer performance associated with massed practice sessions is usually due to muscle fatigue and declining motivation. By contrast, performance is more consistent with distributed practice sessions measured both during and immediately following training. The effects of massed and distributed practice schedules produce conflicting results for skill retention (Farmer et al., 1999; Holding, 1987). Discrepancies in the literature may be due to fatigue, retention intervals, durations of work–rest cycles, and the nature of the task. Schmidt and Lee (2005) suggest that the benefits of distributed over massed schedules of practice must be separated from the effects of fatigue present during training. Moreover, they note that much more is known about the effects of practice schedules on continuous tasks (e.g., tracking) as opposed to discrete tasks (e.g., button press). In fact, they indicate that there may be benefits to massed practice schedules over distributed schedules for discrete tasks.

Training can also be focused on the whole task or parts of the task. Often training on the whole task is not practical. Thus, part-task training is often targeted to critical or more challenging subcomponents of a task. Part-task training can be accomplished by decomposing a task into subcomponents or by fractionalizing the task (i.e., dividing the task into two or more components that are performed together; Wickens and Hollands, 2000). Part-task training has been found to be beneficial for serial tasks, but less so for continuous tasks, especially where there are strong interdependencies among the parts (Schmidt and Lee, 2005).

Another aspect of practice that is crucial for successfully acquiring psychomotor skills is guided training. Wickens and Hollands (2000) noted that under guided training, an individual's progress is monitored so that performance can adhere to the task requirements. Errors in learning are corrected to ensure that they are not repeated. Under guided training, individuals are provided with knowledge of results, which they can use to adjust their actions and reduce the error between current levels of performance and the criterion (Holding, 1987). Wickens and Hollands (2000) suggest that training benefits most when knowledge of results is provided immediately after a task or session.

If the goal is efficient skill performance, then one must understand principles of practice schedules, deliberate practice, part-, and whole-task training. Specifically, psychomotor skills should be learned through distributed practice sessions so that the trainee does not become fatigued or unmotivated. Further, overlearning will enhance the probability that skills will be retained over longer intervals and is absolutely necessary to establish expert-level performance. Also, part-task training should be used if challenging task components need to be practiced to proficiency. Finally, using guided training and providing knowledge of results will help enhance training performance and initial skill performance.

MEDICAL SIMULATORS: PART OF THE SOLUTION

Simulation technology has been proposed as a partial solution to help promote the acquisition and retention of surgical psychomotor skills (Dawson, 2002; Gallagher et al., 2005; Kauffman, 2001; Macintyre and Munro, 1990; Reznick and MacRae, 2006; Satava, 2001). Simulators can be used to help students acquire skills in a manner not possible during clinical training. Kauffman (2001) noted that surgical simulators provide students more time to practice newly acquired skills. Simulators also allow students to make mistakes and learn from them without endangering patients. Further, students can be required to reach a specific level of proficiency before being able to practice their skills on a patient. Perhaps the most important advantage of medical simulation technology is that it can shift the classic teaching model of "see one, do one, teach one" to a more structured training model of "see one, practice many, do one, teach one" (Kauffman, 1999). Beyond the obvious benefits of acquiring new skills, simulators can also be used for aptitude testing, career-long training, procedural rehearsal, board examinations, and credentialing (Dawson, 2006). Obviously, a new model that incorporates additional time for practice is advantageous not only to medical students and residents, but also to the patients.

TYPES OF MEDICAL SIMULATORS

Today, medical simulators address a wide variety of medical specialties and serve numerous purposes (see, Gaba, 2004). Medical simulators can be broadly classified into three categories: mannequin, virtual reality (VR), and hybrid. Mannequin-based simulators are physical representations of the human body and its anatomy. One example of a mannequin-based simulator is the TraumaMan® system by Simulab, Inc. (Figure 20.1). The TraumaMan system is a realistic anatomical model of the neck, chest, and abdomen that has replaceable tissue and fluid components. The TraumaMan system is used for Advance Trauma Life Support (ATLS®) training and allows students to perform procedures on a realistic representation of human anatomy. The main advantage of mannequin-based simulators is that students can practice on a simulator just as they would on a human patient. However, mannequin-based simulators do not provide objective performance assessment. Thus, an experienced physician must assess trainee performance by means of subjective assessments. Also, because mannequin-based simulators are physical models, they often lack variety in patient characteristics.

Virtual reality simulators, by contrast, are based on computer simulation. These simulators include visual, auditory, and haptic displays that enable individuals to see, hear, and feel the effects of their actions. Virtual reality simulators also allow students to interact with the simulator and receive objective feedback in real time (Satava, 2001). Virtual reality simulators can be either whole-task or part-task trainers. An example of a whole-task VR simulator is the Endoscopy AccuTouch® simulator from Immersion Medical, Inc. (Figure 20.2). The Endoscopy AccuTouch simulator has a colonoscopy module that simulates the entire procedure. The trainee manipulates a facsimile of a colonoscope and can insert the scope, visualize the full length of the colon, and photograph suspicious areas, even biopsy growths. Haptic force feedback is provided throughout the procedure and gives cues as to the difficulty of various maneuvers (e.g., when turns and loops of the colon must be navigated). The patient's voice also provides information regarding the quality of the student's performance. Training on the full procedure has advantages because it allows individuals to learn the proper sequence of steps and transitions between steps. However, as noted earlier when first learning to perform a complex procedure, it may be beneficial to practice individual parts of the task and later recombine the parts to perform the full procedure.

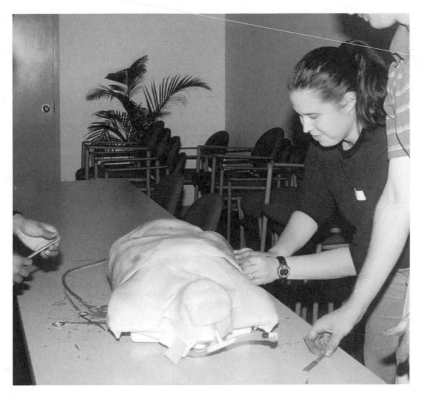

FIGURE 20.1   Student performing a thorocostomy (chest tube insertion) on the TraumaMan® by Simulab, Inc.

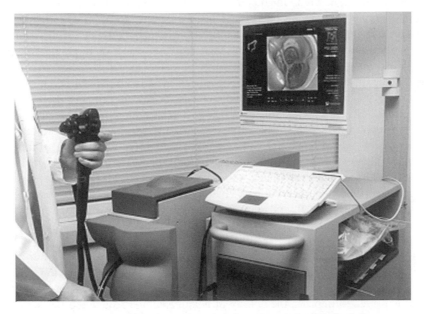

FIGURE 20.2   Virtual reality simulator for colonoscopy from Immersion Medical, Inc.

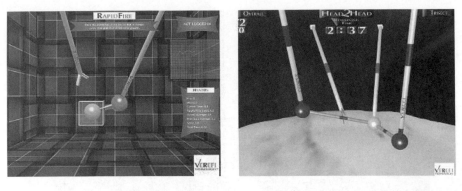

FIGURE 20.3 Screenshots from two virtual reality (VR) laparoscopic training systems; (left) the Rapid-Fire/SmartTutor™ for individuals and (right) the Head2Head system for teams. Printed with permission of Verefi Technologies™, Inc., Elizabethtown, Pennsylvania.

Other VR simulators allow individuals to practice parts of a task or abstract representations of surgical tasks, rather than the whole task. For example, the MIST VR (by Mentice AB) and the RapidFire/SmartTutor™ (by Verefi Technologies™; see Figure 20.3, left) are designed to train laparoscopic surgical skills; however, they do not simulate steps from surgical procedures. Instead, they allow trainees to acquire the psychomotor skills necessary for minimally invasive surgery by performing a variety of fundamental task components (e.g., probing, grasping, transferring objects between hands, etc.). The main advantage of part-task trainers is that individuals can acquire basic skills or focus on challenging subtask components that are less amenable to practice within a full task sequence. Moreover, the SmartTutor system can also adjust the difficulty of the task to adapt to the trainees' skill level in real time.

The Head2Head system (by Verefi Technologies; see Figure 20.3, right) takes training to a new level by allowing two-person teams to collaborate or compete with one another. On collaborative modules, trainees must coordinate their activities to accomplish tasks as they would on genuine surgical procedures (e.g., one individual controls the camera while the other performs the surgical task). The competitive modules pit one trainee against another to improve individual speed and accuracy by obtaining the most points in the shortest time. Thus, the Head2Head system overcomes much of the tedium associated with practicing basic laparoscopic skills by immersing trainees in a game-like atmosphere.

Hybrid simulators are those that incorporate aspects of VR computer-based systems into mannequin simulators (Satava, 2001). These simulators have certain advantages as well. Not only are individuals able to interact with a mannequin that represents typical human anatomy, but they can also receive some objective feedback regarding their performance because the simulator is built on a computer platform. For example, the SimMan® by Laerdal, Inc., is a hybrid training simulator that contains a mannequin and computer and is used for training anesthesia and trauma procedures (Figure 20.4). The system can reproduce a variety of patient conditions, patient responses to treatment, and can record trainee interventions. Hybrid systems are more sophisticated than mannequins, but still use physical models and therefore have limited patient variety. However, they provide a wider range of training scenarios and offer more objective means for assessing performance than mannequins alone.

All of the aforementioned simulators allow trainees to practice in a safe environment. Thus, students are free to make errors and learn from their mistakes without putting patients at risk. Given the concerns regarding patient safety described earlier, the development and use of medical simulators is expected to improve the quality of health care and reduce the incidence of medical errors.

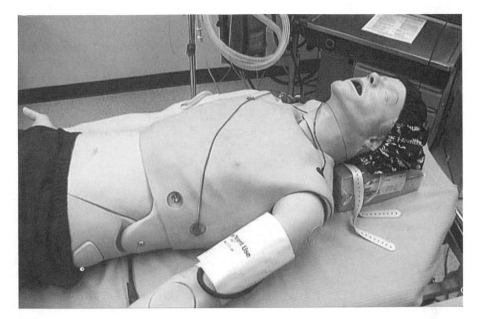

FIGURE 20.4 The SimMan® system by Laerdal, Inc.

LAPAROSCOPIC SURGERY AND SIMULATION TECHNOLOGY

The majority of medical VR simulators available today target laparoscopic skill acquisition. Minimally invasive surgery, via laparoscopy, was quickly embraced during the late 1980s as a safer way to operate on patients. Laparoscopic surgery is performed with instruments and a miniature video camera that are inserted through small incisions in the body. The images from the camera are displayed on a monitor and allow the surgeon to view his or her actions while performing procedures.

Laparoscopic procedures are amenable to VR simulation for many reasons. For example, during laparoscopic procedures, surgeons can only manipulate patient anatomy indirectly with the instruments that pass through the incisions in the body. The indirect access to the patient's anatomy does not allow the surgeon to experience the haptic sensations associated with direct contact of the tissues and organs. In open surgery, although surgeons still manipulate the patient's anatomy with instruments (e.g., scalpel, clamps, etc.), they can also directly touch and feel the patient's tissues and organs, albeit through surgical gloves.

As Biggs and Srinivasan (2002) have noted, the degree of difficulty involved in haptic VR simulation depends on whether the object and user interaction is direct (i.e., with the fingers and hands) or accomplished with a tool (i.e., tip of a laparoscopic instrument). If the haptic simulation can be achieved with a tool, then the haptic interface design is less complex and easier for VR designers to simulate. The reduced complexity is due to point-based haptic interactions that occur when the end of a tool comes in contact with a specific point on an object. In virtual systems, when the end point of a simulated tool contacts a simulated object, collision detection and collision response rules engage the force feedback system and constrain the user's movement (Biggs and Srinivasan, 2002). The collision algorithms are fairly easy to render in a point-based haptic system and therefore lend themselves to laparoscopic procedures, because much of the activity occurs through single points of contact.

The visual representation of surgery is another major issue concerning laparoscopic VR simulators. Designers must represent 3-D anatomy on a 2-D display monitor. Although this is a challenge, it is not as difficult as realistically representing the anatomy in 3-D. Thus, laparoscopic procedures are probably more accessible to designers of VR simulators.

It is indeed fortunate that there are fewer technical issues with simulating laparoscopic procedures, because this type of surgery is more challenging for the surgeon (see following text). Also, because laparoscopic surgery was adopted so quickly, many of the difficulties associated with these procedures did not emerge until after surgeons began performing them. Deziel et al. (1993) surveyed U.S. hospitals regarding patient outcomes for laparoscopic cholecystectomy (i.e., gall bladder removal) and found elevated complication rates. The most common complications were injuries to the patient's bile duct and vascular and bowel tissue. Deziel et al. claimed that despite higher complication rates with laparoscopy, the procedure was generally safe. Moore and Bennett (1995) also assessed laparoscopic cholecystectomy complication rates and found that most complications resulted from relatively inexperienced surgeons (i.e., complications usually occurred within the first 30 cases). Moore and Bennett performed a regression analysis on their data and noted that bile duct injuries could be expected to decrease from 1.7% for the first case to 0.17% after completion of 50 cases. Moore and Bennett also noted that the speed with which the procedure was implemented in the late 1980s, along with the absence of research on training, and risks and benefits to the patient, were likely contributors to the higher complication rates.

Although laparoscopic procedures may have higher complication rates, particularly for less experienced surgeons, it is still the preferred surgical method for many procedures. One reason for its wide acceptance rests with the benefits for the patient (Munz et al., 2004). The most important benefit is a quicker recovery time. Another advantage for patients is the cosmetic appeal of laparoscopy. Patients typically have less visible scarring.

Unfortunately, the benefits that patients gain from laparoscopic procedures come at a cost to surgeons, who must overcome significant challenges to perform this type of surgery. In particular, laparoscopy imposes new perceptual, spatial, and psychomotor demands on the surgeon. Gallagher et al. (2003) point out that, perceptually, the surgeon must translate information that is presented on a 2-D monitor into a 3-D mental model of the human anatomy. Others have also noted that the surgeon performing laparoscopy must compensate for navigating in a 3-D environment with a 2-D monitor by using depth cues other than stereopsis (Ahlberg et al., 2002).

Another perceptual problem encountered by surgeons during laparoscopic procedures is the fulcrum effect (Gallagher et al., 2003). Because laparoscopic instruments pass through small incisions in the body, the amount of space available to move the instruments is limited. Further, the instruments must be pivoted around the insertion point in the patient's body, thereby creating a fulcrum. The fulcrum effect occurs when an instrument is moved in one direction and its image on the display appears to move in the opposite direction. Further, the appearance of objects on the video monitor can be distorted and may also be inconsistent with the surgeon's mental model of the patient's anatomy. For example, the image of the patient's anatomy on the display can look distorted, depending on the magnification of the camera's lens and the position of the laparoscope within the body (i.e., if the laparoscope is too close or too far away from the anatomy).

Recently, DeLucia, Mather, Griswold, and Mitra (2006) studied several mechanisms that could help overcome some of the performance problems associated with laparoscopy, particularly on navigational tasks. They found that adding preview facilitated the formation of one's mental model of 3-D space. Also, changing the viewing aperture from a circular to a rectangular or octagonal shape helped reduce illusions of motion, often exacerbated by the fulcrum effect. Finally, they found some performance benefit to actively controlling one's own camera movements as opposed to viewing those generated by someone else.

There are also numerous ergonomic considerations surrounding laparoscopic surgery. The shape of laparoscopic instruments, the positions of the video monitor and foot controls, the height of the operating table, and the layout of the operating room all force the surgeon to adopt uncomfortable body positions and restrict his or her movement (MacKenzie, Lomax, and Ibbotson, 2004; Matern, 2004). Many of these problems are the result of laparoscopic surgery being performed in operating rooms built for traditional open surgery and not designed to accommodate laparoscopic equipment. In an ergonomic study of display locations, Hanna, Shimi, and Cuschieri (1998) found that moving the position of the video display had measurable effects on performance. Typically, the monitor is placed above and to the side of the surgeon's field of view. Hanna et al. evaluated several different monitor positions in a study of endoscopic knot tying using a simulator. They found that performance time decreased and the overall quality of the knot improved when the monitor was placed slightly below the head and close to the surgeon's hands. In an actual operating room, however, positioning the monitor directly in front of the surgeon and closer to his or her hands may not be possible owing to the need to access the patient in an emergency.

To overcome some of the difficulties associated with laparoscopic procedures, surgeons have turned to a variety of training methods to facilitate skill acquisition outside the operating room. The training methods are tied to two different classes of simulators: box trainers and VR-based systems.

LAPAROSCOPIC BOX TRAINERS

Box trainers are a standard and cost-effective means for surgeons to acquire fundamental laparoscopic skills. They usually consist of a boxlike structure with a camera and light source that displays images from inside the box on a monitor (Figure 20.5). An opaque covering prohibits direct viewing inside the box, allowing only the images on the monitor to be used as cues. Standard laparoscopic instruments are used to manipulate various objects within the box. Typical box trainer tasks include placing objects on a pegboard, cutting fabric, and applying clips.

There is an assumption that the skills learned using a box trainer will transfer to actual laparoscopic procedures. However, this assumption has not been extensively or objectively confirmed in the literature. For instance, Derossis et al. (1998) used a box trainer to develop objective measures of laparoscopic skills. They asked surgical residents to perform a series of laparoscopic box trainer tasks (e.g., peg board transfers, cutting, and suturing) and then assessed their performance speed and precision. Derossis et al. found that those who were further along in their residency performed

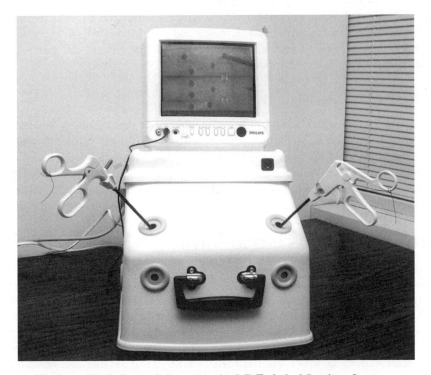

FIGURE 20.5 The laparoscopic box training system by 3-D Technical Services, Inc.

significantly better than newer residents. They suggested that box trainers could provide objective measures of laparoscopic skills because they can differentiate performance on the basis of years in residency and amount of practice. However, a closer look at the results revealed that performance differences were found on only three of the seven tasks: pegboard patterns, pattern cutting, and intracorporeal knot tying.

The results of Derossis et al. (1998) suggest that not all box trainer tasks may be difficult or unique enough to distinguish among different levels of laparoscopic experience. Intracorporeal suturing, or the ability to tie knots within the patient's body, may be an exception because it is widely considered one of the more challenging laparoscopic tasks. In a recent study, Stefanidis, Scerbo, Korndorffer, and Scott (2007) found that the Storz Endoscopy box training system could distinguish between some levels of intracorporeal suturing experience. However, the sensitivity was improved when the suturing task was paired with a secondary spatial memory task competing for the same visual-spatial attentional resources.

Korndorffer and his colleagues (2005) conducted another study of intracorporeal suturing with the Storz Endoscopy box training system and measured knot-tying skills in a porcine laboratory (i.e., on a live pig) before and after training. They observed that the residents needed 151 minutes of practice on the box trainer, on average, to reach performance levels comparable to those of an expert group. Results from the porcine tests showed that the trainees achieved significant gains in performance from the pretest to posttest on several measures, but they did not achieve the same levels exhibited by the experts in the porcine laboratory. The authors concluded that the box training system does produce positive transfer to genuine operating procedures, but at a level lower than what would be expected from expert surgeons.

Macmillan and Cuschieri (1999) used a different box trainer known as the Advanced Dundee Endoscopic Psychomotor Tester (ADEPT) in an attempt to predict how well innate surgical abilities correlate with surgical performance. ADEPT is an advanced box trainer because it uses a computer to determine the training regimen and record performance indices. However, the activities are similar to traditional box trainer tasks, primarily requiring object manipulation. Ten surgical residents were given approximately 1 hour of training on the ADEPT simulator. Expert surgeons then rated the clinical skills of the trainee surgeons. Macmillan and Cuschieri (1999) found a significant correlation ($r = .79$) between participant success rate on ADEPT and clinical skills assessed on actual laparoscopic surgery.

LAPAROSCOPIC VIRTUAL REALITY TRAINERS

Box trainers, though still widely used, are being augmented or replaced by VR-based simulators. Virtual reality trainers have an important advantage over box trainers in that they allow a wider range of performance indices to be quantified and recorded. The MIST VR (described earlier in this chapter), introduced in the late 1990s, is the most widely studied VR laparoscopic training system. It features several basic training tasks including grasping, target transfer, target diathermy, and bowel running.

MIST VR LEARNING CURVES AND SENSITIVITY

Chaudhry et al. (1999) assessed the learning curves on six MIST VR tasks over 10 trials for 11 surgeons and 7 nonsurgeons. Their results showed that the overall scores of the surgeons were significantly better than those of the nonsurgeons on all tasks (demonstrating that the MIST VR has sensitivity); however, there were no significant differences in the learning curves or familiarization rates between the two groups. All participants needed as many as three sessions to familiarize themselves with the tasks and learn the processes, including how to correctly manipulate the instruments. In another study using MIST VR, Grantcharov et al. (2003) did find significant differences in the familiarization curves for surgeons with different levels of laparoscopic experience (e.g., master, intermediate, and beginner). These researchers assessed surgeons on all six MIST VR tasks 10 times over one period and found that master surgeons had steeper learning curves than surgeons with less laparoscopic experience. Further, the familiarization curves for master surgeons differed significantly from those of the intermediate and beginning surgeons on several measures including time, errors, and unnecessary instrument movements. Intermediate surgeons were also found to have steeper familiarization curves than beginning surgeons. Brunner et al. (2004) also studied training with MIST VR over an extended period of time. They found that skills were acquired in successive stages and that even after 7 hours and 30 task repetitions, trainee performance curves had still not reached a plateau. Collectively, these studies demonstrate that MIST VR can differentiate between individuals with different levels of skill and surgical experience.

OVERCOMING THE FULCRUM EFFECT

As noted earlier, the fulcrum effect refers to the incongruity between real and displayed movements that occur during laparoscopic surgery. Gallagher et al. (1999) assessed the degree to which MIST VR could help individuals overcome the fulcrum effect. Half of their participants were trained on the MIST VR, and the other half served as a control group. After completing MIST VR training, all participants were asked to perform a cutting task with a box trainer. Their results showed that individuals trained on MIST VR made significantly more correct incisions in a standard box training task than those in the control group. Gallagher et al. (1999) suggested that the superior performance of those in the MIST VR–trained group could be attributed to their being able to acclimate to the fulcrum effect more quickly. Jordan et al. (2000) also studied the fulcrum effect with the MIST VR. They assigned participants to one of three training conditions: MIST VR, a box trainer with randomly alternating normal and y-axis inverted views, and a box trainer with normal laparoscopic views. Participants in their respective conditions practiced six training tasks and were assessed with a pretest and posttest cutting task using a box trainer. They found that participants trained on MIST VR made significantly more correct incisions on the posttest, followed by those in the randomly alternating condition, and then those in the normal laparoscopic condition. Jordan et al. (2000) suggested that training on MIST VR helped individuals acclimate to the fulcrum effect more quickly than training on a standard box trainer. However, the superior performance of those trained on MIST VR described in these two studies was only demonstrated on box trainer tasks. Obviously, the critical test for MIST VR training requires that the skills learned on the simulator transfer to the operating room with real laparoscopic procedures performed on genuine patients.

TRANSFER OF MIST VR ACQUIRED SKILL

To date, there have been only a few attempts to determine whether skills acquired with MIST VR transfer to real laparoscopic procedures. In one study, skills acquired on MIST VR were assessed on real laparoscopic procedures performed in a porcine laboratory. Alhberg et al. (2002) used fourth-year medical students with no prior endoscopic experience and had half of them train on MIST VR for 3 hours while the other half received no training. All participants then performed an appendectomy on a pig. The surgical sessions were recorded and scored by three observers for five relevant performance metrics (e.g., grasping bowel, cutting ligature, loop ligation, etc.). Alhberg et al. (2002) found no significant performance differences between the MIST VR–trained and untrained groups. They suggested that the absence of any performance benefit for MIST VR might have been due to the lack of haptic feedback. Thus, MIST VR may facilitate hand–eye coordination, but fails to provide the haptic sensations important for real laparoscopic procedures. Therefore, when MIST VR–trained students had to perform the pig appendectomy, they may have been familiar with the visual cues associated with laparoscopic surgery, but had to acclimate to the haptic sensations associated with manipulating tissue.

Unlike Alhberg et al. (2002), Seymour and his colleagues (2002) attempted to determine whether skills acquired on MIST VR would transfer to genuine laparoscopic procedures performed on human patients. Seymour et al. (2002) used surgical residents who were in their first to fourth year of training and assessed their fundamental abilities (i.e., visuospatial, perceptual, and psychomotor abilities). Half were assigned to a standard training condition, and the other half to a MIST VR plus standard training condition. The authors noted that the standard training was appropriate for their level of residency, but did not provide exact details regarding the nature of that training. The group that received training on MIST VR completed 3 to 8 training sessions lasting 1 hour each. Following training, all residents watched a video about laparoscopic cholecystectomy and then performed the procedure under the supervision of a surgeon. All the procedures were recorded and assessed by surgeons who were blind to each participant's condition. Seymour et al. (2002) found that residents who trained on MIST VR and received standard laparoscopic training completed the laparoscopic cholecystectomy in 29% less time than their counterparts in the standard-only training condition. Those trained on MIST VR also committed fewer errors during actual gall bladder removal than those in the standard-only group. Seymour et al. argued that training on a laparoscopic VR simulator did indeed transfer to the operating room. However, it is important to remember that their VR group received standard training *in addition* to hours of practice on MIST VR. Thus, one cannot determine the degree of improvement associated with MIST VR training relative to another group receiving another form of training for a comparable duration.

Collectively, the research to date on MIST VR has shown some benefits for training, but the extent of those benefits is still not known. To date, few studies have pinpointed the advantages of training on MIST VR above and beyond other training devices (e.g., box trainers). Recently, Avgerinos et al. (2005) compared MIST VR with a box trainer and found that the box trainer demonstrated better sensitivity at distinguishing between different levels of surgical experience. On the other hand, Hamilton et al. (2001) compared MIST VR and a video/box training system and found that residents trained on both systems showed improvement. The MIST VR produced higher posttest scores, but the video/box trainer resulted in quicker performance times. However, when both groups were later observed performing genuine laparoscopic procedures, only those residents who practiced with MIST VR showed significant improvement after training.

CONCLUSION

Medical simulators are clearly having a profound effect on the way medicine is being taught. For the first time in the history of medicine, they offer the opportunity for objective assessment of performance with standardized metrics in a safe and controlled environment. They will increase skill proficiency and reduce the performance variance and errors of those who practice medicine, and ultimately, will improve patient safety. However, there are still many challenges that lie ahead for simulation to make its maximum impact in medicine.

Many educators are still leery of the huge discrepancy in realism between current simulation technology and actual patients. Satava (1993) suggested that medical simulators must have adequate fidelity, objective images that behave according to their anatomical properties (e.g., tissue that is displaced properly when touched or grasped), an element of interactivity, and haptic qualities. The MIST VR, for example, is a part-task trainer that uses only abstract representations of laparoscopic tasks. Further, the MIST VR also lacks haptic force feedback. Satava (2001) noted that designers of medical simulators must still address the trade-off between visual fidelity and interactivity; that is, efforts to maximize visual fidelity are often achieved at the expense of interactivity and vice versa. However, Satava (2001) noted that the biggest challenge associated with medical simulators concerns the best ways to incorporate them into a curriculum where they can be used for training and evaluation.

Another criticism of medical simulators is that they may dehumanize the healthcare profession (Issenberg et al., 1999). Some critics fear that by focusing on computerized machines (i.e., simulators) for a portion of medical training, students may be missing the importance of personalized patient care. However, as Issenberg et al. (1999) suggest, patient care can still be learned at a later time, after students have been able to familiarize themselves with medical procedures and pathology. Thus, training with simulators must be balanced with patient interactions.

Although many medical simulators are now being used in education and training, their efficacy must still be considered (Satava, 2001). For a simulator to be truly effective, it must provide more benefits than those currently provided by standard methods of training. Therefore, it is important for educators to be aware of some of the potential limitations associated with different simulator systems. For instance, some simulators allow individuals to acquire skills on only a subset of the tasks needed to perform a full procedure (Scerbo, Bliss, Schmidt, and Thompson, 2006; Scerbo, Schmidt, and Bliss, 2006). Also, as noted earlier, because some simulators are part-task trainers (e.g., MIST VR), they may facilitate the acquisition of fundamental psychomotor skills, but none of the specific steps needed to perform genuine procedures.

The decision to incorporate simulation training into a curriculum is not only dependent on the potential training benefits, but also on the financial costs. Satava (2001) noted some of the financial challenges associated with using simulation for training. For example, because VR simulators are built on a computer platform, the hardware and software required can be very expensive. Thus, the types of medical simulators that are currently available are somewhat simplistic and address procedures that are relatively easy to simulate. Satava (2001) suggests that three areas must be addressed for simulation to be a cost-effective training method. First, simulators should be designed for many different types of surgical specialties. Second, they should accommodate individuals with different skill levels (i.e., students, residents, attendings, etc.). Third, simulators should not only be used for education and training, but also for planning complex surgical procedures. As Satava noted, until medical simulators become more cost-effective, simulation training will likely be limited to less complex procedures.

Additional research is also needed regarding the ideal way to structure training around simulators. Issues concerning schedules of practice, guided training, and overlearning have been studied in other high-risk industries that rely heavily on simulation (e.g., aviation and process plant operations), but need to be reexamined in the medical domain, which has its own unique characteristics and constraints. Further, much of the research regarding simulation training in medicine is not theoretically driven. Principles and theories of learning, training, and skill development are as fundamental to enhancing the effectiveness of simulation-based training in medicine as they are in other domains. Ultimately, it is the need to understand the learner and the requirements for safe and effective performance that is paramount, not the technology. Maintaining a focus on the learner should help instructors seek and apply appropriate knowledge, principles, and theories of education and training to produce better doctors and incorporate simulation where it best serves that goal.

ACKNOWLEDGMENTS

Work on this paper was supported in part by the Naval Health Research Center through NAVAIR Orlando TSD under contract N61339-03-C-0157 and the Office of Naval Research under contract N00014-04-1-0697, entitled "The National Center for Collaboration in Medical Modeling and Simulation," a collaborative project between the Virginia Modeling, Analysis and Simulation Center (VMASC) at Old Dominion University and the Eastern Virginia Medical School. The ideas and opinions presented in this paper represent the views of the authors and do not necessarily represent the views of the Department of Defense.

REFERENCES

Alhberg, G., Heikkinen, T., Iselius, L., Leijonmarck, C. E., Rutqvist, J., & Arvidsson, D., 2002. Does training in a virtual reality simulator improve surgical performance? *Surgical Endoscopy, 16,* 126–129.

American Medical Association, 2005. AMA resident work hours policy. Retrieved July 10, 2007, from http://www.ama-assn.org/ama/pub/category/7094.html

Avgerinos, D. V., Goodell, K. H., Waxberg, S., Cao, C. G. L., & Schwaitzberg, S. D., 2005. Comparison of the sensitivity of physical and virtual laparoscopic surgical training simulators to the user's level of experience. *Surgical Endoscopy, 19,* 1211–1215.

Biggs, J., & Srinivasan, M. A., 2002. Haptic interfaces. In Stanney, K. (Ed.), *Handbook of virtual environments* (pp. 93–116). Mahwah, NJ: Erlbaum.

Brennan, T. A., Leape, L. L., Laird, N. M., Hebert, L., Localio, A. R., Lawthers, A. G., Newhouse, J. P., Welier, P. C., & Hiatt, H. H., 1991. Incidence of adverse events and negligence in hospitalized patients: Results of the Harvard Medical Practice Study I. *New England Journal of Medicine, 324,* 370–376.

Brunner, W. C., Korndorffer, J. R., Sierra, R., Massarweh, N. N., Dunne, J. B., Yau, C. L., & Scott, D. J., 2004. Laparoscopic virtual reality training: Are 30 repetitions enough? *Journal of Surgical Research, 122,* 150–156.

Chaudhry, A., Sutton, C., Wood, J., Stone, R., & McCloy, R., 1999. Learning rate for laparoscopic surgical skills on MIST VR, a virtual reality simulator: Quality of human-computer interface. *Annals of the Royal College of Surgeons of England, 81,* 281–286.

Crossman, E. R. F. W., 1959. A theory of the acquisition of speed skill. *Ergonomics, 2,* 153–166.

Dawson, S. L., 2002. A critical approach to medical simulation. *Bulletin of the American College of Surgeons, 87,* 12–18.

Dawson, S., 2006. Procedural simulation—A primer. *Journal of Vascular Interventional Radiology, 17,* 205–213.

DeLucia, P. R., Mather, R. D., Griswold, J. A., & Mitra, S., 2006. Toward the improvement of image-guided interventions for minimally invasive surgery: Three factors that affect performance. *Human Factors, 48,* 23–38.

Derossis, A. M., Fried, G. M., Abrahamowicz, M., Sigman, H. H., Barkun, J. S., & Meakins, J. L., 1998. Development of a model for training and evaluation of laparoscopic skills. *The American Journal of Surgery, 175,* 482–487.

Deziel, D. J., Millikan, K. W., Economou, S. G., Doolas, A., Ko, S. T., & Airan, M. C., 1993. Complications of laparoscopic cholecystectomy: A national survey of 4,292 hospitals and an analysis of 77, 604 cases. *The American Journal of Surgery, 165,* 9–14.

Ericsson, K. A., Krampe, R. T., & Tesch-Römer, C., 1993. The role of deliberate practice in the acquisition of expert performance. *Psychological Review, 100,* 363–406.

Farmer, E., van Rooij, J., Riemersma, J., Jorna, P., & Moraal, J., 1999. *Handbook of simulator-based training.* England: Ashgate.

Feldman, L. S., Sherman, V., & Fried, G. M., 2004. Using simulators to assess laparoscopic competence: Ready for widespread use? *Surgery, 135,* 28–42.

Gaba, D., 2004. The future vision of simulation in health care. *Quality and Safety in Health Care, 13(Suppl 1),* i2–i10.

Gallagher, A. G., Cowie, R., Crothers, I., Jordan-Black, J. A., & Satava, R. M., 2003. An objective test of perceptual skill that predicts laparoscopic technical skill in three initial studies of laparoscopic performance. *Surgical Endoscopy, 17,* 1468–1471.

Gallagher, A. G., McClure, N., McGuigan, J., Crothers, I., & Browning, J., 1999. Virtual reality training in laparoscopic surgery: A preliminary assessment of minimally invasive surgical trainer virtual reality (MIST VR). *Endoscopy, 31,* 310–313.

Gallagher, A. G., Ritter, E. M., Champion, H., Higgins, G., Fried, M. P., Moses, G., Smith, C. D., & Satava, R. M., 2005. Virtual reality simulation for the operating room: Proficiency-based training as a paradigm shift in surgical skills training. *Annals of Surgery, 241,* 1–9.

Grantcharov, T. P., Bardram, L., Funch-Jensen, P., & Rosenber, J., 2003. Learning curves and impact of previous operative experience on performance on a virtual reality simulator to test laparoscopic surgical skills. *The American Journal of Surgery, 185,* 146–149.

Hamilton, E. C., Scott, D. J., Fleming, J. B., Rege, R. V., Laycock, R., Bergen, P. C., Tesfay, S. T., & Jones, D. B., 2001. Comparison of video trainer and virtual reality training systems on acquisition of laparoscopic skills. *Surgical Endoscopy, 16,* 406–411.

Hanna, G. B., Shimi, S. M., & Cuschieri, A., 1998. Task performance in endoscopic surgery is influenced by location of the image display. *Annals of Surgery, 227,* 481–484.

Hayward, R. A., & Hofer, T. P., 2001. Estimating hospital deaths due to medical errors: Preventability is in the eye of the reviewer. *Journal of the American Medical Association, 286,* 415–420.

Hayward, R. A., McMahon, L. F., & Bernard, A. M., 1993. Evaluating the care of general medicine inpatients: How good is implicit review? *Annals of Internal Medicine, 118,* 550–556.

HealthGrades, 2007. *HealthGrades quality study: Fourth annual patient safety in American hospitals.* Lakewood, CO: HealthGrades.

Holding, D., 1987. Concepts of training. In Salvendy, G. (Ed.), *Handbook of human factors* (pp. 939–962). New York: Wiley.

Issenberg, S. B., McGaghie, W. C., Hart, I. R., Mayer, J. W., Felner, J. M., Petrusa, E. R., Waugh, R. A., Brown, D. D., Safford, R. R., Gessner, I. H., Gordon, D. L., & Ewy, G. A., 1999. Simulation technology for health care professional skills training and assessment. *Journal of the American Medical Association, 282,* 861–866.

Jordan, J., Gallagher, A. G., McGuigan, J., McGlade, K., & McClure, N., 2000. A comparison between randomly alternating imaging, normal laparoscopic imaging, and virtual reality training in laparoscopic psychomotor skill acquisition. *The American Journal of Surgery, 180,* 208–211.

Kauffman, C. R., 1999. Role of surgical simulators in surgical education. *Asian Journal of Surgery, 22,* 398–401.

Kauffman, C. R., 2001. Computers in surgical education and the operating room. *Annales Chirurgiae et Gynaecologiae, 90,* 141–143.

Kohn, L., Corrigan, J., & Donaldson, M. (Eds.), 1999. *To err is human: Building a safer health system.* Washington D.C.: National Academy Press.

Korndorffer, J. R., Dunne, J. B., Sierra, R., Stefanidis, D., Touchard, C. L., & Scott, D. J., 2005. Simulator training for laparoscopic suturing using performance goals translates to the OR. *Journal of the American College of Surgeons, 201,* 23–29.

Lee, T. D., & Genovese, E. D., 1988. Distribution of practice in motor skill acquisition: Learning and performance effects reconsidered. *Research Quarterly for Exercise and Sport, 59,* 277–287.

MacIntyre, J. M. C., & Munro, A., 1990. Simulation in surgical training. *British Medical Journal, 300,* 1088–1089.

MacKenzie, C. L., Lomax, A. J., & Ibbotson, J. A., 2004. Safety and error issues in minimally invasive surgery. In Bogner, M. S. (Ed.), *Misadventures in health care: Inside stories* (pp. 59–74). Mahwah, NJ: Erlbaum.

Macmillan, A. I., & Cuschieri, A., 1999. Assessment of innate ability and skills for endoscopic manipulations by the Advanced Dundee Endoscopic Psychomotor Tester: Predictive and concurrent validity. *American Journal of Surgery, 177,* 274–277.

Matern, U., 2004. The laparoscopic surgeon's posture. In Bogner, M. S. (Ed.), *Misadventures in health care: Inside stories* (pp. 75–88). Mahwah, NJ: Erlbaum.

Moore, M. J., & Bennett, C. L., 1995. The learning curve for laparoscopic cholecystectomy. *The American Journal of Surgery, 170,* 55–59.

Munz, Y., Kumar, B. D., Moorthy, K., Bann, S., & Darzi, A., 2004. Laparoscopic virtual reality and box trainers: Is one superior to the other? *Surgical Endoscopy, 18,* 485–494.

Reznick, R. K., & MacRae, H., 2006. Teaching surgical skills—changes in the wind. *New England Journal of Medicine, 355,* 2664–2669.

Satava, R. M., 1993. Virtual reality surgical simulator. *Surgical Endoscopy, 7,* 203–205.

Satava, R. M., 2001. Accomplishments and challenges of surgical simulation. *Surgical Endoscopy, 15,* 232–241.

Satava, R. M., 2004. Disruptive visions: A robot is not a machine systems integration for surgeons. *Surgical Endoscopy, 18,* 617–20.

Scerbo, M. W., Bliss, J. P., Schmidt, E. A., & Thompson, S. N., 2006. The efficacy of a medical virtual reality simulator for training phlebotomy. *Human Factors, 48,* 72–84.

Scerbo, M. W., Schmidt, E. A., & Bliss, J. P., 2006. Comparison of a virtual reality simulator and simulated limbs for phlebotomy training, *Journal of Infusion Nursing, 29,* 214–224.

Schmidt, R. A., 1975. *Motor skills.* New York: Harper and Row.

Schmidt, R. A., & Lee, T. D., 2005. *Motor control and learning: A behavioral emphasis, 4th ed.* Champaign, IL: Human Kinetics.

Schneider, W., & Shiffrin, R. M., 1977. Controlled and automatic human information processing. I: Detection, search and attention. *Psychological Review, 84,* 1–66.

Seymour, N. E., Gallagher, A. G., Roman, S. A., O'Briend, M. K., Bansal, V. K., Andersen, D. K., & Satava, R. M., 2002. Virtual reality training improves operating room performance. *Annals of Surgery, 236,* 458–464.

Shimada, Y., Nishiwaki, K., & Cooper, J. B., 1998. Use of medical simulators subject of international study. *Journal of Clinical Monitoring and Computing, 14,* 499–503.

Stefanidis, D., Scerbo, M. W., Korndorffer, J. R., Jr., & Scott, D. J., 2007. Redefining simulator proficiency using automaticity theory. *The American Journal of Surgery, 193,* 502–506.

Wickens, C. D., & Hollands, J. G., 2000. *Engineering psychology and human performance.* Upper Saddle River, NJ: Prentice Hall.

21 Communications and Coordination Training with Speech-Interactive Synthetic Teammates:
A Design and Evaluation Case Study

Benjamin Bell, Joan M. Ryder, and Stacie N. Pratt

CONTENTS

INTRODUCTION

SIMULATORS AND THE TEAM TRAINING GAP

Simulation devices have historically emphasized individual skills training, and are seldom designed to provide, as part of the simulated experience, the user's interactions with other members of a crew or team. Despite this limitation, use of simulation for training in complex engineering environments is widespread and enjoys a great deal of user acceptance; the user community has thus evolved techniques for providing team-oriented training with devices designed for individual skills training. The most common way to employ such devices for tasks that involve team performance is through human confederates, or role players. A role player may or may not be getting training—his or her job is to perform the tasks necessary for the simulation to be credible and effective; in other words, to provide behavioral, aural, or visual cueing to the user in a way that simulates how the team would be functioning.

This technique has the advantage of simplicity—the role player participates in the scenario by speaking (directly to the users or through a voice net) and may also operate a workstation. Reliance on such confederates/role players, though, presents several challenges. First, it introduces variability, which makes standardization of training difficult because of the human element influencing events in each scenario. Second, it interferes with performance assessment, because it is often the instructors themselves who are called upon to divide their attention between evaluating trainees and playing roles. Third, it incurs serious penalties in cost and availability of training. Costs arise from the need for role players and from the logistics tail to get them and maintain them at a training facility. Availability is compromised because it can be exceedingly difficult to arrange for role players to staff simulations. Also, the laws of supply and demand interact here so that a shortage of role players can enable paid experts to command high fees. The consequence is that access to team training is measured and scheduled and conducted only at dedicated facilities. Because such training is offered principally at home stations, deployed forces can suffer steep drop-offs in readiness, as any skills that are not practiced while personnel are deployed experience sharp decay (Chatham and Braddock, 2001).

This chapter reports on a successful implementation, evaluation, and fielding of a personal computer (PC)-based simulation that provides training in communication through the use of speech-capable synthetic entities whose behaviors are driven by cognitive models. The goal of this chapter is to showcase the versatility of PC-based simulation when coupled with speech-interactive synthetic agents, to present an instance of this approach in fielded use, and to describe the evaluation methods and findings of an independent analysis of training effectiveness.

THE TRAINING PROBLEM: PILOT COMMUNICATION

Military flying training presents great challenges under the best of conditions; inadequate access to guided practice opportunities contributes to washout and reduces training effectiveness and preparedness. Current technology limitations make training of some skills difficult to accomplish in simulations, limiting opportunities to supplement fieldwork with simulated exercises. When adequate simulators do exist, they are often expensive to operate and require dedicated, fixed hardware. Users can therefore train only in specific locales. The need for expert instructors places additional constraints on training effectiveness and throughput. Simulators as a rule are not equipped to conduct assessment and debrief, which remain largely the responsibility of human instructors.

Desktop flight simulators offer an apparently obvious solution to this problem by providing greater access to operational flight trainers and reducing reliance on human instructor pilots (IPs). Although commercial-off-the-shelf (COTS) simulation technologies can provide low-cost practice opportunities with fidelity that is adequate for some training needs, they currently lack the sophisticated tutoring and assessment required to address training of complex flying skills, such as overhead pattern operations or team coordination in tactical operations. In fact, using simulations in the absence of appropriate instructional feedback, such as that which could be provided by an intelligent tutor, can have a negative impact on performance (Means, Salas, Crandall, and Jacobs, 1993). Simulators that are also devoid of speech-understanding capabilities are unable to train skills related to communications and coordination, such as radio procedures with the other pilots or controllers. Finally, current COTS flight simulators lack the cognitive and pedagogical infrastructure to perform training management tasks such as presenting scenarios that optimally expose the trainee to skills in greatest need of practice, and reporting student performance.

The versatility of PC-based training offers a potential solution for training cognitive-oriented skills such as communication and decision making. This kind of training requires simulations that present realistic problem-solving experiences, dialogue, and interaction. And therein lies a steep challenge—one that can be overcome only through robust, verbally interactive synthetic agents. The kind of agents we have in mind possess capabilities that extend well beyond the scripted, state-machine abilities of computer-generated forces (CGFs), semiautomated forces (SAFs), and game engine artificially intelligent entities, or AIs. Cognitive agents for team training must be able to interact in realistic ways across a broad range of tactical situations and to verbally engage in dialogue with users. Research initiatives in this area have been confined largely to experiments and demonstration prototypes, with few instances of systems making their way to the field.

One recent program that has crossed this chasm is the Virtual Interactive Pattern Environment and Radiocomms Simulator (VIPERS). The VIPERS system, built for the U.S. Air Force (USAF) by CHI Systems, Inc., an OSI Geospatial company, blends advanced cognitive models and speech interaction with PC-based simulation to provide a radio communications and decision-making trainer for use by students in Specialized Undergraduate Pilot Training (SUPT). VIPERS features a verbally realistic simulation of the SUPT pattern in which a user commands an aircraft and interacts through spoken dialogue with synthetic controllers and instructors. Early and frequent collaboration among the Air Force Research Laboratory (AFRL), the Air Education and Training Command (AETC), and the 19th Air Force resulted in VIPERS being fielded for a six-month evaluation by AETC at an active SUPT base, where it was in continuous use by active duty Air Force officers going through SUPT. Usage data on VIPERS was analyzed by the USAF and correlated with performance on training sorties, resulting in a finding of statistically significant correlations between use of VIPERS and performance on three measures selected by the Air Force (situational awareness [SA], communications, and in-flight checks).

VIPERS is a good litmus test for the range of PC-based training systems because of the challenges of creating dialogue-capable agents and because the product was subjected to rigorous evaluation. This chapter will address the instructional approach, the use of synthetic agents both as players in the training scenario and as virtual tutors, and automating performance measurement. We first summarize the evolution of projects demonstrating synthetic teammates for on-demand team training, and then present VIPERS as a case study. Finally, we present details of the USAF formal evaluation of VIPERS: its design, methodology, and findings. Although our training examples are in the aviation domain, we discuss how the principles discussed are applicable to other fields as well.

COMMUNICATION AND COORDINATION TRAINING

Training with Speech-Enabled Synthetic Teammates

The potential for dialogue-capable synthetic teammates to reduce reliance on human role players has generated discussion among those in the training community interested in making team training more accessible, controlling costs, and improving standardization. To employ this technique effectively for team training, synthetic team members require the following capabilities:

1. Simultaneous execution of task work (e.g., flying the aircraft, working the console), teamwork (interacting with other members of the team), and instruction (providing assessment and feedback)
2. Interaction via spoken language (required for team training in verbal environments)
3. Modulating behaviors to replicate various error modes, to allow for varying the proficiency of the synthetic team members (important in team training)

These capabilities were first demonstrated by integrating cognitive models and full-speech interaction for a program called Synthetic Cognition for Operational Team Training (SCOTT; Zachary, Santarelli, Lyons, Bergondy, and Johnston, 2001). SCOTT is a simulation-based practice and training environment in which a single human crewmember of an E-2C tactical crew can train in cross-platform coordination skills by interacting with synthetic teammates, both on and off the E-2C. The system enables an individual to practice crucial advanced team skills on an anytime, anywhere basis with synthetic agents playing the roles of missing teammates. The trainee interacts with these synthetic players via spoken language and receives input from them via synthesized speech. SCOTT maintains detailed performance information during a training exercise and automatically generates both live feedback (delivered through a synthetic teammate) and an after action review (AAR).

The SCOTT prototype has a synthetic E-2C Combat Information Center Officer (CICO), built using CHI Systems' iGEN® cognitive agent software toolkit. The CICO model performs the role of the missing CICO in monitoring the tactical picture, performing command and control task work, interacting with on-board E-2C crew and off-board distributed team members, such as the Force Anti-Air Warfare Coordinator (AAWC) and intelligence sources. The synthetic CICO also monitors the performance of a human E-2C Air Control Officer (ACO) and provides backup and feedback on performance, which can occur online or through after action reviews (AARs). A synthetic Radar Officer (RO) was also developed to replace the missing live RO. The SCOTT test bed includes simulated consoles for the E-2C live and synthetic team members; training management and performance assessment subsystems; an ability to operate in a Joint Semi-Automated Forces (JSAF) or self-contained environment; and voice recognition, speech synthesis, visualization, and other components to support a wide range of training and research applications. The SCOTT network for strike warfare includes the E-2C HAWKEYE 2000 command and control operators, F/A-18 strike pilots, F-14 sweep aircraft, intelligence sources, and a shipboard Force AAWC.

SCOTT broke new ground in demonstrating the application of synthetic teammates to team skill training in realistic, mission-oriented scenarios when it is not possible for the entire team to practice together. It employed new technologies and new software architectures that paved the way for successor programs to move beyond the demonstration prototype stage.

Synthetic Teammates for Realtime Anywhere Training and Assessment (STRATA) was built on the progress made under SCOTT but applied more sophisticated cognitive modeling (enabled by the natural evolution of iGEN and our corresponding methodologies) and incorporated more advanced speech technologies (enabled by the evolution of commercial speech products). The emphasis in STRATA was not only to provide advanced synthetic teammates, but to take seriously the notion of "on-demand team training" by making the instructor and the other team members entirely optional.

In accomplishing this vision, we adopted the premise that for any given set of training objectives there exists a range of acceptable simulation fidelities (National Research Council, 1997; Isdale, Fencott, Heim, and Daly, 2002). For STRATA, we therefore carefully aligned training objectives with the level of fidelity needed to practice and master those objectives (Hays and Singer, 1989; Salas, Bowers, and Rhodenizer, 1998; NAVAIR Orlando Training Systems Division, 2002). The skills we focused on (communication, coordination, and decision making) imply a strong need for cognitive fidelity, meaning users should be immersed in environments that elicit decision-making and team behaviors that closely match the mental processes they apply in actual practices. The visual and physical fidelity requirements associated with airmanship "stick and throttle" training were less stringent for STRATA but were adequate to present a realistic and challenging environment that requires the integration of multiple skills. Results from numerous studies of reduced-fidelity simulation conducted during the past decade point to a trend of greater acceptance of medium fidelity PC-based training, both among pilots in general (Beringer, 1994; Jentsch and Bowers, 1998) and among military pilots (Rogers, 1991; Baker et al., 1993).

The synthetic teammates developed for STRATA provide six key functions:

1. Perform role-based task work/team work (e.g., piloting) as well as teamwork behaviors (e.g., interacting with other members of the team directly), and maintain appropriate situation awareness
2. Provide flexible, realistic communications, because much of the work of the synthetic teammates must be done on verbal channels
3. Commit errors to exercise team backup skill, generating expectations of and providing cues for user-initiated teamwork-oriented backup behaviors
4. Detect and compensate for user error, providing compensatory behaviors when the user makes mistakes, in order to allow the scenario to continue to flow
5. Enhance accuracy of the speech recognition, using internal context to drive and dynamically tailor the speech recognition system by sending commands to the speech recognition engine, in real time, to activate portions of the grammar
6. Modify behaviors based on scenario parameters, flexibly controlled through input parameters represented in Extensible Markup Language (XML)

The synthetic teammates in STRATA facilitate training by engaging the user through verbal and system-mediated communications in the context of various types of close air support (CAS) missions. These agents enable a user to assume the role of a STRATA lead pilot in a CAS two-ship section in order to exercise core CAS-specific skills, including communications, coordination, and target prosecution.

The STRATA synthetic teammates include a Direct Air Support Center (DASC) controller, a Joint Terminal Attack Controller (JTAC), a wingman, and a lead. The JTAC performs the key functions and tasks involved in fixed-wing CAS missions by controlling aircraft in support of ground troops in a forward ground position, as well as inducing errors to invoke instructional opportunities. The wingman is active when no human user is controlling the wing aircraft and performs the standard behaviors required of a wingman in the context of fixed-wing CAS missions as well as responding to certain classes of user error. The lead agent encapsulates knowledge of what the user's tasks are and so originates much of the assessment data that STRATA automatically logs. In addition, the lead can take over the mission and perform simulated CAS scenarios without a user participating.

The most significant result from STRATA was the behavioral and cognitive modeling of human performance in real-time tactical operations. The agent-based models created for STRATA (principally, the JTAC and the strike pilots) are first-in-class exemplars for CAS entities capable of accurately and dynamically participating in close air support simulations. These agents, moreover, are adaptable to other CAS mission types and indeed to other related missions (even seemingly unrelated missions, such as undergraduate pilot training described later). The JTAC synthetic teammate is readily adaptable to simulate forward observers and spotters (for artillery) and air traffic agency controllers (for instance, approach/departure, tower, or sector controllers). The strike pilot model is similarly adaptable to serve as a synthetic teammate for training personnel who control or otherwise interact with airborne assets, including air traffic controllers, combat tactical controllers, forward air controllers (FACs), JTACs, and airborne battle managers.

Another important area of significant progress is spoken dialogue interaction. Speech recognition and speech synthesis each have aroused skepticism within tactical training communities. Speech recognition is often perceived as a risky, brittle, and expensive technology that is not ready for wide-scale use. Speech synthesis is often characterized as artificial and unconvincing, particularly for tactical applications. STRATA's progress has been along both fronts. Our approach to robust speech understanding combines state-of-the-art COTS speech recognition with cognitively driven manipulation of the recognition grammar. The JTAC entity monitors the mission and performs three functions central to reliable speech understanding: First, the model dynamically activates specific grammar sets most relevant to the current phase of the mission. This narrows the range of expected responses so that, for instance, the recognizer would be more likely to capture the utterance "tally target" during the attack portion and less likely to identify a comm as "tally target" during check-in. Second, the model generates specific expectations of comms during challenge–response portions of the mission dialogue (where comms are paired, for instance, during authentication). Third, the model maintains an active grammar that is valid throughout the mission. For instance, user requests to repeat the last comm ("say again") are always valid; user reports of SAM threats, which can appear at any time, are similarly universal to the mission timeline.

Speech synthesis in STRATA presented a need for tactical believability that exceeded the reach of existing text-to-speech synthesis, which lacks the inflection and variation to generate believable human speech and would thus erect end-user acceptance obstacles. Instead, we turned to an open-source concatenated speech tool and enhanced it with an in-house utility to rapidly create human-sounding voices for tactical simulations. The basic speech synthesis itself incorporates a synthesis engine with customized, limited domain voices. These types of voices can be difficult to build because they require extensive markup and must completely cover all words that might be spoken in all parts of speech. For STRATA we developed in-house processes and tools that accelerate the processes of capturing and creating voices and improving their quality. The resulting capability enables STRATA to use prerecorded human voice to create novel utterances. The synthesizer uses recorded phrases that have marked phoneme boundaries, word boundaries, parts of speech, and other characteristics that enable them to be parsed and recombined in real time to create novel phrases.

To enable instructor-optional training, STRATA also yielded gains in automated performance measurement and brief/debrief interfaces. STRATA's performance measurement combines a reusable representation of measures with the assessment capabilities built into the synthetic teammate models. For instance, a measure of comms effectiveness is driven by the JTAC teammate's ability to interpret and assess a user's spoken communications.

The STRATA program thus set the stage for developing a new application that would represent a bold leap forward in how military pilots are trained to communicate. This program would build upon the progress made in STRATA and result in a fielded training aid and a formal evaluation that proved the training benefit.

THE GENESIS OF VIPERS

SUPT is an intensive program that trains successful graduates of Introductory Flight Training (IFT) prior to their being assigned to an advanced training track. This initial pilot training presents student pilots (SPs) with an array of complex skills to acquire and integrate in a dynamic, time-sensitive performance context. Students progressing through the SUPT programs are faced with a critical need for time with instructors and in the airplane (or in simulators of adequate fidelity). Changes in how military pilots are trained are needed in order to ensure cost-effective, sustainable, and scalable solutions to training flight skills that have historically presented problems to students. Current approaches that augment the minimal flying hours with simulation devices have not yet succeeded in providing the interactivity required for some skills (particularly those requiring communication) and have done little to reduce the reliance on an instructor. As a result, training gaps have emerged in the SUPT syllabus that include pattern operations and radio communications (AFRL, 2002).

The need for augmenting formal SUPT classroom and flight instruction with portable, simulation-based training is driven in part by the limited flight time SUPT students have. The training benefit from time in the airplane is compromised whenever an instructor is obliged to review skills and concepts that might have been mastered if appropriate simulation technology were available. Training could be fundamentally improved if students had on-demand access to flight training devices that were sophisticated enough to provide automated instruction in complex, highly interactive flight regimes, yet simple enough for students to operate alone, on low-cost, portable PCs.

To confront these challenges, CHI Systems developed VIPERS in collaboration with AFRL's Human Effectiveness Directorate and AETC. The development team at CHI Systems, working in collaboration with AFRL project scientists and AETC pilots and program officials, built a simulation of a Joint Primary Aircraft Training System (JPATS) pattern environment that provides users with training that realistically replicates the traffic conflicts and radio communications characteristic of SUPT flying training.

TRAFFIC PATTERN AND RADIO COMMUNICATIONS

Joint Primary Pilot Training (JPPT) teaches flying principles and techniques to SPs using the T-6 Texan II aircraft. It includes the following phases: academics, basic, contact, instrument, formation, and navigation. The contact phase is the first phase involving aircraft sorties and is the first time students fly the T-6 in the traffic pattern. Initially, SPs fly under IP supervision (with the IP in the rear cockpit of the aircraft) until qualifying to fly solo. This initial period is referred to as "presolo."

Because of the number of aircraft operating at training bases, there is a standard traffic pattern and established procedures for operating in the pattern (defined in AFMAN 11-248). Although the pattern at each airfield is tailored to the specific terrain, airspace restrictions, and ground references, the traffic pattern has a general configuration conforming to a standard geometry and set of authorized entries and approaches. The overhead pattern is used whenever possible to maximize opportunities to practice landings. The outside portion of the pattern is used when traffic prevents entry to the overhead pattern, when entering the pattern from other areas, when performing a straight-in landing, or when reentering the pattern after breaking out to avoid a conflict. There is also an Emergency Landing Pattern (ELP), which is used to practice the procedures for landing without power. Figure 21.1 shows the normal traffic pattern, identifying the important segments. Figure 21.2 provides a more detailed view of the overhead pattern.

Pilot–controller radio communications in the traffic pattern follow a specific protocol to minimize radio congestion and enhance comprehension. It is important for the SPs to learn and use standard phraseology for these purposes. Furthermore, the communications between other pilots and the controllers in the Runway Supervisory Unit (RSU) provide an important source of SA as they include position reports and clearance requests. Thus, part of learning radio communications is learning to develop SA from listening to radio calls of other pilots in the pattern.

Radio calls are made to report positions and request clearance to perform operations. Each radio call starts with the call sign identifying his or her aircraft to the RSU controller, and then provides the report or request in standard format. The RSU controller responds to some pilot communications but not others. The RSU controller can also direct aircraft without a request. These communications identify aircraft by their position in the pattern rather than by call sign.

Another communication channel for presolo pilots is the intercockpit intercom, which allows the SP in the front cockpit and the IP in the rear cockpit to talk to each other without transmitting on

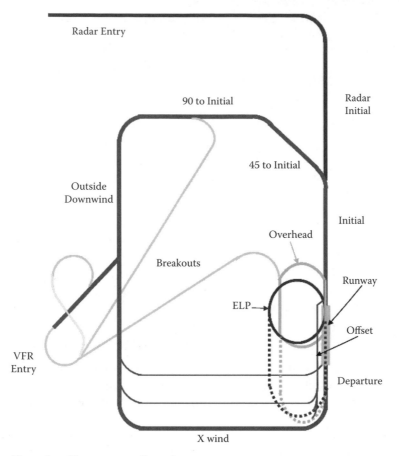

FIGURE 21.1   Normal traffic pattern configuration.

the radio. These communications are less structured and can include coaching and feedback by the IP, but there are specific situations (e.g., times when the SP should be making an in-flight check) that by procedure require a standardized intercockpit communication. Because these communications are within one aircraft, they do not use a call sign.

The RSU is the controlling agency for most training airfields, providing air traffic control functions for a specific runway. Although there are a number of people serving different functions within the RSU, for the purposes of VIPERS, the RSU is treated as a unitary entity. The RSU is situated near the runway to allow visual contact for aircraft in the overhead pattern and on the runway. The responsibilities of the RSU are to facilitate safe and efficient visual flight rules (VFR) traffic pattern operations, including issuing clearances upon pilot request when possible, denying requests that are not safe, or if necessary, directing aircraft actions to avoid conflicts.

INSTRUCTIONAL DESIGN FACTORS

CONCEPT OF OPERATIONS

The overall vision of the VIPERS project is to provide SUPT students with opportunities for guided practice and feedback in radio communications skills and decision making in the JPATS overhead pattern. The format of this practice is simulation-based training with intelligent software agents performing in both tutoring roles and synthetic teammate roles, in a laptop-based portable application for anytime/anywhere training enrichment.

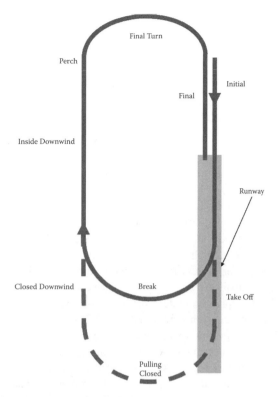

FIGURE 21.2   Overhead pattern: a more detailed view.

The VIPERS concept of operations was driven by the need for improved SA of the traffic in the pattern to be able to determine when to make radio calls and maneuvers. This need is particularly acute in the first few weeks of the contact phase of SUPT, when the SPs are learning the basics of the traffic pattern and radio communications, as well as beginning flying training in the T-6. Thus, that is the focus of the VIPERS training. Following the guidance of AETC, VIPERS is designed to support supplementary on-demand practice rather than be a "syllabus event." The capabilities of the system, however, can also support other means of employing VIPERS as determined by AETC.

The core training technique in VIPERS is scenario-based guided practice (Schank, Fano, Bell, and Jona, 1994; Fowlkes, Dwyer, Oser, and Salas, 1998) in a simulated traffic pattern. The visual representation of the pattern is a 2-D top-down schematic view of the pattern. This representation is an abstracted schematic pattern picture rather than geographically precise representations of a specific airfield. The user controls the aircraft using high-level commands available by button selection (e.g., "B" for break, "C" for pulling closed) rather than with a stick and throttle, to allow focus on communications and decision making rather than on airmanship. The user has a headset and microphone to listen to and make radio communications in the scenarios. The pattern environment simulation includes three types of synthetic entities:

- A synthetic IP that provides coaching and feedback during scenarios and makes assessments to be used in a debrief
- A synthetic RSU controller that maintains knowledge of all aircraft in the pattern and verbally responds to clearance requests and issues directives to all aircraft in the pattern
- Synthetic pilots/aircraft in the pattern behaving appropriately and making radio calls

For each scenario, VIPERS provides a brief giving instructions to the user prior to the scenario and a debrief reviewing performance after the scenario.

In addition to the 2-D simulation, a 3-D mode using a flight simulator, realistic cockpit displays, out-the-window views, and a stick and throttle control was developed but not included in the version evaluated at Laughlin Air Force Base (AFB) as directed by AETC.

TRAINING ANALYSIS AND KNOWLEDGE ENGINEERING

Training analysis and instructional design was based on a detailed survey of published training documents, frequent interchanges with AETC, and numerous discussions and site visits to the 47th Flight Training Wing (FTW) at Laughlin AFB. Documents used as references included *T-6 Primary Flying* (AETC, 2004), *RSU Operations* (AETC, 2006a), *T-6 Aircrew Training* (AETC, 2002), and *T-6 Operations Procedures* (AETC, 2006b).

The initial analysis focused on identifying radio communications, potential conflicts, and decision points for each segment of the pattern. Knowledge engineering sessions also dealt with instructional issues. Periodic sessions were held with subject matter experts (SMEs), primarily IPs, to "walk through" the traffic pattern, identifying at each point the following elements: what an IP would be observing, what feedback/direction would be given and when, any possible conflicts to be aware of, and errors students typically made. This analysis was conducted prior to making a decision on whether the simulation environment should be 2-D or 3-D, so it includes the data related to airmanship. Figure 21.3 provides an example of the results of this analysis, specifying altitude (ALT), airspeed (A/S), aircraft control (AC CTRL), ground track (GR TR), power, radio communications (COMM), and visual clearing, as well as acceptable ranges, IP feedback when the ranges were violated, and possible conflicts. Data from this analysis were used to corroborate the open-source information published by the Department of Defense (DoD) to construct the knowledge of the cognitive agents, particularly the IP model.

Another analysis derived all possible communications and variations for all pattern positions for the SP, the RSU controller, and the IP. For example, at initial, the SP makes the following radio call:

```
Call sign, <Distance>, INITIAL, <Clearance request>, <Fuel Remaining>
```

The range of conditions in which the <optional elements> are needed were enumerated in our analysis. Distance is included if the call is made late (e.g., at 1 mile rather than the standard 2 miles). The clearance requests that could be made at initial include "Request high key" or "For low key," and fuel remaining is given if making a full stop landing. For any one call sign (e.g., Texan 15) and 450 lb of fuel remaining, the following communications could be made at initial:

"Texan 15, initial."
"Texan 15, 1 mile, initial."
"Texan 15, initial, request high key."
"Texan 15, initial, for low key."
"Texan 15, initial, 450."
"Texan 15, 1 mile, initial, request high key."
"Texan 15, 1 mile, initial, for low key."
"Texan 15, 1 mile, initial, 450."

This analysis was used in designing the synthetic agents, to implement the speech generation and recognition, and for developing the automated performance measures.

Further analyses were conducted to derive additional knowledge needed to fully specify the synthetic entity behaviors. This included creating a knowledge map of all possible segments in the pattern, specifying the aircraft parameters (e.g., beginning and ending altitude, airspeed, and ground track) and the range in the segment within which a communication should be made, as well

Aircraft/Pilot Actions/Comms

Altitude: 1000' AGL, +/- 100' level flight

Airspeed: 200 KIAS, +/- 10 KIAS

Aircraft Control: Wings level

Ground Track: Lined-up with runway centerline, 2 miles from beg runway

Power: As required (necessary adjustments required to maintain desired airspeed)

COMM: "Initial" call – few seconds after wings level, at approximately 2 mile point

                 Add "fuel remaining" to call if full stop landing

Measures of Performance/IP Feedback

Altitude: Violation +/- 100' – "check altitude"

                 Trend (no corrective action taken by student) +/- 200' – "you're high/low"

Airspeed: Violation +/-10 KIAS – "check airspeed"

                 Trend (no corrective action taken by student) +/-15 KIAS – "you're fast/slow"

Ground Track: Trend 5° deviation -- "check/watch your runway alignment" or "correct/get back on

                 runway centerline"

COMM: If haven't made call by 1.5 miles to runway – "you need to call initial"

                 If haven't made call by 1 mile to runway – IP will make call

Possible Conflicts

Other aircraft on or approaching Initial (without sufficient spacing)

Other aircraft in pattern on a different runway; *e.g.* center runway

Other aircraft on Straight-in between 5 NM and 2 NM (should know by radio call)

Other aircraft in pattern on instrument approach to other runway; *e.g.*, center runway

Anyone requesting Closed between 2 NM and runway – student has to wait for RSU response before he can

make Initial call.

FIGURE 21.3   Example of analysis of pattern positions.

as all possible following segments (e.g., from initial, the pilot could do a break turn, go straight through, go to high key, or go to low key). This analysis supported development of models of the additional aircraft in the pattern, as well as the knowledge the RSU controller model needed to build its pattern understanding and exercise proper control over the pattern traffic.

Syllabus Elements

Drawn from DoD-published documents distributed via the USAF e-publishing Web site, and in consultation with the 47th FTW and AETC, we developed a pattern operations and radio communications syllabus that offers (1) a "free-play" scenario in which the user begins as the only aircraft in the pattern and continues as the pattern becomes increasingly busy, over a 15 minute scenario; and (2) a library of conflict scenarios, each illustrating a specific pattern conflict and lasting between 1 and 2 minutes. VIPERS also allows missions to be created or modified by IPs or students themselves (see also the subsection on Mission Builder). The interface also provides schematic depictions of the main pattern entries to introduce the student to the basic geometry of the corresponding pattern, and to the radio communications that are required within that pattern. The goal of the scenarios is to provide the student with opportunities to practice navigating through the pattern while making the appropriate radio communications. This flexible structure accommodates a range of needs, from beginners to those seeking refresher training on a specific subset of skills.

There are two instructional components within VIPERS. Each is described in the following subsections.

Pattern Orientation

Pattern Orientation provides a graphical and text introduction to pattern positions, procedures, and communications. It is intended to refresh material in the T-6 Primary Flying Manual (AFMAN 11-248) and in computer-aided instruction (CAI). The Orientation consists of a top-down view of the pattern and steps through each leg/position point of the pattern to present the essential elements of the pattern (Figure 21.4).

This format was chosen to allow the student to gain an overall understanding of the pattern before actually navigating it. The student can move through the pattern by using the PREV and NEXT buttons or can select a specific position point. As the student's aircraft icon moves through the pattern, information corresponding to each position point is displayed at the bottom right of the screen:

> *Name of each position or leg in the pattern.* This is essential to communicate with RSU controllers, who identify aircraft by position rather than by call sign.
>
> *Out-the-window view or spot view* to let the student "see" where the aircraft is in relation to the entire pattern. This supplements the top-down view used to navigate through the pattern.

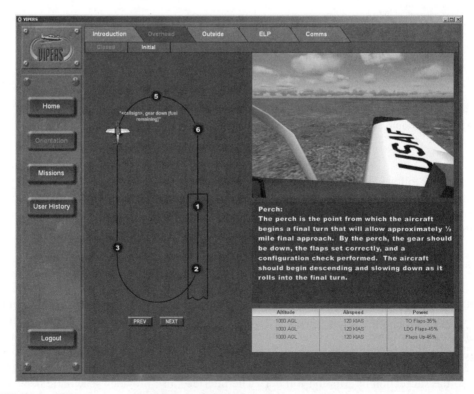

FIGURE 21.4   Example screen from Pattern Orientation.

Aircraft altitude and airspeed to help the student develop a mental model of where the aircraft should be in 3-D space and how fast it should be traveling through the pattern.

Radio calls that are required at each position point. This helps the student to become familiar with proper radio communications and to associate each with a specific position in the pattern.

Missions

The core of VIPERS is scenario-based practice in a simulated traffic pattern. The Mission component provides this practice. VIPERS provides a set of predefined missions including a free-play scenario and missions illustrating specific conflicts.

After selecting the Mission component, the user is presented with a list of scenarios, or missions. Highlighting a mission and pressing the Display Mission Brief button will display a brief giving the user instructions for that mission (Figure 21.5). To select a mission, the user can click the Fly Mission button.

The mission display is a top-down schematic view of the pattern with aircraft icons representing the traffic pattern. In the mission, the user commands the aircraft and makes radio calls as if flying the airplane. The user controls the aircraft using high-level controls (located at the bottom of the screen) indicated by buttons that the user can select either via a standard mouse pointing device or through the keyboard. In addition, the user has a headphone with microphone for transmitting and listening to radio communications. The spacebar on the keyboard is used for engaging the radio microphone, and the "I" key engages the intercom microphone. The simulation includes synthetic aircraft flying in the pattern (represented by aircraft icons on the display) with synthetic pilots making the appropriate radio communications. It also includes a synthetic RSU controller responding to clearance requests and issuing directives to all aircraft in the pattern. The synthetic IP provides

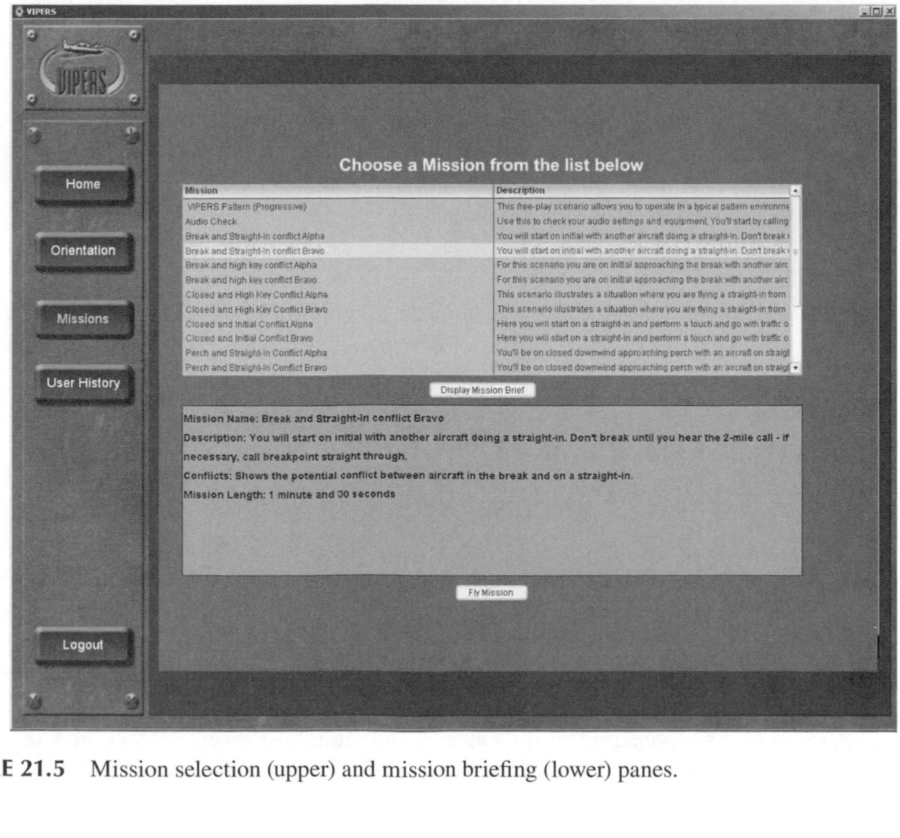

FIGURE 21.5   Mission selection (upper) and mission briefing (lower) panes.

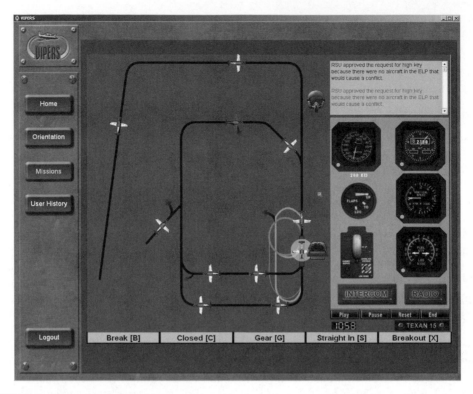

FIGURE 21.6 Example mission screen.

coaching and short feedback as appropriate, reminding the user to make missed calls, and assuming temporary control of the aircraft if needed. A mission screen appears in Figure 21.6.

At the conclusion of the mission, a debrief is provided to the user, reviewing the user's performance on the following four performance measures:

Making correct radio transmissions
Proper performance of in-flight checks (i.e., communications between SP and IP)
Taking appropriate actions in decision situations
Complying with RSU or IP directives

For each measure, the debrief indicates the number of opportunities and the number handled incorrectly, as well as details on each of the errors made. An example debrief is illustrated in Figure 21.7.

AUTOMATED PERFORMANCE MEASUREMENT

CHALLENGES OF ASSESSMENT IN SIMULATED ENVIRONMENTS

To achieve the goal of training that is truly on-demand, the presence of the instructor must be optional, which implies among other things that performance assessment must be automated. Developing adequate measures of cognition and coordination is challenging as those skills do not always have easily definable or observable measures. Significant progress has been made in the last 20 years in characterizing team decision-making skills (e.g., Swezey and Salas, 1992; Brannick, Salas, and Prince, 1997; Cannon-Bowers and Salas, 1997), defining the types of measures that are indicative of those skills (Johnston, Smith-Jentsch, and Cannon-Bowers, 1997), and developing methods for designing scenarios that exercise those skills and provide assessment opportunities

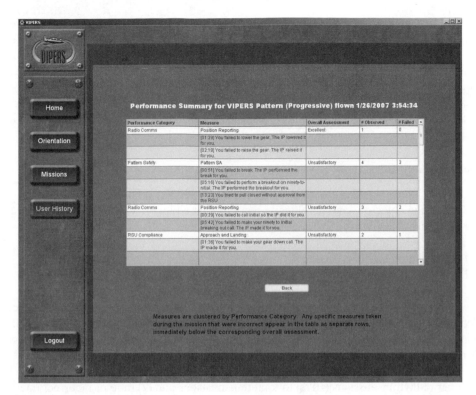

FIGURE 21.7 Example debrief screen.

(e.g., Fowlkes and Burke, 2005). Assessing performance in these environments is critical, particularly in the team context, in which communication is a key skill or important indicator of performance. For instance, assessment of (spoken) radio communications requires careful consideration of context, user intent, and the nuances of language; SA can be measured by inferring from indirect measures (i.e., actions, utterances) the user's mental model of the situation. Even with the automated data capture that some simulators and game environments provide, the need for role players, observers, and instructors, particularly to assess and debrief team-level skills, is still substantial.

A central part of our approach to automated performance measurement is the use of sophisticated cognitive models functioning as synthetic instructor agents that help track user performance and detect errors. These models are multipurpose: they (1) drive the behaviors and discourse for the synthetic teammates, (2) provide expectations to the speech engine to boost recognition rates to the high levels needed for actual training and rehearsal, and (3) provide diagnostic information to the performance assessment engine. The synthetic instructor agent reasons about the situation using encoded knowledge about the mission and the range of behaviors (both communications and actions) that are possible. It also considers which behaviors are appropriate for varying mission phases or tasks. This knowledge, in combination with continually updated situation data, allows the instructor agent to maintain a real-time assessment of the situation. This situation picture enables the instructor agent to generate expected communications and actions against which to compare observed speech and action. The instructor agent also contains performance measure knowledge that supports assessment of the comparison of observed and expected performance. Assessment may involve combining multiple observations, complex assessment algorithms, or comparison to standards for levels of proficiency. The instructor agent is able to use its knowledge of instructional strategies to determine what type of feedback to provide. Feedback can include immediate text feedback, coaching, or evaluative feedback provided by a synthetic instructor or teammate. In addition, the cognitive agent can record performance assessments for later use in the debrief.

Underlying the automated instructor functions is a tight coupling of training objectives, performance measures, and scenario events (Fowlkes and Burke, 2005). Scenarios are populated with events that provide opportunities to evaluate performance related to specific training objectives; automated performance measures then monitor and evaluate user actions in response to these events. The main advantage of this approach is that it makes automated performance assessment more tractable as the assessment can focus on those aspects of behavior that are directly relevant to the events of interest without requiring intelligent tutoring capabilities that track all aspects of user knowledge and behavior (Zachary, Cannon-Bowers, Bilazarian, Krecker, Lardieri, and Burns, 1999).

VIPERS TRAINING OBJECTIVES AND PERFORMANCE MEASURES

Guided by our instructional approach and discussions with the Air Force, we defined the scope of VIPERS training objectives and developed scenarios that address these objectives. There are two primary training objectives for VIPERS:

1. Perform correct radio procedures
2. Demonstrate pattern SA

Assessing performance on these objectives was an important research goal of VIPERS. Voice communication assessment requires careful consideration of context, user intent, and the nuances of language. SA can be measured by inferring from indirect measures (i.e., actions, utterances) the user's mental model of the situation.

In VIPERS, assessments of a user's radio procedures are derived from two measures: (1) ratio of improper radio transmissions (IRTs) to total transmissions and (2) ratio of incorrect intercockpit communications (i.e., communications between SP and IP) to total intercockpit communications. IRTs are further categorized into the following errors:

- Stepping on another transmission (i.e., talking while the radio is being used by another person or talking before a required reply has occurred)
- Making an inaccurate or incorrect call
- Being late with a call
- Missing the call altogether

SA deals with understanding and being able to respond appropriately to any pattern situation. It includes understanding conflict zones and decision points and is demonstrated by avoiding inappropriate requests (e.g., requesting "closed" when it would not be approved), breaking out (to avoid conflict situations), and complying with RSU and IP directives. SA assessments are thus derived from two measures: (1) ratio of decision points correctly managed to total decision points encountered and (2) ratio of directives correctly acted on to total directives received (from the IP and RSU).

SYSTEM ARCHITECTURE AND OPERATION

The VIPERS system consists of integrated, interoperable components that provide simulation-based training of the JPATS SUPT overhead pattern and corresponding radio communications. The selection of an appropriate simulation environment and hardware configuration (i.e., processor, display), as well as an approach for integrating and enhancing speech recognition and speech synthesis software were governed in part by pragmatic considerations. The overriding criterion was a computational infrastructure that was robust enough to properly execute VIPERS. Important secondary criteria also guided the selection of suitable technologies, among them: portability, small computational footprint, ease of use, and avoidance of commercially licensed and export-controlled technologies.

SOFTWARE ARCHITECTURE

The VIPERS software architecture is shown in Figure 21.8. The components include a user interface containing the visual representation of the pattern in both a 2-D top-down view and 3-D simulation environment, a speech recognition engine that interprets user communications, voice generation for the RSU, IP, and other pilot communications, and intelligent agents that play the part of the RSU, IP, and other pilots. There is also a database that stores user information and performance data and is accessible for review at any time. Although developmental spirals of VIPERS employed a High Level Architecture Run-Time Infrastructure (HLA-RTI) network, the final prototype employed a socket-based communications layer to support information exchange among these processes, to minimize the computational footprint, improve performance, maximize reliability, and avoid adding unnecessary licensing costs.

SIMULATION ENVIRONMENT

The simulation environment provides a synthetic JPATS pattern environment, including voice communications and integration with the iGEN-derived cognitive agents (to provide synthetic entities). During our discussions with AETC, it became evident that the training emphasis—pattern SA and radio communications—could be addressed with a schematically rendered, top-down view of the pattern rather than through integration with a flight simulation application. We thus expanded the simulation environment to accommodate two modes of interaction with VIPERS: (1) a flight simulation mode with 3-D cockpit views of the environment and (2) a top-down, schematic view of the pattern environment.

To address the flight simulation mode, we selected a COTS product called Flightgear, because it provided the flight simulation capability we required and because it is an open-source tool, meaning our engineering team could gain complete access to the code base for modifying the application to meet our requirements. For the 2-D schematic view, we selected Macromedia Flash because of its small computational footprint, flexibility, and maturity. To facilitate interoperability and inter-process communication, we adopted the HLA interoperability standard developed by the Defense Modeling and Simulation Office (DMSO), but later moved to a socket-based protocol for the delivered prototype for reasons listed earlier.

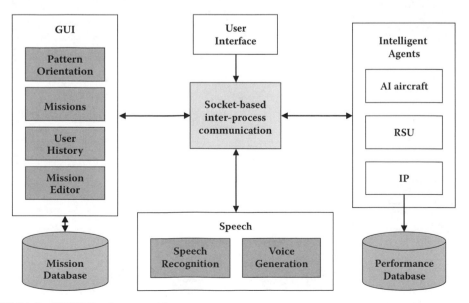

FIGURE 21.8 VIPERS software architecture.

Speech Recognition and Synthesis

Our approach to speech interaction overcomes current limitations in speech recognition by combining conventional recognition with our cognitive agents to enhance performance and yield fieldable-quality voice recognition. For the underlying speech engine we selected a powerful tool in widespread use in the commercial gaming industry called Nuance VoCon 3200. We integrated this engine with our iGEN-derived cognitive agents so that expectations generated by the agents are used to inform the recognition process and thus boost recognition rates. The result is a speech recognition capability that is robust and speaker independent.

For speech synthesis, we adopted a solution that addressed two principal needs: (1) tactically plausible synthetic voices that exhibit the appropriate cadence and inflection of radio communications in a JPATS environment and (2) low-footprint, robust software. Our approach employs a modified form of concatenated text-to-speech by prerecorded voice actors (SPs at the 47th FTW) reading the full range of potential communications, as well as all possible call signs. When a synthetic entity "speaks," the synthesis engine combines the entity's call sign with the voice recording for that communication. The result is a synthesis component that incurs very little computational penalty while providing highly realistic speech.

Hardware Suite

VIPERS was tested on the Alienware M5500 laptop PC running Windows XP and a Sennheiser 155 USB headset with microphone for radio communications. When running in 2-D mode, the trainee uses the keyboard and mouse to control flight actions. When used in 3-D mode, the trainee uses a joystick and throttle control to fly the aircraft (the 3-D mode was not included in the prototype evaluated at Laughlin).

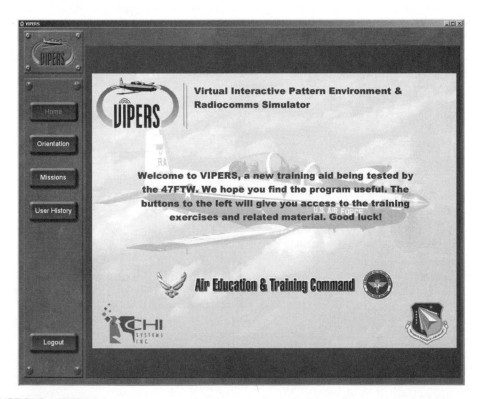

FIGURE 21.9   VIPERS homepage.

Quick Start: Starting/Ending Scenarios   **Quick Start: Viewing the Debrief**

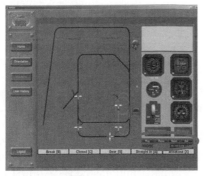

Click "User History", select a mission, click "Load
Selected Debrief". A Performance Summary is displayed.

- "Play"-start or resume
- "Pause"-suspend
- "Reset"-start over and clear the mission log
- "End"-complete the scenario and proceed to debrief

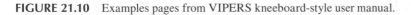

2-5   2-6

FIGURE 21.10   Examples pages from VIPERS kneeboard-style user manual.

Although this was the test configuration, VIPERS will run on most contemporary PCs owing to the low computational footprint.

USER INTERFACE

We developed a Macromedia Flash end-user graphical user interface (GUI) that is used to navigate within the VIPERS system via a menu of selectable buttons (see Figure 21.9). The navigation buttons give the user access to the following interfaces:

Home—takes the user to the homepage
Orientation—schematically depicts the various JPATS patterns, including the Overhead, ELP, and Outside pattern
Missions—simulated sorties that begin with a brief, proceed to the simulated pattern operations, and conclude with a debrief
User History—gives users access to debriefs from their previous VIPERS sessions
Logout—exits the VIPERS system

The specific steps in operating VIPERS were outlined in detail for all users, each of whom received a kneeboard-style user manual explaining calibration, use, and troubleshooting of VIPERS. Figure 21.10 shows two representative pages from the kneeboard.

SYNTHETIC TEAMMATE DESIGN

AGENT APPROACH

To build the cognitive agents to support the synthetic IP, the synthetic RSU controller, and other synthetic SPs, we employed CHI Systems' iGEN cognitive agent development toolkit (Zachary, Le Mentec, and Ryder, 1996). iGEN enabled us to encode rich domain knowledge (perceptual, declarative, procedural, and action) into each agent type in a form that corresponds to the way the knowledge is employed by human decision makers in the JPATS domain. Prior to final deployment of the prototype, these agents were ported to a low-footprint, highly efficient derivative called iGEN-NPC to maximize performance.

SYNTHETIC IP

The IP cognitive agent provides the core intelligence for both real-time and after-action instructional guidance and feedback to the user. The IP agent maintains SA of the user's flight as well as awareness of other aircraft in the pattern. SA is maintained by monitoring voice communications and aircraft location. The IP agent assesses student actions using knowledge of appropriate behavior and intervenes in real time, as would a human IP, via the intercom, when errors of omission or commission are detected. For instance, if a student forgets to call "initial," the IP will first remind the student, and without quick corrective action, will itself make the call.

Additionally, if the student has issued an incorrect aircraft control command or has not issued a necessary command, the IP will intervene by reminding the student of the proper aircraft control action. If the student does not respond, the IP agent can correct the error. For example, if the student has not lowered the gear after a reminder, the IP can perform the gear correction.

The IP agent catalogs missed communications and late communications for review in the debrief. The IP agent also logs user responses to conflicts and to directives from the RSU and IP.

SYNTHETIC RSU CONTROLLER

The RSU cognitive agent is responsible for providing traffic control over the pattern by verbally granting permission or issuing directives to all aircraft in the pattern. Knowledge encapsulated in the RSU agent enables it to maintain SA of all the aircraft in the pattern, recognize and issue directives to resolve possible conflicts, and interpret and respond to pilot (human or synthetic) requests.

The RSU agent represents the pattern as a set of segments (e.g., outside downwind, radar entry). Aircraft location is represented as the pattern segment and the percentage of that segment completed. Conflicts are defined as configurations of aircraft locations. Communications are interpreted based on knowledge of the aircraft location, and responses determined based on the configuration of all aircraft locations within the pattern. When the RSU agent recognizes conflicts between aircraft, it can direct one of them to break out of the pattern as appropriate. For example, if one aircraft is on Radar Initial and another aircraft is on 90-to-Initial, the RSU controller will direct the latter aircraft to break out of the pattern. The RSU agent also provides realistic communications in response to pattern requests from the SPs (human or synthetic) and records inappropriate radio communications for use in the debrief.

In the 2-D representation of the pattern, the simulated aircraft follow a fixed path for each segment, and aircraft location is identified by pattern segment and percentage complete. For use in concert with a flight simulator, an additional reasoning component within the RSU controller computes aircraft location using pattern segments defined in 3-D space. In either case, the RSU agent pushes aircraft location data to the IP and SP agents for computational efficiency.

SYNTHETIC SPs

In addition to the RSU and IP agents, agents in VIPERS control the other aircraft in the pattern, (i.e., synthetic SPs) to provide realistic flying and communications behaviors in the JPATS pattern. The synthetic SP agents fly all legs of the pattern, and have heuristics that govern selection of alternative entries and requests. For example, from initial, an SP may request the ELP 20% of the time. The SP agents make all required radio communications to the RSU and respond to RSU directives or clearance denials (e.g., break out when instructed).

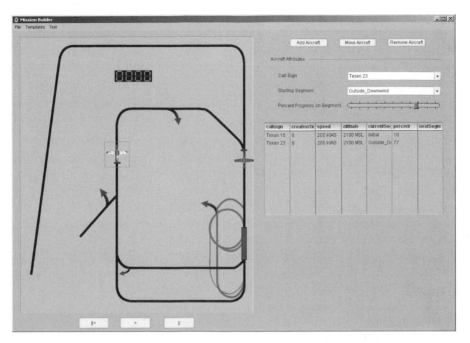

FIGURE 21.11   Mission Builder.

TRAINING MANAGEMENT TOOLS

MISSION BUILDER

The VIPERS Mission Builder (Figure 21.11) gives users graphical and menu-driven scenario-building capability, including drag-and-drop positioning of traffic in the pattern. This mission editor allows IPs to readily create new missions tailored to the specific needs of individual students. The author indicates the starting position by dragging the aircraft icon to a pattern position, and indicates the path of the aircraft by selecting segment names from a pull-down menu. The ">" (play) button provides a preview mode for evaluating the scenario. The mission editor also provides the ability to save defined missions and edit or modify saved missions. The mission editor component was not included in the AETC evaluation of VIPERS.

USER PROFILE

At the conclusion of a session, the user's profile is updated in a training database. The profile contains a record of all missions attempted by the user, with date and performance assessment data. A User History overview display is available, allowing the user to see a summary of missions and to select any for review. Selection of any individual completed mission brings up the corresponding performance summary/debrief.

USABILITY ANALYSIS

Strategies for fielding training technologies must address both engineering factors and end-user acceptance. Because VIPERS introduces a brand-new technique, unit commanders, IPs, and SPs must all voice strong support before the Air Force could commit to adopting it. Gaining this support requires that the training content be doctrinally correct, that the product be easy to use, that the software be reliable, and that the training be effective. Environmental factors such as how, when, and where students have access to the training are also important in gaining end-user acceptance.

Part of the coordination with end users included two separate week-long visits to CHI Systems' facility by an IP from the 47th FTW at Laughlin. Those site visits, conducted by two different IPs, subjected the prototype to rigorous testing and gave the development team a rare opportunity to document existing program inaccuracies and usability shortcomings. In addition, three studies were conducted; two were formative evaluations led by CHI Systems in May 2005 and June 2006. The third was a summative analysis led by AETC (September 2006–May 2007), described later.

PRELIMINARY USER STUDIES AND RESULTS

We conducted a preliminary evaluation of VIPERS on 10–12 May 2005 at Laughlin AFB. This initial tryout was intended as a data collection opportunity, scheduled when sufficient capabilities of VIPERS had been developed to allow potential users at the 47th FTW at Laughlin AFB to interact with the system. This enabled evaluation of the potential benefit of VIPERS and provided an opportunity to obtain comments and suggestions to improve specific components of VIPERS.

This assessment was conducted as an informal study consistent with the objectives stated earlier. Discussions and system evaluations were conducted with IPs and SPs on an as-available basis in order to interfere as little as possible with the ongoing training schedules of the subjects. The basic methodology followed was:

- Introduction (15 minutes)
  - Explain system and goals
  - Overview of session
  - Verbal informed consent
  - Collect demographic data and initial views
- Use of system (30–45 minutes)—followed a think-aloud protocol, with audio recording of comments
- Evaluation (questionnaire) of system (15 minutes)
  - Evaluation of various parts/capabilities and suggestions for improvement (usability evaluation component of session)
  - Evaluation of potential use of VIPERS for other training needs
- Additional discussion as time permitted

Sessions were held with five IPs and three SPs. The IPs had between 2.7 and 4 years as IPs and all were RSU qualified, all were frequent computer users, and two had used PC-based flight simulators on more than a few occasions. The SPs were 2 weeks into the contact phase of their pilot training, so they had just learned the basics of the pattern. All were frequent computer users, and none had used PC-based flight simulators more than occasionally.

Additional discussions were held with other IPs covering specific topics. The general supportable findings from this evaluation are as follows:

- Orientation, Demonstration, Missions, and Debrief were all favorably rated.
- Orientation and Demonstration rated very high in value and usability.
- Missions and Debrief were seen as valuable but not easily understood.
- VIPERS was perceived as important, valuable, and likely to be used.

This formative evaluation was very effective in providing the VIPERS development team with user feedback; as a result we were able to provide a prototype that resolved the most urgent user concerns to AETC for evaluation.

The second evaluation, conducted in June 2006, focused on content validation and usability testing for a VIPERS product that was approximately 3 months from its field trial. This evaluation was less structured than the first in an effort to give representative end users "free-play" opportunities to use and critique the system. Eight SPs participated, with each one being given a 15-minute introduction and 30 minutes of play time. Results from this evaluation revealed a few minor technical flaws, such as nonstandard radio calls from simulated pattern traffic and excessive vertical speeds during landing. However, no reports surfaced of usability issues or any difficulties understanding the interface or operation of the system. Direct observations supported the conclusion that usability factors had been resolved and that the remaining focus should be on doctrinally correct content.

FIELD EVALUATION

The summative evaluation was conducted by AETC's Studies and Analysis Squadron (SAS) with data collection running from October 2006 through February 2007 and analysis completing in May 2007. This purpose of the study was to provide subjective and objective data on users' acceptance of VIPERS, their belief in its training effectiveness, and its actual impact on performance, with the performance impact most heavily influencing decisions on future use of VIPERS by SUPT SPs.

METHOD

The populations used for this study were SUPT students and instructors stationed at Laughlin AFB in Del Rio, Texas. Three (consecutive, nonoverlapping) classes, each consisting of 25–28 SPs, were issued laptop computers loaded with the VIPERS software and headset/microphone appliances for each student. This sample size was deemed sufficient and representative of the SUPT student population as a whole, and struck a balance between the evaluation objectives and minimizing the impact on the flight training schedule. From these three classes a total of 70 students were tested for this study (data from students who left SUPT during the study were not included in the analysis).

At the beginning of each of the three VIPERS classes, the VIPERS laptops and headsets were distributed 2 weeks prior to the first scheduled aircraft sortie. The laptops were set up and made ready for the students to operate. In addition to the laptops and headsets, the students were given manuals on how to run VIPERS and operate the control keys and headsets. In all, the students received a total of 1.5 hours of instruction on how to use VIPERS. This period included sample scenarios that the students were able to run on the computers followed by a question-and-answer session. Subjects were also told that VIPERS is an optional self-study tool and that information about individual performance on VIPERS is anonymous and used only in aggregating data for evaluation of the software.

Following the distribution, the students retained their laptops and used them as desired for approximately 3 weeks while on the flight line. The first test class of SUPT students consisted of 22 males and 3 females, the second class had 22 males and 2 females, and the third had 20 males and 1 female. At the conclusion of each class, subjective and objective data were collected by SAS and usage statistics were extracted from each laptop.

SUBJECTIVE DATA COLLECTION

Subjective data were collected from both IPs and SPs using attitudinal surveys scored on a Likert scale. In addition to the 70 students participating in the study, surveys were administered to 24 of their IPs who also had exposure to the software. The survey measured whether users believed VIPERS to be an effective tool, how it compared with other methods for practicing communications (e.g., chair flying), and subjects' willingness to use it themselves and recommend it to others.

OBJECTIVE DATA COLLECTION

To investigate correlations between use of VIPERS and performance, we instrumented the software to capture detailed usage data for each participant and analyzed each participant's flying performance as recorded by IPs in AETC's Training Integrated Management System (TIMS). This procedure follows standard practice: after every sortie, the IP enters a score (*unsatisfactory, fair, good,* or *excellent*) across a range of measures, each of which is called a maneuver item file (MIF). Thus, the objective data collection for VIPERS was based on an existing assessment framework and introduced neither new procedures nor new measures.

Among the existing measures scored by instructors, AETC identified three that were relevant to evaluating VIPERS' training effects: SA, communications, and in-flight checks (confirming with the IP that the aircraft configuration is appropriate to the flight regime). The next section presents an analysis of the TIMS data for the three MIFs listed earlier.

ANALYSIS

For the subjective (survey) data, a total of 70 student questionnaires were distributed with a 100% return rate as well as a 100% return rate from the 24 instructor questionnaires distributed. A 100% response rate for each item on both surveys was also obtained. A frequency count (percentage of positive and negative responses) was conducted for both surveys.

For the objective data, performance results from the 70 participants (usage data collected by the software and flying performance as captured in TIMS) were investigated through two comparisons. The first comparison looked at high-use (of VIPERS) and low-use groups. These were balanced by selecting a threshold of greater than 1 hour for high use ($n = 23$) and less than 10 minutes for low use ($n = 22$). The second comparison was a simple median threshold of 30 minutes (30 minutes or less: $n = 32$; greater than 30 minutes: $n = 38$).

For assessing performance, we looked at how long it took subjects to establish consistent performance at the *fair* and *good* levels, defining "consistent" for any given level as achieving that level (or above) on four consecutive sorties. We therefore had, for each of the two comparative analyses, three dimensions (SA, communications, and in-flight checks), with two values for each (time in number of sorties to achieve fair and time in sorties to achieve good). The six dependent measures are thus:

- Time to Fair (in-flight checks)
- Time to Good (in-flight checks)
- Time to Fair (communications)
- Time to Good (communications)
- Time to Fair (SA)
- Time to Good (SA)

RESULTS

For the survey data, a frequency distribution was constructed. Results from the instructor surveys showed that more than half (52%) of the instructors recommend continued use of VIPERS in SUPT. Likewise, more than half of the students (57%) said they would recommend the use of VIPERS to future classmates.

For the performance data, we calculated t-tests of the differences between the two comparison groups described previously for each of the six dependent measures. We used $p < .05$ as the criterion for statistical significance because that value is the most commonly used and ensures a 95% chance that any differences resulted from the independent variable and not random error. We also used the more stringent two-tailed test rather than the one-tailed test to examine whether there was an advantage gained from using VIPERS.

For the first test, a comparison of all variables was conducted between two VIPERS usage groups (<10 minutes and >1 hour). For the first comparison, the results show a significant difference for Time to Good for communications, SA, and in-flight checks between students who used VIPERS the most (more than an hour) and those who used it the least (10 minutes or less). A similar

TABLE 21.1
Results from Comparison of High (>1 Hour) and Low (<10 Minutes) Users

Low usage		In-flight checks		Communications		Situational awareness	
		Time to fair	Time to good	Time to fair	Time to good	Time to fair	Time to good
<10 minute use	Mean	5.23	20.64	8.68	20.77	8.95	23.45
(n = 22)	STDEV	1.69	5.81	3.00	6.03	2.10	7.08
	STError	0.37	1.27	0.65	1.32	0.46	1.55
High usage							
>1 hour use	Mean	4.87	16.04	7.00	17.57	8.04	17.43
(n = 23)	STDEV	1.91	5.89	1.88	5.77	2.64	5.48
	STError	0.41	1.26	0.40	1.23	0.56	1.17
t Critical two-tail		2.0167	2.0167	2.0167	2.0181	2.0167	2.0167
P(T ≤ *t*) two-tail		0.5105	**0.0117**	**0.0287**	**0.0489**	0.2083	**0.0026**

trend was observed for the Time to Fair comparisons, but only one variable (communications) was significant. These results are summarized in Table 21.1 and depicted graphically in Figure 21.12.

For the second test a comparison of all variables was conducted between groups on either side of a median usage time (30 minutes). Results mirrored those of the first, in showing that the students obtained a grade of *good* significantly sooner as exposure to VIPERS increased, across all three measures. For Time to Fair, the trend was the same though the differences were not significant. These results are listed in Table 21.2 and shown graphically in Figure 21.13.

DISCUSSION

Results from the survey showed that more than half of both students and instructors would recommend using VIPERS. The purpose of measuring student and instructor attitudes toward VIPERS was to assess confidence levels in the training effectives of VIPERS. Although the survey findings

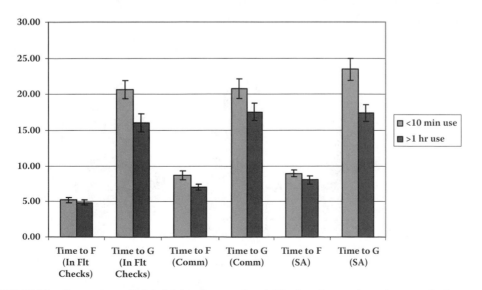

FIGURE 21.12 Comparison of high (>1 hour) versus low (<10 minute) users; bars show standard error.

TABLE 21.2

Results from Comparison of <30 Minute versus >30 Minute Users

Low usage		In-flight checks		Communications		Situational awareness	
		Time to fair	Time to good	Time to fair	Time to good	Time to fair	Time to good
<30 minute use	Mean	5.03	20.47	8.50	20.41	9.06	23.03
($n = 32$)	STDEV	2.06	6.15	2.88	6.73	2.56	6.97
	STError	0.37	1.11	0.52	1.21	0.46	1.25
High usage							
>30 hour use	Mean	4.89	15.74	7.45	16.89	8.18	16.95
($n = 38$)	STDEV	1.71	5.22	1.87	5.38	2.29	5.08
	STError	0.28	0.86	0.31	0.88	0.38	0.83
t Critical two-tail		1.9955	1.9955	1.9955	1.9955	1.9955	1.9955
$P(T \leq t)$ two-tail		0.7622	**0.0009**	0.0704	**0.0180**	0.1347	**0.0001**

suggest that many users remained unconvinced, we interpret these surveys in the context of very busy personnel being asked to devote additional time to evaluate a prototype training device. Seen in that light, we are encouraged by the attitudinal findings, particularly when taken together with the more persuasive results from the performance data.

The results from the performance data over both comparisons show that students who utilized VIPERS more were able to obtain a grade of *good* significantly sooner on all measures than those who used it less. A similar trend was shown for Time to Fair; however, only one item (communications) was significant. A possible explanation as to why significant results were found for each item for Time to Good and for only one item for Time to Fair stems from MIF definitions and the course training standards (CTS). According to the MIF definition, to receive a score of *fair*, a student must perform the item or maneuver safely and in accordance with CTS, but with minimal proficiency. In contrast, to receive a score of *good*, a student must show increased item proficiency and perform the item or

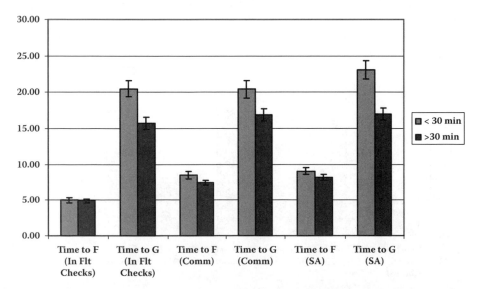

FIGURE 21.13   Comparison of <30 minute versus >30 minute users; bars show standard error of mean.

maneuver satisfactorily while correcting deviations in a timely manner. In other words, by definition, a higher standard of proficiency is required to receive a grade of *good* than for a grade of *fair*. Therefore, a student typically reaches a MIF level of *fair* quickly, but has more difficulty obtaining a MIF level of *good*. Owing to the relative ease of obtaining a *fair*, the training effectiveness of VIPERS was statistically significant only for the one measure most linked to VIPERS: communications. When the students were held to a higher proficiency requirement, statistically significant results were obtained, not only for communications, but for the other measures as well (SA and in-flight checks).

CONCLUSION

VIPERS provides instructor-optional guided practice and feedback in radio communications skills and decision making in the JPATS overhead pattern. The combination of PC-based simulation, intelligent, speech-interactive synthetic teammates, and speech recognition and synthesis increases training availability and reduces dependence on instructors. Data collected from 70 users over a 5-month period show statistically significant training gains from using VIPERS. Specifically, VIPERS use correlated (significantly) with reduced time to achieve a rating of *good* on all three measures (SA, communications, and in-flight checks) identified by the Air Force as being relevant to VIPERS. Time to Fair trended the same way though significance was limited to one of the three measures (communications). We see these findings as providing strong support for the effectiveness of VIPERS: the Time to Good results are consistent across all three measures and the Time to Fair findings reinforce the specific application of VIPERS for communications training.

Findings from the independent (USAF) evaluation provide strong evidence for the training benefit of VIPERS technology, but we see these results as having far broader applicability, along two dimensions: device fidelity and application domain. For the former, although VIPERS was designed and built for easy deployment on commodity laptop PCs, there is nothing in the software architecture that is specific to PC-based, reduced-fidelity simulation. The synthetic teammate implementation relies on standard interoperability protocols and can therefore readily migrate to higher-fidelity training devices (in fact, a recommendation of the AETC final report is to explore the integration of VIPERS into the full-fidelity T-6 simulator). Extending the reach of VIPERS into the realm of full-mission simulators would not only enrich training but also allow the instructor to focus on instruction and not on role playing. The automated performance capture would similarly reduce instructor workload while promoting more effective debriefs.

Just as the software innovations in VIPERS are not specific to PC-based training, the technology similarly is not specific to undergraduate pilot training. Any flying training in which communication and coordination are skills to be acquired and retained can benefit from the on-demand team-oriented guided practice that VIPERS provides. Also, flying missions involve multiple parties, with some team members in the air and others on the ground, so VIPERS can also extend training for ground personnel such as air traffic controllers, battle managers, and tactical control parties.

Nor are the benefits of VIPERS limited to military aviation. Civil aviation training includes radio procedures and effective communication. Pilots flying new routes can practice talking to en route sector and tower controllers within a VIPERS-enabled simulation. Pilots who are non-native speakers of English can use VIPERS technology to master standard aviation English as defined by the International Civil Aviation Organization (ICAO); ICAO's 189 contracting states are required to ensure compliance with this English proficiency standard for licensing of their pilots and controllers effective March 2008.

Finally, VIPERS can enhance training of ground-based domains. Teams that rely on spoken interaction to succeed in time-critical, complex environments could derive the same training benefits as did the pilots in the VIPERS study. Examples include power plant operation, first-responder training, law enforcement, and homeland security.

VIPERS is the first fielded application of synthetic teammates interacting in spoken dialogue that can boast documented verification of measurable training benefit arising from its use. However, the purpose of this chapter is not to claim victory and go home. VIPERS should instead be seen as validation of a concept that has far more potential than has been thus far exploited. The work presented in this chapter, together with some other promising results documented elsewhere in this volume, has merely set the stage for bold new advances that will require principled yet creative frameworks and that will yield important, transformational improvements in how people and teams of people are trained.

REFERENCES

AETC, 2002. *T-6 Aircrew Training* (AFI 11-2T-6, v1). Air Education and Training Command, 1 May 2002.

AETC, 2004. *T-6 Primary Flying* (AFMAN 11-248). Air Education and Training Command, 31 Aug 2004.

AETC, 2006a. *Runway Supervisory Unit (RSU) Operations* (AFI 11-204). Air Education and Training Command, 23 Jan 2006.

AETC, 2006b. *T-6 Operations Procedures* (AFI 11-2T-6, v3). Air Education and Training Command, 19 April 2006.

AFRL, 2002. *Advanced Training Technology Needs for AETC Flying Training* (Final Report, ETTAP Project 02-19). Mesa, AZ: Air Force Research Laboratory.

Baker, D., Prince, C., Shrestha, L., Oser, R., & and Salas, E., 1993. Aviation computer games for crew resource management training. *International Journal of Aviation Psychology, 3*(2), 143–156.

Beringer, D. B., 1994. Issues in using off-the-shelf PC-based flight simulation for research and training: Historical perspective, current solutions, and emerging technologies. *Proceedings of the 38th Annual Human Factors and Ergonomics Society,* 90–94.

Brannick, M. T., Salas, E., & Prince, C. (Eds.), 1997. *Team performance assessment and measurement: Theory, methods and applications.* Hillsdale, NJ: Erlbaum.

Cannon-Bowers, J. A., & Salas, E., 1997. Teamwork competencies: The intersection of team member knowledge, skills, and attitudes. In O'Neil, H. F. (Ed.), *Workforce readiness: Competencies and assessment* (pp. 151–174). Mahwah, NJ: LEA.

Chatham, R. E., & Braddock, J., 2001. *Report of the Defense Science Board Task Force on Training Superiority and Training Surprise.* Washington D.C.: Office of the Undersecretary of Defense for Acquisition, Technology, and Logistics, p. 5.

Fowlkes, J., & Burke, C. S., 2005. Event-based approach to training (EBAT). In Stanton, N., Hedge, A., Brookhuis, K., Salas, E., & Hendrick, H. (Eds.), *Handbook of human factors and ergonomics methods,* (pp. 47-1–47-5). Boca Raton: CRC Press.

Fowlkes, J. E., Dwyer, D., Oser, R. L., & Salas, E., 1998. Event-based approach to training (EBAT). *The International Journal of Aviation Psychology, 8*(3), 209–221.

Hays, R. T., & Singer, M. J., 1989. *Simulation fidelity in training system design: Bridging the gap between reality and training.* New York: Springer-Verlag.

Isdale, J., Fencott, C., Heim, M., & Daly, L., (2002). Content design for virtual environments. In Stanney, K. M. (Ed.), *The virtual environment handbook* (pp. 519–532). Mahwah, NJ: Erlbaum.

Jentsch, F., & Bowers, C. A., 1998. Evidence for the validity of PC-based simulations in studying aircrew coordination. *International Journal of Aviation Psychology, 8*(3), 243–260.

Johnston, J. H., Smith-Jentsch, K. A., & Cannon-Bowers, J. A., 1997. Performance measurement tools for enhancing team decision-making. In Brannick, M. T., Salas, E., & Prince, C. (Eds.), *Team performance assessment and measurement: Theory, methods and applications.* Hillsdale, NJ: Erlbaum.

Means, B., Salas, E., Crandall, B., & Jacobs, T. O., 1993. Training decision makers for the real world. In Klein, G., Orasanu, J., Calderwood, R., & Zsambok, C. E. (Eds.), *Decision making in action: Models and methods* (pp. 306–326). Norwood, NJ: Ablex.

National Research Council, Committee on Modeling and Simulation. 1997. *Modeling and Simulation: Linking Entertainment and Defense.* NRC Computer Science and Telecommunications Board.

NAVAIR Orlando Training Systems Division. 2002. *Training System Functional Description for F/A-18 C/E/F Hornet, Appendix E-Fidelity Analysis* (TSFD Number: 497-FY02-012). NAVAIR ORL TSD: Orlando, FL.

Rogers, B. K. 1991. *Microcomputer-Based Instrument Flight Simulation: Undergraduate Pilot Training Student Attitude Assessment.* (Technical Report No. AL-TR-1991-0039). Chandler, AZ: Williams Air Force Base.

Salas, E., Bowers, C. A., & Rhodenizer, L., 1998. It is not how much you have but how you use it: Toward a rational use of simulation to support aviation training. *International Journal of Aviation Psychology, 8*(3), 197–208.

Schank, R. C., Fano, A., Bell, B. L., & Jona, M. K., 1994. The Design of Goal Based Scenarios. *The Journal of the Learning Sciences, 3*(4), 305–345, 1994.

Swezey, R. W., & Salas. E. (Eds.)., 1992. *Teams: Their training and performance.* Norwood, NJ: Ablex.

Zachary, W., Cannon-Bowers, J., Bilazarian, P., Krecker, D., Lardieri, P., & Burns, J., 1999. An intelligent embedded tutoring system for tactical team training: the Advanced Embedded Training System (AETS), *International Journal of Artificial Intelligence in Education, 10*, 257–277.

Zachary, W., LeMentec, J. C., & Ryder, J. 1996. Interface agents in complex systems. In Ntuen, C., & Park, E. (Eds.), *Human interaction with complex systems: Conceptual principles and design practice* (pp. 35–52). Norwell, MA: Kluwer Academic.

Zachary, W., Santarelli, T., Lyons, D., Bergondy, M., & Johnston, J. 2001. Using a community of intelligent synthetic entities to support operational team training. In *Proceedings of the Tenth Conference on Computer Generated Forces and Behavioral Representation,* 215–224. Orlando: Institute for Simulation and Training.

Appendix A: Glossary of Modeling Terms

Compiled by Michael G. Lilienthal, Ph.D., CPE, director, Research Development and Acquisition, Modeling and Simulation, Office of the Deputy Assistant Secretary of the Navy; and William F. Moroney, Ph.D., CPE, Director, Human Factors Program, University of Dayton, Ohio.

Term	Definition
Activity models	Models of the processes that make up the functional activity showing inputs, outputs, controls, and mechanisms through which the processes of the functional activity are (or will be) conducted.[e]
Analytical model	A model consisting of a set of solvable equations. For example, a system of solvable equations that represents the laws of supply and demand in the world market.[a,j]
Black box model	A model whose inputs, outputs, and functional performance are known, but whose internal implementation is unknown or irrelevant. For example, a model of a computerized change-return mechanism in a vending machine that is in the form of a table indicating the amount of change to be returned for each amount deposited.[a,j] Syn. input/output model. Cf. glass box model.
Computational model	A model consisting of well-defined procedures that can be executed on a computer. For example, a model of the stock market in the form of a set of equations and logic rules.[j]
Conceptual model	A statement of the content and internal representations that are the user's and developer's combined concept of the model. It includes logic and algorithms, and explicitly recognizes assumptions and limitations.[a]
Concrete model	A model in which at least one component represented is a tangible object. For example, a physical replica of a building.[a,j]
Constructive model or simulation	Models and simulations that involve simulated people operating simulated systems. Real people stimulate (make inputs) to such simulations, but are not involved in determining the outcomes.[d] See Appendix B: Live, virtual, and constructive simulation.
Continuous model	A mathematical or computational model whose output variables change in a continuous manner.[a,j] Cf. discrete model.
Data model	A description of the organization of data in a manner that reflects the information structure of an enterprise.[e,f,h] In a database, the user's logical view of the data in contrast to the physically stored data or storage structures.

Continued

Term	Definition
Descriptive model	A model used to depict the behavior or properties of an existing system or type of system. For example, a scale model or written specification used to convey to potential buyers the physical and performance characteristics of a computer.[a,j] Cf. prescriptive model.
Deterministic model	A model in which the results are determined through known relationships among the states and events, and in which a given input will always produce the same output. For example, a model depicting a known chemical reaction.[a,j] Cf. stochastic model.
Discrete model	A mathematical or computational model whose output variables take on only discrete values; i.e., in changing from one value to another, they do not take on the intermediate values. For example, a model that predicts an organization's inventory levels on the basis of varying shipments and receipts.[a,j] Cf. continuous model.
Dynamic model	A model of a system in which there is change, such as the occurrence of events over time or the movement of objects through space. For example, a model of an aircraft wing under a variety of loads or a model that describes the mechanical stress on an individual lifting a load.[a,j]
Enterprise model	An information model that presents an integrated top-level representation of processes, information flows, and data.[c,e]
Error model	(a) A model used to estimate or predict the extent of deviation of the behavior of an actual system from the desired behavior of the system. For example, a model of a communications channel used to estimate the number of transmission errors that can be expected in the channel. (b) In software evaluation, a model used to estimate or predict the number of remaining faults, required test time, and similar characteristics of a system.[a,j]
Glass box model	A model whose internal implementation is known and fully visible. For example, a model of a computerized change-return mechanism in a vending machine, in the form of a diagram of the circuits and gears that make the change.[a,j] Cf. black box model. Syn. white box model.
Graphical model	A symbolic model whose properties are expressed in diagrams. For example, a decision tree used to express a complex procedure.[a,j] Cf. mathematical model, narrative model, software model, and tabular model.
Hierarchical model	A model of information in which data are represented as trees of records connected by pointers.[k]
Iconic model	A physical model or graphical display that resembles the system being modeled. For example, a nonfunctional replica of a computer tape drive used for display purposes.[a,j] See also: scale model.

Continued

Term	Definition
Information model	A model that represents the processes, entities, information flows, and elements of an organization, and all relationships between these factors.[f]
Interactive model	A model that requires human participation.[a] Syn. human-in-the-loop.
Logical data model	A model of the data stores and flows of the organization derived from the conceptual business model.[f]
Markov chain model	A discrete, stochastic model in which the probability that the model is in a given state at a certain time depends only on the value of the immediately preceding state.[a,j] Syn. Markov model.
Mathematical model	A symbolic model whose properties are expressed in mathematical symbols and relationships. For example, a model of a nation's economy expressed as a set of equations.[a] Cf. graphical model, narrative model, and tabular model.
Metamodel	A model of a model. Metamodels are abstractions of the M&S being developed that use functional decomposition to show relationships, paths of data and algorithms, ordering, and interactions between model components and subcomponents. Metamodels allow the software engineers who are developing the model to abstract details to a level that subject matter experts can validate.[m]
Model	(a) A physical, mathematical, or otherwise logical representation of a system, entity, phenomenon, or process.[a,b,d,m] (b) A functional form of a system, generally reduced in scale, near or at operational specification. Models will be sufficiently hardened to allow demonstration of the technical and operational capabilities required of the final system.[n]
Modeling	Application of a standard, rigorous, and structured methodology to create and validate a physical, mathematical, or otherwise logical representation of a system, entity, phenomenon, or process.[e]
Modeling and simulation (M&S)	The use of models, including emulators, prototypes, simulators, and stimulators, either statically or over time, to develop data as a basis for making managerial or technical decisions. The terms modeling and simulation are often used interchangeably.[m]
Narrative model	A symbolic model whose properties are expressed in words. For example, a written specification for a computer system.[a,j] Syn. verbal descriptive model. Cf. graphical model, mathematical model, software model, and tabular model.
Natural model	A model that represents a system by using another system that already exists in the real world. For example, a model that uses one body of water to represent another.[a,j]

Continued

Term	Definition
Normative model	A model that makes use of a familiar situation to represent a less familiar one. For example, a model that depicts the human cardiovascular system by using a mechanical pump, rubber hoses, and water.[a,j]
Numerical model	(a) A mathematical model in which a set of mathematical operations is reduced to a form that is suitable for solution by simpler methods such as numerical analysis or automation. For example, a model in which a single equation representing a nation's economy is replaced by a large set of simple averages based on empirical observations of inflation rate, unemployment rate, gross national product, and other indicators. (b) A model whose properties are expressed by numbers.[a,j]
Object model	A specification of the objects that are intrinsic to a given system, including descriptions of the object characteristics (attributes), and the static and dynamic relationships that exist between them.[i]
Parametric model	A model using parametric equations that may be based on numerical model outputs or fits to semiempirical data to succinctly describe a particular process, feature, or effect.[m]
Physical model	A model whose physical characteristics resemble those of the system being modeled. For example, a plastic or wooden replica of an airplane; a mock-up.[a,j] See also: iconic model, scale model. Cf. symbolic model.
Predictive model	A model in which the values of future states can be predicted or are hypothesized. For example, a model that predicts weather patterns on the basis of the current value of temperature, humidity, wind speed, and so on, at various locations.[a,j]
Prescriptive model	A model used to convey information regarding the required behavior or properties of a proposed system. For example, a scale model or written specification used to convey to a computer supplier the physical and performance characteristics of a required computer.[a,j] Cf. descriptive model.
Probabilistic model	See: stochastic model.[a]
Process improvement modeling	Defines and documents the current ("as is") and desired future ("to be") processes and information requirements of a functional activity. Two types of process improvement models are activity models and data models.
Process model	A model of the processes performed by a system. For example, a model that depicts the software development process as a sequence of phases.[a] Cf. structural model.
Queuing network model	A model that describes a process as a network in which each node represents a service facility for rendering a given type of service and a queue for holding entities waiting to be served. For example, a model depicting a network of shipping routes and docking facilities at which ships must form queues in order to unload their cargo.[a,j]

Continued

Term	Definition
Reliability model	A model used to estimate, measure, or predict the reliability of a system. For example, a model of a computer system that is used to estimate the total down time that will be experienced.[a,j]
Scale model	A physical model that resembles a given system, with only a change in scale. For example, a replica of an airplane one-tenth the size of the actual airplane.[a,j]
Semi-Markov model	A Markov chain model in which the length of time spent in each state is randomly distributed.[a,j]
Static model	A model of an entity or system in which there is no change. For example, a scale model of a bridge that is provided for its appearance rather than for its performance under varying loads.[a,j]
Stochastic model	A model in which the results are determined by using one or more random variables to represent uncertainty about a process, or in which a given input will produce an output according to some statistical distribution. For example, a model that estimates the total dollars spent at each of the checkout stations in a supermarket, based on probable number of customers and probable purchase amount of each customer. [a] Syn. probabilistic model. See also: Markov chain model. Cf. deterministic model.
Structural model	A representation of the physical or logical structure of a system. For example, a representation of a computer network as a set of boxes connected by communication lines.[a,j] Cf. process model.
Symbolic model	A model whose properties are expressed in symbols. Examples include graphical models, mathematical models, narrative models, software models, and tabular models.[a,j] Cf. physical model.
Tabular model	A symbolic model whose properties are expressed in tabular form. For example, a truth table that represents a Boolean logic "OR" function.[a,j] Cf. graphical model, mathematical model, and narrative model.
Time step models	Dynamic models in which time is advanced by a fixed or independently determined amount to a new point, and the states or status of some or all resources are updated as of that new point in time.[l]

Source: Most of the Department of Defense (DoD)-related documents cited in this glossary are available at http://dodssp. daps.dla.mil (click on ASSIST and then Quick Search) or through http://www.dtic.mil/. Others are available through the agency or organization listed in the source list.

[a]Department of Defense (August 1995). DIS Glossary of M&S Terms. A Glossary of Modeling and Simulation Terms for Distributed Interactive Simulation (DIS).

[b]Department of Defense (January 4, 1994). DoD Directive 5000.59. DoD Modeling and Simulation (M&S) Management.

[c]Department of Defense (October 27, 1992). DoD Directive 8000.1. Defense Information Management Program.

[d]Department of Defense (October 1995). DoD Modeling and Simulation Master Plan of 1995. (5000.59-P).

[e]Department of Defense (March 29, 1994). DoD 8320.1-M. Data Administrative Procedures.

[f]Department of Defense (April 1998). DoD 8320.1-M-1. Data Element Standardization Procedures.

[g]Defense Systems Management College (DSMC; September 1994). DSMC 1993–94 Military Research Fellows Report. Systems Acquisition Manager's Guide for the Use of Models and Simulation.

[h]American National Standards Institute (ANSI; February 1, 1991). American National Dictionary for Information Systems. (FIPS Pub 11-3).

[i]Department of Defense (April 1995). High Level Architecture Glossary.

[j]Institute of Electrical and Electronics Engineers (IEEE; 1990). IEEE Standard Glossary of Modeling and Simulation Terminology. (IEEE Std 610.3).

[k]Department of Defense (February 1995). *Military Handbook for Joint Database Elements for Modeling and Simulation (M&S).*

[l]Military Operations Research Society (MORS; October 27, 1989). A Taxonomy for Warfare Simulation (SIMTAX). (MORS Report).

[m]Naval Air Warfare Center Training Systems Division (NAWC-TSD; April 28, 1994). Modeling and Simulation Educational Training Tool (MSETT) Glossary. (MSETT NAWC-TSD Glossary).

[n]DoD 5000.2R, April 5, 2002.

Appendix B: Glossary of Simulation Terms

Compiled by Michael G. Lilienthal, Ph.D., CPE, director, Research Development and Acquisition, Modeling, and Simulation, Office of the Deputy Assistant Secretary of the Navy; and William F. Moroney, Ph.D., CPE, Director, Human Factors Program, University of Dayton, Ohio.

Term	Definition
Activity-based simulation	A discrete simulation that represents the components of a system as they proceed from activity to activity. For example, a simulation in which a manufactured product moves from station to station in an assembly line.[a]
Advanced distributed simulation (ADS)	A set of disparate models or simulations operating in a common synthetic environment in accordance with the distributed interactive simulation (DIS) standards. The ADS may be composed of three modes of simulation: live, virtual, and constructive, which can be seamlessly integrated within a single exercise.[a]
Built-in simulator	A simulator that is built into the system being modeled. For example, an operator training simulator built into the control panel of a power plant such that the system can operate in simulator mode or in normal operating mode.[a,j]
Computer simulation	A dynamic representation of a model, often involving some combination of executing code, control/display interface hardware, and interfaces to real-world equipment.
Constrained simulation	A simulation where time advances are paced to have a specific relationship to wall clock time. These are commonly referred to as real-time or scaled real-time simulations. Here, the terms constrained simulation and (scaled) real-time simulation are used synonymously. Human-in-the-loop (e.g., training exercises) and hardware-in-the loop (e.g., test and evaluation simulations) are examples of constrained simulations.[i]
Constructive model or simulation	Models and simulations that involve simulated people operating simulated systems. Real people stimulate (make inputs) to such simulations, but are not involved in determining the outcomes.[d] See: live, virtual, and constructive simulation.
Continuous simulation	A simulation that uses a continuous model.[a,j]
Critical event simulation	A simulation that is terminated by the occurrence of a certain event. For example, a model depicting the year-by-year forces that lead to a volcanic eruption, and is terminated when the volcano in the model erupts.[a,j]
Discrete simulation	A simulation that uses a discrete model.[a,i]

Continued

Term	Definition
Distributed interactive simulation (DIS) compatible	Two or more simulations (or simulators) are DIS compatible if they are DIS compliant, and their models and data that send and interpret protocol data units (PDUs) support the realization of a common operational environment among the systems (coherent in time and space).[a]
Environmental simulation	A simulation that depicts all or part of the natural or man-made environment of a system. For example, a simulation of the radar equipment and other tracking devices that provide input to an aircraft tracking system.[j]
Event-oriented simulation	A simulation in which attention is focused on the occurrence of events and the times at which those events occur. For example, a simulation of a digital circuit that focuses on the time of state transition.[a,j]
Fast time	The simulation is presented at a rate greater then real-time. Thus events which transpire in one minute in the real world could transpire in 30 seconds in the simulation (i.e. twice real-time).
Human–machine simulation	A simulation carried out by both human participants and computers, typically with the human participants asked to make decisions and a computer performing the processing on the basis of those decisions.[a]
Hybrid simulation	A simulation that combines constructive, live, and/or virtual simulations, typically in a distributed environment. Such simulations usually combine simulators with actual operational equipment, prototypes of future systems, and realistic representations of operational environments.[m]
In-basket simulation	A simulation in which a set of issues is presented to a participant in the form of documents on which action must be taken. For example, a simulation of an unfolding international crisis presented as a sequence of memos describing relevant events and outcomes of the participant's actions on previous memos.[a,j]
Instructional simulation	A simulation that is intended to provide a simulation equivalent of a real or hypothesized stimulus that could occur in the synthetic environment, for the purpose of training.[a]
Interval-oriented simulation	A continuous simulation in which simulated time is advanced in increments of a size suitable to make implementation possible on a digital system.[a,j]
Live simulation	A simulation involving real people operating real systems. One of several categories of simulation.[d] See: live, virtual, and constructive simulation.
Live, virtual, and constructive simulation	A broadly used taxonomy for classifying simulation types. The categorization of simulation into live, virtual, and constructive is problematic because there is no clear division between these categories. The degree of human participation in the simulation is infinitely variable, as is the degree of equipment realism. This categorization of simulations also suffers by excluding a category for simulated people working real equipment (e.g., smart vehicles).[d]

Continued

Term	Definition
Modeling and simulation (M&S)	The use of models, including emulators, prototypes, simulators, and stimulators, either statically or over time, to develop data as a basis for making managerial or technical decisions. The terms modeling and simulation are often used interchangeably.[m]
Monte Carlo simulation	A simulation in which random statistical sampling techniques are employed such that the result determines estimates for unknown values.[a]
Outcome-oriented simulation	A simulation in which the end result is considered more important than the process by which it is obtained. For example, a simulation of a radar system that uses methods far different from those used by the actual radar, but whose output is the same. Cf. process-oriented simulation.
Process-oriented simulation	A simulation in which the process is considered more important than the outcome. For example, a model of a radar system in which the objective is to replicate exactly the radar's operation, and duplication of its results is a lesser concern.[a,j] Cf. outcome-oriented simulation.
Real-time	The simulation is presented in standard time (e.g., events which transpire in one minute in the real world transpire in one minute in the simulation).
Real-time simulation	Same as constrained simulation.[i]
Simuland	The system being simulated by a simulation.[a]
Simulated time	Time as represented within a simulation. Syn. virtual time. See also: fast time, real-time, and slow time.[j]
Simulation	A method for implementing a model over time. Also, a technique for testing, analysis, or training in which real-world systems are used, or where real-world and conceptual systems are reproduced by a model.[b,d]
Simulation entity	An element of the synthetic environment that is created and controlled by a simulation application through the exchange of distributed interactive simulation protocol data units (DIS PDUs; e.g., tanks, submarines, carriers, fighter aircraft, missiles, bridges). It is possible that a simulation application may be controlling more than one simulation entity.[a,j]
Simulation environment	(a) Consists of the operational environment surrounding the simulation entities including terrain, atmospheric, bathyspheric, and cultural information. (b) All the conditions, circumstances, and influences surrounding and affecting simulation entities, including those stated in (a).[a]
Simulation game	A simulation in which the participants seek to achieve some agreed upon objective within an established set of rules. For example, a management game, a war game. Note: The objective may not be to compete, but to evaluate the participants, increase their knowledge concerning the simulated scenario, or achieve other goals. Syn. gaming simulation.[a,j]

Continued

Term	Definition
Simulation object model (SOM)	A specification of the intrinsic capabilities that an individual simulation offers to federations. The standard format in which an SOM is expressed provides a means for federation developers to quickly determine the suitability of simulation systems to assume specific roles within a federation.[i]
Simulation process	The imitative representation of the actions of platform(s), munitions(s), and life form(s) by computer program(s) in accordance with a mathematical model and the generation of associated battlefield entities. May be fully automated or partially automated. In the latter case, the human-in-the-loop injects command-level decisions into the process and is not intended to be a "trainee."[a]
Simulation time	(a) A simulation's internal representation of time. Simulation time may accumulate faster, slower, or at the same pace as real-time. (b) The reference time (e.g., Universal Coordinated Time) within a simulation exercise. This time is established by the simulation management function before the start of the simulation and is common to all participants in a particular exercise.[a,j]
Simulator	(a) A device, computer program, or system that performs simulation. (b) For training, a device that duplicates the essential features of a task situation and provides for direct human operation.[a]
Slow time	The simulation is presented at a rate less then real-time. Thus, events which transpire in one minute in the real world could transpire in two minutes in the simulation (i.e., one-half of real-time). This is often used in "reenactments," or where additional detail is needed.
Stimulate	To provide input to a system to observe or evaluate the system's response.[a,j]
Stimulation	The use of simulations to provide an external stimulus to a system or subsystem. An example is the use of a simulation representing the radar return from a target to drive (stimulate) the radar of a missile system within a hardware/software-in-the-loop simulation.[g]
Stimulator	(a) A hardware device that injects or radiates signals into the sensor system(s) of operational equipment to imitate the effects of platforms, munitions, and environment that are not physically present. (b) A battlefield entity consisting of hardware and/or software modules that injects signals directly into the sensor systems of an actual battlefield entity to simulate other battlefield entities in the virtual battlefield.[a]
Time-slice simulation or time-interval simulation	A discrete simulation that is terminated after a specific amount of time has elapsed. For example, a model depicting the year-by-year forces affecting a volcanic eruption over a period of 100,000 years.[a]

Continued

Term	Definition
Unconstrained simulation	A simulation where there is no explicit relationship between wall clock time and the rate of time advancements. These are sometimes called "as-fast-as possible" simulations, and the two terms are used synonymously here. Analytic simulation models and many constructive "war game" simulations are often unconstrained simulations.[i]
Virtual simulation	A simulation involving real people operating simulated systems. Virtual simulations inject human-in-the-loop in a central role by exercising motor control skills (e.g., flying an airplane), decision skills (e.g., committing fire control resources to action), or communication skills (e.g., as members of an air traffic control team).[d] See: live, virtual, and constructive simulation.

Source: Most of the Department of Defense (DoD)-related documents cited in this glossary are available at http://dodssp. daps.dla.mil (click on ASSIST and then Quick Search) or through http://www.dtic.mil/. Others are available through the agency or organization listed in the source list.

[a]Department of Defense (August 1995). DIS Glossary of M&S Terms. A Glossary of Modeling and Simulation Terms for Distributed Interactive Simulation (DIS).

[b]Department of Defense (January 4, 1994). DoD Directive 5000.59. DoD Modeling and Simulation (M&S) Management.

[c]Department of Defense (October 27, 1992). DoD Directive 8000.1. Defense Information Management Program.

[d]Department of Defense (October 1995). DoD Modeling and Simulation Master Plan of 1995. (5000.59-P).

[e]Department of Defense (March 29, 1994). DoD 8320.1-M. Data Administrative Procedures.

[f]Department of Defense (April 1998). DoD 8320.1-M-1. Data Element Standardization Procedures.

[g]Defense Systems Management College (DSMC; September 1994). DSMC 1993–94 Military Research Fellows Report. Systems Acquisition Manager's Guide for the Use of Models and Simulation.

[h]American National Standards Institute (ANSI; February 1, 1991). American National Dictionary for Information Systems. (FIPS Pub 11-3).

[i]Department of Defense (April 1995). High Level Architecture Glossary.

[j]Institute of Electrical and Electronics Engineers (IEEE; 1990). IEEE Standard Glossary of Modeling and Simulation Terminology. (IEEE Std 610.3).

[k]Department of Defense (February 1995). *Military Handbook for Joint Database Elements for Modeling and Simulation (M&S)*.

[l]Military Operations Research Society (MORS; October 27, 1989). A Taxonomy for Warfare Simulation (SIMTAX). (MORS Report).

[m]Naval Air Warfare Center Training Systems Division (NAWC-TSD; April 28, 1994). Modeling and Simulation Educational Training Tool (MSETT) Glossary. (MSETT NAWC-TSD Glossary).

[n]DoD 5000.2R, April 5, 2002.

Appendix C: Glossary of Verification, Validation, and Accreditation Terms

Compiled by Michael G. Lilienthal, Ph.D., CPE, director, Research Development and Acquisition, Modeling and Simulation, Office of the Deputy Assistant Secretary of the Navy; and William F. Moroney, Ph.D., CPE, Director, Human Factors Program, University of Dayton, Ohio.

Term	Definition
Accreditation	The official certification that a model, simulation, or federation of models and simulations and its associated data are acceptable for use for a specific purpose.[b]
Accreditation agent	The organization designated to conduct an accreditation assessment for a modeling and simulation (M&S) application.[a]
Accreditation criteria	A set of standards that a particular model, simulation, or federation must meet to be accredited for a specific purpose.[a]
Data verification and validation (V&V)	The process of verifying the internal consistency and correctness of data, and validating that it represents real-world entities appropriate for its intended purpose or an expected range of purposes. The process has two perspectives: the producer and the user process.[a]
Department of Defense (DoD) component verification, validation, and accreditation (VV&A) focal point	An organization designated by each DoD Component as its authoritative, single point of contact for information and data on, at minimum, its VV&A policies and procedures, V&V results, and accreditation documentation. The DoD Component VV&A focal point shall be the designated point of contact to work with the DoD VV&A focal point on VV&A issues.
Face validation	The process of determining whether a model or simulation seems reasonable to people who are knowledgeable about the system.[c]
Independent verification and validation	The conduct of verification and validation of a model or simulation by individuals or agencies that did not develop the model or simulation.[c]
Logical verification	The identification of a set of assumptions and interactions that the model and simulation correctly produces the intended results.[c]
Validation	The process of determining the degree to which a model and its associated data are an accurate representation of the real world, from the perspective of the intended uses of the model.[b]
Validation agent	The person or organization designated to perform validation of a model, simulation, or federation of models and/or simulations and the associated data.[a]

Continued

Term	Definition
Verification	The process of determining that a model implementation and its associated data accurately represent the developer's conceptual description and specifications.[b]
Verification agent	The person or organization designated to perform verification of a model, simulation, or federation of models and/or simulations and the associated data.[a]

Source: The Department of Defense (DoD) documents cited in the glossary are available at http://dodssp.daps.dla.mil (click on ASSIST, then Quick Search).

[a]DoD Instruction 5000.61 (April 29, 1996). DoD Modeling and Simulation (M&S), Verification, Validation, and Accreditation (VV&A).

[b]Department of Defense Directive (DoDD) 5000.59 (January 4, 1994). DoD Modeling and Simulation (M&S) Management.

[c]DoD 5000.59-M (January 15, 1998). DoD Modeling and Simulation (M&S) Glossary.

Index

GOOD WOOD
FINISHES

GOOD WOOD
FINISHES

Albert Jackson & David Day

BETTERWAY BOOKS
CINCINNATI, OHIO

GOOD WOOD FINISHES
Conceived, edited and designed at Inklink,
Greenwich, London, England

Text: Albert Jackson and David Day

Design and art direction: Simon Jennings

Project consultant: Ronnie Rustin

Text editors: Ian Kearey
and Albert Jackson

Illustrators: Robin Harris and David Day

Studio photography: Ben Jennings, Paul Chave,
and Neil Waving

Indexer: Ian Kearey

Proofreader: Mary Morton

U.S. consultant editor: R. Adam Blake

First published in North America
in 1997 by Betterway Books,
an imprint of F & W Publications, Inc.
1507 Dana Avenue
Cincinnati, OH 45207
1–800/289–0963

ISBN 1–55870–440–X

Text set in Franklin Gothic Extra Condensed, Univers Condensed
and Garamond Book Condensed by Inklink, London
Colour reproduction by Colourscan, Singapore

Printed in Singapore

Jacket design: Simon Jennings
Jacket photograph: Paul Chave
Jacket illustrations: Robin Harris and David Day

CONTENTS

INTRODUCTION

Applying a protective finish is invariably the final and arguably the most rewarding stage in any wood-working project. One can take pride in well-crafted joints, wafer-thin woodturning or intricate marquetry, but there are few delights to compare with the satisfaction of building a surface coat of polish or varnish which transforms an apparently mundane piece of wood into a uniquely beautiful object. And you don't have to be a skilled woodworker to enjoy wood finishing. It is such a varied and absorbing activity that individuals can spend years practicing and perfecting their skills, so it is hardly surprising that, even in professional woodworking circles, finishing is quite often undertaken by a specialist. Similarly, a great many amateurs take up wood finishing in order to renovate inexpensive antiques for profit or merely to put new life back into much-loved heirlooms.

ACKNOWLEDGEMENTS

Consultants
The help and specialist advice provided by our technical consultants is gratefully acknowledged:

A chemist by training, **Ronnie Rustin** has a wealth of practical experience and a thorough knowledge of traditional and modern wood-finishing techniques. He is also the Managing Director of Rustins Ltd., a company famous for developing many innovative wood-finishing products. Ronnie Rustin's generous contribution to the book has been invaluable.

Tim Bizley of Touchstone Design is a professional wood grainer and marbler who has worked as a specialist decorator and muralist for over twelve years. He is also a craft-based member of the Interior Decorators and Designers Association. Tim Bizley acted as technical advisor on graining techniques and supplied all the examples of work illustrated in the chapter on wood graining.

Designer-makers
The authors and producers would like to thank the following for permission to reproduce images of their work:

John Hunnex, page 91 (CL)
Stewart Linford, page 90, 122
Paul Mathews, page 73
Wendy Maruyama, page 77
Derek Pearce, page 65 (T)
Hugh Scriven, page 39
Wales & Wales, page 40
Richard Williams, page 91 (BR)
Raymond Winkler, page 65 (BL)

Reference material and equipment
The authors and producers are grateful to the following for supplying reference and equipment used in this book:

Abrasives
CSM Trade Supplies, Brighton, East Sussex, UK
General wood finishes
Foxell & James, London EC1, UK
Langlows Products Division, Palace Chemicals Ltd., Chesham, Bucks, UK
Liberon, New Romney, Kent, UK
E. Parsons & Sons Ltd., Nailsea, Bristol, UK
Ronseal Ltd., Chapeltown, Sheffield, UK
Rustins Ltd., London, NW2, UK
Graining tools and materials
A. S. Handover Ltd., London, N1, UK
Shellac
A. F. Suter & Co. Ltd., London, E3, UK
Wm. Zinsser & Co. Inc., Somerset, NJ, USA
Spray equipment
Clarke International, London, E5, UK

Photography
The studio photographs for this book were taken by Ben Jennings, with the following exceptions:

Neil Waving, pages 18, 21, 22, 24 (BR), 53, 81
Paul Chave, pages 10, 32, 45, 60, 76, 80

The authors and producers also acknowledge additional photography by, and the use of photographs from, the following individuals and companies:

Robert Bosch Ltd., Uxbridge, Middlesex, page 23
Clarke International, London E5, page 82
Cuprinol Ltd., Frome, Somerset, pages 62, 64 (CL, BR)
David Day, Page 63 (T)
John Hunnex, Woodchurch, Kent, page 91 (CL)
Langlows Products Division, Palace Chemicals Ltd., Chesham Bucks, page 96
Stewart Linford Furniture (Derek St Romain), High Wycombe, Bucks, pages 90, 122
London Guildhall University (Hellena Cleary), London, E1, page 103 (C, BR, BL)
Alan Marshall, page 34
Wendy Maruyama (Cary Okazaki Studios), San Diego, California, page 77
Paul Mathews, Buckinghamshire College, High Wycombe, Bucks, page 73
Derek Pearce, London, SW 13, page 65 (T)
Ronseal Ltd., Chapeltown, Sheffield, pages 52, 91 (TR)
Sadolin UK Ltd., St Ives, Cambs, pages 47, 64 (TR)
Hugh Scriven, Shrewsbury, Shropshire, page 39
A. F. Suter & Co. Ltd., Bow London E3, page 51
Wales & Wales (Michael Hemsley FBIPP), Lewes, East Sussex, page 40
Richard Williams, Buckinghamshire College, High Wycombe, Bucks, page 91 (BR)
Raymond Winkler, Buckinghamshire College, High Wycombe, Bucks, page 65 (BL)
Shona Wood, page 63B

The authors and producers also thank the following for the use of their photographic archives:
Peter Cornish and Philip Hussey, Buckinghamshire College, High Wycombe, Bucks
John Cross, London Guildhall University, Restoration and Conservation Dept, London, E1

Key to credits
T = top, B = bottom, L = left, R = right, TL = top left, TC = top center, TR = top right, CL = center left, C = center, CR = center right, BL = bottom left, BC = bottom center, BR = bottom right

CHAPTER *1* Good-quality paint may obliterate minor imperfections, but a coat of varnish or lacquer can do nothing to improve the appearance of wood that has been inadequately prepared. The very first application of clear finish invariably exposes flaws that were completely undetectable before. Work systematically, eradicating all obvious blemishes, before sanding the wood smooth with progressively finer abrasives.

PREPARATION

FILLING CRACKS AND HOLES

Although any woodworker rejects timber with glaring defects such as end splits and shakes, it is difficult to guarantee that a batch of timber will be completely faultless, without at least some minor cracks or evidence of wood-boring insects. Try as you may to select only the better sections of the wood, you must invariably fill or patch a few cracks and holes before starting to sand to a smooth finish. However, there are a number of materials and techniques you can draw upon, depending on the dimensions of the crack or hole, and the type of finish you intend to apply.

STOPPER

WAX FILLING STICKS

LIBERON

ELECTRIC SOLDERING IRON

SHELLAC STICKS

Cellulose filler for paintwork
You can use a commercially prepared or home-made stopper when preparing wood for painting, or you can fill small holes and cracks with ordinary decorator's cellulose filler. Supplied ready-made in tubs or as a dry powder for mixing with water, cellulose filler is applied and sanded flush like wood putty.

Wood putty or stopper
Traditional filler made from wood dust mixed with glue still has its uses, but most wood finishers prefer to employ commercially prepared wood putty, or stopper, sold as a thick paste in tubes or small cans, for filling indentations. Stoppers are made in a range of colors to resemble common wood species.

Most stoppers are one-part pastes, formulated for either interior or exterior woodwork. Once set, they can be planed, sanded and drilled along with the surrounding wood; they remain slightly flexible, to absorb any subsequent movement that may be caused by the timber shrinking and expanding.

Catalysed two-part stoppers, intended primarily for larger repairs, set even harder than the standard pastes. Take care not to overfill when using them, or you may find yourself using up a great deal of sandpaper just to achieve a flush surface. Use a two-part putty if you want to build up an edge or broken corner.

Reconstituting stopper
To keep wood stopper in usable condition, replace the lid or screw cap as soon as you have taken enough for your requirements. If you find that stored water-based stopper has stiffened, try standing the tin in warm water or place the container on a radiator to make the filler pliable.

MAKING YOUR OWN STOPPER
To make your own filler, collect sawdust or, better still, the dust created by sanding a workpiece or an offcut. Mix plenty of dust with a little PVA glue to make a thick paste – a glue-rich filler tends to reject stains and polishes, creating a visible repair. As an alternative to glue, try using some of the finish you intend to apply. If color matching proves to be a problem, try adding a drop or two of compatible stain or some powdered pigment to the mix.

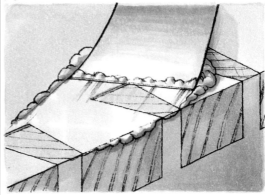

Disguising joints
Filled shoulder lines are almost always discernible, but you can make passable repairs to gappy joints that have visible end grain, using a home-made filler.

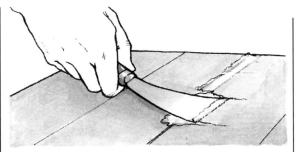

Using wood putty

Make sure the wood is clean and dry. Using a flexible filling knife, press putty into the indentations, leaving the filler slightly raised for sanding flush after it has set. Drag the knife across a crack to fill it, then smooth the putty by running the blade lengthways. Fill deep holes in stages, allowing the stopper to harden between applications.

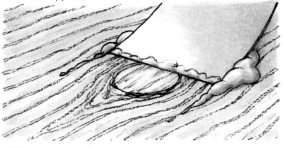

Filling large holes

Plug deep knotholes with solid wood. When the glue has set, fill gaps around the patch with wood stopper.

Coloring putty to match

To match the color of your workpiece, make a test piece by applying stain and one finish coat to an offcut of the same wood. Select a putty that resembles the lightest background color of the wood and, using a white ceramic tile as a palette, add compatible wood dye one drop at a time. Blend the dye into the putty with a filling knife to achieve the required tone. Mix a color that is slightly darker than your test piece to allow for the fact that putty will be a shade lighter when dry.

Alternatively, add powdered pigments to color the putty, plus a drop of compatible solvent if the paste becomes too stiff.

FILLING STICKS

Sticks of solidified shellac in various colors are made for melting into holes in the wood or for building up broken moldings. Shellac can be used as a preparatory stopper for use with most surface finishes However, it may prevent an acid-catalysed cold-cure lacquer from curing properly.

Carnauba wax, mixed with pigments and resins, is ideal for plugging small wormholes. Although wax filler can be applied to bare wood that is to be French-polished or waxed, it is often best to wait until the wood is finished.

Wax sticks are made in a range of colors. If necessary, cut pieces of wax from different sticks, blending them with the tip of a soldering iron to match a specific color. This method of filling is known as beaumontage.

Filling with shellac

Use a heated knife blade or a soldering iron to melt the tip of a shellac stick, allowing it to drip into the hole. While it is still soft, press the shellac flat with a wood chisel dipped in water. As soon as the filler hardens, pare it flush with a sharp chisel, finishing with a fine abrasive.

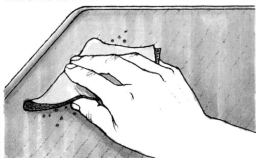

Using wax filling sticks

Cut off a small piece of wax and put it on a radiator to soften. Using a pocket knife, press wax into the holes. As soon as it hardens, scrape the repair flush with an old credit card. Fold a piece of sandpaper, and use the paper backing to burnish the wax filling.

PATCHING AND PLUGGING

It pays to fill a wide crack with a sliver of timber or veneer, rather than relying on stopper which could fall out. Dead knots and holes that are too large to fill successfully can be cut out and patched with solid wood. Diamond-shape patches tend to blend in better than square or rectangular ones.

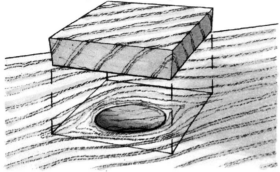

1 Cutting a diamond-shape patch
Select and cut out a diamond-shape patch from wood that matches the workpiece in grain pattern and color. Plane a shallow bevel on all four edges of the patch.

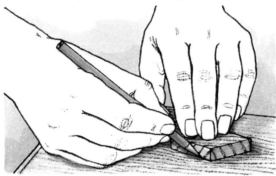

2 Cutting the recess
Hold the replacement patch over the knothole and draw round it with a pencil, then chisel out a tapered recess to receive the patch.

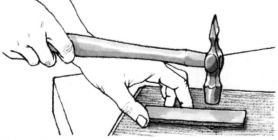

3 Inserting the patch
Tap the glued patch into the recess, cleaning off excess adhesive with a damp cloth. Leave the glue to harden, then plane flush.

Filling cracks with veneer
Although one would never wish to buy split timber, if you are refinishing an old table top or cabinet, you may not have the choice. Enlarge a tapered crack with the tip of a dovetail saw until it is wide enough to accommodate a strip of glued veneer. When the adhesive has set, plane the repair flush.

Filling a crack with a tapered lath
To patch a wide crack or an open joint in a solid-wood panel, cut a lath from matching timber and plane a shallow bevel along both sides. Scrape any dirt and old wax polish from the crack, and tap the glued lath in place with a hammer. Plane the lath flush after the glue has set.

PLUG CUTTERS

Patch unsightly flaws with a circular patch cut with a plug cutter. These cutters are designed to exactly match holes bored with a drill bit or router cutter. You can use similar plugs to mask the sunken heads of screw fixings.

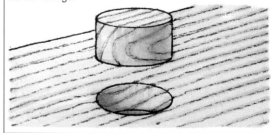

DISGUISING REPAIRS

Whether you use wood putty, shellac or solid wood to fill holes and cracks, it is often difficult to match color and grain pattern exactly. Apply a single coat of the surface finish to see how the filling will react; if your repair is still noticeable, paint it to simulate the appearance of the surrounding wood.

Only an expert can copy grain pattern perfectly, but the aim is to fool the eye so that it is not automatically drawn to the repair. A handy trick is to paint a filled hole to look like a small knot, rather than attempt to reproduce the grain; provided the wood contains similar knots, the eye will accept the obvious difference between the patch and the background as a natural feature.

It is convenient to use artist's oil paints thinned with mineral spirit, but professional retouchers mix powdered pigments, available from most suppliers of wood finishes, with transparent shellac polish. Thin the polish with alcohol if it becomes too viscous. A white tile or a piece of glass make ideal palettes for mixing colors.

RAISING DENTS IN TIMBER

A misplaced hammer blow or an unprotected clamp head can leave an unsightly dent in an otherwise perfect surface. You could fill the dent with wood putty, but to avoid having to color-match the repair, apply water or steam, which make the crushed wood fibres swell and lie flush with the surface.

Applying water
Using a pointed brush, drip hot water into the dent. Allow time for the wood to absorb the moisture, adding more water from time to time until the surface is flush.

Using steam
If soaking with water is unsuccessful, lay a damp cloth over the dent and apply the tip of a soldering iron to the spot. The steam generated causes the wood fibres to expand rapidly. Let the wood dry out thoroughly, then sand it smooth.

1 Painting the background color
Using a pointed artist's paintbrush, mix pigments and shellac to approximate the palest background color of the surrounding grain. Seal the wood, then copy the linear pattern across the patch, extending your painted grain onto the wood to blur the outline of the repair. Keep the paintwork as thin as possible.

2 Touching in darker grain
Paint in the darker flecks of grain in a similar way, softening and blending the edges to mimic actual figure. Let the shellac dry thoroughly, then protect it with another coat or two of finish. If you are using French polish, apply it lightly to avoid smudging your repair artwork.

REPAIRING VENEERS

Because they are cut so thinly, veneers are somewhat fragile until they are glued firmly to the groundwork. Even then, the occasional accident or a lack of glue can result in a raised blister or chipped veneer that has to be repaired before you can finish the work satisfactorily. The likelihood of needing to repair damaged veneer is even greater if you are restoring old furniture that has been used, and perhaps abused, for many years.

Detecting blisters

A blister usually occurs where a patch of groundwork was missed as glue was spread, prior to laying up. The blister may be obvious as soon as the work is taken out of the press, but sometimes you can only detect a patch of loose veneer by tapping the surface with your finger-tips; a change in sound from that of solid, adhered veneer denotes a blister.

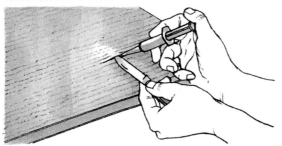

1 Injecting glue

In order to introduce glue beneath the veneer, dampen the blister and slit it lengthways with a sharp knife. Work some PVA glue through the slit with the knife blade or, better still, inject some with a plastic syringe.

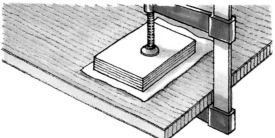

2 Clamping the veneer

Press the blister flat to squeeze out air and glue, wiping surplus adhesive from the surface with a damp cloth. Lay a small piece of polythene over the repair and clamp it down, using a block of scrap wood to spread the load. After the glue has set, remove traces of glue with sandpaper or a cabinet scraper.

Removing a foreign body

A speck of coarse sawdust or a piece of grit trapped beneath veneer will form a blister that cannot be pressed flat until the foreign body is extricated. Wet the patch thoroughly and cut a V-shape flap in the vicinity of the blister. Peel back the flap and scrape out the speck with a knife blade. Brush some glue onto the groundwork and clamp down the veneer.

PRESSING OLD VENEER

Until comparatively recently, veneer was invariably laid using animal glue. Although in many ways it is the ideal glue for veneering, animal glue is not water-proof, and veneer is prone to buckling if moisture is able to penetrate, perhaps through a hairline crack. One of the great advantages of animal glue is that it can be softened with heat and the veneer pressed down without having to slit the blister to introduce fresh adhesive.

Ironing a blister

Place a piece of brown paper over the blistered veneer and apply a warm iron, gradually flattening the veneer as the glue softens. Although you can accelerate the process by substituting a damp cloth for the paper, the steam will spoil the surface finish; however, this may not be a problem if you are in the process of re-polishing.

Patching veneer

It is relatively easy to cut out a flaw, such as a knot hole or cigarette burn, and insert a patch of veneer. Provided you are repairing new work, it should be possible to find a piece of veneer that is identical in thickness, with closely matched grain pattern and color.

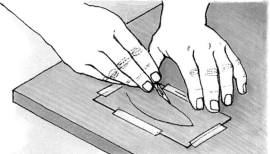

1 Cutting a patch

Tape the piece of veneer over the blemish, aligning the grain, and trace a boat-shape patch with a sharp knife. Cut through both layers, down to the groundwork.

2 Removing the waste

Lay the patch aside and cut out the waste with a wood chisel to reveal the groundwork. Scrape the groundwork clean, then glue and clamp the patch in place.

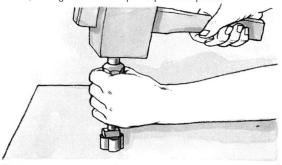

Using a veneer punch

Special punches, with wavy cutting edges, are made for stamping patches out of thin sheets of veneer. Holding the punch upright, give it one firm blow with a mallet to cut an irregular-shape patch from your chosen veneer. Place the punch over the flaw and cut out an identical recess for the patch.

Repairing chipped veneer

Unless the edge of a veneered panel is lipped with solid wood, the unprotected veneer is very vulnerable. If you accidentally chip the edge, repair it immediately with glue before the sliver of veneer gets swept away. If you are restoring old veneer, insert a patch to disguise the damage.

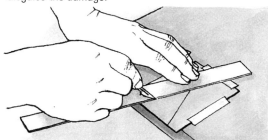

1 Trimming the veneer

Tape down a small piece of veneer so that it just overhangs the chipped edge, and cut a V-shape patch through both layers. Make sure you don't score the groundwork too deeply.

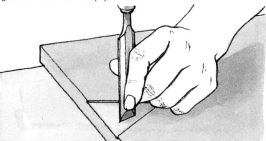

2 Paring down to the groundwork

Carefully pare out waste, and scrape the groundwork with a wood chisel to leave a clean recess. Tape the glued patch in place and clamp it down, using a layer of polythene to prevent the softening block from sticking to the work.

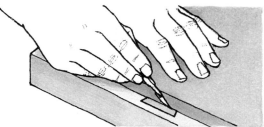

3 Trimming the overlap

When the glue has set, turn the work face-down and trim the patch flush with the edge of the panel. Sand the top surface and touch in the grain as required (see page 13).

ABRASIVES

The surfaces of wood must be brought to as near-perfect a finish as possible before beginning to apply varnish, lacquer or any other clear coating. Rubbing wood smooth with abrasives is the usual way of getting the desired result, and woodworkers are today presented with an enormous range of products to achieve their aims.

Not only is the wood itself smoothed with abrasives, but each coat of finish is also rubbed over lightly, to remove specks of dust and other debris that become embedded as the finish sets.

Although sandpaper as such is no longer manufactured, the term is still used to describe all forms of abrasive, and we still 'sand' wood by hand and with power tools. Most abrasives are now manufactured using synthetic materials that are far superior to the sandpaper of old.

The structure of modern abrasives

An abrasive for woodworking is made by gluing irregular particles of natural or synthetic grit to a backing sheet, usually of paper or cloth. The efficiency, or the rate at which the abrasive wears away the wood, depends on several factors: the size of the particles and the ability of the material to retain its cutting edges; the degree to which the sandpaper can resist clogging with wood dust and sticky resins; and the quality of the bond between grit and backing, without which the particles become detached and are swept away.

Abrasive materials

You can choose from a number of abrasive grits, depending on their relative costs and the nature of the material you are finishing.

Crushed glass is used to make inexpensive abrasive paper, intended primarily for sanding softwood that is to be painted. When compared with other abrasives, glass is fairly soft and wears rapidly. Glasspaper can be recognized easily by its sand-like color.

Garnet is a natural mineral which, when crushed, produces relatively hard particles with sharp cutting edges. It has the added advantage that the grains tend to fracture before they become dull, presenting fresh cutting edges – in effect, they are self-sharpening. Reddish-brown garnet paper is used by cabinetmakers for sanding softwoods and hardwoods.

1

2

7

6

SELF-LUBRICATING
SILICON CARBIDE

SILICON CARBIDE

GARNET

16

Aluminium oxide is used to manufacture a great many abrasive products for sanding by hand and with power tools. Available in a number of different colors, aluminium oxide is especially suitable for sanding dense hardwoods to a fine finish.

Silicon carbide is the hardest and most expensive woodworking abrasive. It is an excellent material for sanding hardwoods, MDF and chipboard, but it is most often used for manufacturing abrasive paper and cloth for rubbing down between coats of varnish and paint. Water is used as a lubricant when smoothing finishes with black to dark-grey 'wet-and-dry' paper. A pale-grey, self-lubricating paper is available for rubbing down finishes that would be harmed by water.

ALUMINIUM-OXIDE

1 Paper- or cloth-backed rolls
Economical and ideal for sanding turned legs and spindles.

2 Slashed cloths
They can be crumpled in the hand and applied to work on the lathe.

3 Velour-backed strips
Peel-off strips for sanding blocks and power sanders.

3

4

CRUSHED GLASS

5

Backing

The backing is basically nothing more than a vehicle that carries the grit to the work. Nevertheless, the choice of backing material can be crucial to the performance of the abrasive.

Paper is the cheapest backing material used in the manufacture of woodworking abrasives. It is available in a range of thicknesses or 'weights' – flexible lightweight papers are ideal for sanding by hand, although medium-weight backing is perhaps better for wrapping round a sanding block. Thicker papers are used with power sanders. Paper backings are designated by letter, according to their thickness or flexibility, ranging from A, the lightest, to F.

Cloth or woven-textile backings provide very tough and durable, yet flexible, abrasive products. You can crease a good cloth backing without it cracking, splitting or shedding its grit. Cloth makes ideal belts for power sanders and strips for smoothing turned spindles.

Non-woven nylon-fibre pads, impregnated with aluminium-oxide or silicon-carbide grains, are ideal for rubbing down finishes and for applying wax polish and oil. The large cavities within the pad will not become clogged, and it can be washed out under running water. The abrasive coating extends throughout the thickness of a pad so that, as the fibres get worn away, fresh abrasive is exposed. Abrasive belts, rolls and discs are all made with nylon-fibre backing.

Nylon fibre is frequently used for stripping old finishes (see page 33), and, because it does not rust, it is ideal for applying water-based products. Nylon-fibre pads are safe to use on oak, which is prone to staining when minute particles from steel wool get caught in its open grain.

Non-abrasive polishing pads make excellent applicators for wood dyes, oils and wax polishes.

Foamed plastic is used as a secondary backing when you need to spread even pressure over a contoured surface. You can buy paper-backed silicon-carbide glued to thin sponges, for rubbing down varnished moldings, turned legs or spindles.

4 Foam-backed pads
Flexible pads follow the contours of a workpiece.

5 Non-woven pads
Nylon fibre impregnated with abrasive material.

6 Standard-size sheets
Sandpaper or cloth sheets measure 280 x 230mm (11 x 9in).

7 Flexible-foam pads
Ideal for sanding moldings.

Bond

The bond, or method of gluing abrasives to the backing, is vital, both in ensuring that the grit stays put, and because it affects the characteristics of sandpaper.

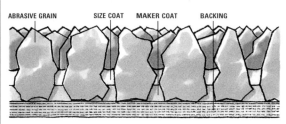

ABRASIVE GRAIN   SIZE COAT   MAKER COAT   BACKING

As the abrasive particles are embedded in the first, or maker, coat of adhesive, an electrostatic charge orientates each grain so that it stands perpendicular to the backing, with its sharp cutting edges uppermost. A second layer of adhesive, known as the size coat, is sprayed onto the abrasive to anchor the grains and provide lateral support.

Animal glue, which softens with heat generated by sanding, is used when flexibility is a requirement. Resin, on the other hand, is heat-resistant, making it ideal for power sanding. Because it is waterproof, resin is also used for the manufacture of wet-and-dry papers. A combination of adhesives modifies the properties of a paper. Resin over glue, for example, would make a relatively heat-resistant paper that would be more flexible than a resin-over-resin combination.

Additives

A third coating of stearate, a powdered soap, packs the spaces between the grains, presenting a finer abrasive surface to the work and reducing premature clogging with wood dust. Stearate, and other chemical additives, act as dry lubricants for abrasives used for rubbing down coats of hard finish.

Antistatic additives in the size coat reduce clogging dramatically and increase the efficiency of dust extractors. This leads to a decrease in dust deposits on the work, surrounding surfaces and power tools – a distinct advantage when you may have to sand work-pieces and apply finishes in the same workshop.

Storing abrasives

Wrap sandpaper or cloth in plastic to protect it from damp or humid conditions. Store sheets flat, and don't let the abrasive surfaces rub together.

GRADING SANDPAPER

Sandpapers are graded according to particle size, and are categorized as extra-fine, fine, medium, coarse or extra-coarse. For most purposes, these classifications are adequate but, should you want to work through a series of precisely graded abrasives, each category is subdivided by number. There are several different grading systems in operation, none of which make for exact comparison. However, as the chart below demonstrates, you can safely assume that the higher the number, the finer the grit.

Sandpaper grades		
Extra-coarse	50	1
	60	½
Coarse	80	0
	100	2/0
Medium	120	3/0
	150	4/0
	180	5/0
Fine	220	6/0
	240	7/0
	280	8/0
Extra-fine	320	9/0
	360	-
	400	-
	500	-
	600	-

Closed or open coat

Sandpapers are also categorized according to the density of grit. A closed-coat sandpaper, with densely packed abrasive grains, cuts relatively quickly, as it has a great many cutting edges for a given area. An open-coat sandpaper has larger spaces between the grains, which reduces clogging and is more suitable for resinous softwoods.

SANDING BY HAND

Most woodworkers resort to power sanding in the early stages of preparing a workpiece, but it is usually necessary to finish by hand, especially if the work includes moldings. You can, of course, do the whole thing by hand – it just takes longer.

Always sand parallel to the grain, working from coarser to finer grits so that each application removes the scratches left by the previous paper or cloth. Stroking abrasives across the grain leaves scratches that are difficult to remove.

You will find it easier to sand most components before assembly, but take care not to round over the shoulders of a joint or create a slack fit by removing too much wood. Restoring old furniture presents additional problems of sanding up to corners and of possibly sanding cross grain where one component meets another.

Sanding flat surfaces
Stand beside the bench so that you can rub a sanding block in straight strokes, parallel with the grain; sweeping your arm in an arc tends to leave cross-grain scratches. Work at a steady pace, letting the abrasive do the work. It pays to change the paper frequently, rather than tiring yourself by rubbing harder to achieve the same ends.

Cover the surface evenly, keeping the block flat on the wood at all times, especially as you approach the edges of the work, or you may inadvertently round over sharp corners.

Sanding end grain
Before sanding, stroke end grain with your fingers to determine the direction of fibre growth. It will feel smoother in one direction than the other; to achieve the best finish, sand in the smoothest direction.

SANDING BLOCKS
It is much easier to sand a flat surface evenly if you wrap a piece of abrasive paper around a sanding block. You can make your own from an offcut of wood with a piece of cork tile glued to the underside, but this is hardly worth the trouble when factory-made cork or rubber sanding blocks are so cheap.

Most blocks are designed to be wrapped with a piece of sandpaper torn from a standard sheet, but you can buy sanding blocks that take ready-cut self-adhesive or velour-backed strips of abrasive that are peeled off when they need replacing. Double-sided blocks are made with firm plastic foam on one side, for sanding flat surfaces, and a softer sponge on the reverse, for moldings and curved profiles.

Velcro-lined foam plastic   **Double-sided**   **Cork**   **Rubber**

Tearing sandpaper
Fold a sheet of sandpaper over the edge of a bench, and tear it into strips that fit your sanding block. Wrap a piece of the paper around the sole of the block, gripping the sides with fingers and thumb.

Sanding small items
It is impossible to clamp and sand small items using conventional methods. Instead, glue a sheet of sandpaper face-up on a flat board and rub the workpiece across the abrasive.

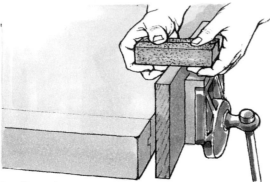

Sanding edges

It is even more difficult to retain sharp corners when sanding narrow edges. To keep the block level, clamp the work upright in a vise and, holding the block at each end, run your fingertips along each side of the work as you rub the abrasive back and forth. Finally, stroke the block lightly along the corner to remove the arris and prevent splinters.

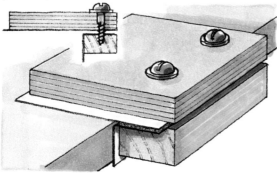

Making an edge-sanding block

It is especially important to sand edges accurately when working on edge-veneered boards. Screw together two pieces of wood to make an edge-sanding block, trapping two pieces of sandpaper face-to-face between them. Fold back one piece of paper to form a right angle. Rub the block along the edge of the work, simultaneously sanding both adjacent surfaces.

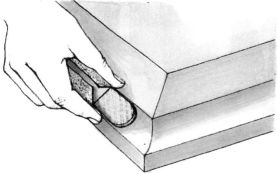

Sanding moldings

Wrap sandpaper around a shaped block or dowel when sanding moldings. Alternatively, use foam-backed paper or an impregnated nylon-fibre pad.

SANDING SEQUENCE

Every woodworker develops his or her preferred sequence for preparing a workpiece for finishing, but the following will serve as a guide to suitable grades of abrasive to achieve the result. You may need to experiment and modify the sequence when dealing with different woods. Sanding a close-grain hardwood with an extra-fine abrasive, for example, tends to burnish the surface, making it more difficult to apply wood dye subsequently.

Start with 120 grit aluminium-oxide or garnet paper followed by 180 grit, until the surface appears smooth and free from tool marks and similar blemishes. You only need to resort to anything as coarse as 80 to 100 grit if the wood is not already planed to a reasonably smooth surface.

Remove the dust between sandings, using a tack rag – a sticky cloth designed for picking up dust and fine debris. If you fail to keep the work clean, abrasive particles shed during the previous sanding may leave relatively deep scratches in the surface.

Sand again for no more than 30 to 60 seconds, using 220 grit, then raise the grain by wiping the surface with a damp cloth. Wait for 10 to 20 minutes, by which time the moisture will have caused the minute wood fibres to expand and stand proud of the surface. Lightly skim the surface with a fresh piece of 220 abrasive to remove these 'whiskers', leaving a perfectly smooth surface. It is particularly important to raise grain before applying water-based products.

At this stage, you can safely apply a surface finish, but if you feel the workpiece demands an extra-special finish, raise the grain once more and rub down very lightly, using 320 grit paper or an impregnated nylon-fibre pad.

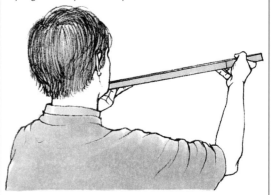

Checking a sanded surface

Inspect the workpiece against the light at a shallow angle, to check that the surface is sanded evenly and that you have removed all obvious scratches.

POWER SANDING

Nowadays, portable sanding machines relieve the woodworker from the tiresome chore of sanding for long periods, but even orbital sanders are apt to leave tiny whorls or scratches on the wood that show up only after the first coat of finish is applied. As a safeguard, raise the grain with a damp cloth after you have finished power sanding, and rub over lightly by hand, using a fine abrasive paper or nylon-fibre pad.

Belt sander

Belt sanders
These are heavy-duty power sanders that are capable of reducing even sawn timber to a smooth finish. As a result, they remove a great deal of wood very quickly, and have to be carefully controlled to avoid rounding over the edges of a workpiece or wearing through a layer of veneer. Special accessories that frame the sanding bed are helpful in preventing the tool from tilting, especially as you approach the edge of a panel. Belt sanding creates a great deal of dust, so fit a collecting bag or use an extractor (see page 24).

Sanding belts
Cloth- and paper-backed belts are made for the average 60 to 100mm (2⅜ to 4in) wide sanders. They are held taut between two rollers, the front one being adjustable to control tension and tracking. Operating a lever releases the tension so that you can change a belt; once the sander is running, adjust a small knob to center the belt on the rollers. Use medium-to-fine abrasive belts for most applications.

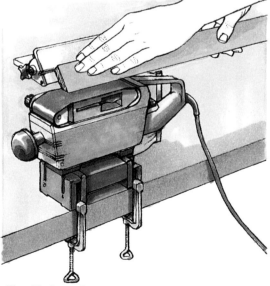

Using a belt sander
There are few occasions when you would need a belt sander for fine woodwork, but it is useful for smoothing large baulks of timber or some man-made boards. Switch on and gradually lower the sander onto the work. As soon as you make contact, move the sander forward – allowing the tool to remain stationary or dropping it heavily onto the surface will score the wood deeply. Sand in the direction of the grain only, keeping the tool moving and using parallel overlapping strokes. Lift the sander off the work before switching off.

Fixed belt sanders
Using a purpose-made clamp, you can attach a portable belt sander upside-down on a bench, allowing you to sand small components by applying them to the moving belt. You can use a fence to guide the work, and you can shape curved workpieces over the end roller.

Orbital sanders

Provided you work through a series of progressively finer abrasives (see page 20) and take the trouble to raise the grain before the final light sanding, an orbital sander will produce a surface that, to all intents and purposes, is ready for finishing. Before applying a clear finish, however, always inspect the surface carefully to make sure there are no swirling scratches caused by the elliptical motion of the base plate. Some orbital sanders can be switched to a straight reciprocal stroke to eliminate this possibility.

Orbital sander

Palm-grip sander

Palm-grip sanders

The majority of orbital sanders are designed to be held in both hands, but lightweight, palm-grip sanders are also available.

Sanding sheets

Strips of sandpaper are made specifically for use with orbital sanders. Designated as half, third and quarter sheets, their proportions are based on the standard-size sheets made for hand-sanding (see page 17). They are held in place by a wire clamp at each end of the sander's base plate; alternatively, strips are velour-lined or self-adhesive for easy replacement. To preserve your health and reduce clogging, choose a sander that incorporates dust extraction; the base plate and sandpaper are both perforated so that dust is sucked directly from beneath the tool into a collecting bag or vacuum cleaner (see page 24).

Perforating sandpaper

Ready-made sheets are very convenient, but you can make considerable cost savings by perforating plain sandpaper strips or rolls. Using a soft pencil and white paper, make a rubbing of the perforations in your sander's base plate. Use it as a pattern for drilling matching holes in a piece of MDF, and glue into them short lengths of pointed dowel rod.

Attach a strip of abrasive to the base plate, and then press your sander down onto your perforator to pierce the sandpaper.

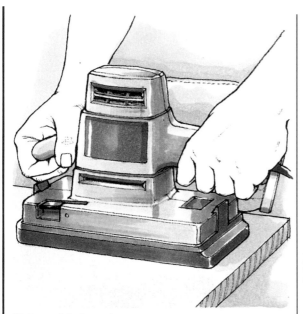

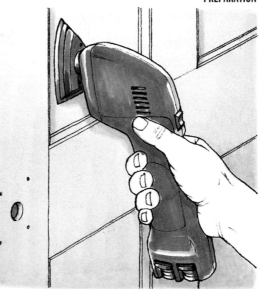

Using orbital sanders

Don't apply excessive pressure to an orbital sander, as this tends to overheat the abrasive, causing dust and resin to clog the grit prematurely. A sensation of pins and needles in your fingers after prolonged sanding indicates that you are pressing too hard.

Keep the tool moving back and forth with the grain, covering the surface as evenly as possible. If you are using a variable-speed sander, select the slowest rate for coarser grits and gradually increase the speed as you progress with finer abrasives.

Cordless sanders

There are obvious advantages to be gained from using a battery-powered sander: there's no electrical flex to get caught up on the workpiece, and you can work outside if you wish, completely independent of a mains supply. However, only a few cordless sanders are currently available.

RANDOM-ORBITAL SANDERS

The combined rotational and eccentric motions of a random-orbital sander practically eliminate discernible scratches on a wood surface. The circular base plate takes sanding discs, along with the usual options – Velcro or self-adhesive attachment, and perforations for dust extraction. Some sanders can cope with flat and curved surfaces, while others have interchangeable base plates so that you can increase the sanding area for working on large boards or panels. The only disadvantage is that you cannot sand into corners (see left).

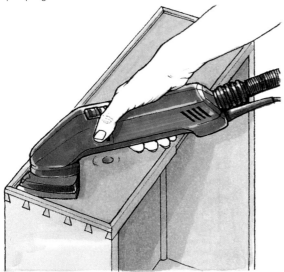

Sanding into corners

With a well-designed orbital sander, it should be possible to sand into right angles and up to the ends of fixed rails or panels. However, for really tight corners and cross-grain miters, use a delta sander, which has a triangular base plate.

Disc sanders

With the exception of bench-mounted machines, cabinetmakers seldom use disc sanders, which can score deep scratches in the wood. However, wood-turners employ the combined actions of disc sander and lathe to their advantage for sanding bowls and platters.

Flexible-shaft sanders and discs

Arbor-mounted foam pads, from 25 to 75mm (1 to 3in) in diameter, are made for use in portable power drills or, better still, highly manoeuvrable, flexible-shaft sanders. Velour-lined or self-adhesive abrasive discs, with cloth or paper backing, come ready-made to fit every size of foam pad.

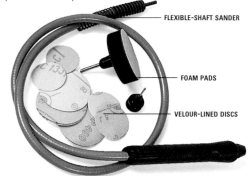

FLEXIBLE-SHAFT SANDER

FOAM PADS

VELOUR-LINED DISCS

Advantages for woodturners

Miniature disc sanders are ideal for intricate woodwork such as carving or modelmaking, but they are especially suited to woodturners, because the soft-foam pads conform to the changing contours of a wooden bowl or vase, ensuring an even distribution of pressure without generating too much heat. More importantly, since both the disc and workpiece rotate simultaneously, you can remove tool marks rapidly without scratching the wood.

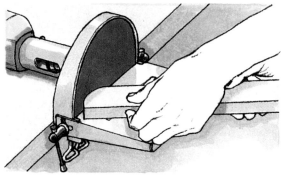

Bench-mounted sanders

A relatively large-diameter metal disc sander, mounted rigidly to the bench, is perfect for finishing end grain. Using coarse to fine grits, you can also shape work-pieces with a disc sander. Keep the workpiece moving, and press the end grain lightly against the downward-rotating side of the disc. Applying excessive pressure invariably scorches the wood.

PROTECTING YOURSELF FROM DUST

Power sanders are not especially dangerous, provided they are used with care. However, the dust generated by sanding can be very injurious to health, and may also constitute a fire hazard.

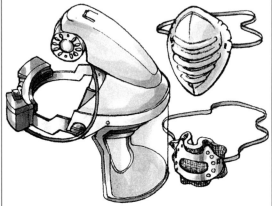

Face masks and helmets

At the very least, make sure you wear a face mask to cover your nose and mouth when sanding. Cheap disposable masks are available from any tool store, and are usually supplied as part of the kit when you hire power sanders.

A battery-powered respirator, built into a light-weight helmet, offers the ultimate protection. A stream of filtered air, blown behind the transparent face screen, prevents you breathing airborne dust.

Dust extractors

Good-quality power sanders are fitted with an extractor port that discharges dust into a bag, for disposal after work or when the bag is full. For greater efficiency, attach a sander to an industrial vacuum cleaner that sucks the dust directly from the work surface. A purpose-made extractor is activated as you switch on the sander.

SCRAPING WOOD

Even though sanding is the most-used method for smoothing timber, scraping the surface, which removes minute shavings instead of dust particles, produces a superior finish. Because a scraper can take such a fine cut, you can use it on areas of wild grain that are difficult to plane well.

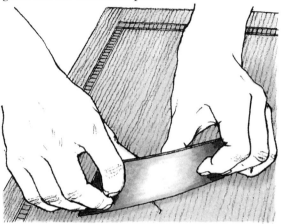

Controlling a cabinet scraper
Holding the scraper in both hands, lean it away from you and push the tool forwards. Bending a scraper, by pressing with your thumbs near the bottom edge, concentrates the forces in a narrow band, so that you can scrape small blemishes from the wood. By experimenting with different curvatures and angles, you can vary the action and cutting depth to suit the particular task.

Levelling wood panels
To scrape a panel flat and level, work in two directions at a slight angle to the general direction of grain. To finish, smooth the wood by scraping parallel with the grain. Use a similar method when scraping out small patches of dried glue or scorching, to avoid leaving a deep hollow.

Cabinet scrapers
The standard cabinet scraper is nothing more than a small rectangle of tempered steel. For shaped surfaces and moldings, you need a scraper with a pair of curved edges, or a goose-neck scraper that is shaped to accommodate a great many convex and concave radii. Before using a scraper, you must prepare and sharpen its cutting edges.

1 Filing a scraper
Clamp the scraper in a bench vise and draw-file its two long edges to make them perfectly square. To prevent the file rocking, steady it by running your fingertips against each face of the scraper.

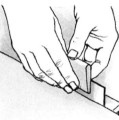

2 Honing the scraper
Filing leaves rough edges that must be rubbed down with an oiled slipstone. Keep the stone flat on the faces of the scraper, and rub it along both sides of each cutting edge.

3 Raising a burr
Stretch the metal along both cutting edges with a smooth metal burnisher. If you can't get the proper tool, use the curved back of a gouge. Holding the scraper on the bench top, strop each edge firmly four or five times, drawing the burnisher towards you while keeping it flat on the scraper.

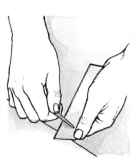

4 Turning the burr
For the scraper to function, the raised burrs must be folded over at right angles. Holding the burnisher at a slight angle to the burred edge, draw the tool firmly along the scraper two or three times.

FILLING AND SEALING GRAIN

An open-grain timber, such as oak or ash, looks good when coated with a satin varnish or oil, but when French polish or gloss varnish sinks into each pore, the result is a speckled, pitted surface that detracts from the quality of the finish.

Perhaps the ideal solution is to apply coat after coat of the finish itself, rubbing down between applications until the pores are filled flush, but this is a slow, laborious process, which is why the majority of woodworkers opt for a ready-mixed grain filler. Most general-purpose fillers are thick wood-color pastes. Choose a color that closely resembles the species you are finishing, always erring on the darker side when a perfect match is impossible.

1 Applying grain filler
Make sure the surface is completely clean and dust-free. Dip a pad of coarse burlap into the grain filler and rub it vigorously into the wood, using over-lapping circular strokes.

2 Removing excess filler
Before the paste dries completely, wipe across the grain with clean burlap to remove excess filler from the surface. Use a pointed stick to remove paste embedded in moldings or carving.

3 Rubbing down
Leave the grain filler to dry thoroughly overnight, then sand lightly in the direction of the grain, using 220 grit, self-lubricating silicon-carbide paper. Rub down moldings or turned pieces with an abrasive nylon-fibre pad.

Filling stained timber
It is debatable whether it is better to color the wood before or after grain filling. To fill first may result in patchy, uneven color, but if you apply filler over stained timber, there is the possibility that you may wear through the color when sanding at a later stage. One solution is to stain the timber first, then protect it with sanding sealer, or two coats of transparent French polish, before applying a grain filler mixed with some of the same compatible wood dye.

SANDING SEALER

Sealing serves more than one purpose. On porous woods it prevents the finish being absorbed, just as a primer does for paint, and can be used as the first base coat for French polish. Perhaps most important of all, shellac-based sanding sealer makes an excellent barrier coat, preventing wood stains being re-dissolved and also sealing in contaminants, such as silicone oil, that affect the setting of the final finish. For this reason, it often makes sense to seal old furniture that has been stripped prior to refinishing (see page 33). However, since sanding sealer prevents some varnishes from setting satisfactorily, check the manufacturer's instructions before starting.

Applying sanding sealer
Sand the work well and pick up the dust with a tack rag. Brush sanding sealer onto the wood and leave it to dry for an hour or two. Rub the surface with fine sandpaper, an abrasive pad, or 0000-grade steel wool before applying your chosen finish. You may need a second sealing coat on very porous timber.

CHAPTER 2 Most experts agree that when it comes to restoring nicely aged wood finishes, it is best to do as little as possible, erring on the side of preservation rather than renewal. The subtle shading of color and tone – the patina of antique finishes – is all too easily lost, yet is extremely difficult to replicate.

REPAIRING FINISHES

CLEANING OLD FINISHES

Over a prolonged period of use, a piece of furniture or a wooden utensil gradually collects a layer of dirty wax polish or oil that masks the color and grain pattern. Just as we become used to the appearance of a painting obscured by discolored varnish, it may be hard to imagine how a finish may once have looked and how much of an improvement can be made. However, it is safe to say that most old pieces benefit from cleaning and, in some cases, this is all that is required to restore the quality of a finish.

Cleaning fluids
There are a number of preparations on the market that dissolve accumulated layers of grime, but ordinary mineral spirit is perfectly adequate.

1 Applying cleaning fluid
Dip a pad of burlap or 000-grade steel wool into the fluid, and rub the dirty wood in the direction of the grain. A liquid slurry of cleaner and dissolved wax forms on the surface; wipe it off with a clean cloth pad or paper towel before it congeals.

2 Cleaning moldings
Use steel wool or an abrasive nylon pad to clean out crevices, corners and moldings where wax and dirt tend to collect most thickly. Don't rub too hard in case you should wear through the finish on high points. Finally, clean all surfaces with a soft cloth or a non-abrasive polishing pad (see page 17) dipped in mineral spirit.

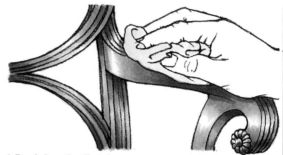

3 Reviving the finish
The combined action of mineral spirit and abrasives leaves the original finish looking clean but lacking vitality. You can buy proprietary creams and emulsions to burnish the surface, or use any liquid abrasive, such as metal polish or car-paint cleaner. Pour some onto a soft-cloth pad and rub the matt surface vigorously to restore its glossy finish, then apply a light dressing of wax polish.

Don't use a burnishing cream or liquid if you have stripped a wax finish down to the bare wood.

PATCHING THE FINISH
Burnishing alone may not be sufficient to restore badly worn or scuffed areas of a finish. Whatever the finish, it is possible to use wax polish to restore the color locally but, if there are very thin patches that need rebuilding, you need to identify the original polish or varnish.

Identifying the finish
Any piece made around the turn of the century is probably French-polished; check by rubbing an inconspicuous area with a white cloth dampened with alcohol, wrapped round your fingers. French polish will stain the cloth brown, but if you are picking up nothing but surface dust make a similar test for cellulose lacquer using the appropriate thinner. Cellulose thinner will also dissolve acrylic varnishes but, since these finishes were not available until quite recently, the age of the piece should give you a clue. Most modern varnishes are completely insoluble in anything other than a purpose-made chemical stripper.

REMOVING SCRATCHES

You would be hard-pressed to find a piece of furniture that has seen years of service without getting scratched to some degree, and most of the time we are content to ignore this type of superficial damage. However, it's a different story when you accidentally drag a sharp object across a newly polished surface. Only an expert can hope to make scratches invisible, but there are ways to render them less conspicuous, depending on the severity of the damage. Treat deep scratches individually, filling them flush with wax or some of the original finish. On the other hand, it's better to burnish out minor scratches or blend them into the background color.

Filling with wax sticks
Sets of colored-wax sticks are sold for filling relatively deep scratches. Rub the sharp edge of a stick across the scratch until it is filled flush, adjusting the color with other sticks until you achieve a close match. If your workshop is cold, warm the sticks very slightly before using them. Smooth the deposit and wipe excess wax from the surface with a soft cloth, then cover the repair with a light dressing of wax polish.

Burnishing a scratched surface
Burnish out fine scratches with an abrasive reviver (see page 28). Don't persist for too long; it is better to disguise scratches rather than risk wearing through the polish in an attempt to eradicate them altogether.

Disguising hairline scratches
Surface scratches are pale in color, and tend to stand out more than blemishes that are darker in tone. Conceal a mass of fine scratches by rubbing over the damaged area with a proprietary scratch cover, a liquid blend of waxes and coloring agents.

Retouching scratches
Touch in individual scratches with a special felt-tip pen filled with wood dye. Ten minutes later, you can dress the surface with a coat of shellac or wax polish.

ADDING SHELLAC POLISH OR VARNISH
Professional restorers melt stick shellac (see page 11) into deep scratches, but it takes practice to avoid overfilling and perhaps creating a repair that is larger than the original flaw. A slower but more controllable process is to fill the scratch with ordinary shellac polish (see pages 52–3) that has been poured into a shallow dish and left exposed to the air to thicken slightly. Employ a similar technique, using varnish straight from the can to repair a modern finish.

Filling with shellac polish
Using a fine artist's paintbrush, run some thickened polish along the scratch and let it set. If necessary, add more polish until it just stands proud of the surface, then leave it to harden thoroughly. Wrap fine self-lubricating silicon-carbide paper around a very small cork block, and use it to sand the repair flush. Burnish the surface with a liquid finish reviver (see opposite) or wax polish.

ERADICATING STAINS

Disfiguring stains, in the form of white rings or dark patches, are often found on old tables and sideboards. They are invariably caused by water or alcohol being left to etch the surface of the finish, most usually French polish. Very little water or alcohol is required to do the damage. Ring stains are typically the result of moisture trapped beneath a flower vase or tumbler. A mug of coffee or a hot plate will have a similar effect, but this damage usually goes deeper.

In every case, the problem is soluble without having to refinish the piece, provided the moisture has not penetrated to the wood itself and left a dark patch. Your only solution then is to strip the finish and bleach out the stain.

Smearing with petroleum jelly
Smear a white patch liberally with petroleum jelly and leave it to soak in for 24 hours. Wipe off excess jelly with a soft cloth and, provided the damage was not too severe, the stain will have disappeared.

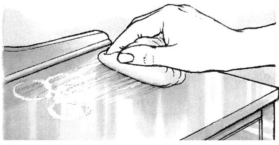

Wiping with alcohol
Since French polish is soluble in denatured alcohol, it is sometimes possible to 'pull over' a white stain. Moisten a soft cloth pad with alcohol (see page 57) and wipe it lightly across the stain. Make sure the cloth is never more than damp, or there is a very real risk of spoiling the finish. Leave the alcohol to evaporate, then repeat the treatment until the stain disappears.

Burnishing stains
Whatever the finish, you can burnish out white rings with a proprietary finish reviver, liquid metal polish, or car-paint cleaner on a pad of soft cloth. Having removed the stain, burnish the rest of the surface lightly to an even finish, then dress it with a coat of wax or French polish.

BLEACHING STAINS

Crazing or hairline cracks allow moisture to seep below the finish, where it stains the wood, forming dark irregular patches. Your only recourse in this situation is to strip the finish from the surface (see pages 32–5) and bleach out the stain with a solution of oxalic acid. Specialist wood-finishing suppliers stock oxalic-acid crystals, or you may be able to buy them from your local pharmacist. Oxalic acid is extremely toxic and must be stored out of the reach of children.

Ventilate the workspace when mixing and using wood bleaches, and wear protective gloves, goggles, and an apron. Half-fill a glass jar with warm water and gradually add crystals, stirring with a wooden spatula until no more will dissolve. Never pour water onto oxalic-acid crystals.

Applying the bleach
Leave the solution to stand for about 10 minutes, then paint it onto the stain, using a white-fibre or nylon brush. Let the wood dry, then apply more bleach if the stain persists. Finally wash the wood with water and leave it to dry thoroughly. Wearing a face mask, sand the raised grain with fine abrasive paper. Dispose of any remaining solution safely.

STRIPPING FINISHES

Purists would argue that you should never strip an old finish, because the color and general patina of the original polish add greatly to the value of antique furniture. In principle, this is good advice, and it would certainly be counterproductive to refinish a valuable table or cabinet simply to brighten it up, but there are circumstances that leave you with few alternatives.

Fire or water damage, for example, can be so severe that the original finish is irretrievably damaged, so you lose nothing by stripping it. Also, you will have to remove a finish if you need to bleach out small stains, but in this case strip just enough polish to make the repair and the refinishing as straightforward as possible.

Remember that not all old furniture is valuable, and that stripping and refinishing may make it more serviceable. Similarly, built-in cupboards may benefit from stripping if you are to make a decent job of redecorating.

Having decided that stripping is appropriate, there are a number of alternative methods and materials to consider. Your final decision will rest on factors such as the type of finish to be removed, the size and quality of the workpiece and, to some extent, cost and convenience.

1 Panelled doors
Painted cupboard doors can usually be stripped safely in a chemical dip (see page 34), but a hot-caustic dip may split thin panels.

2 Solid-wood chairs
Another potential candidate for industrial stripping, especially as having to strip by hand a number of chairs with turned legs and spindles is time consuming.

3 Bentwood chairs
A hot-caustic dip may distort bentwood furniture. If you don't want to remove the finish by hand, have these items stripped in a cold-chemical or warm-alkali dip.

4 Carved woodwork
Industrial stripping is safe for most solid-wood items, but sanding raised grain from carved wood is a real chore. It may be better to strip these items yourself with a chemical paint or varnish remover (see pages 32-3).

5 Antique woodwork
It is always best to strip antiques by hand. This allows you the option of removing just some of the finish to undertake a repair (see page 34).

6 Veneered pieces
Hot caustic soda can lift veneers off the groundwork. It would be unwise to use any industrial process unless the company concerned is prepared to guarantee their safety.

CHEMICAL STRIPPERS

Perhaps the most efficient method of removing finishes from any item of woodwork, be it a fine piece of furniture or an old pine door, is to apply a chemical stripper that partially dissolves the varnish, paint or polish, making a thick sludge that you can scrape and wash from the surface. You can strip wax polish with mineral spirit, and small areas of French polish using denatured alcohol (see page 34), but commercially prepared paint and varnish removers are far more potent and will enable you to strip any finish, even if you cannot identify it precisely.

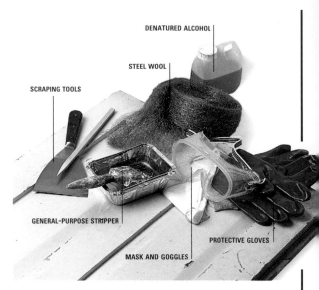

DENATURED ALCOHOL

STEEL WOOL

SCRAPING TOOLS

GENERAL-PURPOSE STRIPPER

PROTECTIVE GLOVES

MASK AND GOGGLES

Commercial paint and varnish removers
An extensive range of products is available, so you should be able to find a stripper that will suit your requirements. Most types of finish remover are available from any hardware store that stocks paints and varnishes.

General-purpose strippers
These are the most commonly available strippers, form-ulated to remove any finish, including water-based paints and varnishes. They are generally fairly corrosive substances and should be handled with care. Since some of them also exude unpleasant fumes, it pays to wear a face mask when using them.

SAFETY PRECAUTIONS
Using chemical strippers is not dangerous, provided you follow sensible precautions and always comply with the printed instructions supplied with each particular stripper.

• Work outdoors or in a well-ventilated workshop.
• Wear a face mask or respirator to protect yourself from harmful fumes.
• Wear protective gloves, goggles and old clothes when handling corrosive strippers.
• Cover the workbench and floor with sheets of polythene or newspaper.
• Check with your local authority on how best to dispose of hazardous waste materials.

Varnish removers
Since a few modern finishes are resistant to general-purpose strippers, some manufacturers also market special strippers that will soften the toughest varnish. They may be even more potent than general-purpose strippers, so follow the maker's handling instructions with care.

Safe strippers
So-called safe strippers, the latest generation of finish removers, do not release harmful fumes and can generally be handled without wearing protective gloves. Allow extra time when working with safe strippers, as the chemicals react relatively slowly with certain finishes.

Liquid and gel strippers
Many finish removers are available in two consistencies, to suit the nature of the workpiece. Thick gel-like strippers cling to any vertical or horizontal surface, and are therefore the best choice for built-in furniture or any workpiece that cannot be laid flat on a bench. A liquid version of the stripper is better able to cope with delicate carvings and moldings, but is more difficult to control.

Spirit- or water-washable
Having removed the softened finish, it is necessary to wash the workpiece to remove all traces of stripper. Water is often recommended by the manufacturer, and is a good choice to avoid an excess of solvent fumes in the workshop. However, to protect marquetry and other delicate veneers from the effects of water, choose a stripper that can be washed off with mineral spirit.

Using chemical strippers

Unless a manufacturer suggests other methods for using a particular chemical stripper, you can assume the following procedures apply to any type of paint or varnish remover. Prepare the workshop, pour some stripper into a shallow dish, and select an old paintbrush to apply it.

1 Applying the stripper

Brush a liberal coat of finish remover onto the workpiece, stippling it into carving and moldings. Some varnishes and paints might be slow to react, but eventually the surface will begin to wrinkle.

After 10 to 15 minutes, check that the finish has softened right through to the wood by scraping a small area. If the lower coats of finish are still intact, apply fresh stripper, stippling the partly softened layers back down again.

2 Scraping off the surface

Leave the stripper to penetrate for another few minutes, then scrape the softened finish from the wood with a wide-blade paint scraper and wipe it onto a thick wad of newspaper. Fold the newspaper to wrap the waste and place it outside to dry, ready for disposal.

3 Cleaning irregular surfaces

Use a shavehook to scrape finish from moldings, then rub along them with fine steel wool to clean out the residue, turning the pad inside out as it becomes clogged. Use an abrasive nylon pad on oak and to wipe softened paint or varnish from turned legs and spindles. Sharpen a short length of dowel to pick solvent and paint from deep carving and tight corners.

4 Washing the workpiece

Clean every speck of finish out of the grain by rubbing the wood with balls of steel wool or a nylon pad dipped in fresh stripper. Wash the workpiece thoroughly with water or mineral spirit, and leave it to dry.

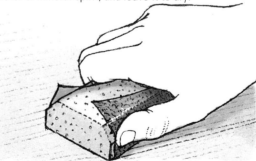

5 Rubbing down and sealing

Sand the wood lightly to remove raised grain (see page 19) and, unless you know the history of the workpiece, apply a sanding sealer (see page 26) to make sure there is no chance of silicone oil contaminating the new finish. If you are afraid sanding sealer might affect the clarity of the finish, seal the wood with a coat of transparent shellac polish.

Stripping small areas

If you need to expose just a small area of wood, perhaps to bleach out a dark stain (see page 30), there is no need to strip the entire piece. To make the job of matching the original finish as easy as possible, strip an area with definable edges, a table top, for example, a drawer front or side panel. Set up the piece so that the area you intend to strip is horizontal, and use a gel-consistency stripper for better control.

If you can identify the finish (see page 28), you may be able to use its solvent to soften and remove it. Being relatively gentle, straightforward solvents enable you to feather the edge of a stripped patch, keeping the area to a bare minimum. However, color matching the finish is likely to be more critical and the liquid nature of solvents makes them difficult to control.

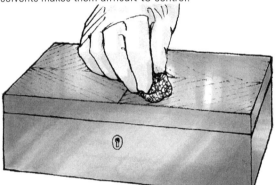

Removing French polish

Pour some denatured alcohol into a shallow dish and dip a small ball of fine steel wool into it. Gently rub away at the finish until it begins to soften, then wipe it off with a cloth pad.

If there is a risk of alcohol running onto adjacent areas of polish, dampen a cloth pad with alcohol and use it to wet the surface, then abrade the polish gently with dry steel wool or an abrasive nylon pad.

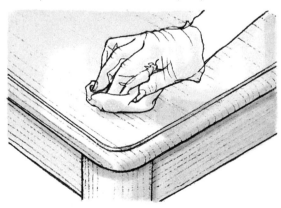

Stripping wax polish

You can use a similar process to remove a patch of wax polish from a workpiece, using mineral spirit.

INDUSTRIAL STRIPPING

To save time and effort, consider having large items stripped professionally. Industrial stripping tanks accommodate most items of furniture and joinery, and many companies will collect them from your house and deliver them after stripping.

Hot caustic dip

The most economical process involves immersing workpieces in hot caustic soda, followed by a thorough hosing with water to wash the chemical out of the wood. This is a most efficient system for removing finishes, but consider carefully the risks involved before you submit old furniture to what, after all, is fairly harsh treatment for items made from wood. Exposure to heat and water causes the wood to expand and contract considerably, often leading to weak joints, warped components and split panels. At the very least, you can expect raised grain and perhaps some staining. Since the same conditions soften animal glues, veneered pieces may blister or even delaminate.

Cold-chemical dip

Some companies operate with a cold-chemical solution that is less harmful for solid-wood items, but is relatively expensive compared with caustic soda. You must expect a certain amount of raised grain, and it would be unwise to have veneered items stripped unless the company will guarantee their safety.

Warm-alkali dip

You can have pieces dipped for a few minutes only in a warm-alkali solution. This is a carefully controlled process that is safe for all man-made boards, including plywood, but you should still ask for advice before having old veneered furniture stripped.

HOT-AIR STRIPPERS

You can strip oil-based finishes by heating them until they are soft enough to be scraped from the wood. Using a traditional gas torch is a little risky because, until you get used to handling the tool, it is fairly easy to scorch the wood. However, after a little practice, anyone can use an electric hot-air stripper to remove paint from larger items of built-in furniture and joinery. Being lightweight, a modern stripper, which can be fitted with various nozzles to direct the heat, is easy to control and use for long periods.

1 Softening the finish
Holding the nozzle of the stripper about 50mm (2in) from the surface of the workpiece, squeeze the trigger and move the tool slowly from side to side until the paint begins to blister and lift off the wood.

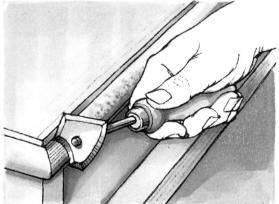

2 Scraping off softened paint
As soon as the finish softens, switch off the stripper and lift the paint from the wood, using a decorator's scraper. Use a shavehook to scrape softened paint from moldings, taking care not to gouge the wood with the blade points.

3 Cleaning the surface
It may prove impossible to scrape every speck of paint from the pores of an open-grain timber. This doesn't matter if you plan to repaint the piece; simply fill any blemishes, sand the wood lightly and apply a primer. If you want to apply a clear finish, clean out the grain with steel wool or an abrasive nylon pad dipped in chemical paint stripper, then wash and seal the wood (see page 33).

MECHANICAL STRIPPING
Because you have to sand the wood in any case, removing a finish with a power sander would appear to be a viable option. However, it is practically impossible to avoid sanding away some of the wood, the dust created is particularly hazardous, and all but fairly coarse abrasives clog almost immediately. In addition, you still have to sand anything but flat surfaces by hand.

A cabinet scraper creates less dust and is more controllable, but even so scraping a finish from a large item would be somewhat laborious. A scraper comes into its own when you need to remove just a small patch of finish to repair the wood beneath, especially if there are adjacent areas that you want to protect from moisture, heat, or chemical strippers.

DEALING WITH INFESTATION

There is no point in refinishing an old piece of furniture that is infested with wood-boring insects until they have been eradicated. The furniture beetle, better known as woodworm, is not a common pest in all areas of the country, but the thriving market in used furniture means that a wormed piece can crop up just about anywhere.

The damage is the result of the insect larvae burrowing deeply into the wood for a period of three to four years. However, the first signs of infestation are usually a few round flight holes in the surface of the wood where the adult beetles emerged, prior to laying their eggs elsewhere.

Checking the extent of infestation
Most outbreaks of woodworm are treatable, provided the wood is still structurally sound. Use the point of a knife blade to probe the wood in the vicinity of obvious infestation; if the wood crumbles under pressure, that component will have to be repaired or even replaced. If the wood appears to be firm, treat it with a chemical preservative, formulated to kill any remaining larvae and prevent future infestation.

DETECTING WOODWORM
Although you may detect flight holes in polished surfaces, the beetle lays its eggs on unfinished wood, so always check those parts for signs of infestation. Take out the drawers, for example, and inspect them all round, including the bottom panels. Similarly check the backs of cabinets and the undersides of tables and sideboards. Pale-colored flight holes and traces of fine wood dust indicate recent infestation.

A used piece of furniture that you have acquired may have been treated for woodworm already. However, if there is any doubt, it pays to treat the piece yourself.

1 Injecting flight holes
The inside of infested wood is probably honeycombed with interconnecting tunnels. Inject a chemical preservative deep into the wood by squirting the fluid into a flight hole every 50mm (2in) or so. Fluid is supplied in cans with pointed nozzles for this purpose, or in aerosol cans fitted with narrow plastic hoses. Always protect your eyes, in case fluid shoots out from another flight hole under pressure.

2 Treating bare wood
Since it is impossible to know how far the larvae have burrowed, pour some fluid into a dish and paint it onto all unfinished surfaces. Preservative smells unpleasant so, if possible, work outside and wear a face mask. Leave the work to dry out, then treat it a second time. After the preservative has dried a second time, you can apply any finish to the wood.

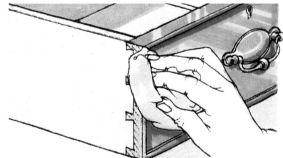

3 Treating polished areas
There is no point in painting preservative onto polished surfaces, since it cannot penetrate the wood. As an extra precaution against future infestation, apply an insecticidal polish to old finished surfaces. Fill flight holes with colored wax sticks (see page 11).

CHAPTER 3 The idea of artificially coloring a piece of wood may seem unnecessary when the various species of timber are so colorful already. However, stains are mostly applied to enhance the natural color of a particular workpiece, or perhaps to unify several similar pieces of wood that vary slightly in their hue or tone.

COLORING WOOD

BLEACHING WOOD

Woodworkers often resort to bleaching in order to obliterate staining. For this, you should use a comparatively mild bleach, such as a solution of oxalic acid (see page 30). However, it may also be desirable to reduce the depth of color of a workpiece, perhaps so that you can stain it to resemble a different species, or maybe to stain several components the same color. To alter the color of timbers drastically, you need a strong proprietary two-part bleach. This is usually sold in kit form, comprising a pair of clearly labelled plastic bottles, one containing an alkali and the other hydrogen peroxide. However, the bottles are invariably labelled A and B, or 1 and 2.

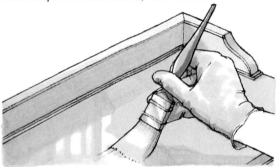

1 Applying solution A
Pour some of the contents of bottle A into a glass or plastic container and, using a white-fibre or nylon brush, wet the workpiece evenly. Don't splash bleach onto adjacent surfaces and, if you have to work on a vertical surface, start at the bottom to avoid runs streaking the surface.

2 Applying solution B
About 5 to 10 minutes later, during which time the wood may darken, take another brush and apply the second solution. The chemical reaction causes foaming on the surface of the wood.

Testing the effectiveness of bleach
Because some woods bleach better than others, it is worth testing a sample before you treat the actual workpiece. As a rough guide, ash, beech, elm and sycamore are easy to bleach, whereas you may have to bleach other woods, such as mahogany, rosewood, oak and padauk, a second time to get the color you want.

3 Neutralizing the bleach
When it is dry, or as soon as the wood is the required color, neutralize the bleach by washing the work with a weak acetic-acid solution, comprising one teaspoon of white vinegar in a pint of water. Put the work aside for about three days, then sand down the raised grain and apply the finish.

SAFETY PRECAUTIONS
Wood bleach is a dangerous substance which must be handled with care and stored in the dark, out of the reach of children.

• Wear protective gloves, goggles and an apron.

• Wear a face mask when sanding wood that has been bleached.

• Ventilate the workshop or work outside.

• Have a supply of water handy so that you can rinse your skin immediately if you splash yourself with bleach. If you are going to work outside, fill a bucket with water.

• If you get bleach in your eyes, rinse well with running water and seek medical attention.

• Never mix the two solutions except on the wood, and always apply them with separate brushes. Discard any unused bleach.

LIMING WOOD

Strictly speaking, liming does not actually change the color of the wood, but because its open pores are filled with a special white wax, the appearance of the wood alters dramatically. Liming wax, a proprietary blend of waxes and pigments, is available from most wood-finish suppliers.

Prepare the workpiece, sanding it smooth, then wipe the surface with a cloth dampened with mineral spirit to remove traces of grease.

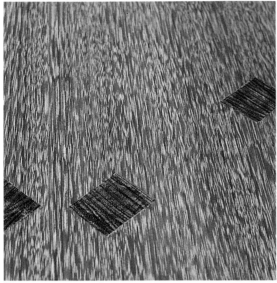

Liming wax accentuates large open pores

1 Opening the grain
Using a bronze-wire brush, scrub the wood in the direction of the grain to clean out the pores. Glance across the work from time to time to check your progress, ensuring that you cover the surface evenly. Wipe the debris from the surface with a tack rag.

2 Staining the wood for contrast
Because the effect of liming depends on the contrast between the wax and the color of the wood, it often pays to stain the work first. Use a water stain and seal in the color with a coat of transparent shellac polish (see page 53). When the sealer coat is dry, smooth the surface with an abrasive nylon pad.

3 Applying liming wax
Dip a pad of burlap into liming wax and apply it to the work, using firm circular strokes to force it into the pores. When you have covered the surface, wipe across the grain to remove excess wax. After 10 minutes or so, gently burnish the surface in the direction of the grain, using a soft cloth pad.

4 Finishing the work
Leave the liming wax to harden for 24 hours, then apply an ordinary paste wax polish (see page 91) to enhance the color of the wood.

Liming wax prevents varnish or cold-cure lacquer setting properly. If you want to apply one of these finishes, follow the procedure described above, but use white decorator's undercoat instead of liming wax. Having rubbed paint into the pores, wipe it from the surface, using a paper towel slightly dampened with mineral spirit.

CHEMICAL STAINING

It was once common practice to color oak and other woods that are rich in tannic acid by exposing them to ammonia fumes. Depending on the length of exposure, fuming will cause a piece of oak to turn anything from a pale honey color to a fairly dark golden brown. The color is even and permanent, yet does not obscure the grain pattern. You might decide to fume new components before assembling them or, depending on its size, fume the completed workpiece.

Fume the wood before filling blemishes, as wood putties and fillers are not affected by ammonia fumes. Even more importantly, any steel that is in contact with the wood causes black stains, so make sure that no screw heads are exposed, and avoid fitting metal hardware until after fuming.

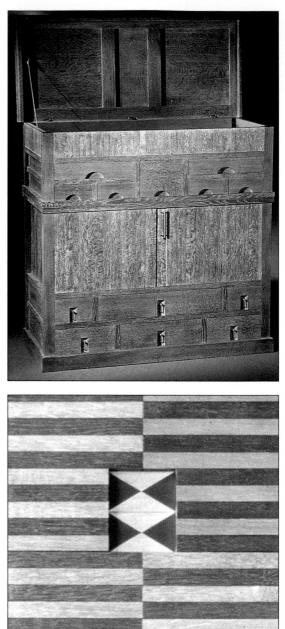

Fumed and limed European-oak cabinet (top)

Detail of cabinet constructed from strips of fumed and natural oak (above)

Sycamore shelf unit with fumed-oak drawer cabinet (left)

Obtaining ammonia

You can fume wood using ordinary household ammonia, but the process will be relatively slow. For faster results use 26 per cent ammonia, also known as '880' or 'eight-eighty', which you can buy from a pharmacist. For safety, wear protective gloves and a respirator when handling this strong ammonia solution and, if possible, work outside.

Making and using a fume tent

To concentrate the ammonia fumes, enclose the workpiece inside a makeshift timber framework, draped with black plastic sheeting. If you are fuming separate components, support them face-side up on wooden wedges or pyramids to keep the points of contact to a minimum. Place shallow dishes of ammonia inside the fume tent, then make it airtight by sealing all joints with adhesive tape. Oak will turn a medium-dark color after about 24 hours of exposure, but check on progress from time to time, and remove the work when it is just slightly lighter than required – the wood continues to change color for a while after you take it out of the tent.

EBONIZING

The tannic-acid content of wood can also be used to turn it black, a process known as ebonizing. Traditionally, ebonizing was carried out with vinegar in which pieces of iron had been left for several days.

Ebonizing a workpiece

Leave a handful of rust-free steel nails in a jar of white vinegar for about a week, then paint it liberally and evenly onto the wood. Try diluting with water to achieve different tones. Let the wood dry, then brush on some ammonia to neutralize the acetic acid. Leave the work to dry again and apply a sealer.

PLASTIC SHEET

CONSTRUCT FRAME FROM SCRAP WOOD AND BOARD

FINISHED WORKPIECE

TAPE JOINTS

SHALLOW DISH CONTAINING AMMONIA

SUPPORT SEPARATE COMPONENTS ON WEDGES

Temporary fume tent

STAINING WOOD

A wood stain or dye is fundamentally different from a surface finish such as paint or varnish. Paint, which colors the wood by depositing a relatively dense layer of pigments on the surface, also forms a protective coating on the workpiece, and clear varnish is essentially a paint without the colored pigments. A true penetrating dye or stain soaks into the wood, taking the color deep into the fibres. However, it provides no protection at all, and so a clear finish is always applied to a stained workpiece afterwards.

Modern stains often contain translucent pigments that lodge in the pores of the wood, accentuating the grain. However, without thorough testing, it can be difficult to determine which ready-made stains contain pigments because a manufacturer may create a whole range of stains, only some of which contain pigments to create particular colors. Successive applications of a pigmented stain gradually darken the wood, whereas applying more than one coat of a non-pigmented stain has little effect on the color.

1 Solvent or oil stains
2 Acrylic stains
3 Denatured alcohol
4 Ready-mixed water stains
5 Mineral spirit
6 Ready-mixed alcohol stains
7 Concentrated water stains
8 Powdered water stains

42

Solvent or oil stains

The most widely available penetrating stains, made from oil soluble dyes, are thinned with mineral spirit. Known as solvent stains or oil stains, these wood dyes are easy to apply evenly, will not raise the grain and dry relatively quickly. Oil stains are made in a wide range of wood-like colors, which you can mix to achieve intermediate shades. Some solvent stains contain translucent pigments that make them fade-resistant.

Alcohol stains

Traditional alcohol stains are made by dissolving aniline dyes in denatured alcohol. The main disadvantage with alcohol stains is their extremely rapid drying time, which makes it difficult to get even coverage without leaving darker patches of overlapping color. Some manufacturers supply ready-mixed stains, and they are also available in powder form which you can mix with alcohol and a little thinned shellac as a binder. Concentrated powder stains, which come in a limited range of strong colors, are used mainly for tinting French polish.

Water stains

Water stains are available from specialists as ready-made wood-color dyes. You can also buy them as crystals or powders for dissolving in hot water so that you can mix any color you want. Water stains dry slowly, which means there is plenty of time to achieve an even distribution of color, but you must allow adequate time for the water to evaporate completely before you apply a finish. They also raise the grain, leaving a rough surface, so it is essential to wet the wood and sand down prior to applying water stains (see page 20).

Acrylic stains

The latest generation of water stains, based on acrylic resins, are emulsions that leave a film of color on the surface of the wood. They raise the grain less than traditional water stains and are more resistant to fading. As well as the usual wood-like colors, acrylic stains are made in a range of pastel shades; it can, however, be difficult to predict the final color produced by these pastel-colored stains on dark hardwoods. All acrylic stains need diluting by about 10 per cent when used on dense hardwoods.

COMPATIBILITY

You can create practically any color you like by mixing compatible wood stains or dyes, and you can reduce the strength of a color by adding more of the relevant solvent. However, you should guard against overlaying a penetrating stain, even one that has dried out, with a surface finish that contains a similar solvent. As you drag a brush or pad across the surface, the solvent may reactivate the color, causing it to 'bleed' into the surface finish.

As a basic rule, select a stain that will not react with the finish you want to apply, or seal the stain first to prevent solvent disturbing the color. It is always worth testing the stain and finish before applying either to a workpiece.

Solvent stains

Seal a solvent stain (oil stain) with shellac or sanding sealer before applying a varnish, lacquer or wax polish that is thinned with mineral spirit, turpentine or cellulose thinner.

Alcohol stains

You can use an alcohol stain under any finish, except for French polish. When the stained surface is completely dry, gently wipe it with a clean rag before applying a finish.

Water and acrylic stains

Allow a stain thinned with water to dry for 48 hours before overlaying with a solvent-based finish – any moisture that has not evaporated can cause the finish to develop a white haze or milkiness. Although a dry water stain should not react with a water-based finish, always test the finish in an inconspicuous place before you apply it.

If you forget to raise the grain before applying a water stain (see page 20), rub down the stained surface very lightly with 220 grit abrasive paper, and then pick up the dust with a tack rag before applying any finish.

Gel stains

Gel or wiping stains are thixotropic in nature, which means they are particularly easy to control – no drips and no overlap marks. Because these stains do not penetrate deeply into the wood, absorption is fairly consistent, even between end grain and side grain.

APPLYING PENETRATING STAINS

Wet the surface to get some idea of what a particular workpiece will look like under a clear finish, and if in doubt, apply some of the actual finish you intend to use. If you are unhappy with its depth of color, or if you feel it doesn't quite match another piece of wood you are working with, take a scrap piece of the same timber and make a test strip to try out a stain before coloring the workpiece itself (see opposite).

Setting up for staining
Plan the work sequence in advance, to minimize the possibility of stain running onto adjacent surfaces or one area of color drying before you can 'pick up' the wet edges. If you have to color both sides of a workpiece, stain the least important side first, immediately wiping off any dye that runs over the edges.

Staining large panels
If possible, set up the workpiece so that the surface to be stained is horizontal. Lay a large panel or door on a pair of trestles so that you can approach it from all sides.

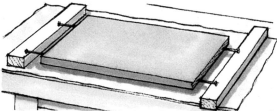

Batch production
It is sometimes convenient to stain components before assembly, setting them aside to dry while you complete the batch.

To color a number of adjustable bookshelves, for example, drive a pair of nails or screws into each end. Lay each shelf on a bench, with the nails or screws resting on battens to raise the shelf off the work surface. Having stained each side in turn, stand the shelf on end against a wall until the stain is dry.

Applicators
You can use good-quality paintbrushes, decorators' paint pads covered with mohair pile, non-abrasive polishing pads (see page 17), or a wad of soft cloth to apply penetrating stains. You can also spray wood dyes, provided you have adequate extraction facilities (see page 83). Wear PVC gloves and old clothes or an apron when applying wood stains.

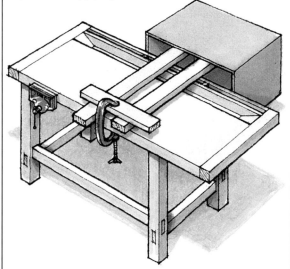

Supporting drawers and cabinets
After staining the inside of drawers or small cabinets, support them at a comfortable working height to complete the job, using cantilevered battens clamped or screwed temporarily to a bench.

Preparing a workpiece for staining
Sand the workpiece well (see pages 19–24), making sure there are no scratches or defects that will absorb more stain than the surrounding wood. In addition, scrape off any patches of dried glue that could affect the absorption of stain.

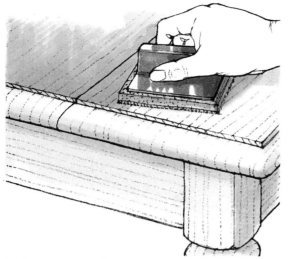

Staining a flat surface

Pour enough stain to color the entire workpiece into a shallow dish. Brush or swab the stain onto the wood in the direction of the grain, blending in the wet edges before the dye has time to dry. When you have covered the surface, take a clean cloth pad, and mop up excess stain, distributing it evenly across the workpiece. If you splash stain onto the wood, blend it in quickly to prevent a patchy appearance.

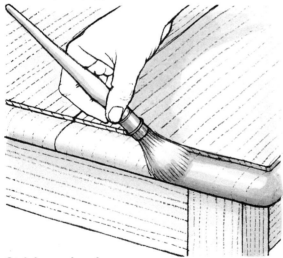

Staining end grain

Exposed end grain appears darker than the rest of the workpiece because the orientation of the cells allows it to absorb more penetrating stain. Painting the end grain with a coat of white shellac or sanding sealer will reduce the amount of color taken up by the wood. Alternatively, you can use thinned varnish, but you should wait 24 hours before you stain the wood.

MAKING A TEST STRIP

Before you color an actual workpiece, make a test strip to see how the wood will be affected by the stain you intend to use. It is important that the test strip is sanded as smooth as the workpiece you will be staining, because coarsely sanded wood absorbs more dye and will therefore appear darker than the same piece of wood prepared with a finer sandpaper.

Apply a coat of stain and allow it to dry. As a general rule, stains dry lighter than they appear when wet. Apply a second coat to see if it darkens the wood, leaving part of the first application exposed for comparison. If you apply more than two full coats of stain, the color may become patchy due to uneven absorption of the liquid.

A second coat of a non-pigmented stain may not change the color appreciably, but you can modify it by overlaying with a compatible stain of a different color.

Once the stain is completely dry, paint one half of the test strip with the intended finish to see how it affects the color of the stain.

CLEAR FINISH UNFINISHED CLEAR FINISH UNFINISHED

Test strip, using pigmented stain   **Test strip, using non-pigmented stain**

45

Coloring veneer

You can treat modern veneered panels like solid wood. However, old furniture was invariably veneered using water-soluble animal glue, and it would pay to use an alcohol or solvent stain to color such items.

You can stain veneer patches (see page 15) or pieces of marquetry before gluing them in place. Dipping scraps of veneer in a dish of wood dye ensures even coloring.

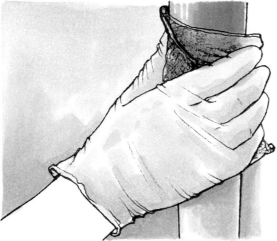

Staining turned spindles

Apply stain to turned legs and spindles with a rag or a non-woven polishing pad. Rub the dye well into turned beads and fluting, then cup the applicator around the leg or spindle and rub it lengthways.

Since turned work exposes end grain it is very difficult to obtain even coverage.

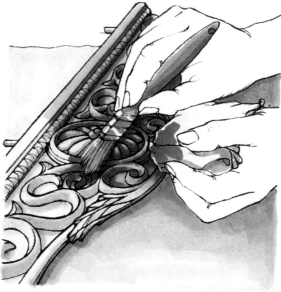

Staining carved work

Use a soft brush to apply penetrating stain to carving or intricate moldings, absorbing surplus stain immediately with rag or a paper towel.

STAINING SOFTWOOD

It is advisable to apply stain to softwood with a cloth pad rather than a paintbrush; highly absorbent wood tends to draw extra stain from a heavily loaded brush at the first point of contact, thus creating a patch of darker color.

The different rates of absorption between early-wood and latewood often give stained softwood a distinctly striped appearance. With some colors, this can be very attractive, but if it doesn't suit your requirements, try coloring the wood with varnish stain or staining wax (see opposite).

Softwood colored with penetrating stain (left) and varnish stain

STAINED FINISHES

Certain products enable you to modify the color of wood and provide a protective finish at the same time. Stained finishes do not have the same clarity as a penetrating wood dye and, because they lie on the surface of the wood, applying too many coats tends to obscure the grain. Varnish stains and protective wood stains are brushed onto the wood. Apply staining wax like wax polish (see pages 92–3).

Staining waxes

There are numerous colored wax polishes that can be used directly on bare wood, but they cannot match the depth of color of a penetrating wood dye. Their primary value is in modifying the color of a finished piece and blending in faded patches.

Colored waxes look very much darker in the tin than they do on a workpiece. Even deep-brown polish, for example, will add a deep rich tint to pine without obliterating the grain.

Protective wood stains

Protective wood stains are translucent finishes for exterior joinery. Being water-vapour-permeable, they allow the wood to exude moisture while protecting it against adverse weather conditions. As a result, protective stains are long-lasting finishes that resist flaking and cracking.

The majority of protective wood stains are tinted, but there is also a clear variety for refurbishing previously stained wood without altering the color. Protective wood stains are either water-based or solvent-based, and some are one-coat finishes. The water-based variety may not dry properly if applied during wet or humid weather.

Varnish stains

Varnish stains are basically tinted polyurethane or acrylic varnishes that contain coloring agents in the form of translucent pigments or oil-soluble dyes. They are ideal for putting color back into a dowdy workpiece that is already varnished. Although stained varnishes are tough finishes, it pays to overlay them with clear varnish, to prevent scratches and heavy wear that will reveal the paler wood beneath the layer of color. Varnish stains must be brushed on evenly to avoid a streaky appearance.

Exterior wood stain brings protection and color to a softwood deck

MODIFYING THE COLOR

No matter how practiced you become at judging colors and mixing dyes, inevitably there comes a time when the dried stain is not quite the color you had in mind. If it's too dark, you may be able to remove some stain, but don't make the mistake of trying to alter the color by applying layer upon layer of dye – this will simply lead to muddy colors or poor finish adhesion. Instead, add washes of tinted finish to modify the color gradually.

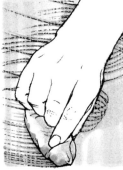

Adding tinted shellac

If the wood is to be French-polished, dissolve some powdered stain in alcohol and add it to a pale shellac (see page 58). Apply a coat of the tinted shellac and allow it to dry. Keep adding washes of shellac, adjusting the color with alcohol stain, until you achieve the right shade.

Applying tinted varnish

If you plan to varnish the workpiece, you can apply a sealer coat of tinted shellac. Alternatively, use a thinned wash of varnish stain, or add diluted wood dye to a compatible clear varnish. Gradually build up to the required tone with a series of thin coats, then apply a protective coat of full-strength varnish.

Toning with wax

If the color match is still not perfect, you can finally tip the balance by adding a dressing of colored staining wax. Rub on the wax in the direction of the grain, using an abrasive nylon pad or very fine steel wool, then buff it to a satin finish with a soft cloth.

Removing color

If a solvent-stained workpiece dries streaky or too dark in tone, wet the surface with mineral spirit and rub it with an abrasive nylon pad. Wipe the surface with a cloth to lift some of the stain and redistribute the remainder more evenly. At this stage, you can modify the color of the wood by applying another, paler stain while the wood is still damp.

ACCENTUATING MOLDINGS AND CARVING

You can bring a workpiece to life by using color to add depth to carving and intricate moldings. The process imitates the effects of natural wear, adding considerably to the appeal of antique or reproduction furniture and picture frames.

Highlighting

The simplest method is to wipe color from the high points while the stain is wet. Alternatively, sand these areas lightly with an abrasive pad after the stain has dried, and wash off the dust, using a cloth dampened with solvent.

Shading

You can add depth to the most delicate of raised patterns, using dark stain mixed into diluted French polish (see left). Seal the stained surface, then paint tinted shellac liberally onto carved and molded areas of the workpiece, allowing it to flow into all the nooks and crannies. Wipe the color off high points immediately, using a soft cloth, and allow the shellac to dry before applying a clear finish.

CHAPTER 4

French-polishing is the traditional method of applying shellac dissolved in denatured alcohol, using a soft cloth pad to rub the polish onto the wood. It is an essential skill to master if you want to restore reasonably priced antique furniture, because during Victorian times it was as common a finish as polyurethane varnish is today.

FRENCH POLISH

SHELLAC PRODUCTION

Shellac, the basic ingredient for French polish, is derived from an insect, *Laciffer lacca*, a native of India and the far East. The larvae of the lac insect secrete a protective resin that builds up in thick layers on the twigs and branches of trees on which they feed. The spread of the insect is encouraged by tying infested shoots to other suitable host trees. Eventually, when twigs become encrusted with hardened lac resin, they are 'harvested' as stick lac for refining into a wide variety of products, including shellac polish.

Handmade shellac

Although the production of shellac has been largely mechanized, traditional methods that have been practiced for hundreds of years still account for approximately 15 per cent of the world's shellac.

The crop of encrusted twigs is pounded and scraped to remove the lac resin, which is then crushed and sieved to extract wood fragments and insect remains. The crushed resin is washed in water, then rinsed and spread out in the sun to dry. After drying, it is sieved again and winnowed to produce a commercial grade of resin known as seed lac.

Blended seed lac is packed into a narrow canvas tube which is suspended in front of a charcoal fire. As the resin melts, the tube is twisted, wringing molten shellac through the weave of the canvas. The shellac is transferred to a cylindrical ceramic jar filled with hot water, where it is smoothed out to an even thickness. Peeling the sheet of soft shellac from the cylinder, a skilled worker stretches it in front of the fire, using his hands, feet, and even his teeth. Once it is removed from the heat, the shellac cools rapidly and is crushed to make flake shellac.

A different variety of handmade shellac is made by dropping the molten lac onto cold stone or sheets of galvanized iron, where it solidifies into flat discs, 50 to 75mm (2 to 3in) in diameter. These translucent discs, which can be inspected against the light for possible impurities, are reserved for the best-quality button polish. Button lac is also produced by pouring the molten shellac into molds.

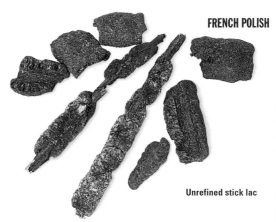

Unrefined stick lac

Modern production methods

Though traditional methods are still employed at village level, modern manufacturing processes are geared to producing flake shellac in various qualities and colors.

Seed lac is heated with steam until it becomes molten enough to be filtered in hydraulic presses, and then is passed through rollers which produce long continuous sheets of shellac.

Alternatively, seed lac is dissolved in industrial alcohol, and the solution is filtered to remove impurities. The alcohol is boiled off to leave molten shellac which is passed through rollers.

Stretching shellac which will be crushed into flakes when cool

1 Machine-made flakes
Modern manufacturing processes produce very fine flake shellac.

2 Handmade flakes
Traditional handmade flakes are relatively thick.

3 Stick lac
Coarse lac resin scraped from twigs and branches.

4 Seed lac
Crushed and processed stick lac becomes commercial seed lac.

5 Button lac
Translucent discs of best-quality shellac.

6 Blond shellac flakes
De-waxed flakes for making your own almost-clear French polish (see page 53).

7 Bleached shellac
Bleached de-waxed shellac for manufacturing commercial transparent polish (see page 53).

KNOTTING AND SANDING SEALERS

As well as being the basic ingredient for French polish, shellac is also useful as a sealer, forming an effective barrier that prevents contaminants affecting a surface finish. An application of French polish or shellac-based sanding sealer, for example, prevents wood stain migrating into a top coat of varnish (see page 26). Shellac is also used to manufacture fast-drying knotting which, when painted over knots and end grain, seals in softwood resins that might otherwise stain paint or varnish. If you plan to use a catalysed lacquer, however, use only de-waxed shellac as a sealer.

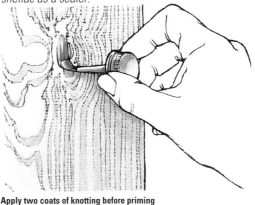

Apply two coats of knotting before priming

51

READY-MADE POLISHES

It is possible to buy flake shellac from which you can make your own polish but, unless cost is of prime importance, it is invariably more convenient to use one of the many varieties of commercially prepared shellac polishes.

Standard polish

The basic medium-brown French polish is manufactured from orange shellac flakes. It is suitable for polishing all dark hardwoods and for tinting pale-colored species. Standard polish is widely available from most outlets, including hardware and paint suppliers.

French polish, prized for its glass-like finish, is ideal for elegant period-style furniture

White polish

Bleached seed lac is used to make a milky-white variety of polish, ideal for finishing pale-colored hardwoods and for sealing wood prior to waxing. If standard white polish is too soft, you can buy one with additives that create a harder finish. White polish may not set properly after it has been in stock for about two years.

UNFINISHED MAHOGANY

BUTTON POLISH ON MAHOGANY

GARNET POLISH ON MAHOGANY

WHITE POLISH ON SYCAMORE

Pound cut

The 'strength' or viscosity of French polish is designated by how much shellac is dissolved in one gallon of alcohol, and is referred to as the 'cut', particularly in the USA. This specification is used even when polish is sold in litres. A ready-to-use 3 pound cut, for example, comprises about 30 per cent shellac, making it suitable for most general applications. A thinner, 1 pound cut would be more suitable as a sealer coat; in practice, however, most polishers would simply dilute the thicker 3 pound cut with alcohol.

Transparent polish

Shellac contains a small amount of wax which is insoluble in alcohol. It is this wax that accounts for the milkiness of white polish, and which settles out of other shellacs when they are left undisturbed for a period of time. Washing bleached shellac in petroleum solvent dissolves the wax, resulting in an almost clear polish that does not alter the natural color of wood. Like white polish, transparent polish has a shelf life of about two years.

Button polish

The term button polish generally implies a superior-quality, golden-brown shellac polish. Although most ready-made polishes are made from good-quality flake shellac, some manufacturers still import traditional hand-made button lac for their polish.

De-waxed button polish is referred to as 'special' or 'transparent' button polish, and produces a harder finish than the standard variety.

Garnet polish

This is a deep red-brown French polish, popular with antique restorers. It is sometimes used to impart a reddish color to mahogany and other similar woods.

Ebony polish

Black-stained ebony polish provides the typical glossy French-polish lustre, but obscures the grain if too much is applied. Ebony polish is the traditional piano finish, but is also used for polishing very dark woods.

Exterior French polishes

Exposure to water leaves white staining on all French polishes, except for a range of special dark and pale polishes that are specifically formulated for use on exterior woodwork.

BLONDE SHELLAC

Bleaching seed lac alters its properties, so that it becomes insoluble in alcohol after about three days. Because of its short shelf life, bleached shellac is only sold as ready-mixed polish (see above left). For wood finishers who prefer to make their own almost clear French polish, de-waxed blonde shellac flakes are available for dissolving in alcohol.

TRADITIONAL FRENCH-POLISHING

It is hard to imagine how French-polishing could have acquired a reputation for being so difficult to master when nineteenth-century polishers would have thought themselves unworthy of the title if they were unable to conjure up the perfect shellac finish. Now that we have become used to fast-drying varnishes and one-coat finishes, we seem to have lost the confidence to tackle a technique that requires time and patience to perfect. To become skilled at every aspect of French-polishing would take years of experience but, by practicing basic techniques on pieces of scrap wood or veneered boards, any reasonably competent woodworker should be able to produce an acceptable result.

Although the Victorians French-polished practically every type of furniture imaginable, shellac is not particularly hard-wearing. It may be the perfect finish for a delicate side table, a sewing box, or even the best sideboard, but it would not be the ideal choice for a kitchen table or worktop, where it would be subjected to harsh treatment and regularly exposed to water, alcohol and heat (see page 30).

The type of wood you are using also affects whether to use shellac. French polish is at its best when applied to beautifully figured, close-grain hardwoods, such as mahogany, satinwood or walnut, but it seems inappropriate for open-grain oak or ash and the more mundane softwoods.

Creating a suitable environment

A clean, dust-free environment is necessary, whatever finish you are applying, but French polish is especially vulnerable to changes in temperature and humidity. Keep your workshop warm and dry, and draughtproof windows and doors.

If possible, set up your workbench in front of the main source of natural or artificial light so that it falls across the surface of the workpiece – you will be able to see how the polish is going on and detect foreign bodies or specks of dust immediately.

Making a cloth pad

Generations of polishers have refined and developed the techniques of French-polishing to suit individual tastes and requirements, but the essential elements remain the same – shellac is applied patiently over a period of days, gradually building a translucent film, using a pad of cotton wool wrapped in cloth.

Make the pad to suit the size of your hand and surface area you will be polishing. The dimensions given in the following sequence are for a general-purpose pad, but you may want to make smaller pads for specialized work.

1 Folding the square of wadding
Upholsterer's wadding is the ideal material for a French-polishing pad. Tear off a 150 to 225mm (6 to 9in) square of wadding, fold it in half, then fold over each half of the rectangle to make a triangle.

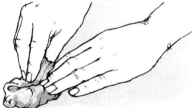

2 Shaping the wadding
Fold two corners of the triangle towards the center, making a roughly sausage-shaped pad. If you are unable to obtain upholsterer's wadding, take a handful of ordinary unmedicated cotton wool and squeeze it into an egg-shape pad.

3 Inserting the wadding
Place the wadding diagonally across the center of a 225 to 300mm (9 to 12in) square of soft cotton or linen. A piece of fabric torn from an old sheet or pillowcase is ideal, or you could use a large plain handkerchief.

4 Folding over the covering
Taking hold of the corner, fold one half of the fabric over the end of the wadding pad.

5 Wrapping the wadding
Holding the wadding down with one hand, wrap the remaining corners over the pad to make a neat package.

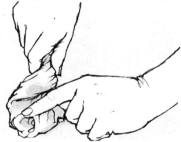

6 Twisting excess fabric
Twist the fabric into a tail behind the pad to tighten up the package, then fold the tail over onto the pad to form a grip that fits in the palm of your hand.

7 Holding the cloth pad
Hold the pad in one hand so that you can pinch the sides between forefinger and thumb, forming a pointed end with which to apply polish into tight corners. Make sure there are no creases or stitched hems running across the sole of the pad.

8 Charging the pad
You should never dip the pad into polish, nor pour polish directly onto its sole. Instead, place the pad in the palm of one hand and carefully unwrap it. Pour shellac polish onto the wadding, squeezing it gently until it is thoroughly wet but not completely saturated.

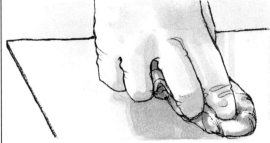

9 Stimulating the flow of polish
Re-wrap the pad and press the sole against a flat surface to encourage the shellac to permeate the fabric, squeezing out excess polish that would build up in ridges on the workpiece. Use a piece of scrap wood or cardboard, or even the front rail of your bench, but make sure it is clean and free from dust. It will be necessary to recharge the pad from time to time as the polish is used up.

STORING A CLOTH PAD
To keep your polishing pad soft and supple between applications, store it in an airtight jar. A pad may last for months, but always discard it as soon as a hole wears in the fabric, before it begins to scar the polish. Even then, the used wadding without its cloth wrapping is useful as a 'fad' for sealing a workpiece with French polish (see page 56).

APPLYING FRENCH POLISH

Traditional polishing is a process that cannot be rushed. Any attempt to push on before applications of polish have been allowed to dry and harden inevitably leads to problems that retard progress rather than accelerate it.

French-polishing comprises three main stages. The wood must first be sealed as a prelude to the all-important 'bodying up', the process of building a satisfactory film of polish; this may take several days to complete. Finally, burnishing with alcohol removes excess oil and gives shellac its unique glossy finish. Although not absolutely essential, it pays to wear disposable gloves while polishing, to keep your hands clean.

1 Preparing the surface
Like most translucent finishes, French polish will accentuate the slightest flaw on the surface of the wood, so prepare the workpiece thoroughly. Repair any obvious blemishes, then sand the wood smooth (see pages 9–25). If necessary, color the wood with stain (see pages 42–46) and apply a grain filler (see page 26). Alternatively, fill open grain by applying successive coats of polish, rubbing down with silicon-carbide paper between coats, until the pores are filled flush with shellac.

2 Sealing the wood
Professional polishers often use a 'fad' – a piece of used cotton wadding – to apply the first sealer coats of shellac polish, but a newly made cloth pad charged with slightly thinned polish works just as well. Apply the polish in long, overlapping strokes, parallel to the grain of the wood. In the early stages, you need apply very little pressure to the pad; but as the work progresses, squeeze the pad lightly to encourage more polish to flow. Don't go back over the work, even if you notice slight blemishes. When you have covered the entire work surface, leave the polish to harden for about an hour.

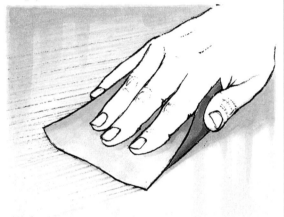

3 Rubbing down the sealer coat
Lightly sand the polished surface with fine silicon-carbide paper, in the direction of the grain only. If the first sealer coat is very uneven, apply another similar coat of polish.

4 Bodying up
Charge the cloth pad with full-strength polish, then begin building up the body of polish. The key to this stage is to keep the pad moving while it is in contact with the work, preventing the sole sticking to the polish. Sweep the pad onto the surface, making small, overlapping, circular strokes until you have coated the workpiece, then sweep the pad off again.

5 Polishing into corners

Make sure you polish right into closed or internal corners every time you coat a surface with French polish. This is where the pointed end of the cloth pad comes into play. Place your forefinger on top, then sweep the pad into and out of the corner with one continuous movement.

6 Lubricating the pad

As the work progresses, you will notice the pad does not slide quite so easily across the surface; this is caused by the alcohol re-dissolving polish that has already begun to harden. Lubricate the pad as soon as it begins to 'drag' by smearing a drop of linseed oil onto the sole with your fingertip.

7 Combining different strokes

To distribute the polish evenly, go back over the surface again, this time with figure-of-eight strokes, making sure you work right up to the edges. Finally, apply the polish with straight overlapping strokes, parallel to the grain. Leave the polish to dry for about 30 minutes, then repeat the whole process, perhaps three or four times. Put the workpiece aside to allow the polish to harden overnight.

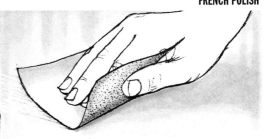

8 Rubbing down

The next day, inspect the workpiece for specks of embedded dust or other blemishes and, if necessary, sand the surface very lightly, using self-lubricating silicon-carbide paper.

9 Building a protective body of polish

Continue to build up a thickness of polish, coating the surface three to four times per day, with a half-hour break between each coat, then allow the polish to harden overnight. Repeat the process over a period of days until you are satisfied with the general color and appearance of the work.

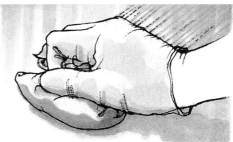

10 Removing the oil

Lubricating the sole of the pad leaves the polished surface streaky. To remove the oil from the polish and bring the surface to a gloss finish, add a little alcohol to the pad and squeeze it almost dry. Sweep the pad across the work with straight parallel strokes, gradually increasing pressure until the pad begins to drag, then leave the polish to harden. Repeat the process every two to three minutes until streaking disappears. Wrapping the pad with fresh fabric may help absorb the oil. After half an hour, polish the surface with a duster, then put the work aside for about a week to let the polish harden thoroughly.

Burnishing to a high gloss

If a polished surface does not shine to your satisfaction, you can burnish it after the shellac has hardened for a week. Rub the surface vigorously with a soft cloth moistened with a special-purpose burnishing cream or car-paint cleaner (see page 28). Both are extremely fine abrasives that will produce a deep shine. Finally, buff the polish with a dry duster.

Creating a satin finish

If a high gloss is not to your taste, you can cut back a newly French-polished workpiece, using a pad of 000-grade steel wool dipped in wax polish. Rub the hardened polish very lightly with the grain, until the entire surface appears to be matted evenly. Burnish gently with a duster.

Polishing carving and moldings

It is impracticable to French-polish a deeply carved workpiece, or one with intricate moldings, using a cloth pad. Instead, apply slightly diluted shellac polish with a soft squirrel-hair brush. Let the polish flow smoothly, but not too thickly, leaving it to settle naturally; over-brushing shellac leaves brushmarks in hardened polish.

Once the polish has hardened, burnish the high points, using a pad moistened with alcohol (see page 57), but don't rub too hard. Polish with a duster.

ADJUSTING THE COLOR

Perhaps the pinnacle of the French-polisher's art is the ability to modify the color of the finish as the job progresses, a skill that requires great subtlety and which can only be learnt from experience.

There may be any number of reasons why modification might be necessary. If you are restoring old furniture, you may need to enrich a partly faded finish, for example, or perhaps you will want to adjust the shade of a component that does not quite match the color of a new piece you are polishing.

As you build up the layers of polish, stand back from the work from time to time, and inspect it from all angles and in different lights to make sure it is progressing to your satisfaction.

Coloring shellac polish

A shift in color is achieved by applying a wash coat or two of tinted shellac polish. These coats can be included at any time during the French-polishing process, then sealed and protected with subsequent layers of full-strength polish.

You can mix ready-made alcohol stains with shellac, but professionals use powdered aniline dyes to tint French polish. They are available from specialist suppliers in a limited range of colors, typically red, black, yellow, green, blue, orange, and brown. The right combination of these colors will achieve any wood shade you require.

The secret is to mix very pale colors, so that you can overlay one with another to achieve the exact shade and tone required. Powdered dyes are very strong, so dissolve tiny amounts in alcohol and mix the solution in equal proportions with shellac polish.

Applying wash coats

After testing the colored polish for strength on a piece of paper or scrap wood, apply it very thinly to the work with a fad or cloth pad. Try to blend it in, making sure there are no obvious edges to the colored area. If using a pad is impracticable, float it onto the work with a soft brush.

Let the polish dry, check it for accuracy and, if necessary, apply another wash coat to alter the balance of color. If the edges of the tinted area are obvious, try sanding them lightly with a fine silicon-carbide paper.

Once you are satisfied with the result, continue bodying up the polish, using a cloth pad. Apply the first coats very gently to ensure you do not disturb or alter the color.

BRUSHING SHELLAC

The idea of applying shellac by brush is not new. In the past, tradespeople such as coffin makers, whose work would probably not be viewed over-critically, tended to build up a body of polish by painting thinned shellac onto the wood. The traditional hand-rubbed appearance could always be achieved by finishing the job with a cloth pad.

If you have neither the inclination nor the time to learn true French-polishing, try one of the special brushing shellac polishes which contain additives to retard drying, enabling you to paint the shellac onto a workpiece without leaving permanent brushmarks in the finish. Use a soft, natural-bristle paintbrush.

Prepare and color the work as recommended for traditional French-polishing.

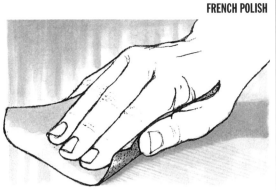

2 Rubbing down
Some brushing polishes dry faster than others, but an hour should be plenty of time. Using fine silicon-carbide paper, rub down the first coat lightly until it feels smooth, then apply two more coats of shellac. There's no need to rub down the second coat unless you notice any blemishes.

3 Waxing the finish
The result may be perfect for your needs straight from the brush, but you can modify the finish, to render it indistinguishable from a similar French-polished job, by rubbing it with fine steel wool dipped in wax polish. Apply the polish gently and evenly, making sure you don't cut through the layer of shellac.

1 Applying the polish
Don't attempt to spread the finish as if it were varnish, but let the polish flow naturally from the brush, using straight strokes parallel with the grain. You can pick up runs or ridges of polish, provided you do it reasonably quickly. Flexing the bristles against the edges of the work tends to promote runs, so wipe them with a clean rag before the polish has time to set. If you notice too late, leave the runs to set, then rub them down later.

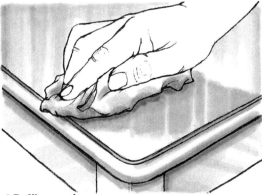

4 Buffing up the wax
Leave the wax to harden for 15 to 20 minutes, then burnish vigorously with a soft duster.

FAULTS AND REMEDIES

The following is a check list of common problems and solutions associated with French-polishing.

Pitted surface
Failing to fill grain adequately allows shellac to sink into the open pores as it sets.
Let the polish harden, rub it down with silicon-carbide paper wrapped round a sanding block and re-polish until the pores are filled flush with shellac.

Blushing
Moisture trapped in the polish gives shellac a cloudy appearance soon after it is applied. This can be caused by humidity during polishing, or perhaps a water stain was not allowed to dry out adequately. Alternatively, the wood itself was left slightly damp.
Because blushing usually penetrates to the wood, the usual recourse is to strip the shellac and re-polish.

Blooming
A cloudy deposit, similar to the bloom found on the skins of grapes, can occur on shellac, whatever its age.
Use a rag barely dampened with water to wipe blooming from the surface, then rub it dry with a duster or paper towel.

Polishing disturbs previous layers
Attempting to apply fresh shellac before previous coats have time to harden smears the polish.
Let each application dry for at least 30 minutes and put the work aside overnight to allow each coat to harden thoroughly (see page 57).

Scars
If the cloth pad is allowed to come to rest on the surface of the polish, it will leave an imprint of the fabric in the shellac.
Leave the polish to harden overnight, then sand out the scar with silicon-carbide paper. Don't concentrate too much on a small area, or you will wear a pale-colored patch in the finish.

Ridges in the polish
Ridges will be raised by applying too much pressure to a slightly overcharged cloth pad.
Treat as for scars.

Runs
Shellac polish will run or 'curtain' just like paint that is applied too thickly without brushing out. This will most likely occur when thinned shellac is being applied, or the cloth pad or paintbrush is passed across raised moldings or against a sharp edge.
Don't attempt to spread runs while the polish is still soft. Let it harden, then treat as for cloth-pad scars.

Scratches
If you find that the act of polishing is scratching coats applied previously, check the sole of the polishing pad for specks of dust or grit. Remake the pad if you notice a seam running across the sole. A polishing pad made from synthetic-fibre cloth may also scratch the surface of the polish.
Make sure you wipe the work after rubbing down, and check that you do not press a freshly charged cloth pad against a dirty surface (see page 55). Sand out scratches and other blemishes when the shellac has hardened overnight.

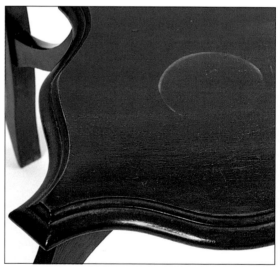

White rings
Circular white stains are caused by the damp base of a vase or glass left in contact with a French-polished surface. Alcohol and heat will have a similar effect.
There are a number of solutions to this problem (see page 30), including burnishing with a proprietary finish reviver, car-paint cleaner or liquid metal polish.

CHAPTER 5

Modern production methods have made available a large range of varnishes and lacquers, each with its own specific properties – durability, weather-resistance, ease of application, drying speed, and so on. Such is their versatility, there is almost certainly a varnish or lacquer that will meet your requirements.

VARNISH & LACQUER

A FINISH FOR EVERY SITUATION

At one time, the terms 'lacquer' and 'varnish' were used to describe specific finishes. Lacquer was for the most part a clear coating that dried quickly by evaporation of the solvent, whereas a conventional varnish was a mixture of resins, oil and solvent that dried by a combination of evaporation and oxidation. Nowadays, a great many finishes are so complex that they no longer fit exactly into either category, but manufacturers have continued to use the familiar terms so as not to disorientate their customers. As a consequence, the labels 'lacquer' and 'varnish' have become interchangeable; to avoid further confusion, the terms used here are those that you are most likely to encounter when buying wood finishes.

The bulk of varnishes and lacquers are clear to amber-colored finishes, designed primarily to protect the wood and accentuate its natural grain pattern. There are also modified finishes that contain colored dyes or pigments.

Clear polyurethane varnish is a tough and attractive finish for all interior wood surfaces

Oil varnishes

Traditional oil varnish is composed of fossilized tree resins blended with linseed oil and thinned with turpentine. In the manufacture of modern oil varnishes, these natural resins have been superseded by synthetic ones, such as phenolic, alkyd and polyurethane resins, with mineral spirit as the solvent.

Oil varnishes, frequently referred to as solvent-based varnishes, dry as a result of oxidation. After the solvent has evaporated, the oil absorbs oxygen from the air, chemically changing the varnish in such a way that applying mineral spirit does not soften the dried film.

Grained softwood door protected with exterior-grade varnish

Floor sealers are especially hardwearing clear varnishes

The ratio of oil to resin has an effect on the properties of the varnish. Varnishes with a high percentage of oil, known as long oil varnishes, are relatively tough, flexible and water-resistant, making them suitable for finishing exterior woodwork. Short oil varnishes, made with less oil and a higher proportion of resin, dry more quickly and with a harder film than long oil varnishes, and can be polished to a gloss finish. These are also called rubbing varnishes, and are classed as interior woodwork finishes.

The choice of resin also affects the characteristics of a varnish. Exterior-grade varnishes, for example, are often made from alkyd resin blended with tung oil to provide resilience and weather resistance. Manufacturers adopt terms such as spar varnish, marine varnish or yacht varnish to describe superior-quality exterior finishes that will cope with polluted urban environments and coastal climates. Polyurethane resin is favoured for interior oil varnishes, including floor sealers, which need to be tough enough to resist hard knocks and abrasion.

Oil varnishes are supplied ready for use, except for those containing pigments or matting agents, which need to be stirred first (see page 66).

Spirit varnishes

Spirit varnish is manufactured from natural resins, most often shellac, dissolved in alcohol. It dries quickly by evaporation of the alcohol, but the film can be softened again by applying the solvent. A spirit varnish has a higher proportion of shellac than a brushing shellac or French polish. Spirit varnishes are seldom used for wood finishing these days, but they are useful when sealing creosoted wood before painting it.

Two-pack polyurethane varnish

In order for this varnish to set hard, the user is required to mix in a precise amount of isocyanate curing agent just prior to application. The result is a clear, tough finish that is better than standard oil varnish in terms of durability and resistance to heat, alcohol and other chemicals. Its one real disadvantage is that, during the curing process, the varnish exudes extremely unpleasant fumes that can be injurious to health, especially to people who suffer from any form of respiratory illness. Consequently, many countries have banned the use of two-pack polyurethane varnishes except in controlled industrial premises fitted with adequate exhaust ventilation.

Protective wood stains (right)

Available as solvent-based and water-based finishes, protective wood stains fall somewhere between exterior varnish and paints. Most are translucent wood-colored or pastel-shade finishes, but some are completely opaque. These finishes, which should not be confused with genuine penetrating wood stains (see pages 42–3), provide color and protection for exterior doors and window frames.

For perfect adhesion, wood stains should be applied to bare wood or to previously stained joinery that has been washed thoroughly. Although you usually have to strip conventional varnish or paint, some stains are made to obliterate old paintwork. (See also page 47.)

Acrylic varnishes (above)

The most recently developed wood varnishes are composed of acrylic resins dispersed in water to form an emulsion. The varnish is milky white when applied; it becomes a clear transparent finish after going through a two-stage evaporative process.

Acrylic varnish contains a small percentage of solvents known as coalescing agents which, after the water has evaporated, fuse the particles of resin into a cured film. This process can only take place in a relatively warm, dry atmosphere. In very humid or damp conditions, the coalescing agents may evaporate in advance of the water, leaving a film that cannot set properly. Once it has set, however, the varnish is impervious to water; it can be softened with cellulose thinner if necessary.

Acrylic varnishes have many advantages over solvent-based finishes. They are non-toxic and practically odourless, and dry so fast that you can complete most tasks in a single day. There's no risk of fire, and you can wash out your brushes in ordinary tap water.

Varnish stains (below)

Tinted solvent-based and acrylic finishes allow you to varnish and color the wood in one operation. Varnish stains are made in various translucent colors, mostly formulated to imitate common wood species; some ranges also include pastel shades. (See also page 47.)

Cold-cure lacquers

Cold-cure lacquers, which set hard by a process known as cross-polymerization, require the addition of an acid catalyst to start the reaction. When cured, the molecules of resin are bonded chemically, forming an extremely tough, non-reversible film which is highly resistant to solvents, heat and abrasion. Because cold-cure lacquers do not rely on evaporation of the solvent or on oxidation for setting, they can be applied in relatively thick coats.

Swimmers table
Glass top supported on carved bathers coated with cold-cure lacquer and colored with compatible glitter powder.

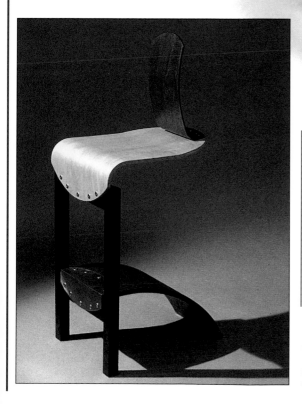

Some lacquers are supplied pre-catalysed, so that the curing process begins automatically as soon as the solvent evaporates. Other cold-cure lacquers are supplied in two parts, requiring the user to add the acid hardener before applying the finish.

Cold-cure lacquers are usually manufactured with butylated urea-formaldehyde resins, plus melamine for heat resistance, and alkyd resin as a plasticizer. The lacquer forms an exceptionally clear film that does not yellow in time; you can also choose from opaque white or black finishes.

Laminated stool
Dye-stained laminated beech, finished with clear catalysed lacquer.

PROPERTIES OF VARNISH AND LACQUER

Manufacturers are able to vary the formulae of varnishes and lacquers to give them whatever properties are required for a particular need. Listed below are the characteristics most likely to be included in sales literature or user instructions.

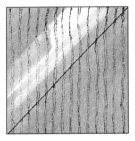

Finish – gloss, satin, matt

Varnishes and lacquers dry to a gloss finish, except when matting agents have been included to make them semi-gloss (satin) or completely matt when set. Most manufacturers make a range of varnishes or lacquers in all three; when a varnish stain, for example, is only available in one finish, you can modify it by coating over it with the appropriate clear varnish.

Clarity and color

Most varnishes and lacquers are transparent finishes that enhance the color of the wood without masking the grain pattern. Even finishes described as perfectly clear will darken wood slightly; water has a similar effect. Varnish stains and protective wood stains, which contain pigments or dyes, impose a completely different color on the wood.

Non-yellowing

Oil varnishes are prone to darkening or turning yellow with age. Both acrylic varnish and cold-cure lacquer retain their clarity.

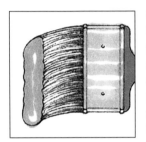

Viscosity

Varnishes and lacquers are usually liquid in consistency, but some, which are described as thixotropic or non-drip, are supplied as a thick gel that flows when brushed onto the work.

Durability

Modern varnishes and lacquers that can take a great deal of wear and tear are described as being resistant to scratches, abrasion and impact.

Heat resistance

The term heat-resistant implies that you can place hot plates or dishes onto a varnished or lacquered surface without damaging the finish.

Water resistance

A water-resistant coating will not absorb moisture or be stained by spilled water.

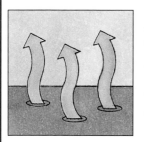

Solvent resistance
A solvent-resistant coating will not be softened or stained when subjected to solvents, including alcohol.

Weather resistance
All exterior-grade finishes are weather-resistant. They form a flexible coating that does not flake or crack and is ultra-violet (UV) resistant, thus preventing the wood from fading.

Microporous or water-vapour permeable
Terms used to describe an exterior varnish or protective wood stain that repels rainwater, yet allows moisture vapour to permeate.

Low odour
The low-solvent content of acrylic varnishes makes them practically odourless. There is also a reduced health risk when using low-solvent finishes and they are less harmful to the environment.

Toxicity
Manufacturers are bound by law to include advice on the effects of swallowing a finish or breathing its fumes. Regulations on the use of wood finishes for children's furniture and toys are especially rigorous.

Flammability
Solvent-based wood finishes exude flammable vapours. Acrylic varnishes and other water-based products are non-flammable.

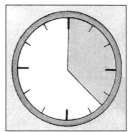

Drying and setting times
Manufacturers invariably quote the period of time it takes for a finish to be 'touch dry', and a much longer setting time, after which it can be re-coated. Drying and setting times of different wood finishes vary a great deal. Although a fast drying time enables you to complete a job quickly, a slow-setting varnish allows more time to spread the finish evenly without leaving brushstrokes. There is, however, a greater chance of airborne dust becoming embedded in a slow-setting finish.

BRUSHING VARNISH

You can spray varnishes onto wood – except for those that are thixotropic – but it is cheaper and more convenient for most amateur woodworkers to apply varnish with a paintbrush. Provided you use good-quality equipment and work patiently, you can achieve perfect results.

NATURAL-BRISTLE PAINTBRUSHES

SYNTHETIC-BRISTLE BRUSH

OVAL VARNISH BRUSH

Choosing brushes

Any good-quality paintbrush is suitable for applying oil varnish, but natural-bristle brushes that spread the finish well without shedding loose bristles are the best choice. There are also oval-shape varnish brushes, specially designed for greater carrying capacity and improved edge control.

Use synthetic-bristle brushes to apply water-based acrylic varnish. Most varnish manufacturers recommend nylon brushes.

Choose a 50mm (2in) brush for general work and a 25mm (1in) cutting-in brush for varnishing glazing bars and narrow moldings. A 100mm (4in) brush will be helpful when varnishing floors, but using a brush wider than that becomes tiring after a while.

Whatever brushes you decide to use, reserve them for varnishing woodwork so that they do not become contaminated with specks of dry paint.

When varnishing a floor, consider using a paint roller attached to a long extension handle.

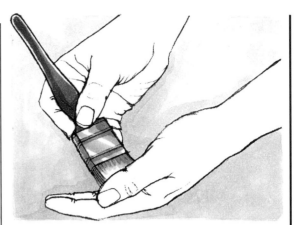

1 Preparing a new brush

Before you use a brand-new brush to apply oil varnish, flex it against the palm of your hand to tease out any loose bristles.

2 Soaking the bristles

Prepare the new brush by soaking the bristles in linseed oil for about 24 hours. If you stand the brush on end in a jar of oil, the bristles will become splayed and useless. Instead, suspend the brush from a short length of stiff wire pushed through a small hole drilled just above the metal ferrule.

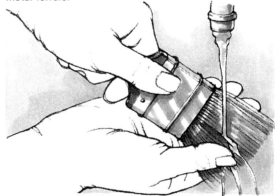

3 Washing out oil

Squeeze excess oil from the bristles, then brush back and forth on clean brown paper or cardboard. Rinse the brush in mineral spirit and wash it in hot soapy water. When the brush is dry, it is ready for use.

Cleaning and storing brushes

Brushes used for acrylic varnish should be washed immediately in clean water. If they are left to become hard, use cellulose thinner to soften the varnish.

Between applications of oil varnish, suspend the brush in water to keep the bristles soft. Before using it again, blot the brush with paper towelling. When the work is finished, rinse the brush with mineral spirit, then wash the bristles in hot water and detergent.

Re-shape the wet brush and wrap the bristles in brown paper. Slip an elastic band over the ferrule to hold the paper in place. Lay the brush flat on a shelf, or suspend it from a wall-hung wire rack.

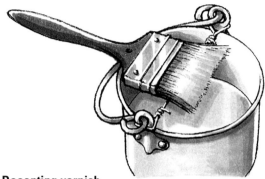

Decanting varnish

Gently stir matt, satin or tinted varnish until you can feel there is no sediment left at the bottom of the container. Thixotropic varnish does not need to be stirred.

You can take varnish straight from the can, but it pays to decant just enough for your immediate needs into a clean paint kettle; replace the can lid to seal in the rest of the varnish. Stretch a length of wire across the top of the kettle to support your brush temporarily.

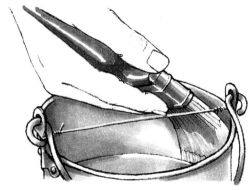

Loading the brush

Dip the first third of the bristles into the varnish; when a brush is overloaded, varnish can set hard in the roots of the bristles, reducing their flexibility. Press the loaded bristles against the side of the kettle to squeeze out excess varnish that might drip from the brush; it is not good practice to drag the bristles across the rim of the kettle, as this tends to create air bubbles.

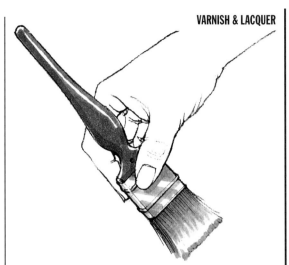

Holding the brush

There are no hard-and-fast rules about how to hold a paintbrush, but when using the pen grip you can move the brush in any direction simply by flexing your wrist. Grip the ferrule between your thumb and fingertips.

PREPARING WOOD

Work in a warm, dry, dust-free atmosphere. However, remember to ventilate the workshop, particularly when applying solvent-based finishes. Don't wear dusty work clothes, or woollen sweaters that could shed fibres.

New or bare wood

Make sure the work is clean, smooth, and free from grease or wax. Wipe oily hardwoods with a cloth dampened with mineral spirit.

As a precaution, seal stripped wood with sanding sealer to prevent residues of silicone oil from wax polishes contaminating the varnish (see page 26), but always check first with manufacturers' instructions, to ensure that the varnish you are using will set when applied over sanding sealer.

Previously varnished wood

Strip badly chipped or flaking varnish (see pages 31–5). Wash sound varnish to remove dirt and traces of grease. Key gloss varnish with fine wet-and-dry abrasive paper.

Exterior woodwork

Exterior varnishes should be applied on a warm, dry day, preferably after a spell of dry weather. Acrylic varnishes are especially sensitive to levels of humidity and temperature (see page 64).

APPLYING VARNISH

There are no special skills to master when applying solvent-based or acrylic varnishes. However, a few basic procedures can help avoid some of the less obvious pitfalls.

Varnishing a flat panel

Supporting a large panel horizontally on a pair of trestles makes varnishing marginally easier, but there are few problems with finishing a hinged door or fixed panel, provided you guard against the varnish running.

1 Applying a sealer coat of oil varnish

Thin oil varnish by about 10 per cent when applying a first sealer coat to bare wood. You can brush it onto the wood, but some woodworkers prefer to rub it into the grain with a soft cloth.

2 Rubbing down the first coat

Leave the sealer coat to harden overnight, then hold the work in a good source of light to inspect the varnished surface. Rub it down lightly in the direction of the grain, using fine wet-and-dry paper dipped in water. Wipe the surface clean, using a cloth moistened with mineral spirit, and dry it with a paper towel.

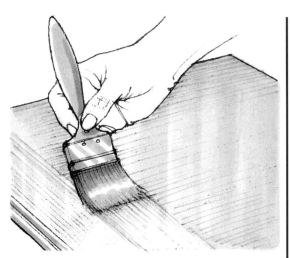

3 Brushing full-strength varnish

Paint oil varnish onto the wood, brushing first with the grain then across it to spread the finish evenly. Always brush towards the area you have just finished, to blend the wet edges. It pays to work at a fairly brisk pace; varnish begins to set after about 10 minutes, and re-brushing it tends to leave permanent brushmarks. Finally 'lay off' along the grain with very light strokes, using just the tips of the bristles to leave a smoothly varnished surface. When varnishing vertical surfaces, lay off with upward strokes of the brush.

Two full-strength coats of oil varnish should be sufficient; for a perfect finish, rub down lightly between each hardened coat.

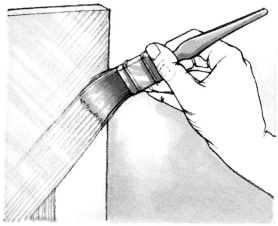

Varnishing edges

As you approach the edges of a panel, brush outwards away from the center. If you flex the bristles back against the sharp arris, you will cause varnish to dribble down the edge.

It is best to blend in the edges of a workpiece as the work progresses, but if that proves troublesome, try varnishing the edges of a panel first and letting them dry. When you coat the flat surfaces, wipe runs from the edges with a rag.

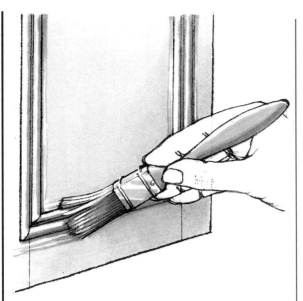

Varnishing moldings

Flexing a brush across a molding usually causes a tear-drop of varnish to run down the surface. Avoid this by brushing along the molding only.

When finishing a panelled door, varnish the moldings first and then varnish the panel, brushing out from each corner towards the center.

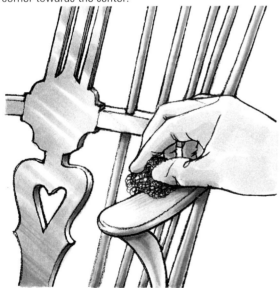

Matting a gloss varnish

Matt and satin oil varnishes have very finely textured surfaces that serve to scatter the light. These look perfect, but you can achieve a smoother-feeling surface on components such as wooden chair arms or a table top by rubbing down a gloss varnish to a matt finish.

Rub the varnish with 000-grade steel wool dipped in wax polish. Leave the wax to harden, then burnish it with a soft duster.

APPLYING ACRYLIC VARNISH

Many of the techniques employed when applying oil varnish are just as relevant to the application of acrylic varnish. The aim is still to acquire a flat, even coating without runs or brushmarks, but the chemical properties of acrylic varnish make it behave slightly differently from oil varnish.

Grain-raising characteristics

When a piece of wood absorbs water, its fibres swell and stand up proud of the surface. Because it is water-based, acrylic varnish has the same effect, making the final finish less than perfect. The solution is either to wet the wood first, and sand it smooth before applying acrylic varnish (see page 20), or to sand the first coat of varnish with fine wet-and-dry paper dipped in water before re-coating the work. Wipe up the dust with a cloth dampened with water; a tack rag may leave oily deposits that will spoil the next coat of acrylic varnish.

Problems with rust

Applying any water-based finish over unprotected steel or iron fittings, including woodscrews and nails, will cause them to rust. Either remove metal fittings before you varnish the work, or protect them with a coat of de-waxed transparent shellac (see page 53).

Don't use steel wool to rub down acrylic varnish; tiny slivers of metal that get caught in the grain may rust, creating black spots on the wood. Use copper wool or an abrasive nylon-fibre pad (see page 17).

Applying the varnish

Acrylic varnish must be applied liberally, first by brushing across the grain, then laying off evenly as described for applying oil varnish (see opposite).

Acrylic varnish dries in only 20 to 30 minutes, so you need to work fast, especially on a hot day, to avoid leaving permanent brushmarks in the finish.

You can apply a second coat after two hours. A total of three coats is sufficient for maximum protection.

APPLYING COLD-CURE LACQUER

This is a very different finish from conventional varnish. Although cold-cure lacquer is no more difficult to apply, it is important to be aware of how the curing process can be affected by inadequate preparation and inappropriate procedures.

Mixing cold-cure lacquer

Mix recommended amounts of hardener and lacquer in a glass jar or polythene container. Metal containers and other plastics may react with the hardener, preventing the lacquer from curing.

Once mixed, some cold-cure lacquers are usable for about three days. However, you can extend the pot life to about a week by covering the jar with polythene, held in place with an elastic band. This type of lacquer will last even longer if you keep the sealed container, clearly marked, in a refrigerator.

Brush care

Apply cold-cure lacquer with any good-quality paintbrush. It can also be sprayed, and can even be applied to large areas with a plastic-foam paint roller.

Once polymerization is complete, cold-cure lacquer becomes insoluble, so wash brushes in special lacquer thinner as soon as the work is complete. The brush can be left suspended in the mixed lacquer between coats, provided the whole container, including the brush, is wrapped in polythene.

Preparing the surface

As with any wood finish, the work must be smooth and clean; remove every trace of wax, which might prevent the lacquer curing. Any wood dye applied to the work must be compatible with the acid catalyst in the lacquer, so check the manufacturers' recommendations before coloring the wood.

Applying cold-cure lacquer

Adequate ventilation is important, especially when you are lacquering a floor, but keep the workshop warm.

Brush on lacquer liberally, using a flowing action and blending in wet edges as you go. Apply it relatively thickly, taking care to avoid runs or sagging.

The lacquer will be touch dry in about 15 minutes; apply a second coat after about an hour. If a third coat is required, apply it the following day.

There is no need to rub down between coats, except to correct blemishes. It you use stearated abrasives (see page 18), wipe the sanded surface with special lacquer thinner.

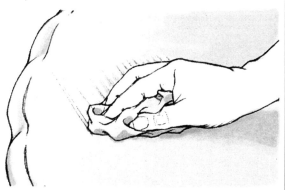

Modifying the finish

To achieve a perfect gloss finish, let the last coat harden for a few days, then sand it smooth with wet-and-dry paper and water until the surface appears matt all over; a shiny patch indicates a hollow. Using a burnishing cream on a slightly damp cloth, buff the surface to a high gloss, and then rub it with a duster.

To create a satin finish, rub the hardened lacquer with 000-grade steel wool lubricated with wax polish. Use coarser steel wool for a matt finish.

CELLULOSE LACQUER

Cellulose lacquer dries solely by evaporation of its solvent, leaving a film that will re-dissolve readily when cellulose thinner is applied to the surface. As a result, each successive coat partially dissolves and melds with the previous application, eventually becoming one integral film of lacquer.

This is a water-clear finish that hardly changes the color of the wood. It also sets very rapidly – it is re-coatable after only 30 minutes – which all but eliminates the problem of dust contamination.

Cellulose lacquer is not as resistant to heat, water or abrasion as polyurethane varnish or cold-cure lacquer, for example, but it does compare favourably with shellac polish. Ventilation is essential when applying cellulose lacquer, and you should wear an approved respirator (see page 125). The lacquer is highly flammable.

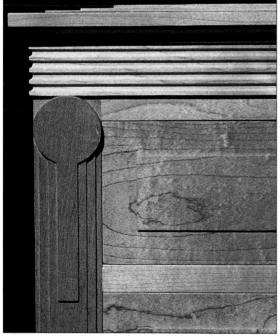

Spraying and brushing lacquer
Conventional cellulose lacquer dries so quickly that spraying is the only practicable method of application (see pages 80–8). If your workshop is not equipped with the required spray gun, compressor and ventilation system, use a specially formulated lacquer made with slow-evaporating solvent so that it can be brushed on to the wood.

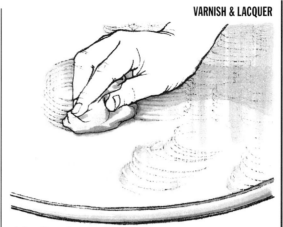

1 Sealing the work
Using a cloth pad, apply a sealer coat of lacquer diluted by 50 per cent with cellulose thinner.

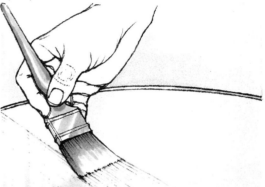

2 Applying full-strength lacquer
Brush on additional full-strength coats, laying on the lacquer with a flowing action. Hold the brush at a shallow angle to the surface, applying the finish with long, straight, overlapping strokes. Don't spread the lacquer like varnish or you run the risk of leaving visible brushmarks in the rapidly setting finish.

3 Burnishing the finish
After about an hour, rub down the final coat of lacquer to remove any minor blemishes. You can use fine wet-and-dry paper or self-lubricating silicon-carbide paper. Rub to the required finish, using burnishing cream.

FAULTS AND REMEDIES

The following is a check list of problems that are commonly encountered when using varnish and cold-cure lacquer.

VARNISH
Runs and sagging
Excess varnish runs or sags if not brushed out sufficiently.
Wipe upwards against the flow of fresh runs, using an unloaded brush.

Rub down runs that have set hard, using wet-and-dry paper dipped in water. If practicable, first pare down hardened runs with a sharp chisel, to minimize rubbing down.

Embedded dust particles
There is very little you can do to prevent the occasional speck of dust from settling on wet varnish.
If the varnish is still wet, pick up a speck of dust with a pointed toothpick; the varnish will flow back to fill the hollow, forming a smooth coat.

If the varnish has begun to set, leave embedded dust until the next day, then rub the surface down with wet-and-dry paper.

Embedded bristles
Even the best brush will shed the occasional bristle.
Scoop up a dropped bristle with the tip of the brush. If you don't notice a detached bristle until the varnish has set, pick it out with the point of a sharp knife and rub down with wet-and-dry paper.

Varnish rolls up into tiny balls and clogs abrasive paper when rubbing down
The varnish has not been left to harden sufficiently. If the original coat was applied too thickly, it may be touch dry but still soft beneath. As a test, press your thumbnail into the varnish; if it leaves an impression, the varnish is too soft to rub down.
Leave the work for another 24 hours and rub down with wet-and-dry paper.

Brushstrokes set permanently in the varnish
Marks are caused by brushing back over a coating that has just begun to set.
If you accidentally brush into setting varnish, don't attempt to rectify the damage; it simply gets worse. Leave it to dry overnight, then rub down.

Cissing or fish-eye
Traces of silicone wax left in the pores of the wood can repel a finish, resulting in miniature craters.
See page 88.

Acrylic varnish dries to a white powder
If acrylic varnish is applied in damp or humid conditions, the coalescing agents evaporate before the water does, and the varnish dries to a white powder.
Brush the powder off the surface and re-varnish.

Acrylic varnish dries too fast to be brushed out effectively
Hot, dry weather reduces the drying time of water-based varnish considerably.
Dilute the varnish by about 10 per cent.

COLD-CURE LACQUER
Film does not dry within expected time
Failing to remove all traces of grease or wax from the wood, using a liming wax to fill the grain, adding insufficient hardener, and applying the finish in a temperature of less than 19°C (65°F) can all delay the drying process.
If you leave the workpiece in a warm room, the lacquer will dry eventually, but it may take several days. You can protect a lacquered floor with a sheet of polythene until the finish has set hard.

Second coat of lacquer wrinkles or blisters
The solvent in the lacquer affects an underlying coat that has not set hard.
Leave the workpiece in a warm room for a few days.

Lacquer appears misty after burnishing
It is not possible to burnish lacquer to a high gloss until it has set hard.
Re-burnish after leaving the work in a warm room for several days.

Poor adhesion
Using stearated abrasives to rub down cold-cure lacquer leaves dust that can affect the adhesion of subsequent coats.
Wipe up dust with a cloth dampened with the special lacquer thinner before applying fresh lacquer.

CHAPTER 6

Paints and varnishes are made from similar resins and solvents, and have many characteristics in common. The one real difference is that paints contain colored pigments that obliterate the grain pattern, and as a result are more often used for finishing inexpensive hardwood joinery, softwoods and boards.

PAINT FINISHES

PRIMERS, UNDERCOATS AND TOP COATS

When applying a protective body of varnish or lacquer, the same material is used for each coat, but conventional paintwork is a combination of three slightly different paints – a single coat of primer effectively seals the wood and provides a surface to which subsequent coats will adhere well, two to three coats of dense matt undercoat form the protective layer, and a colorful top coat provides a satin or gloss finish.

PRIMERS
Solvent-based wood primer
You can choose from white or pink primer, depending on which will work best with the color and tone of subsequent coats of paint. A combination of red lead and white lead accounted for the color of traditional pink primer; pink remains the preferred color, even though lead is no longer added to non-trade paints. Leave solvent-based primers to dry overnight.

Acrylic wood primer
Water-based acrylic primers, which can be used as a base for oil or acrylic paints, dry in about four hours. Except for those specially formulated for finishing metals, water-based paints cause steel fittings to rust unless they are protected with a coat of transparent shellac (see page 53).

Aluminium wood primer
Solvent-based primers that contain aluminium particles contribute towards good weather resistance. Aluminium primers are also recommended for sealing all hardwoods, especially oily ones, resinous softwoods and timber treated with dark-colored wood preserver. They are also the primers to choose if you are painting woodwork that has been scorched while being stripped with heat.

UNDERCOATS
Solvent-based undercoat
Undercoat, which is formulated to obliterate wood grain and primer, dries to an even, matt finish, and can be rubbed down with wet-and-dry paper to a perfectly flat surface. Solvent-based undercoats, which are usually available in white, grey and a limited range of colors, should be left to harden overnight.

Acrylic undercoat
Water-based acrylic undercoats dry so fast you can complete the average job, including the top coat, in a single day; some paints are ready for another coat after only one hour. A few manufacturers market a single acrylic paint that can be used for both priming and undercoating. Acrylic undercoat can be overlaid with solvent-based or water-based top coats.

Bare wood
Grain raised and sanded smooth.

Primer
Seals the wood and provides the ideal base for other paints.

Undercoat
Two to three coats obliterate primer and build a protective body of paint.

Top coat
Final paint finish provides colorful, wipe-clean surface.

TOP COATS

Solvent-based paint

A top coat forms the final decorative surface and is generally available as a high-gloss finish or with a subtle satin sheen. Although few paint manufacturers distinguish between exterior and interior finishes, gloss paint is generally more weather-resistant than satin.

Non-drip thixotropic paints do not require stirring unless the medium has settled out during storage, in which case allow the paint to gel again before using it. Solvent-based top coats are touch-dry within two to four hours, and set completely overnight.

One-coat paint

Solvent-based one-coat gloss and satin paints do not require separate undercoats, thus saving time. They are made to a creamy consistency, with a relatively high proportion of pigments. One-coat paints are especially useful for obliterating old paintwork and strong colors. They must be applied liberally to be fully effective, and should not be spread too thinly.

Acrylic paint

Water-based acrylic paints are similar to acrylic varnishes in many ways. The most obvious similarity is that both set by evaporation of the water, followed by coalescing agents that fuse the resin into a hard film. This means that acrylic paints may not set satisfactorily if they are applied on a cold damp day or during a period of high humidity (see page 64).

Although acrylic paints are available as gloss and satin finishes, water-based paints are not quite as glossy as the solvent-based variety.

Acrylic paints dry quickly; they are also non-toxic, non-flammable, and practically odourless. Check with the manufacturer's recommendations to make sure that a particular acrylic paint is suitable for finishing exterior joinery.

Milk paint

Formulated to recreate an authentic nineteenth-century finish, milk paints are supplied as colored powders for mixing with water. They are made from milk protein, lime and clay, plus a subtle range of earth pigments. Milk paints dry with a matt finish, but can be burnished if you prefer a satin sheen. For additional protection, apply a coat of clear varnish.

These paints are aimed primarily at restorers, but they are equally suitable for new work. You don't need to prime bare wood, but a special primer is available for use on ready-painted surfaces.

Metallic paint

Manufacturers offer a range of gold, silver, copper and bronze paints, primarily for finishing picture frames, boxes, and other small decorative objects. They are not protective coatings in their own right, but you can cover them with slightly thinned clear varnish if the object is to be handled.

Metallic paints must be stirred thoroughly before use, and applied with a soft paintbrush.

APPLYING PAINT FINISHES

Compared with spraying, applying paint with a brush or pad is a relatively slow process and one where it is difficult to achieve the same quality of finish. However, since it avoids the cost of specialized equipment, and because almost everyone has used a paintbrush, painting by hand is still most woodworkers' preferred method of applying paint finishes.

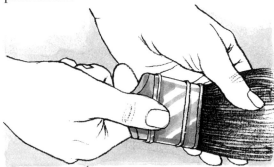

Choosing a good-quality brush
Check the quality of a brush by fanning the bristles with your fingers. The bristles should be densely packed, and they should spring back to shape readily. The bunch of bristles, known as the filling, should be glued firmly into the metal ferrule which, in turn, must be fixed securely to the wooden or plastic handle. A 50mm (2in) brush is ideal for general paintwork, and you will need a 25mm (1in) brush for precise work.

Cleaning pads and brushes
As soon as you have finished painting, blot a pad or paintbrush on a layer of old newspaper, rinse it in mineral spirit, then wash the bristles or pile with hot water and detergent. Wash out brushes used with acrylic paint immediately with water. Re-shape clean brushes and wrap them for storage (see page 69).

Soften hardened oil paint by soaking the bristles in proprietary brush cleaner or paint stripper, then wash the brush thoroughly with soap and water. Cellulose thinner will soften hardened acrylic paint.

Brushes, paint pads and rollers
When choosing brushes for painting, the same rules apply as for varnishing (see page 68). The best brushes for solvent-based paints are made from tough, resilient hog hair. Slightly cheaper ones are a mixture of natural bristles, usually hog, ox or horse hair. Synthetic bristles mimic natural hair, tapering to a tip which is flagged; they divide at the very tip into even finer filaments that hold a finish well. Use these for water-based paints.

Mohair-lined, foamed-plastic pads are the modern equivalent of the paintbrush for finishing large flat surfaces. Some painters also use a smaller version, known as a sash pad, for glazing bars, spindles and moldings. Gently brush a new pad with a clothes brush to remove any loose filaments from the pile.

You could use a small mohair roller to paint a large door or panel.

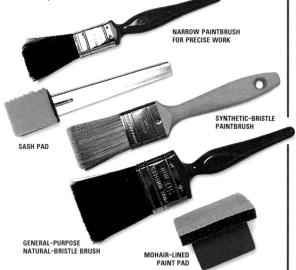

NARROW PAINTBRUSH FOR PRECISE WORK

SYNTHETIC-BRISTLE PAINTBRUSH

SASH PAD

GENERAL-PURPOSE NATURAL-BRISTLE BRUSH

MOHAIR-LINED PAINT PAD

LOADING PAINT PADS
Paint pads are sold with a special tray that has a roller built into one end. As you draw the pad across the roller, paint is distributed evenly across the pile.

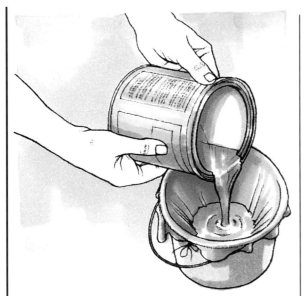

Pouring paint into a kettle

Pour just enough paint for your needs into a plastic paint kettle to make loading a paintbrush easier (see page 69).

If using paint left over from a previous job, it pays to filter it through a piece of muslin or old tights stretched over the kettle; don't, however, do this with thixotropic paint. If old paint has skinned over, cut round the edge with a knife and lift out the skin with a stick before filtering the paint.

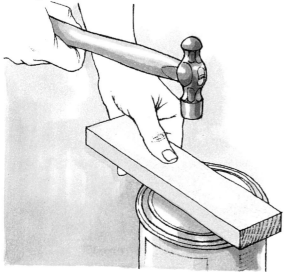

Sealing a can of paint

When re-sealing the can, always wipe paint from the rim with a cloth pad and tap down the lid, using a hammer and a block of wood. Shaking the can after-wards helps prevent a skin forming over the paint.

APPLYING PAINTS

Make sure the work is clean and sanded smooth before brushing on the first coat of paint. Acrylic primer and milk paint are water-based, so be sure to raise the grain before applying them (see page 20).

Although paints are opaque, they will not hide the effects of resinous knots which will eventually discolor the paintwork. Seal suspect knots with shellac-based knotting (see page 51) before painting with solvent-based or acrylic paints.

Strip off chipped or flaking paint (see pages 31–5), and wash sound paintwork to remove dirt and traces of grease. Key gloss paint with fine abrasive paper.

Choosing your moment

Paint exterior woodwork during warm dry weather. Avoid working on a windy day, or airborne dust might ruin your paintwork.

Applying solvent-based paint

When using conventional oil paint, apply a primer and a minimum of two undercoats, followed by a single top coat. Rub down between coats with wet-and-dry paper, wiping off the sludge with a cloth dampened with mineral spirit.

Spread the paint with vertical and sideways strokes, laying off with the tips of the bristles for a smooth finish. Avoid visible brushmarks and runs as described for applying varnish (see pages 70–1).

There is no need to spread thixotropic paint; apply it fairly liberally, smooth it out using virtually parallel strokes, then lay off lightly.

Applying acrylic paint

Brush on water-based paint as you would acrylic varnish (see page 71), blending wet edges quickly.

SPRAYING FINISHES

Spraying wood finishes is not only faster than brushing but, once you have mastered the basics, it also guarantees superior results. Sprayed paintwork, in particular, has a smooth, even quality that is difficult to achieve by any other method, and it is worth spending time developing your technique by practicing on scrap wood and boards before you tackle an actual workpiece.

Spraying systems

In industry and building construction, various hands-on and semi-automated systems are employed for spraying anything from furniture to motor cars, and for decorating interior and exterior surfaces. However, amateur wood finishers require a versatile system, and one that is reasonably inexpensive, compact and reliable. For most people, this means using a small electric-powered compressor that delivers pressurized air to a finely adjustable, hand-held spray gun.

Basic spraying equipment can be hired if you don't want to invest a lot of money at one time, but if you are going to the trouble of constructing a spray booth with built-in extraction, you would do best to equip yourself with a suitable system.

Spray guns

All spray guns atomize a fluid finish, depositing it as a fine mist onto the workpiece, where it flows together to form a perfectly even surface coating. Squeezing the trigger allows compressed air to flow through the spray gun, where it is mixed with paint or other finishes drawn from a reservoir that is mounted above or below the gun.

A gravity-feed cup, attached to the top of the gun, will hold up to about half a litre (1 pint) of paint or clear finish. A filter at the base of the cup prevents dirt particles blocking the gun's nozzle. Gravity-feed guns, often made with relatively lightweight plastic reservoirs, are suitable for spraying most wood finishes, but may not be able to cope with heavily pigmented paints.

A suction-feed spray gun is more versatile because it can handle any wood finish, including metallic paints. Compressed air flows through the gun creating a vacuum that draws finish from a reservoir carried below. Suction-feed reservoirs are invariably larger than gravity cups, so require refilling less often. However, a canister that holds up to a litre (2 pints) of paint can make the spray gun unwieldy, and you have to guard against striking the work with the reservoir slung below the gun.

High-volume, low-pressure (HPLV) spray guns are becoming popular for home spraying, as they produce little overspray and paint waste. They can be run with compressed air or continuous air supplied by a turbine.

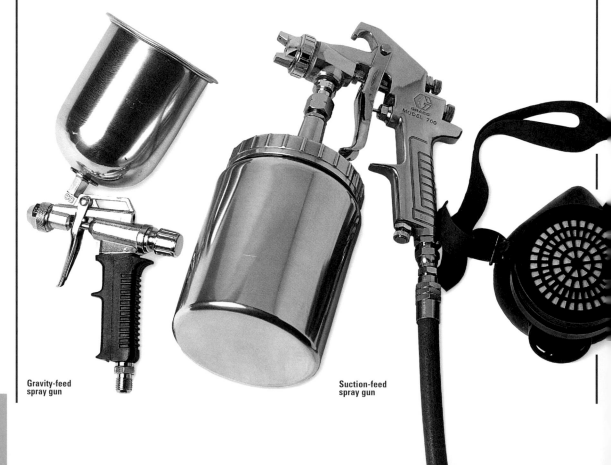

Gravity-feed
spray gun

Suction-feed
spray gun

Spray-gun controls

A top-of-the-range gun has sophisticated controls for balancing air pressure, fluid output and spray pattern.

Fluid tip

The fluid tip is where paint and compressed air are brought together. Air escapes from holes surrounding the central nozzle, from which the wood finish emerges. Squeezing the gun's trigger opens the valve that controls the flow of air momentarily before it also withdraws a spring-loaded needle from the nozzle, allowing paint or varnish to flow.

Fluid-output adjuster

A screw mounted at the rear of the spray gun is used to govern how far the needle can be withdrawn from the fluid-tip nozzle in relation to the trigger, thereby regulating the flow of finish from the gun.

Air valve

Air pressure to the gun is set at the compressor, but an adjustment screw fitted to some spray guns allows you to fine-tune the pressure. Adjust air pressure until it is as low as possible while still maintaining effective atomization.

Air-flow adjuster

Another adjustment screw, usually fitted at the back of the gun, controls the amount of air that flows through the fluid tip to the horns. This allows you to modify the spray pattern, from a narrow cone to the maximum width of fan.

FITTING A SUCTION-FEED RESERVOIR

When attaching the reservoir to the spray gun, make sure that the bent pipe that leads to the base of the canister faces towards the nozzle of the gun. This ensures that the pipe will pick up more of the finishing material in the cup when the gun is tilted slightly forward of horizontal (see page 86).

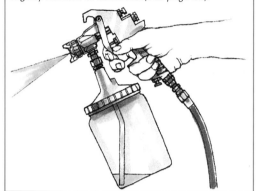

External-mix air cap

The fluid-tip nozzle protrudes from the center of the air cap. A narrow gap surrounding the nozzle is the outlet for air that is directed into the stream of fluid, atomizing it into extremely fine droplets. Some of the compressed air, diverted to 'horns' mounted on each side of the cap, compresses the spray pattern from cone to fan-shaped.

LOCKING RING
AIR CAP
HORN
FLUID -TIP NOZZLE
HORN
AIR-FLOW ADJUSTER
FLUID-OUTPUT ADJUSTER
GRACO
MODEL 700
TRIGGER
DL
AIR VALVE
AIR-SUPPLY HOSE
RESERVOIR

Matched sets

Although many wood finishers make do with a single combination of air cap, fluid tip and needle, pigmented finishes and metallic paints, for example, may require a different set-up. Spray-gun manufacturers publish guides recommending matched sets of needle, cap and tip for various finishes, compressor sizes and scales of production.

Controls of a suction-feed spray gun

COMPRESSORS

Small portable compressors are designed to work with simple, constant-bleed spray guns that have very basic controls. To operate spray guns with the full range of controls described on page 81, you need a compressor incorporating an air receiver or reservoir, from which compressed air is drawn off through a flexible hose running to the gun.

Choosing a compressor

A typical compressor for the home workshop has a single- or twin-cylinder air pump driven by an electric motor, either by means of a drive belt or, more commonly, direct-coupled as a single unit. Compressed air is pumped into a receiving tank and the motor cuts out when the tank is full. As air is drawn off by the spray gun, the pressure in the tank begins to fall; on its reaching a pre-set level, the motor cuts in to top up the tank again.

Choose a compressor with a 2HP motor that can deliver 8cfm (cubic feet per minute). If space is limited,

select a compact unit with a 25 litre (6.5 US gal) air receiver; however, a 50 litre (13 US gal) receiver can cope with a whole range of additional air tools.

Compressors are also rated according to maximum working pressure, typically 120 to 150psi (pounds per square inch). Since you need an operating range of something like 30 to 50psi for spraying and perhaps 80 to 100psi for air tools, the maximum working pressure of most compressors is more than sufficient. Always follow the manufacturers' instructions when setting the air pressure.

MOTOR

FILTER REGULATOR

AIR-HOSE CONNECTION

AIR RECEIVER

DRAIN COCK AT BASE OF RECEIVER

2HP electric compressor

Regulators and filters

Most compressors are manufactured with a built-in regulator to ensure that air is delivered to the spray gun at a constant pressure; a gauge on the instrument records the air pressure, which can be adjusted by turning the regulator valve. The hose is attached by simple quick-fit connectors.

On some models, the regulator incorporates a filter to remove moisture and other contaminants before the air reaches the gun; water droplets collect at the bottom of the reservoir where they can be drained off at regular intervals. If you need to operate with a long hose, it may be necessary to fit a second filter closer to the spray gun to remove any moisture that may have condensed in the line. In-line filter regulators have a drain cock for removing any water collected at that point.

Constructing a spray booth

Spraying is a wasteful process, depositing only about 30 per cent of the paint or varnish onto the work-piece. The rest is lost to the atmosphere as overspray and, if it were not extracted in some way, would fill the workshop with a highly flammable mist of fumes and paint particles. Some woodworkers cope by spraying in the open air or by setting up the work-piece just inside the open doors of a workshop or garage, so that the overspray is directed outside. However, neither situation is entirely satisfactory, and it is better to construct a spray booth fitted with an extractor fan that will in effect collect the overspray, filtering out the solids and depositing the fumes outside the workshop.

Unless you intend to spray water-based finishes only, you need a filtered extractor fan with a shielded motor that prevents sparks igniting solvent fumes. Any switches and light fittings installed in the spray booth must also be explosion-proof.

Building a basic booth

Construct a three-sided box from a softwood frame-work covered with hardboard or MDF panels. Mount the extractor fan in the rear wall of the booth. Line the inside of the booth with sheets of paper that can be replaced after each job.

Arrange a light source above you or on each side of the booth, to avoid throwing your shadow on the work. Light reflected off the back wall will help you judge the condition of the paintwork.

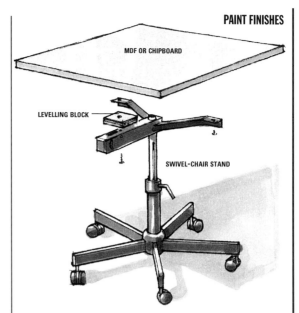

MDF OR CHIPBOARD

LEVELLING BLOCK

SWIVEL-CHAIR STAND

Making a turntable

To avoid being covered with overspray, always position the workpiece between you and the extractor. The easiest way to accomplish this is to make a turntable for the work, so that you can rotate the workpiece to present unfinished surfaces to the spray gun in turn. You can buy proprietary turntables, but it may be cheaper to convert a swivel-chair stand.

SAFETY WHEN SPRAYING

Before you invest too much money on equipment, check with your local authority, fire department and possibly your insurance company to ensure you are able to comply with any requirements or regulations for building a spray booth and operating paint-spraying equipment in your workshop.

• Always work outside or install an approved extractor to remove solvent fumes from the workshop.

• When spraying, wear goggles, overalls and an approved respirator.

• Don't smoke when spraying, and extinguish naked flames in the workshop.

• Don't point a spray gun at yourself or anyone else.

• Disconnect a spray gun from the supply hose before attempting any service or repair work (see page 85).

• Keep a fire blanket and extinguisher close to hand.

ADJUSTING AND TESTING SPRAY GUNS

Adjusting spray equipment to get the best results each time will become automatic with experience, but initially it is worth experimenting with the range of adjustments to see how your particular system operates. Unless you are working with cellulose lacquer, which is usually sold in a sprayable consistency, you will need to dilute the finish with an appropriate solvent.

Thinning wood finishes

Check the manufacturers' recommendations for the ideal ratio of finish to thinner when preparing paint, varnish or cold-cure lacquer. To avoid having to mix a second batch to the same consistency, always make up enough thinned finish to complete the job.

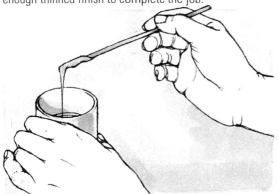

Checking consistency

Stir the thinner into the finish with a wooden stick, then lift out the stick to see how well the diluted finish runs from the tip. If it is still too thick, the finish will drip or run intermittently from the stick, but if it runs smoothly, in a steady continuous stream, the paint or varnish is about ready for spraying. Before spraying a workpiece, test the finish on a practice board – an overdiluted finish will run almost immediately.

Using a viscosity cup

For a more scientific test of consistency, you can run the fluid through a viscosity cup, a type of funnel that will empty at a precise rate when the finish is thinned accurately.

Adjusting the controls

To test the controls of a spray gun, set up a piece of plywood or MDF in the spray booth. Fill the gun's reservoir to the recommended level with paint so that you can see the effects of adjusting the controls.

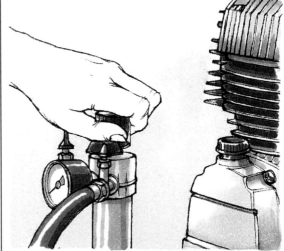

1 Setting the air pressure
The easiest way to set the required air pressure is to open fully the air valve on the gun's handgrip, then adjust the valve on the compressor's regulator until the gauge reads the required pressure; about 30psi is a good starting point.

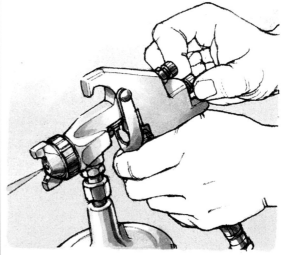

2 Adjusting fluid output
Start with the fluid-output screw fully closed. Aim the gun at the workpiece, holding the nozzle about 200mm (8in) from the surface, and squeeze the trigger. Gradually open the fluid-output adjuster until you begin to wet the surface with paint. If the adjuster is opened too far, too much fluid will be sprayed onto the surface and begin to run.

3 Fine-tuning

Experiment with the controls, using the air valve or the regulator to increase and decrease air pressure, and balancing the effects by adjusting the fluid flow.

Another test is to move the gun closer to the work-piece and then bring it away, to gauge when too much fluid is applied to the surface and, conversely, when the paint only settles as a dry dusting. The relative humidity of the atmosphere and the rate at which the thinner evaporates will also affect the quality of finish.

Maintaining compressors

Drain water from the receiver and filter regulator each day or after every spraying session.

Following the manufacturer's instructions, check the oil level regularly and change the air-intake filter when necessary. Remove accumulated dust from the compressor's cooling fins.

CLEANING A SPRAY GUN

Having to replace a ruined paintbrush is not a disaster, but if you neglect to clean out a spray gun you will be faced with a hefty bill for replacement parts, or even a completely new gun.

As soon as you have finished spraying, empty the reservoir and add thinner. Operate the gun until clean thinner begins to emerge from the nozzle. If you have run out of a specific thinner, cellulose thinner can be used to clean out most modern finishes.

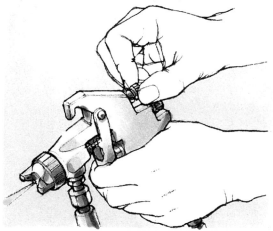

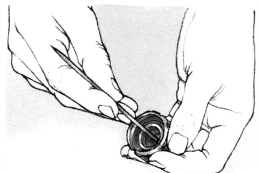

4 Setting the spray pattern

With the air-flow adjuster fully closed, the gun will emit a narrow cone of atomized paint. With the horns set horizontally, gradually open the adjuster, watching how the spray pattern changes to a wide vertical fan. Slacken the locking ring on the air cap, turn the horns to a vertical position and hand-tighten the locking ring again; in this configuration, the gun produces a horizontal, fan-shaped spray pattern.

Cleaning the air cap and fluid tip

Close the valve that delivers air to the hose, squeeze the gun's trigger to clear the hose, then disconnect the spray gun. Remove the air cap so that you can wipe it and the fluid tip clean with a piece of soft rag. Remove any obvious blockages, using a wooden toothpick and the synthetic-bristle brush supplied with the gun. Wipe the inside of the reservoir and the outside of the gun with a rag moistened with thinner.

SPRAYING TECHNIQUES

As a general rule, it is best to apply several thin coats of wood finish, rubbed down between applications with wet-and-dry paper to remove specks of dust and other blemishes. Sprayed finishes tend to become touch-dry relatively quickly, but you will need space to put workpieces aside to harden properly; dampen the floor to keep airborne dust to a minimum.

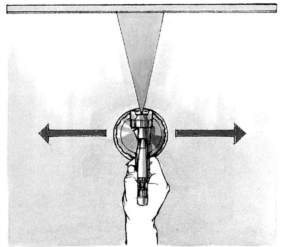

Pointing the gun
To achieve a perfectly even finish, it is important to keep the gun pointed directly at the work. When spraying a wide panel, for example, flex your wrist so that you move the gun on a path parallel to the surface of the work.

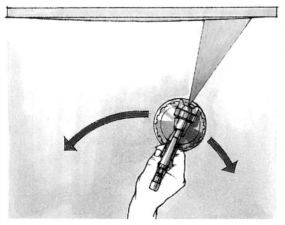

Uneven coverage
If you make the common mistake of swinging the gun in an arc, you will deposit insufficient paint or varnish along each side of the workpiece, leaving a strip of thicker finish down the center.

Spraying a flat panel
Before spraying a vertical board or panel, adjust the gun to produce a fan-shape spray pattern (see page 85).

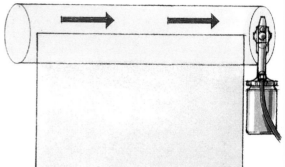

1 Making the first pass
Aligning the nozzle with the top edge of the workpiece, aim the gun to one side of the panel. Squeeze the trigger and make one continuous pass at a steady pace across the panel. Don't release the trigger until the gun is aiming well clear of the panel.

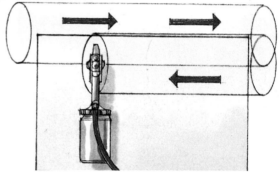

2 Overlapping with the return pass
Squeeze the trigger again and make a second pass in the opposite direction, overlapping the first application by 50 per cent. To coat the entire panel evenly, overlap each subsequent pass in a similar way, squeezing and releasing the trigger at the start and end of each pass; spraying continuously may seem easier, but is very wasteful of paint or varnish.

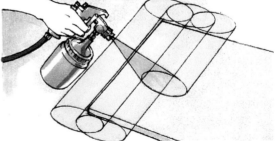

Spraying a horizontal panel
You may find it easier to lay a small panel flat on your turntable. Working away from you, make overlapping parallel passes, holding the gun at an angle of about 45 degrees to the work.

SPRAYING ASSEMBLED WORKPIECES

Spraying individual components, such as panels, doors or shelves, is relatively straightforward (see opposite), but when you are finishing assembled pieces, work out a sequence that will enable you to coat all surfaces in turn, and will also allow you to move the workpiece without spoiling the finish.

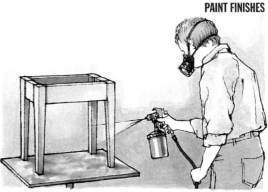

Spraying a table

It is always more convenient to spray a table top and underframe separately. Set the gun to produce a cone-shape spray pattern for finishing narrow legs and rails, spreading the pattern into a fan for spraying the top.

- Spray the underside of the top and put it aside to dry.
- Stand the underframe on the turntable and spray the inside of the legs and rails. When spraying square legs, aim the gun at one corner so that you coat two surfaces at once.
- Spray the outside of the legs and rails.
- Return the table top to the turntable, supporting it on small blocks of wood. Spray the edges all round, then coat the top surface evenly (see opposite).

Spraying a cabinet

Finish the doors as individual panels before fitting them to a cabinet. Spray the inside of the cabinet first, trying not to aim the gun directly into a right-angle corner.

Depending on the size of the cabinet, either set the gun to produce a horizontal fan-shape spray pattern (see page 85), or use a cone-shape pattern for finishing interior surfaces.

- Finish the underside of the top panel.
- Spray down one side of the cabinet, then across the back panel.
- Coat the remaining side panel, then complete the interior by spraying the bottom of the cabinet.
- Spray the exterior of the cabinet, treating each panel individually.

Spraying a chair

Set a cone-shape pattern for chair legs and stretcher rails and, if necessary, open it out into a small fan for finishing the seat and back rest.

- Turn the chair upside down on the turntable so that you can spray the insides of the legs and rails.
- Spray the underside of the seat.
- Stand the chair on its feet and spray the outside of the legs and stretcher rails.
- Spray the edges of seat followed by the top surface.
- Finish the inside of armrests and chair back.
- Spin the chair round to coat the outside of the arm-rests and chair back.

FAULTS AND REMEDIES

Brushed-on varnishes, lacquers and paints exhibit certain faults that result from poor preparation or from their sensitivity to temperature or humidity (see pages 74 and 79). You are likely to encounter similar problems when the same finishes are sprayed. The following is a list of problems that are directly related to spraying or that occur most often when a finish is applied with a spray gun.

'Orange peel'
The finish dries with a wrinkled appearance similar to the skin of an orange. In most cases, this is the result of holding the gun too close to the workpiece or of spraying a fluid that has not been diluted sufficiently.
Let the finish harden, then rub down and respray.

Runs and sagging
Instead of forming a perfectly even coating, the finish runs or sags, sometimes forming a thick roll along one edge of the workpiece. This will occur when the finish is applied too thickly or the finish is overdiluted.
Let the finish dry hard, then rub down with wet-and-dry paper before applying the next coat.

Cissing or fish-eye
A newly sprayed surface develops miniature craters where the finish has been repelled by traces of wax, oil or water. An old piece that has been stripped of its finish may be contaminated by silicone oil or wax from previous finishes. Alternatively, if the compressor receiver or air line has not been drained properly, water or oil may be deposited in the new finish.
When the finish has set, scrape or sand it flat with wet-and-dry paper and wipe the surface clean, using a cloth dampened with mineral spirit. After draining the spray-gun system, spray a small area to see whether the problem has been eradicated.

If the symptoms recur, rub down again and add a proprietary anti-cissing (fish-eye) agent to the finish to reduce its surface tension.

As a last resort, strip the finish back to bare wood (see pages 31–5) and apply a shellac-based sealer (see page 26) before respraying.

Finish dries with a powdery appearance
A dry, finely textured surface may be the result of excessive air pressure or overspray settling on previously sprayed paintwork. Alternatively, you may be holding the gun so far from the surface that the finish is almost dry when it reaches the surface.
Let the finish dry thoroughly, then rub down and respray.

TYPICAL SPRAY-GUN PROBLEMS
Some faults are caused by not cleaning and servicing a spray gun regularly.

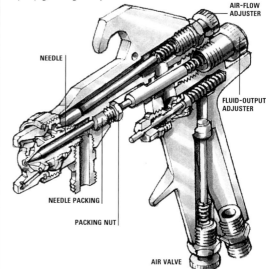

AIR-FLOW ADJUSTER

NEEDLE

FLUID-OUTPUT ADJUSTER

NEEDLE PACKING

PACKING NUT

AIR VALVE

Gun flutters or spits drops
If the gun begins to flutter or spit drops of paint or varnish onto the workpiece while spraying, check to see if the reservoir is nearly empty or the delivery pipe is not in the correct position to pick up the fluid (see page 81). Check also that the air vent in the top of the reservoir has not become blocked. If all seems to be well with the reservoir, try thinning the fluid slightly. Tighten the needle-valve packing nut to ensure it does not allow air into the fluid passages.

Fluid runs from the nozzle
If paint or varnish seeps from the nozzle when the gun is not being operated, the needle packing may be too tight. Lubricate the packing with a spot of light oil and check the adjustment of the packing nut. If this does not solve the problem, the needle itself may be worn or damaged, or may not be seating properly in the fluid tip. Have the gun checked by an expert.

Fluid leaks from the packing nut
Tighten the packing nut; if this does not work, replace the needle packing.

CHAPTER 7

Waxing wood is a long-established tradition, and one which is frequently employed by antique restorers. That is not to say that the subtle qualities of wax polish have gone unnoticed by other woodworkers, especially as a finish for open-grain timbers or as a dressing over lacquer, varnish or French polish.

WAX POLISH

COMMERCIAL POLISHES

Making wax polish from basic ingredients is sometimes advocated by traditionalists, but since there is such a variety of excellent polishes readily available, there seems little point in introducing a complication into what is otherwise one of the simplest of wood-finishing processes. Most commercially prepared wax polishes are a blend of relatively soft beeswax and hard carnauba wax, reduced to a usable consistency with turpentine or mineral spirit.

A traditional wax finish gives a sympathetic patina to a Georgian-style dressing table and chair

Paste wax polish

The most familiar form of wax polish is sold as a thick paste, packed in flat tins or foil containers. Paste wax, applied with a cloth pad or fine steel wool, serves as an ideal dressing over another finish.

Liquid wax polish

When you want to wax a large area of oak panelling, for example, it is probably easiest to brush on liquid wax polish that has the consistency of cream.

Floor wax

Floor wax is a liquid polish formulated for hardwearing surfaces. It is usually available as a clear polish only.

Tinted brushing polish deepens the color of pine furniture

Woodturning sticks

Carnauba wax is the main ingredient for sticks that are hard enough to be used as a friction polish on work-pieces being turned in a lathe.

Colored polishes

White to pale-yellow polishes do not alter the color of the wood to a great extent, but there is also an extensive choice of darker shades, sometimes referred to as staining waxes, that can be used to modify the color of a workpiece and to hide scratches and minor blemishes. Dark-brown to black polish is a popular finish for oak furniture; it enhances the patina of old wood and, by lodging in the open pores, accentuates the grain pattern. There are warm golden-brown polishes, made to put the color back into stripped pine, and orange-red polishes to enrich faded mahogany. Applying one polish over another creates even more subtle shades and tints.

It is not a good idea to wax chairs or benches with dark-colored polishes in case your body heat should soften the wax and stain your clothing. The same goes for finishing the insides of drawers; long-term contact could discolor delicate fabrics.

Silicones

Silicone oil, which is added to some polishes to make them easier to apply and burnish, will repel most surface coatings should the piece require refinishing in the future (see page 88). Sealing the wood beforehand is a wise precaution, but applying a chemical stripper at a later date may still allow silicone oil to penetrate the pores. You should therefore decide from the beginning whether it would be better to finish a piece with a silicone-free wax polish.

Wax-dressed walnut display cabinet

APPLYING WAX POLISHES

Finishing wood with a wax polish could hardly be simpler, as it requires only careful application and sufficient energy to burnish the surface to a deep shine. However, as with any wood finish, the workpiece must be sanded smooth and any blemishes filled or repaired before you can achieve a satisfactory result (see pages 10–26). Wipe the surface with mineral spirit (see page 28) to remove traces of grease and old wax polish.

Although there is no need to fill the grain, it is always best to seal the work with two coats of French polish or sanding sealer before applying wax polish, especially if you have colored the wood with solvent stain. Rub down the sealer coats with fine silicon-carbide paper.

WAX-POLISHING BRUSHES

Professional wood finishers sometimes use a bristle brush to burnish hardened wax polish. You can use a clean shoe brush, but you might want to buy a purpose-made furniture brush fitted with a handle to keep your knuckles out of the way when burnishing into awkward corners and recesses. In addition, there are circular brushes designed to fit the chuck of a power drill; when you are using one of these, apply light pressure only and keep the brush moving across the polished surface.

HAND BRUSH FOR WAX POLISH

DRILL BRUSH

SHOE BRUSH

FURNITURE BRUSH

1 Applying paste wax polish
Dip a cloth pad in paste wax and apply the first coat, using overlapping circular strokes to rub the wax into the grain. Cover the surface evenly, then finish by rubbing in the direction of the grain. If the polish proves difficult to spread, warm the tin on a radiator.

2 Building up a layer of polish
After about 15 to 20 minutes, use 000-grade steel wool or an abrasive nylon pad to rub on more wax polish, this time working along the grain. Put the work aside for 24 hours so that the solvent can evaporate. On new work, apply four or five coats of wax in all, allowing each one to harden overnight.

3 Burnishing the polish
When the wax has hardened thoroughly, burnish vigorously with a soft cloth pad. Some polishers prefer to use a furniture brush because it raises a better shine, particularly when burnishing carved work. Finally, rub over all polished surfaces with a clean duster.

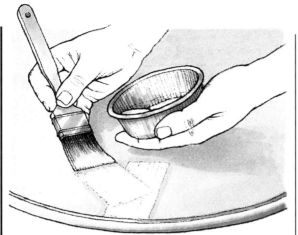

1 Brushing liquid wax polish
Decant some polish into a shallow dish and brush it liberally onto the wood, spreading the wax as evenly as possible. Let the solvent evaporate for about an hour.

2 Applying subsequent coats
Apply a second coat of wax with a soft cloth pad. Use circular strokes at first, and finish by rubbing parallel to the grain. An hour later, apply a third coat if required.

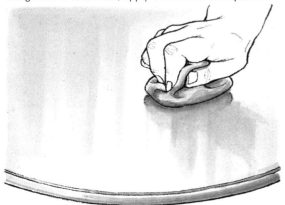

3 Buffing the surface
Leave the polish to harden, preferably overnight, then burnish the workpiece in the direction of the grain with a clean soft duster.

Maintaining a wax finish
The color and patina of a wax finish improve with age, provided the finish receives regular care. Mop up any spilled water immediately, and dust a polished surface frequently to pick up dirt that might otherwise sink into the wax and discolor the finish. If you cannot raise a satisfactory shine by burnishing with a soft cloth, it is time to apply a fresh coat of wax. Very dowdy wax polish can be removed with mineral spirit, in preparation for refinishing (see page 28).

APPLYING A WAX DRESSING
If you want to achieve the typical mellow finish of wax polish but prefer something more hardwearing, you can apply a thin wax dressing over polyurethane varnish or cold-cure lacquer.

Dip 000-grade steel wool or an abrasive nylon pad in paste polish, and rub the finished surface using long straight strokes, parallel with the grain. Leave the wax to harden for 15 to 20 minutes, then polish it with a soft cloth.

1 Waxing a turned workpiece

Sand the work smooth with fine abrasive paper or cloth, rub a damp cloth along it to raise the grain, then sand the wood a second time when the water has evaporated. Hold a special hard-wax turning stick against the workpiece as it rotates in a lathe at a slow speed – move the stick across the work as friction begins to melt the wax, coating the wood evenly.

You can apply a cloth pad dipped in ordinary paste wax polish to a turned piece, but you may need several coats of wax to build a satisfactory finish.

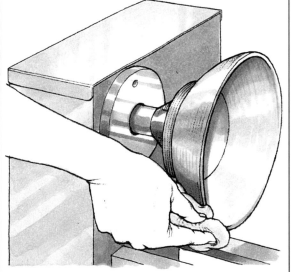

2 Burnishing with the lathe running

Let the wax harden, then hold a soft cloth pad against the rotating workpiece to raise a shine. Move the cloth slowly across the work, keeping the pad away from rotating parts of the lathe. Although you need to apply sufficient pressure to smooth the surface of the wax, pressing too hard can tear the polish.

Polishing floors

After cleaning or sanding wooden floorboards, seal the bare wood with a proprietary floor sealer. Pour clear liquid floor wax into a shallow dish and apply two coats of polish to the wood, using a 100mm (4in) paintbrush. Leave the wax to dry, then burnish the wood with a bristle brush held in a power drill or hire a polishing machine to finish a large floor.

You may need to wax polish a floor every four to six months, depending on the wear it receives; it should be burnished every few weeks to recreate the shine.

FAULTS AND REMEDIES

Wax polishing is so straightforward that there is very little that can go wrong, and even a complete novice can achieve perfect results. Most problems that do occur are caused by impatience.

Uneven finish

Burnishing a polished surface before the solvent has evaporated redistributes the wax, resulting in a patchy, uneven finish. You may also find you are leaving fingerprints in the soft wax.

Leave the wax to harden, then use a 000-grade steel-wool pad to apply a light dressing of fresh wax to even out the finish. Let this coat dry overnight before burnishing with a soft duster.

Surface breaks up when burnishing

The wax has not hardened completely, and rubbing too hard pulls flakes of wax off the surface.

Remove the wax with a steel-wool pad dipped in mineral spirit. Wipe the dissolved wax off the wood with a paper towel and re-polish.

Wax develops a bloom

Occasionally a wax finish will develop a cloudy bloom as the solvent evaporates.

This effect is usually temporary, and can be removed with a soft duster.

CHAPTER 8

Unlike varnish and paint, which lay on the surface, wood-finishing oil penetrates deeply into the pores, forming a resilient finish that will not crack, peel or chip. As a result, most oil finishes are ideal for exterior joinery and garden furniture, and require no more than annual maintenance to protect the wood from weathering and preserve its appearance.

OIL FINISHES

TYPES OF OIL FINISH

Some woodworkers consider oil finishes as being suitable only for hardwoods such as teak or afrormosia; this is primarily because they are associated in people's minds with the fashion for 'Scandinavian-style' furniture and interior design. In fact, oil makes a handsome finish for any timber, especially pine, which turns a rich golden color when oiled.

Pine staircase finished with hardwearing gelled oil

Linseed oil

Traditional linseed oil, derived from the flax plant, is rarely used nowadays for finishing wood, mainly because it can take up to three days to dry.

Manufacturers have been able to reduce drying time to about 24 hours by heating the oil and adding driers, producing 'boiled' linseed oil. Neither type of oil should be used as an exterior finish.

Tung oil

Also known as Chinese wood oil, tung oil is obtained from nuts grown in China and parts of South America. A tung-oil finish is resistant to water, alcohol and acidic fruit juice, takes about 24 hours to dry and is suitable for exterior woodwork.

Finishing oil

Commercial wood-finishing oils, based on tung oil, include synthetic resins to improve their durability. Depending on temperature and humidity, finishing oils dry in about six hours. Often referred to as teak oil or Danish oil, finishing oil is an excellent finish for any environment, and can also be used as a sealer coat for oil varnish or paint.

Non-toxic oils

Pure tung oil is non-toxic, but some manufacturers add metallic driers to it, so don't use tung oil for items that will come into contact with food unless the maker's recommendations state specifically that it is safe to do so. As an alternative, you can use ordinary olive oil or one of the special 'salad-bowl' oils, sold for finishing food receptacles and chopping boards.

Gelled oil

A blend of natural oils and synthetic resin is available in a thick gel that behaves more like a soft wax polish. It is packed in tubs so that the gel can be picked up on a cloth pad. Gelled oil can be applied to bare wood and, unlike other oil finishes, it can also be applied over existing finishes such as varnish and lacquer.

Preparing the surface

Since oil is a penetrating finish, it cannot be applied to a pre-varnished or painted workpiece; strip a surface finish using chemical stripper (see pages 31–4). When finishing previously oiled timber, use mineral spirit to clean old wax from the surface (see page 28). Prepare bare wood thoroughly (see pages 10–26), sanding it smooth with progressively finer abrasive papers.

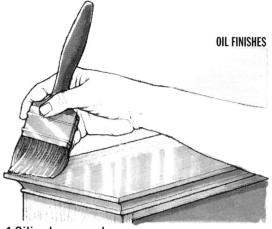

1 Oiling bare wood
Shake the container before decanting some oil into a shallow dish. Apply the first coat, using a fairly wide paintbrush to wet the surface thoroughly. Leave the oil to soak in for about 10 to 15 minutes, then ensure that coverage is even by wiping excess oil from the surface with a soft cloth pad.

2 Applying additional oil with a pad
After six hours, use an abrasive nylon-fibre pad to rub oil onto the wood in the general direction of the grain. Wipe excess from the surface with a paper towel or cloth pad, then leave it to dry overnight. Apply a third coat in the same way.

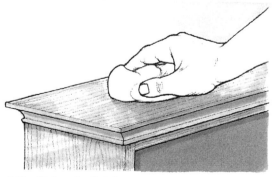

3 Modifying the finish
Leave the last coat to dry thoroughly, then burnish the surface with a duster to raise a soft sheen.

For a smooth satin finish, dress interior woodwork with wax polish, using a clean abrasive nylon pad or fine steel wool (see page 93).

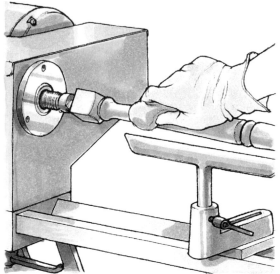

Oiling turned pieces

After sanding a turned workpiece, switch off the lathe while you rub oil onto the wood. Let it soak in for a short while, wipe off excess oil, then restart the lathe and burnish by holding a cloth pad against the slowly rotating workpiece.

Applying gelled oil

Apply gelled oil to bare wood, using a soft cloth pad to rub the finish vigorously in the direction of the grain until the surface is touch-dry. Two coats are usually sufficient, but apply more gelled oil to a workpiece that will be subjected to heavy wear and hot dishes; allow four hours between coats. Apply gelled oil sparingly over an existing finish.

Since gelled oil dries naturally to a soft sheen, there is no need to burnish the workpiece again, but allow a full 48 hours before you put it to use.

From time to time, wipe the workpiece with a damp cloth to remove surface marks and fingerprints.

Maintaining an oiled finish

An oiled surface is very hardwearing, and under normal circumstances requires nothing more than an occasional wipe with a damp cloth to maintain the finish. A faded finish can be revitalised by applying a light coat of oil, provided you remove any wax dressing first (see page 28). Wipe the surface dry before oiling.

Oil exterior woodwork at regular intervals, taking care to treat all surfaces with at least one coat.

Fire precautions

As oil oxidizes it generates heat, which can cause oil-soaked rags to burst into flames. Spread out used rags to dry thoroughly outside, or soak them in a bucket of water overnight before disposing of them.

FAULTS AND REMEDIES

Oiling wood is so easy that success is practically guaranteed, provided you have prepared the workpiece adequately and you don't leave the oil to become sticky.

Sticky surface

If you leave excess oil on the surface for longer than about an hour, it thickens and becomes sticky.
Don't attempt to wipe off oil if it reaches this stage. Instead, use an abrasive nylon pad to apply a light dressing of fresh oil to wet the surface again, then wipe over with a cloth pad or absorbent paper towel.

White rings

Hot plates or dishes may leave white rings on an oiled surface.
These blemishes are usually temporary and disappear of their own accord within a short time.

CHAPTER 9

Covering wood with genuine gold leaf is a particularly skillful process, and is best left to an expert. However, applying paper-thin sheets of gold-colored base metal is far less demanding and relatively inexpensive. And if you want to spruce up old picture frames and mirrors, you may be able to achieve the desired result with a ready-to-use gilt cream or varnish.

GILDING

GILDING WITH CREAMS AND VARNISHES

Gilding does not have to be an expensive process. If all you require is an attractive gold-colored surface, you can use proprietary finishes that are akin to wax polishes and metallic varnishes. Similar products are perfect for improving the appearance of cheap gilded photo mounts and picture frames.

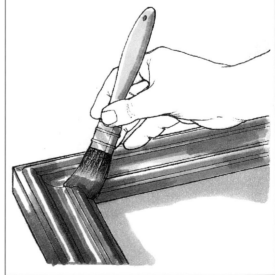

FONTENAY BASE

GILT VARNISH

GILT CREAM

GILT-FINISHING LIQUID

Gilt cream
Soft creamy wax is ready-made in a variety of metallic shades for finishing new work or restoring old gilded furniture and frames. Gilt creams are very easy to apply and mix on the surface of a workpiece.

Gilt varnish
Use non-tarnishing gilt varnish to decorate both new and stripped workpieces. You can apply it directly to the wood or over a traditional red base (see below), and it can be used as a base coat for gilt cream. Gilt varnish is especially useful for picking out small areas of a decorative frame or for finishing separate slip moldings. Stir gilt varnish thoroughly to avoid a streaky finish.

Fontenay base
Before applying a gilt finish, you can seal the wood with Fontenay base, a special dark-red matt varnish that adds depth to the gold color. A black base coat, that creates an undertone for silver and pewter finishes, is also available.

Gilt-finishing liquid
Gilt-finish suppliers provide a clear gloss copal varnish for sealing gilt cream. Apply gilt-finishing liquid with a soft paintbrush.

APPLYING FONTENAY BASE
When gilding new work, fill the grain (see page 26) and sand the wood carefully. Rub down paintwork with wet-and-dry paper.

Brush Fontenay base onto the work, leave it to dry, then rub down with very fine steel wool or silicon-carbide paper. If necessary, apply a second base coat to create an even matt finish.

1 Applying gilt cream

Apply gilt cream with a soft cloth wrapped round a fingertip. Use small overlapping circular strokes to spread the cream evenly, finishing with straight parallel strokes. Work cream into carvings and decorative moldings with an old toothbrush.

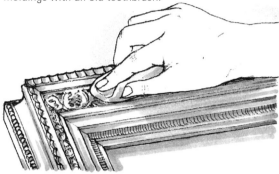

2 Burnishing and sealing gilt cream

Allow the solvent to evaporate for at least 12 hours, then burnish the gilded surface with a soft cloth pad. Unless you want an aged appearance, take care not to rub so hard that you expose the base coat on the high points. Apply extra cream to cover any bare patches.

Gilt cream provides a permanent finish similar to ordinary wax polish; for additional protection, coat it with gilt-finishing liquid.

Applying gilt varnish to new work
Using a soft paintbrush, apply gilt varnish evenly and leave it to dry for at least three hours before handling the workpiece. For an extra-rich finish, rub on a darker gilt cream after the varnish has set.

AGEING A GILT FINISH

Good-quality metallic varnishes and creams provide a beautiful finish with a deep glow, but period-style furniture and genuine old pieces often benefit from a little 'ageing' to provide them with a distinguished, care-worn appearance.

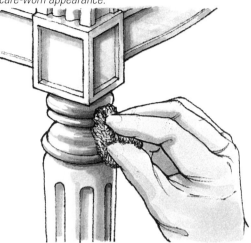

Exposing the basecoat
Using a small ball of fine steel wool or an abrasive nylon-fibre pad, gently rub the gilding from the high points until the red base coat just begins to show through the gold. Take care to keep the treatment subtle, or the effect will be spoiled.

Applying colored wax
Rub dark-brown wax polish over a newly gilded workpiece, if necessary using a brush to stipple the polish into all the crevices. Take a soft cloth and rub excess wax from the high points, leaving the darker color to accentuate the decorative details. Create a similar effect by rubbing one or more dark-gold creams over a pale gilt finish, then polish the high spots with a cloth pad.

MAKING MINOR REPAIRS WITH GILDING WAX

It generally pays to exercise restraint when restoring old gilding. Even run-of-the-mill picture frames become more characterful when natural wear starts to expose the dark base color and the gilding begins to take on a mellowed patina. The best policy is to patch up only those faults that draw attention to themselves, disguising them with a blend of wax sticks and gilt cream.

FILLING STICKS

RETOUCH CRAYONS

Disguising open miters
You can fill a less-than-perfect miter joint with a soft wax crayon. Rub the sharp edge of the stick across the open miter until it is filled flush with wax. Wrap a soft cloth around your finger, and rub along the joint to smooth the filling and remove excess wax from the surface. If necessary, blend the color with a fingertip dipped in gilt cream.

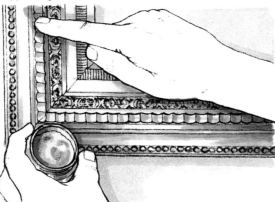

Hiding scratches
Fill a deep scratch that has exposed the red base color or white gesso ground (see page 104) with a soft wax crayon (see above), and hide minor scratches by rubbing over them with gilt cream.

Wax filling sticks and retouch crayons
Use gilt-colored wax sticks to fill holes and repair minor chips and damaged moldings. Softer-wax crayons will help disguise scratches and inaccurate miter joints. Both types of wax stick are available in a wide range of colors and tones, from deep bronze to pale gold and silver. Melting two or more sticks and blending the wax allows you to match an existing finish exactly.

Filling holes
When restoring an old picture frame, fill small holes with a gilt filling stick of hard wax. Soften a pea-size piece of wax on a radiator until you can knead it easily between your fingers, then use a penknife to press the softened wax into each hole. Scrape it level with your thumbnail or a plastic credit card, and burnish the wax filling with the smooth paper backing of abrasive paper. Disguise the repair by smearing it with gilt cream.

GILDING WITH METAL LEAF

Base-metal leaf is not a cheap modern substitute for genuine gold leaf. For hundreds of years it has been employed for work that did not merit the expense of being coated with pure gold, so metal leaf can be used legitimately to make attractive repairs as well as for gilding new work

Gilded sconce (right)
Flickering candlelight will accentuate the quality of genuine gold leaf or base-metal gilding.

Empire-style couch (below)
The appeal of this elegant couch is greatly enhanced by its ebonized frame with gilded details.

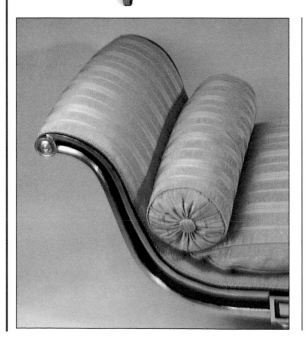

103

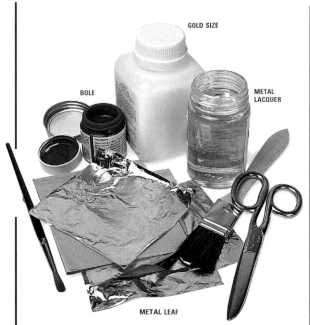

GOLD SIZE

BOLE

METAL LACQUER

METAL LEAF

Metal leaf

Also known as common leaf or Dutch leaf, metal leaf, an alloy of copper and zinc, is available as thin 100 to 125mm (4 to 5in) squares bound into books of 25 sheets. Being slightly thicker than gold leaf, metal leaf is relatively easy to apply and, when burnished, makes a passable substitute for the real thing.

Gesso and bole

Far from hiding uneven grain or surface blemishes, thin metal leaf will highlight imperfections as soon as it is burnished. Consequently, bare wood is coated with gesso, a paste made from rabbit-skin glue and chalk, which can be sanded to a perfectly smooth base for gilding. It can also be used as a glue for re-attaching broken pieces of old gesso. Colored gesso is sometimes referred to as bole.

Gold size

Size is a glue-like preparation used to stick metal leaf to a gesso ground. Depending on the type you use, size will dry in anything from 2 to 24 hours.

Metal lacquer

Base metal will tarnish unless it is coated with a water-clear transparent lacquer formulated to protect metal.

PREPARING METAL LEAF

Before you handle metal leaf, wash your hands and dust them with talcum powder to prevent the leaf sticking to your fingers.

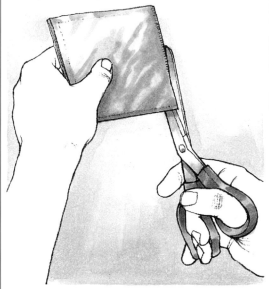

Cutting the leaves to size

Remove the outer covers from a book of metal leaf and cut off the spine with scissors. Leaving the tissue backing intact, trim each individual sheet into squares or rectangles to fit the work in progress.

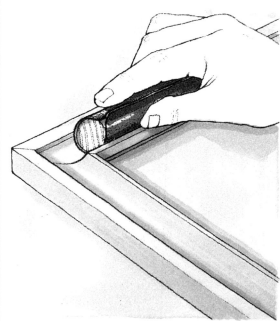

Preparing the surface

Fill any holes and cracks, then sand the wood as smooth as possible. Wipe the surface with mineral spirit to remove dust and grease.

1 Applying bole to the work

Warm a pot of ready-made dark-red bole in a *bain-marie* or glue pot until it becomes liquid enough to be brushed smoothly onto the prepared surface. Don't allow the bole to run or collect in the hollows.

Leave the surface to harden overnight, then rub it down lightly with fine wet-and-dry paper. Apply up to five coats of bole.

2 Sealing the bole with shellac

Mix up a sealer comprising equal amounts of standard French polish and denatured alcohol. Apply the thinned shellac with a cloth pad or a soft paintbrush; when brushing up to sharp edges or moldings, take care that the sealer does not run or collect in grooves or hollows.

3 Rubbing down with steel wool

Allow the shellac to harden, then remove blemishes by rubbing down gently with 0000-grade steel wool lubricated with soapy water. Wipe the surface dry with a clean cloth.

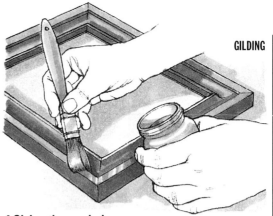

4 Sizing the workpiece

Apply a thin, even coat of adhesive gold size, brushing it out carefully to avoid leaving bare patches. Since metal leaf must be applied to the size at exactly the right moment, divide a large workpiece into smaller, manageable sections.

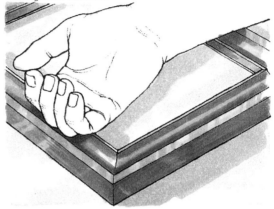

5 Testing the size

Temperature and humidity will affect the time it takes for gold size to dry. Check by gently touching your knuckles against the sized surface; when it feels firm but slightly tacky, the size is about ready.

6 Applying metal leaf

Holding a leaf of metal in both hands, lay it face-down onto the sized workpiece. Smooth it down firmly with your fingertips, then peel off the tissue backing.

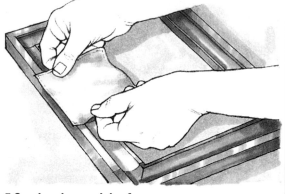

7 Overlapping each leaf

Apply the next strip of metal leaf in the same way, overlapping its neighbour by about 3mm (⅛in). Continue to lay additional strips until you have gilded the entire workpiece, or at least one sized section.

8 Blending the joints

Remove the overlaps and blend the joints between strips of leaf by brushing them with the tip of an ox-hair paintbrush. Brush only in the direction of the overlaps, collecting the tiny scraps of leaf on a piece of paper placed beneath the workpiece. These 'skewings' are used to patch small areas at the next stage.

9 Patching with skewings

Inspect the work carefully for areas of red ground that may have been missed. Anything that is too small to be covered with a small patch of metal leaf can be obliterated with skewings brushed lightly onto the surface and tamped down firmly onto the still-tacky size with the tip of a brush.

10 Burnishing the leaf

The following day, burnish the metal gently with a cotton-wool pad until you have raised a soft sheen. Preserve the finish by brushing the workpiece with a thin coat of transparent metal lacquer.

GILDING CARVED WORK

Gilding a carved workpiece takes more time and patience. Consequently, plan to size and gild sections in turn, so that you can apply leaf to one part of the work while the size is becoming tacky on another. This may entail working from the bottom up, to avoid skewings contaminating a section that is still drying.

Applying leaf to shaped groundwork

Cut or tear small pieces of leaf to fit the shape of the area you are working on, pressing them into place with your fingertips until you have completed a section, then tamp the metal with the tip of a brush to ensure it conforms to the shape of the groundwork and adheres to the size.

CHAPTER 10

Graining is the art of simulating the appearance of real wood with colored glaze. Although it would be unrealistic to expect to copy actual species of timber without expert tuition, the techniques covered in this chapter will enable you to paint convincing wood effects, using easily available materials and a minimum of specialized brushes and tools.

WOOD GRAINING

GRAINING TOOLS

You can use household-decorating tools to make a reasonable attempt at straightforward graining, but better results and a wider range of subtleties can be achieved if you also invest in a few specialized graining tools.

Professional graining brushes are not cheap, but you should never have to replace them, provided they are kept clean and stored carefully.

A set of metal combs is also relatively expensive, but you can get similar effects from cheaper rubber or plastic combs; you can also cut your own from plastic sheet or cardboard.

You may be able to buy some graining tools from a good general paint stockist, but you will probably have to seek out a specialist tool store or craft supplier to get the full range.

Brushes
Use ordinary decorator's paintbrushes to apply glaze and create simple wood graining. Good-quality brushes are always best for general-purpose work, but cheap or worn paintbrushes may prove to be invaluable for special one-off dragged effects (see page 112-13).

1 Mottler
A mottler, with its short soft bristles, is used to simulate the bands of highlights that are often displayed across wavy-grain woods and veneers, such as fiddleback sycamore or ripple ash. Although a genuine mottler is a useful tool to have in your kit, you can produce similar effects with an ordinary paintbrush.

2 Lining tool
This paintbrush, with its square-trimmed filling of bristles, is ideal for removing excess color that has accumu-lated around the edges of a panel or down the sides of dragged grain. However, you can perform similar tasks using any convenient brush.

3 Softener
A 100mm (4in) hog-hair softener is the one specialist brush you cannot do without. The application of a softener spreads and blends marks left by other brushes and tools, turning them into delightful impressions of real wood grain.

4 Flogger
A flogger has extra-long stiff bristles that are used to strike wet glaze, leaving a texture that realistically simulates large open pores. Although you will not use a flogger for every job, it is difficult to achieve the same results with any other brush.

Combs and heart grainers

Dragging the teeth of ready-made or improvised combs through wet glaze leaves a pattern of stripes that is strongly reminiscent of wood grain.

1 Heart grainers

These are special combing tools that leave a highly realistic impression of heart-wood grain. The convex working surface of each heart grainer is molded with raised concentric ridges, centered on one edge of the tool. A handle is molded or fitted to the back. Heart grainers are made in coarse, medium and fine grades.

2 Improvised combs

Many wood grainers make their own combs, using thick cardboard or stiff plastic sheet. Cut rectangles or triangles with perfectly flat sides then, using a sharp craft knife, cut a series of deep notches to form the teeth. Depending on the effect you want to create, cut a row of identical teeth or space them irregularly. You can also experiment with ready-made tile-adhesive spreaders.

3 Rubber or plastic combs

Rubber or plastic graining combs, which often have different-size teeth on each edge, produce relatively large striations in the colored glaze.

4 Steel combs

You can buy sets of precision-made steel combs in three grades – coarse, medium and fine. Combs 75 to 100mm (3 to 4in) wide are the most useful, but you will find 25 and 50mm (1 and 2in) combs perfect for graining narrow rails and stiles.

CHECK ROLLER

This very specialized roller is made up of a number of serrated steel discs mounted side-by-side on a central spindle. Its sole function is to print a representation of the deep elongated pores found on open-grain woods, especially oak. Although a check roller is not an essential item, it would be very laborious to create a similar effect by other means.

109

PAINTS AND GLAZES

Standard solvent-based eggshell paint is used to provide the background color for wood-grain effects. The paint is applied to prepared solid wood or a groundwork cut from man-made board.

Choose a paint that matches the lightest color in the grain pattern of the wood being simulated; this invariably is found within a limited range of colors, often a pale beige which you may want to tint to a warmer or cooler shade. Accurate color matching comes with experience and the knowledge of how a background color is affected when it is overlaid with different glazes. It pays to develop your sense of color by practising on sheets of stiff card.

Oil glaze
Glaze is a ready-made, practically colorless finish, similar in consistency to conventional paint. However, unlike paint, which is designed to form a flat even covering, oil glaze or 'scumble' is formulated to retain brushstrokes and the marks left by dragging combs across a wet surface.

Artist's oil paints
You can buy wood-colored glazes, but you will have greater control over the tones and shades of your work if you tint colorless glaze with tubes of oil paint, sold by art-material stockists. The best-quality paints are expensive, but you can use cheaper student-quality oil paints. Earth colors — such as raw and burnt umber, raw and burnt sienna and Vandyke brown – are the most useful for wood graining. You will also need a tube of black paint to alter the tone of the colors where appropriate.

Varnish
After the initial work has dried thoroughly, protect finished wood graining with one or two coats of satin-finish oil varnish (see pages 68–71). You can include mottling in the first coat of varnish (see page 119).

Preparing surfaces
New wood must be sound, clean and dry. After sanding the surface smooth, treat resinous knots with shellac-based knotting (see page 51) before applying a primer and undercoat.

Sand previously finished wood to create a good key for the background color. Scrape and sand peeling paintwork back to sound feathered edges. Prime bare patches, then obliterate the old color with a suitable undercoat (see page 76).

When the undercoat is dry, brush or spray the work with two coats of eggshell paint, rubbing down with wet-and-dry paper between applications.

OIL GLAZE

ARTIST'S OIL PAINTS

VARNISH

Applying glaze to groundwork

Whatever your intended final effect, apply the colored glaze the same way, brushing in all directions to cover the work. You can include irregular streaks of color by occasionally wiping the brush across the open end of an oil-paint tube and blending the neat paint into the applied glaze. Finish by brushing roughly parallel to the direction of the grain pattern.

The glaze will be perfect for tooling after about five minutes, and will remain workable for up to an hour. When graining a large area, apply the glaze to small, self-contained sections.

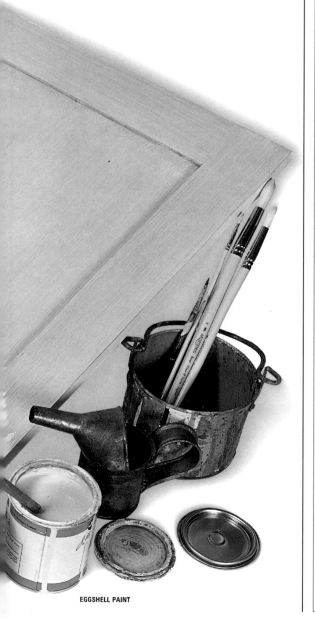

EGGSHELL PAINT

MIXING GLAZE

Professionals frequently carry out wood graining with watercolor glazes, but an oil glaze is easier for amateurs to handle, because it leaves plenty of time to create the desired effects. Oil glaze, which is thinned to a usable consistency with mineral spirit, can be purchased from craft shops or trade suppliers.

Diluting oil paint

Squeeze a 50mm (2in) length of oil paint onto an old saucer, and use a paintbrush to blend in enough mineral spirit to make the paint very slightly liquid. Blend in other oil-paint colors until you have mixed the shade you want.

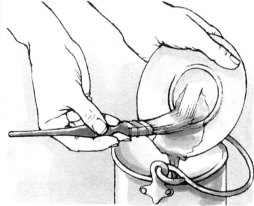

Coloring the glaze

Pour some colorless glaze into a paint kettle – 25mm (1in) of glaze in a 1 litre (2 pint) kettle will be enough for the average room door. Add about 20 per cent mineral spirit and mix it in thoroughly, then gradually add the thinned oil paint until the glaze appears to be the required color and consistency. If you add too much mineral spirit, the glaze may not adhere properly and may dry before you complete the work. If you don't add enough, ridges will form in the glaze as it sets.

Test the glaze by brushing it onto a small area of the prepared work – it should appear darker than the painted groundwork but should retain brushmarks, allowing the base color to show through.

BRUSH-GRAINING

Before attempting to paint an impression of wood grain, it is essential to examine a few examples of the real thing, in order to get some idea of what different grain patterns look like. This contributes immeasurably to a convincing representation. However, no two pieces of wood are exactly the same, so be prepared to accept the happy accidents that are bound to occur, rather than risk becoming frustrated by striving for a slavish copy.

One of the most immediate techniques is simple brush-graining, which recreates the true character of straight-grained wood.

Graining with a wet paintbrush

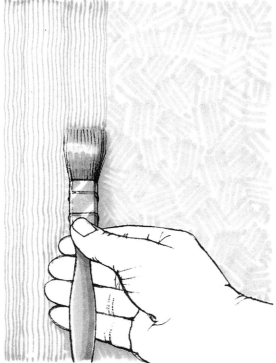

Using a wet brush
You can produce muted linear effects by graining with a brush that is still wet from the glaze previously applied to the work. Holding the paintbrush lightly between your thumb and fingertips, drag it from top to bottom at a shallow angle to the work surface, allowing the bristles to disperse the colored glaze naturally. There is no need to apply excessive pressure, but keep the brush moving throughout the stroke. Apply successive strokes alongside until you have covered the working area.

Using a dry brush
Brush-graining with a dry brush not only displaces the glaze but also removes some color at the same time, creating relatively bold stripes. Don't be afraid to wobble the brush slightly as you make the strokes, because this adds to the naturalistic appearance, but be sure to follow any diversions when you make successive strokes. Regularly wipe the tips of the bristles onto an absorbent rag to remove excess glaze.

Experiment with different brushes to see what effects they produce; ordinary decorator's paintbrushes, hog-hair softeners, floggers, and even old glue brushes will leave distinctive tracks in the glaze.

A dry brush creates a relatively bold linear texture

Softening the grain

If brush-graining appears too strident, use a softener to blur the lines. Softening also introduces attractive and convincing random factors to the work. Hold the brush at 90 degrees to the surface, and gently stroke the bristles along the painted grain, reducing its intensity without entirely losing the linear effect. Softening across the grain is faster, but you may lose the linear effect altogether.

FLOGGING OPEN-GRAIN TEXTURE

Superimpose a coarse open-grain texture over bold linear grain or painted heartwood (see page 114-15).

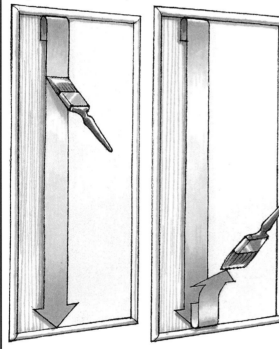

Brush-graining a door panel

Brush-graining panels surrounded by rails, stiles or muntins requires a slight variation in technique.

First paint colored glaze over the entire panel, then start each graining stroke by pushing the tips of the bristles up against the underside of the top rail and dragging the brush to the bottom.

Reverse the paintbrush and push the bristles down to meet the bottom rail, then draw the brush upwards to meet the initial stroke, lifting it off the surface in one continuous movement. Disguise a poor match by softening the grain (see top right) or texturing the panel with a flogger (see right).

Using the flogger

Hold the flogger just above and parallel to the surface. Working up from the base of the panel, strike the wet glaze with a series of short over-lapping strokes, using the flat of the brush, until you gradually texture the whole area. To blend the texture near the bottom of the panel, reverse the brush as described left. Use the edge of the brush on narrow workpieces.

PAINTING HEARTWOOD

Wall panelling and frame-and-panel doors are greatly enhanced by the inclusion of bold grain patterns. Mature wood, found near the center of a tree, produces various irregular grain patterns, depending on how the tree is converted to boards or veneers. The techniques described here simulate a typical pattern of concentric heartwood grain, as found on crown-cut veneer, with straight-grained wood on each side.

For a relatively soft, muted effect, paint the grain pattern onto a background already wet with colored glaze. For greater contrast, perhaps for work that will be seen from a distance, paint the grain with colored glaze onto dry groundwork or onto a background that has been 'oiled-in' sparingly with colorless glaze applied with a rag.

Highly figured panels usually appear most attractive when the surrounding stiles and rails are finished with simple brush-graining.

Painting onto dry ground
When the groundwork is left unglazed, more of the pale background color is exposed and the edges of the heartwood banding remain distinct, even after they have been softened or flogged.

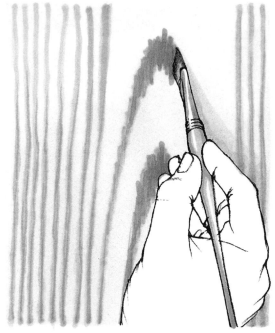

1 Painting concentric bands
Starting from the base of the panel, use an artist's flat fitch to paint concentric bands of colored glaze. Use the thin edge of the brush for the vertical strokes, painting the pointed apex of each band with the wider face of the brush. You can afford to be quite bold at this stage.

2 Softening the grain pattern
Stroke the softener vertically along the center of the grain pattern, streaking the pointed tip of each band of color, then brush to the left and right at an angle of about 30 degrees from the center. Finish with light vertical strokes.

3 Brush-graining on each side of the banding
Cover the panel on each side of the grain pattern with colored glaze, then drag the bristles of a paintbrush or softener through the glaze (see pages 112–13), following the general direction of the banding. Soften this brush-graining.

GRAINING RAILS AND STILES

Work to a sequence that allows you to grain up to the joints between rails, stiles and muntins without obliterating the work you have just completed.

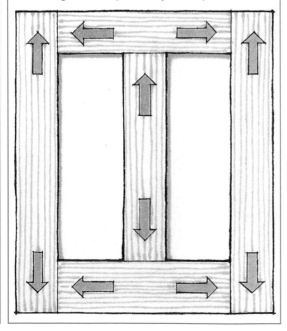

Painting onto wet glaze
When you paint onto groundwork wet with glaze, there is inevitably less contrast between the simulated grain and background color. If required, you can compensate by mixing a slightly darker glaze for painting the grain.

Begin by applying colored glaze to the entire background, then brush-grain roughly with the wet paintbrush (see page 112). Take some of the colored glaze and add more oil paint to darken the tone, thinning it slightly with mineral spirit.

Paint and soften heartwood banding (see opposite), then complete the panel with brush-graining on each side of the central grain pattern.

Blotting highlights
If, having softened the work, you require more contrast between grain pattern and background, fold an absorbent rag into a pad and use one edge to blot some of the glaze from between the bands of color. Lightly soften or flog the work.

COMB-GRAINING

When done well, combing is highly evocative of coarse open-grain wood, and sometimes exhibits attractive interference patterns that are similar in appearance to silky oak. The basic techniques are not difficult to master, and with practice you will discover the degree of variation required to avoid an over-repetitive, mechanical effect. Combing is employed primarily to produce the near-parallel linear patterns of straight-grained wood, but you can use steel or rubber combs to blur painted or dragged oak heartwood and to break up coarse brush-graining.

When combing, it pays to add a little more mineral spirit to the glaze, to avoid ridges building up where the comb's teeth push the glaze aside.

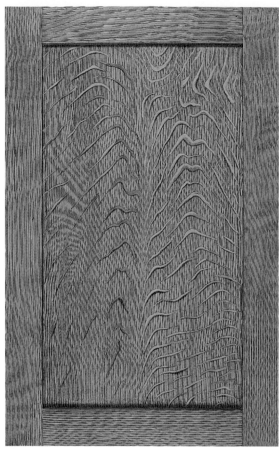

Oak grain pattern created with steel combs

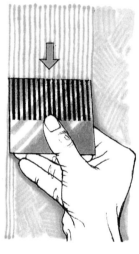

1 Using steel combs
Cover the surface with thinned glaze and brush it out well, then draw a 100mm (4in) medium steel comb from top to bottom in a series of overlapping vertical strokes. Keep the strokes more-or-less parallel, but imitate real grain by allowing the comb to waver from side to side occasionally. Wipe excess glaze from the tips of the teeth between strokes.

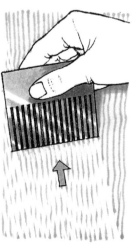

2 Reverse combing
Break up the linear pattern with a fine comb, dragging it upwards at an angle of about 10 degrees to the first series of strokes. Blend in excess color at the top and bottom of a panel by stippling with a lining tool. Go back over the same area a second time if you want to create a finer texture, or blur parts of the work by stippling gently with a softener.

Dragging with a wrapped comb
To create a relatively subdued effect, wrap a piece of absorbent rag tightly over the teeth of a coarse or medium comb. Drag the wrapped comb through the glaze, pulling a clean section of the rag over the tips of the teeth after each vertical stroke. Cover the work-piece once, and then break up the pattern with an unwrapped fine comb, as described left.

USING A HEART GRAINER

A heart grainer is employed exclusively to simulate the pattern of dense heartwood grain. It is used much like a comb, in that it is drawn across the work to leave impressions in the wet glaze, but by presenting its convex surface to the work at different angles, you can create an almost infinite variety of bold patterns with a single tool.

Rubber grainers are molded with coarse, medium or fine ribs – a coarse grade is ideal for oak heartwood, whereas the finer grades are more reminiscent of pine.

Holding a heart grainer
Hold the grainer between thumb and fingertips, with the concentric curved ribs centered on the bottom edge of the tool.

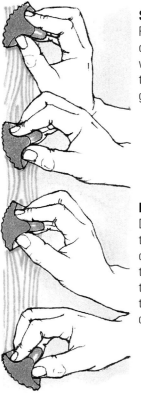

Starting the stroke
Position the grainer near one end of the workpiece, with the bottom edge of the tool resting on the glazed surface.

Making the stroke
Draw the grainer slowly to the bottom of the panel in one continuous stroke, at the same time rocking the tool over and back to vary the pattern left in the colored glaze.

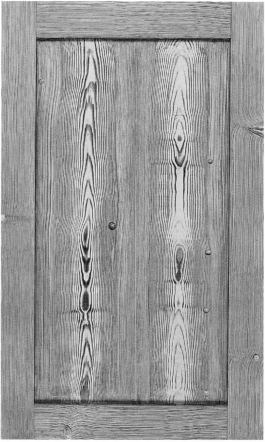

Pine door panel painted with a heart grainer and dry brush

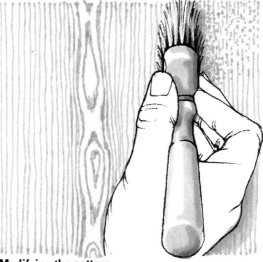

Modifying the pattern
Create a suggestion of straight grain on each side of the heartwood pattern, following its outline roughly with a brush or comb, then soften and blend both grain patterns (see pages 114–15). Alternatively, you can modify the work with light flogging, or retain better definition by stippling with a softener.

ADDITIONAL FIGURING

Small details applied to basic brush- or comb-graining add variety and interest, making each panel or frame a unique piece of work. Such detailing must be done with care to be convincing, but this does not mean that its application has to be laboured; a degree of spontaneity is vital in producing lively work. One essential requirement is a familiarity with the effects you are trying to create; this can best be achieved by collecting examples of real wood or accurate color reproductions from which to work.

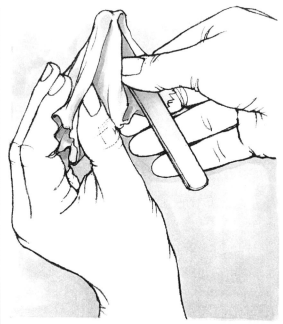

Improvising a veining horn
Professional grainers use a flat pointed tool, known as a veining horn, wrapped in absorbent cloth for wiping out ray flecks. Some grainers improvise by wrapping a coin, but a simple wooden spatula or ice-cream stick is easier to handle. Stretch the fabric tightly over the rounded tip of the stick, re-folding the rag at intervals to maintain a clean working edge.

Creating quartered oak
Quarter-sawing logs reveals a grain pattern crossed with ray-fleck figure in some hardwoods, especially oak. These pale-colored flecks can be found running ribbon-like down a piece of straight-grained wood, or perhaps flanking a central band of bold figure.
    Reproduce ray flecks by wiping them out of combed or brushed-and-flogged graining.

Wiping out individual flecks
Draw the cloth-covered tool through the glaze, turning the stick to make short twisting lines that taper sharply towards their ends. No two flecks are identical in shape or size, but they tend to follow a similar pattern across the work.

Grouping ray flecks

Wipe out staggered rows of ray flecks, making them smaller and fainter as you approach the edge of a panel. Lightly soften the work with a brush or comb, but take care not to lose too much definition.

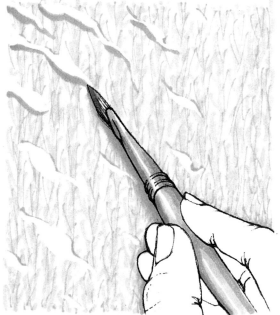

Underlining flecks

When the work is to be seen from a distance, you can create depth and variety by underlining some ray flecks with dark glaze. Use an artist's fitch to apply the glaze freely, then soften the marks or blend them with light stippling.

Mottling

There are several ways to produce the silky mottle of reflective grain pattern exhibited by hardwoods such as mahogany and satinwood, but perhaps the easiest method is to create the effect when applying the final protective coats of varnish. Darken the varnish with slightly thinned oil paint, then brush it evenly onto the workpiece. Because oil varnish dries faster than glaze, you may find it necessary to mottle a large workpiece in manageable stages.

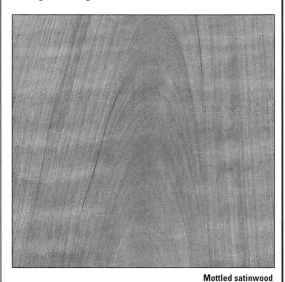

Mottled satinwood

Using a mottler

Holding the mottler at 45 degrees to the surface, remove narrow strips of varnish by waggling the brush from side to side. Create a band of separate, slightly random, impressions in the varnish. Keep the bristles dry by wiping them on an absorbent rag.

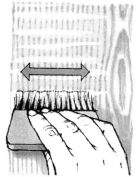

Mottling with a paintbrush

Squeeze the bristles of a household paintbrush between your fingers and thumb to produce a narrow, slightly wavy tip. To soften mottling, gently stroke the bristles of a softener along the impressions – never across them.

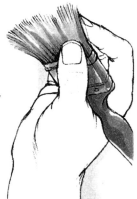

Including knots

Knots can be found in practically any species of timber, but they are particularly prevalent in softwoods. It can enliven grain patterns if you include the occasional knot when painting.

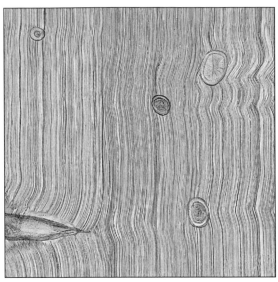

Detail of knotty pine

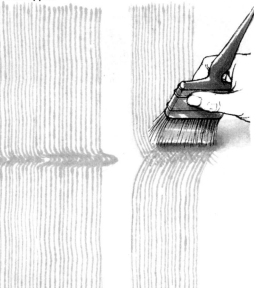

Placing knots

You can place a small knot almost anywhere that would benefit from some additional interest, but for special emphasis consider the placing of knots while applying the initial graining. For example, while drawing a brush through wet glaze, make a sharp kink to one side; a knot would nestle realistically in the bend.

Alternatively, manufacture some wild grain by flicking the brush to one side in the down stroke, then draw the brush up from the base of the work, flicking the brush in the same direction where the strokes meet.

Imprinting knots

It is surprisingly easy to imprint a realistic knot in wet glaze, using the end of a dowel or even your fingertip if you are wearing protective gloves. The simple act of touching the glaze disperses the color, leaving a pale patch with a darker rim and sometimes a small dark dot in the center.

If a knot needs still further emphasis, paint in small concentric circles very freely with the point of an artist's brush, stippling afterwards to soften the effect. Don't make all the knots the same shape or size.

PRINTING DEEP PORES

Some cuts of oak, walnut and, to a lesser extent, beech, exhibit deep, elongated pores. These can be printed over brushed or combed grain once the initial work is dry, using a check roller.

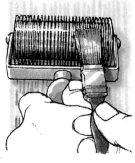

Using a check roller

Apply a dark-colored glaze with a paintbrush held against the serrated discs of a check roller as you push the tool across the work. The pores should run at a very slight angle across the general direction of the grain.

CHAPTER **11** The patina of old woodwork – greatly admired and respected by restorers and collectors – is acquired naturally by long exposure to light, the gradual accumulation of dust and grease, and by moderate wear and tear. Although it is not that easy to reproduce the subtleties of a genuine patina, you can give both new and older pieces an attractive aged appearance by gently 'distressing' their finishes.

ANTIQUE FINISHES

SHADING A CLEAR FINISH

Shading is a technique that reproduces the modulations of color and tone found on old polished or varnished items. The parts of a piece that are handled regularly or that receive the most wear are generally paler than those areas that are protected. Similarly, large flat areas, which are polished and dusted regularly, are cleaner than corners and crevices where dirt is able to collect.

Shading suggests the accumulation of dirt and old polish

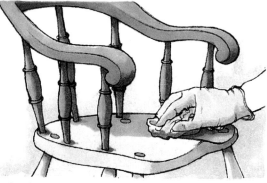

1 Applying stain
Prepare the workpiece, sanding it smooth, then apply a penetrating wood stain (see pages 42–6). Because you will be removing much of the color in the next stage of the process, use a stain that is darker than you would normally choose for coloring similar pieces.

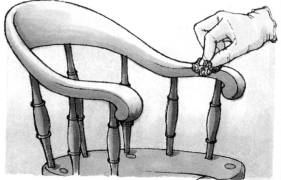

2 Removing color
When the stain is dry, use a pad of fine steel wool to remove some of the color. Concentrate on those areas that would have been rubbed and handled regularly, such as chair backs, seats and arms, and suggest a degree of wear on stretcher rails. Similarly, lightly scuff moldings, carvings and edges to remove color from the high points.

3 Shading door panels
Create a pale patch in the center of a door panel, with a gradual transition from light to dark towards the perimeter of the panel. Rub in the direction of the grain only, avoiding sudden changes of tone.

4 Finishing touches
Carefully wipe the surfaces with a cloth dampened with solvent to remove dust and particles of metal.

If required, accentuate moldings and carving by brushing tinted French polish into the deeper crevices (see page 48). Finish the workpiece with a dark-brown paste wax polish, emphasizing the gradual changes of color and tone that you have created.

DISTRESSING PAINTWORK

A perfectly finished item may look incongruous in a country setting or when placed among older, weathered pieces. Give new paintwork a suitably well-used patina with colored wax polishes or a wash coat of tinted oil glaze. Finish the workpiece with matt or eggshell paint. There is no need to strive for a perfect finish; ageing processes work best with slightly uneven paintwork.

Paintwork distressed with colored wax polish

1 Applying colored wax polish
When the paint is dry, use an abrasive nylon pad to apply colored paste wax polish to the entire workpiece. Rub in all directions to encourage wax to lodge in the recesses, including scratches and other imperfections. Take care not to wear through the paint at this stage. Applying two different colors to vary the overall tone makes for an interesting effect.

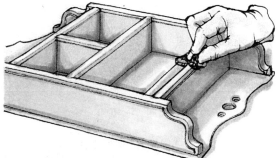

2 Modifying the color
Leave the colored wax to dry, then use a clean abrasive pad dipped in colorless wax polish to clean the dark color from the surfaces, especially the high points. Be sure to remove most of the color from the central areas of flat panels, leaving more of the dark polish where dirt would collect naturally. Don't worry if you happen to wear through the paintwork on a few high points and edges – it only adds to the overall effect.

Remove excess wax with a soft cloth and, the next day, burnish to a soft sheen.

DISTRESSING WITH OIL GLAZE
As an alternative to wax polish, distress new paintwork with oil glaze tinted to the required color with artist's oil paint (see page 111). Allow the base coat of eggshell paint to dry, then brush the tinted glaze freely across all surfaces.

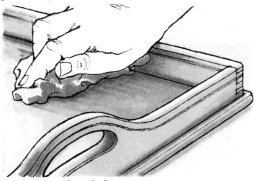

Removing colored glaze
After about five minutes, wipe off most of the glaze with a pad of soft absorbent cloth, leaving the residue to settle in the recesses and deeper blemishes. If the effect is not to your liking, you have plenty of time to wash off the glaze with a cloth dampened with mineral spirit.

Once the first coat is dry, you can apply more glaze to areas that need greater emphasis. Protect the finished result with a clear varnish.

CRACKING FINISHES

One of the cardinal rules of wood finishing is to avoid using incompatible finishes, but a purpose-made cracking varnish takes advantage of the different drying rates of oil-based and water-based finishes to create a most convincing aged surface. The required materials, usually known as ageing varnish and cracking varnish, are stocked by specialist suppliers.

Although the techniques are simple, perfect results rely on perfect timing, so a little experimentation pays dividends.

Preparation

To simulate crazed varnish, prepare the wood in the usual way, sealing the surface with a coat of matt acrylic varnish. Depending on the degree of ageing you want to suggest, you may want to apply a suitable wood stain beforehand.

To age existing paintwork, wash the surface to remove dirt and grease; rub down a gloss finish with wet-and-dry paper.

1 Applying ageing varnish

Paint a coat or ageing varnish onto the sealed or painted surface. Since the thickness of this initial coat determines how wide the final cracks will be, you can vary the effect by applying thicker varnish in those areas where you want to see more intense cracking.

2 Timing the process

Leave the varnished workpiece in a warm atmosphere until it feels dry when you run a fingertip lightly across the surface; it should feel slightly tacky if you press hard. To apply cracking varnish before this stage will result in a wrinkled finish with only a minimal amount of cracking.

3 Applying cracking varnish

Paint an even coat of cracking varnish onto the workpiece and warm it gently with a hairdryer until the varnish begins to exhibit cracks, then leave the workpiece to dry hard in a warm room.

4 Emphasizing cracks

To simulate a discolored crazed finish, rub artist's oil paint vigorously into the cracks, blending dark brown and black to create irregular coloring. Gently wipe paint from the surface to leave color in the finer cracks. If the work is to be handled, apply a protective coat of oil varnish, but only after the artist's oil paint has dried thoroughly.

HEALTH AND SAFETY

Many wood finishes contain substances that are potentially harmful to your health, and some are also highly flammable. In addition to the following precautions, always observe manufacturers' instructions to protect yourself from health hazards and accidents when using or storing finishes.

Breathing solvent fumes
Breathing solvent vapours can be dangerous; if you begin to experience headaches, dizziness, fatigue or drowsiness, leave the workshop immediately.

If someone else feels faint, take them into fresh air, keeping them warm and at rest. Don't give him or her anything to eat or drink until fully recovered. If they are unconscious, put them in the recovery position and get urgent medical attention. If breathing has stopped, administer artificial ventilation (respiration).

• To protect yourself from solvent fumes, provide good natural ventilation when working with finishes; when spraying, fit an extractor in the spray booth.

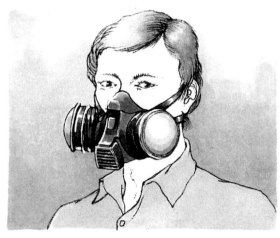

• When it is impossible to provide adequate natural ventilation, and always when spraying substances, wear a gas-cartridge respirator. The filter can be changed to one that will protect you from wood dust when sanding.

Protecting your eyes
Wear goggles to protect your eyes from liquid splashes.

• If you get wood finishes or thinners in your eyes, flush them with running water for at least 10 minutes, holding your eyelids apart. If you wear contact lenses, remember to remove them first. Seek medical advice.

Skin contact
Repeated or prolonged contact with some wood finishes and thinners may lead to dermatitis. If in doubt, wear disposable gloves when applying finishes.

• Wash with soap and water or a proprietary skin cleanser; never use solvents or thinners to clean finishes from your skin.

Swallowing substances
If a child appears to have swallowed any wood finish or solvent, do not induce him or her to vomit. Keep the child calm and at rest, and obtain medical attention.

Fire precautions
Substances marked flammable should be handled and stored with care. Good ventilation is essential.

• Don't smoke in the workshop, and extinguish naked flames where workpieces are finished or left to dry.

• The fine mist created by spraying solvent finishes is highly flammable. It is important to install an explosion-proof (flame-proof) extractor fan, light fittings and switches in a spray booth.

• Sweep up shavings and dust regularly, and don't leave oil- or solvent-soaked rags in the workshop.

• Keep a fire extinguisher and fire blanket close at hand. Have the extinguisher checked regularly.

Storing finishes
If possible, store finishes and thinners in a locked shed or outhouse. If you need to transfer substances, label the containers clearly and avoid using food or drink cans or bottles that could be misidentified. Keep finish or solvent containers closed except when in use.

Disposing of substances
Don't pour solvents or finishes into drains or water courses. Contain and collect spills with a non-combustible absorbent material such as sand or earth.

• Ask your local authorities for advice on where and how to dispose safely of waste products, including empty containers.

See also:
Protecting yourself from dust, page 24.
Chemical strippers, page 32.
Bleaching wood, page 38.